NATURAL ENVIRONMENT RESEARCH COUNCIL

INSTITUTE OF GEOLOGICAL SCIENCES

MEMOIRS OF THE GEOLOGICAL SURVEY OF GREAT BRITAIN
ENGLAND AND WALES

The Geology of the Country around Weymouth, Swanage, Corfe & Lulworth

(*Explanation of Sheets 341, 342, 343,
with small portions of Sheets 327, 328, 329*)

W. J. ARKELL, M.A., D.Sc.

with contributions by

C. W. Wright, M.A., and H. J. Osborne White, F.G.S.

Sylvia Newman June 2006

LONDON

HER MAJESTY'S STATIONERY OFFICE

1947

The Institute of Geological Sciences was formed by the incorporation of the
Geological Survey of Great Britain and the Museum of Practical Geology with
Overseas Geological Surveys and is a constituent body of the Natural Environment
Research Council

ISBN 0 11 884010 X

PREFACE

The area dealt with is substantially the same as that covered in 1898 by a Geological Survey memoir written by the late Sir Aubrey Strahan on ' The Geology of the Isle of Purbeck and Weymouth.' It includes the whole of the coastal region within Sheets 341 (West Fleet), 342 (Weymouth) and 343 (Swanage), while northwards it extends inland to the South Winterbourne and Frome in Sheet 328 (Dorchester) and to Poole Harbour in Sheet 329 (Bournemouth). It also enters the south-east corner of Sheet 327 (Bridport), but to a less extent than did Strahan's original area, because a separate memoir on the Bridport sheet is shortly to appear.

The region is a natural entity, containing a series of inter-dependent structures and a range of stratigraphy of quite unusual variety and interest. It is not surprising that from the early part of the nineteenth century it has attracted a great deal of geological attention. This aspect is briefly treated in Chapter I. Strahan's original memoir included a chronological bibliography, but it has not been thought necessary to repeat this feature on the present occasion, since a select bibliography was published in 1935 by Mr. G. M. Davies in his ' Dorset Coast, A Geological Guide '.

Sir Aubrey Strahan's memoir served its day excellently, but some years ago it passed out of print. Much additional information and many new interpretations had by this time accumulated, and it seemed expedient to issue an independent memoir rather than a revised edition. The preparation of the new memoir was entrusted to Dr. W. J. Arkell, who, though not a member of the Geological Survey, had special qualifications for the task. He had not only a life-long association with the district, which had borne fruit in many scientific papers dealing with its tectonics and stratigraphy, but he also had produced a comprehensive treatise on the Jurassic System in Britain. Throughout his career, Dr. Arkell has been influenced by Sir Aubrey Strahan's 1898 memoir, but he has not hesitated to advocate modifications of interpretation, where such have seemed desirable.

Dr. Arkell has accepted assistance from other workers, which he desires to acknowledge as follows:

" Realising the importance of abundant field-experience of Chalk stratigraphy and palaeontology for the elucidation of the difficult but vital exposures in the zone affected by the Ridgeway Fault, I enlisted the help of Mr. H. J. Osborne White, who accordingly in 1936 examined all the Chalk pits from Abbotsbury to Chaldon and Winfrith, determining so far as possible the attitudes and zonal positions of the beds exposed. Most of these exposures had been already visited by me, and some of them were revisited by us together and discussed on the spot. I wish to record how greatly I personally, as well as the memoir, benefited by this collaboration. Mr. White's copious notes have been freely drawn upon in the last pages of Chapter XI, dealing with Chalk stratigraphy, and in Chapter XIII, describing the tectonics.

" In 1937 I made the acquaintance of Mr. C. W. Wright, then a freshman and classical scholar of Christ Church, Oxford. Finding that he was already familiar with the Upper Cretaceous rocks of Dorset, as well as of most other parts of England, and was a specialist in Cretaceous palaeontology, of which he and his brother, Mr. E. V. Wright, had made a collection of extraordinary breadth and excellence, I invited him to undertake Chapters X and XI on the Gault and Upper Greensand and the Chalk. He immediately began to discover ammonites and other fossils previously unknown in the district, and to track down most of the rarities to their proper horizons. The amount of new and valuable matter contained in his chapters speaks for itself.

" I wish to acknowledge especially the generosity of the Chief Geologist, Dr. G. M. Lees, and the other geologists of the D'Arcy Exploration Company, in putting all the results of their borings and other geological explorations at my disposal. Their activities largely transformed the tectonic picture over much of the district, and I was fortunate indeed to have the opportunity to follow and discuss with them their discoveries step by step.

" It will be obvious that much of this memoir is owed to the labours of others, and more indirectly to collaboration and discussion with them. While alone responsible for the accuracy of such matter as is not directly acknowledged to other sources, I would like to mention by name the following :— Mr. F. W. Anderson, Mr. D. F. W. Baden-Powell, Sir Edward Bailey, Dr. C. T. Barber, Mr. E. J. Bowen, Mr. P. C. S. Bradley, Mr. C. P. Chatwin, Dr. L. R. Cox, Mr. P. T. Cox, Lieut.-Col. C. D. Drew, Mr. P. E. Kent, Mr. J. F. Kirkaldy, Dr. G. M. Lees, Mr. B. H. Mottram, Mr. A. H. Taitt, Mr. H. J. Osborne White, Mr. C. W. Wright, Mr. A. Wrigley. Other authorities have been consulted on specific points and their valuable help is acknowledged in the text.

" Most of the fossils have been specially drawn for this memoir by Miss O. F. Tassart; but the drawings of Purbeck and Wealden ostracods (Figs. 28, 34) are by Mr. F. W. Anderson, and those of Purbeck fossils, Wealden, Lower Greensand and Bembridge gastropods (Figs. 29, 35, 37, 47), and also parts of Fig. 3 nos. 1-3), Fig. 4 (no. 5), Fig. 18 (no. 6) and Figs. 17 and 27 are by me. The flint implements (Figs. 80, 81) have been specially drawn by Mr. C. O. Waterhouse of the Department of British and Mediaeval Antiquities at the British Museum."

References are given in footnotes. Sir Aubrey Strahan's memoir is referred to throughout as *Purbeck Memoir*, 1898. Other titles are also often contracted after their first appearance in any individual chapter.

The memoir had reached the stage of corrected galley-proof in November, 1939. Publication had to be delayed on account of the war. The authors have taken the opportunity to make some small emendations and have added a few new references in footnotes in page-proofs in August, 1944. But otherwise the memoir remains essentially as written in 1939.

W. F. P. McLintock,
Director.

Geological Survey Office,
Exhibition Road,
South Kensington,
London, S.W.7.
21st August, 1946.

CONTENTS

		PAGE
PREFACE BY THE DIRECTOR		iii
LIST OF ILLUSTRATIONS		vi
CHAPTER I.—INTRODUCTION		1
CHAPTER II.—MIDDLE JURASSIC ROCKS.	Bathonian and basal Callovian Stages: Fuller's Earth, Forest Marble, Cornbrash ...	15
CHAPTER III.—UPPER JURASSIC ROCKS.	Callovian and Lower Oxfordian Stages: Kellaways Beds and Oxford Clay	25
CHAPTER IV.— ,, ,, ,,	Upper Oxfordian Stage: Corallian Beds ...	36
CHAPTER V.— ,, ,, ,,	Kimmeridgian Stage: Kimmeridge Clay ...	64
CHAPTER VI.— ,, ,, ,,	Portlandian Stage: Portland Beds ...	89
CHAPTER VII.— ,, ,, ,,	Purbeckian Stage: Purbeck Beds	123
CHAPTER VIII.—LOWER CRETACEOUS ROCKS.	Neocomian Stage: Wealden Beds ...	148
CHAPTER IX.— ,, ,, ,,	Aptian Stage: Lower Greensand	163
CHAPTER X.—UPPER CRETACEOUS ROCKS.	Albian Stage: Gault and Upper Greensand	178
CHAPTER XI.— ,, ,, ,,	Cenomanian, Turonian and Senonian Stages: The Chalk	195
CHAPTER XII.—EOCENE AND OLIGOCENE ROCKS		215
CHAPTER XIII.—TECTONIC STRUCTURE		242
CHAPTER XIV.—DEVELOPMENT OF THE TOPOGRAPHY AND DRAINAGE. PLEISTOCENE AND RECENT DEPOSITS		313
CHAPTER XV.—ECONOMIC GEOLOGY		354
APPENDIX I.—LIST OF GEOLOGICAL SURVEY PHOTOGRAPHS ...		362
APPENDIX II.—SHORT LIST OF BOOKS AND ARTICLES OF GENERAL INTEREST		368
INDEX		369

LIST OF ILLUSTRATIONS

TEXT-FIGURES

		PAGE
FIG. 1.—Sketch-map of the area, showing geology and sheet lines	...	2
FIG. 2.—Locality-map of the shores and hinterland of the Fleet	...	14
FIG. 3.—Fuller's Earth fossils		16
FIG. 4.—Forest Marble fossils		17
FGI. 5.—Lower Cornbrash fossils...		20
FIG. 6.—Upper Cornbrash fossils...		22
FIG. 7.—Oxford Clay fossils		28
FIG. 8.—Corallian Beds fossils		38
FIG. 9.—Corallian Beds fossils		40
FIG. 10.—Sketch-map of the Bran Point fault		43
FIG. 11.—Corallian Beds at Bran Point		45
FIG. 12.—Corallian Beds at Black Head		49
FIG. 13.—Corallian Beds at Redcliff and Ham Cliff		52
FIG. 14.—Sections of the Corallian Beds in the cliffs near Weymouth		55
FIG. 15.—Kimmeridge Clay fossils		65
FIG. 16.—Cliff-section at Kimmeridge		75
FIG. 17.—Ammonites with virgatotome ribbing		77
FIG. 18.—Portland Beds fossils		96
FIG. 19.—Cliff-sections, Freshwater Steps to St. Alban's Head	...	98
FIG. 20.—Profiles of the Portland Stone at the principal exposures in Purbeck		100
FIG. 21.—Portland Sand at Emmit Hill		104
FIG. 22.—Portland Sand at Gad Cliff		106
FIG. 23.—Cherty Series and Portland Sand at Dungy Head		109
FIG. 24.—Portland Beds at Burning Cliff, Ringstead Bay		112
FIG. 25.—Comparative sections of the Portland Beds and subjacent strata		120
FIG. 26.—The Great Dirt Bed in Portland Island		125
FIG. 27.—Jaws and teeth of Purbeck mammals		127
FIG. 28.—Ostracods of the Purbeck Beds		129
FIG. 29.—Purbeck invertebrate fossils		131
FIG. 30.—Swanage Stone shaft-head		134
FIG. 31.—Purbeck Beds, Durlston Bay		136
FIG. 32.—Broken Beds at Lulworth Cove		140
FIG. 33.—Purbeck Beds, Isle of Portland		146
FIG. 34.—Ostracods of the Wealden Beds		151
FIG. 35.—Gastropods of the Wealden Beds		153
FIG. 36.—Cliff-section of the Wealden Beds, Swanage Bay		155
FIG. 37.—Lower Greensand gastropods...		168
FIG. 38.—Lower Greensand fossils		170

	PAGE
FIG. 39.—Gault and Upper Greensand ammonoids	183
FIG. 40.—Gault and Upper Greensand fossils	187
FIG. 41.—Lower and Middle and Upper Chalk fossils	198
FIG. 42.—Upper Chalk fossils	201
FIG. 43.—Pipe-clay open working at Corfe	219
FIG. 44.—Cliff-section of Tertiary strata, Studland Bay	222
FIG. 45.—Geological map of Creechbarrow and its surroundings	233
FIG. 46.—Horizontal section north-south through Creechbarrow and the Chalk ridge	236
FIG. 47.—Bembridge fossils identified from Creechbarrow	239
FIG. 48.—Tectonic sketch-map of the Weymouth district	245
FIG. 49.—Section through Abbotsbury	250
FIG. 50.—Section at Upwey	250
FIG. 51.—Sketch of a chalk pit at Portisham	252
FIG. 52.—Sketch of a chalk pit at Corton Down	253
FIG. 53.—Section through Ridgeway Hill	254
FIG. 54.—Section through The Knoll, near Broadwey	261
FIG. 55.—Section through the Bincombe inlier	261
FIG. 56.—Section seen in a pipe-trench at Green Hill	265
FIG. 57.—Plan of faults at East Hill, Sutton Poyntz	269
FIG. 58.—Section through East Hill spur, Sutton Poyntz	270
FIG. 59.—Section through the Spring Bottom ridge, Ringstead	270
FIG. 60.—Section through the Poxwell boring	273
FIG. 61.—Geological map and section of the Chaldon structure	276
FIG. 62.—Map of contours drawn on top of the Middle Chalk, Lulworth area	280
FIG. 63.—Sketch-map of the foreshore, cliffs and stream at Osmington Mills	283
FIG. 64.—Section through the Purbeck foresyncline, Bat's Head	286
FIG. 65.—The Purbeck foresyncline as seen in the cliff, Bat's Head	287
FIG. 66.—Bat's Head, showing shears in vertical chalk	289
FIG. 67.—Man-o'-War Head from the east	290
FIG. 68.—Faults in the Chalk, St. Oswald's Bay	291
FIG. 69.—Faults in Purbeck Beds, Durdle Cove	292
FIG. 70.—Structures at Stair Hole	294
FIG. 71.—Section in the cliffs, Lulworth Cove	295
FIG. 72.—View of the chalk cliff, Lulworth Cove	297
FIG. 73.—Crumpled Purbeck Beds, Peveril Point	304
FIG. 74.—Cliff-section showing the Ballard Down fault	306
FIG. 75.—Diagrams for Clarke's underthrust hypothesis	309
FIG. 76.—Diagrams for normal faulting hypothesis	310
FIG. 77.—Diagrams illustrating 'onion-scale faulting'	311
FIG. 78.—Sketch-map of the Chaldon Inlier to illustrate the drainage area of Winfrith Brook	320
FIG. 79.—Sketch-map showing the Pleistocene deposits of the area and the nature of the beaches	322
FIG. 80.—Palaeolithic implements from Moreton gravels	326
FIG. 81.—Palaeolithic implements from Moreton gravels	328
FIG. 82.—'Head' at Chesilton	335
FIG. 83.—Sketch-map of blown sand area, South Haven Peninsula	347
FIG. 84.—Old maps of South Haven Peninsula, Studland	349

PLATES

In this edition the Plates preceed the main text

PLATE   I.—View eastwards over Bacon Hole and Mupe Rocks. The Mupe Rocks are of Portland Stone capped by Broken Beds, upon which follows the rest of the Purbeck Beds completely exposed. The gap in the Chalk cliffs on the left, behind, is Arish Mell, the western boundary of Purbeck. Right of it are Flowers Barrow, Worbarrow Bay and Gad Cliff. Swyre Head in the distance on the right. (Geological Survey photograph no. A.1338)

PLATE   II.—Ammonites from the Lamberti Zone, Tidmoor Point. For detailed explanation see p. 30

PLATE   III.—Ammonites from the Mariae and Cordatum Zones of the Upper Oxford Clay, and from the Corallian Beds. For detailed explanation see p. 34

PLATE   IV.—Ammonites from the Lower Kimmeridge Clay. For detailed explanation see p. 74

PLATE   V.—Ammonites from the Upper Kimmeridge Clay. For detailed explanation see p. 78

PLATE VI.—A. Hounstout Cliff from Freshwater Steps. The cascade and steps are at the small dark headland in the centre. Hounstout Cliff rises to 501 ft. above the sea beyond the small bay called Egmont Bight. Most of the cliff displays the Pavlovia Zones; about the highest quarter consists of Portland Sand capped with Portland Stone. (Photograph by the author)

        B. Rope Lake Head from the east. Typical cliff of Upper Kimmeridge shales, with the White Band near the top and the Basalt Stone Band near the base. The shore is covered with black boulders of basalt-like dicey cementstone and white slabs of hard paper shale from these two bands. Note the cementstone ledge in the sea, exposed by the ebb-tide. (Photograph by the author)

PLATE VII.—A. Ammonites from the Portland Stone. The largest belong to the Perisphinctid genus *Titanites*. The black and white ruler is 1 ft. long. (From an exhibit in the Geological Survey Museum ; Geological Survey photograph)

B. Durlston Head from Tilly Whim Caves. The so-called caves are old quarries, worked until the beginning of the nineteenth century. The platform in the foreground, forming the floor of the quarries, is the top of the Cherty Series. The brow of the cliff shows the basal Purbeck Beds. A huge fallen block of the oyster bed lies in the left foreground. (Geological Survey photograph no. A.1290)

PLATE VIII.—A. Gad Cliff from the east. Overhanging crags of Portland Stone and Purbeck Beds, dipping 25° to 35° landwards, above an undercliff of Portland Sand and Kimmeridge Clay. The White Band crops out at the foot of the cliff. (Photograph by Professor S. H. Reynolds)

B. Durdle Door. The arch is of Portland Stone, the higher cliff on the left of Purbeck Beds, standing nearly vertical. The detail of the Purbeck Beds is shown in Fig. 69, p. 292. (Geological Survey photograph no. A.1326)

PLATE IX.—A. The Fossil Forest, Lulworth. Two silicified tree-trunks encased in tufa (size shown by walking stick), and the tufa-coated stumps (" burrs ") from which they were broken in Purbeck times. (Geological Survey photograph No. A.1335)

B. Purbeck Dirt Bed with stones, Bacon Hole. The Dirt Bed, or ancient soil with stones, is overlain by a bed of tufa (on which the hammer rests). The silicified trees and cycads occur in this tufa. (Photograph by Professor S. H. Reynolds)

PLATE X.—A. Durlston Bay, Peveril Point and Ballard Down, from Durlston Head. Durlston Bay and Peveril Point show the classic section of the Purbeck Beds. Beyond is Swanage Bay, hollowed out of the Wealden Beds, and at the back the Chalk ridge of Ballard Down, ending in the cliffs and stacks of Handfast Point. The Eocene plateau of Bournemouth shows as a faint line on the horizon. (Geological Survey photograph no. A.1291)

B. Swanage Bay in 1883 ; dressed stone awaiting shipment. The stone wharf was at the foot of Park Road. Notice the hand-made stone sinks in front, and in the distance the Wealden cliffs with fields stretching from the cliff edge to the downs, where New Swanage now stands. (Photograph by Powells', Sea Front, Swanage)

PLATE XI.—A. Portland Beds—Gault unconformity, Holworth House, Ringstead. On the left the light Portland Stone is seen to be tilted at 30° to the left (north) and overlain by dark Gault clay, the sharp line of contact dipping about 12° to the right (south). Beyond is the cliff of Upper Greensand and Chalk forming White Nothe, curtained with slips on the Gault and Kimmeridge Clays beneath. (Geological Survey Photograph no. A.1367)

B. Albian—Cenomanian—Turonian section, White Nothe. The lowest of the three white pointers indicates the exposed junction of the Kimmeridge Clay and the Gault ; the middle pointer shows the Chloritic Marl ; the highest pointer shows the Plenus Marl, separating the Lower and Middle Chalk. (Photograph by the author)

PLATE   XII.—A. Chalk stacks, Handfast Point. The stack on the right is Old Harry. The gap on the left was breached in the winter 1920-21. It formed an island which will eventually no doubt break up into several new stacks. (Geological Survey photograph no. A. 12237)

B. The Pinnacle, a chalk stack on which peregrine falcons have nested for many years. The Foreland, Swanage. (Geological Survey photograph no. A. 12238)

PLATE XIII.—A. View of Studland Heath, typical scenery of the Bagshot Beds, with heather in bloom. In the foreground is the mass of iron-cemented gritstone called the Puckstone ; in the distance is the much larger mass called the Agglestone. (Photograph by the author)

B. Creechbarrow Hill from the south-east. The view is taken from the chalk ridge and in the foreground is the chalk pit in the vertical Mucronata Zone, in which are vertical pipes containing flints of Creechbarrow type. The profile of Creechbarrow shows the summit cap of Bembridge Limestone and the south-west spur (left) and the east spur (right), caused by outcrops of flint gravel. (Photograph by the author)

PLATE XIV.—A. View looking east along the foresyncline and steep middle limb of the Purbeck anticline, from east of White Nothe. In the foreground Upper Chalk with bands of flint dipping gently south (seaward) towards Middle Bottom, which coincides with the foresyncline, in the centre of the picture. In the cliff beyond, the Micraster Zones rise in a steeply increasing curve until at the first headland, Bat's Head, they and the Planus Zone are vertical. The vertical hardened chalk forms the high ridge which strikes half left into the distance. The second headland is Dungy Head, of Portland Stone dipping about 45°N. In the distance is the plateau of Purbeck, where the Portland and Purbeck Beds lie nearly flat on the axis of the anticline. (Geological Survey photograph no. A. 12571)

B. Stair Hole, Lulworth. The arches through which the sea enters are cut in topmost Portland Stone and basal Purbeck Beds. The cliff at the far (east) end shows the Lulworth Crumple in the Middle Purbeck Beds. (Geological Survey photograph no. A. 12223)

PLATE   XV.—The Ballard Down Fault. The curved fault-plane can be seen, separating hard vertical chalk on the left (south) from soft curved chalk on the right (north) the curved bedding running parallel to the fault-plane. (Photograph by H. E. Armstrong, reproduced from A. W. Rowe " The Zones of the White Chalk of the English Coast, II. Dorset," *Proc. Geol. Assoc.*, vol. xvii, pt. 1, pl. viii, 1901)

PLATE   XVI.—A. Corfe Castle from the west, looking across the Corfe River gap. Vertical chalk bedding can be seen in the side of the conical hill below the castle wall. The pit on the left is in highly sheared and hardened chalk close to the Tertiary base. (Geological Survey photograph no. A. 1308)

B. Plateau Gravel of the Lower Palaeolithic terrace filling a channel eroded in Bagshot Sand. Warmwell Pits Ltd. (1938). The marks on the survey rod indicate feet. Note current-bedding in both gravel and Bagshot Sand. The Plateau Gravel has been artificially removed except from the channel, where it was at least twice the normal thickness. (Photograph by the author)

PLATE XVII.—A. Chesil Beach and Portland Island, from the air. The Fleet backwater is well seen, apparently closed at the far end by Portland Harbour Beach, beyond which is the harbour with warships at anchor. The narrows in the foreground are $1\frac{1}{2}$ miles west of Langton Herring Church ; the next inlet, reaching the edge of the photograph, is the mouth of Rodden Brook ; the next narrows are at Herbury peninsula, beyond which is the East Fleet
(Photograph by *The Times*, by permission)

B. Cliffs at Portland Bill, capped by the raised beach. The base of the raised beach coincides with the top of the crane, from which it runs almost horizontally to the right (east) and rises gradually to the left (west), to reach the skyline to the left of the large triangle of black shadow, but before reaching the first of the next two smaller vertical bars of shadow (caused by joints in the Portland Stone and basal Purbeck Beds). (Photograph by Kestin's, Weymouth)

PLATE XVIII.—A. Boring for oil at Poxwell Circus, 1937. The photograph shows the derrick, 100 ft. high, which stood on the summit of the hill between Moigns Down and the Stone Circle for about a year. (Photograph by Dr. W. F. P. McLintock)

B. A Stone quarry on Portland Island. The quarry is west of Easton and the church (completed 1766 ; architect Thomas Gilbert of Portland) stands near West Weare Cliff. The method of quarrying and the tackle used are typical of the island. (Geological Survey photograph no. A. 4957)

PLATE   XIX.—Geological map of the folded and faulted country north and north-west of Weymouth. The folded and faulted region was re-mapped on the 6-inch scale in 1938 by W. J. Arkell. The remaining lines (dots and dashes) are from A. Strahan's and C. Reid's 6-inch field-maps of about 1888-1890. The Tertiary boundary was surveyed by Clement Reid, *At the* the rest by A. Strahan. The horizontal section *end of* is generalized and superficial deposits are omitted. *book*

The Geology of the Country around Weymouth, Swanage, Corfe and Lulworth

ADDENDA AND CORRIGENDA, 1952

VARIOUS new contributions to our knowledge of the Weymouth area have been made since this memoir was published in 1947. It has not proved practicable to include references to them in the text of the present reprint, but they are listed below, together with a number of corrections, mainly to the palaeontology. These addenda and corrigenda have been supplied by Dr. W. J. Arkell, F.R.S., Mr. C. W. Wright, M.A., and Mr. R. V. Melville, M.Sc. A review by Dr. Arkell of progress of geological investigations in Dorset from 1940 to 1950, with bibliography, is given in *Proc. Dorset Nat. Hist. Arch. Soc.*, vol. 72, pp. 176-94 (1951).

p. 15.   FULLERS' EARTH : A borehole at Compton Valence, made in 1948 proved the Lower Fullers' Earth to be 164 ft. thick. The total thickness of Fullers' Earth therefore, exceeds 350 ft. See Falcon, N. L. and P. E. Kent. 1950. *Geol. Mag.*, vol. lxxxvii, p. 302.

p. 16.   FIGURE 3 (4A-C) : For " Davidson " read " (Davidson) ".

p. 17.   FIGURE 4 (6A-B) : also p. 19, lines 2 and 3 : For "*Ostrea (Catinula) minuta* (J. de C. Sowerby) " read " *Ostrea ancliffensis* Cox and Arkell."

p. 18.   LINE 5 : For "*Belemnopsis bessina* (d'Orbigny) " read " *Belemnopsis fusiformis* (Parkinson)".

p. 19.   LINES 2 AND 3 : For "*Ostrea (Catinula) minuta* (J. de C. Sowerby) " read " *Ostrea ancliffensis* Cox and Arkell." LINE 9 FROM BOTTOM : For " *Oxytoma costata* (J. Sowerby) " read " *Oxytoma costatum* (Townsend) "

p 20.   FIGURE 5 (4) : For " *Trigonia rolandi* Cross " read " *Trigonia crucis* Sharp " (*T. crucis* Sharp ex Lycett MS. *Quart. Journ. Geol. Soc.*, 1870, vol xxvi, p. 383 ; this is a prior name).

p. 21.   LINE 12 FROM BOTTOM: and p. 22, FIGURE 6 (1) : For " (?*Microthyridina*) " read " (*Digonella*) "

p. 26.   KELLAWAYS BEDS : It is now known that these beds are not faulted out near East Fleet. See Arkell, W. J. 1948. *Proc. Dorset Nat. Hist. Arch. Soc.*, vol. lxix, p. 122.

p. 27.   DESCRIPTION OF PUTTON LANE BRICKYARD : Delete " *Erymnoceras* " ; for " *Sigaloceras* " read " *Gowericeras* "; for " *braamburiensis* (J. Sowerby) " read " *braamburiensis* (J. de C. Sowerby)".

p. 28   FIGURE 7 (4): For " *Trigonia sp.* cf. *irregularis* Seebach " read " *Trigonia (Myophorella) scarburgensis* Lycett ".

p. 29.   DESCRIPTION OF CROOK HILL BRICKYARD : Delete " ? Jason Zone" and " *Kosmoceras* cf. *jason* (Reinecke)". Bed 1 is now included in the Coronatum Zone. See Arkell, W. J. 1948. *Proc. Dorset Nat. Hist. Arch. Soc.*, vol. lxix, p. 124.

p. 34.   LINE 18: For " *Perna* " read " *Isognomon* ".

p. 40.   FIGURE 9 (9): For " *Cidaris* " read " *Paracidaris* ".

p. 46.   BED 16, LIMESTONE : For " 10 ft." read " 1 ft 10 in.".

p. 46.   LINE 22 ; p. 48, LINE 17 ; p. 52, LINE 5 ; p. 62, LINE 4 : for " *Gervillia aviculoides* " read " *Gervillella aviculoides* "

p. 67.   UNDER HEADING ' ZONES ' IN BOXED LIST : for " *Gavesia* " read "*Gravesia* ".

p. 72.   BED 26 : for " Shales, mainly hard, 5½ ft." read " Shales, mainly hard, 10 ft."

p. 77.   FIGURE 17 (2) : for " *Provirgatites* " read " *Zaraiskites* ".

p. 124. TABLE OF OSTRACOD ZONES: Mr Sylvester-Bradley has published a revision of the zonal indices of the Upper and Middle Purbeck Beds as follows :—

Upper Purbeck	Cypridea setina (Anderson)	$\begin{cases} C. \ setina \ \text{s. str.} \\ C. \ rectidorsata \\ \text{Sylvester-Bradley} \end{cases}$
Middle Purbeck	C. granulosa (J. de C. Sowerby)	$\begin{cases} C. \ fasciculata \ (\text{Forbes}) \\ C. \ granulosa \ \text{s. str.} \end{cases}$

Mr. F. W. Anderson defined C. setina as Langtonia setina Anderson ; Mr. Sylvester-Bradley considers Langtonia to be synonymous with Pseudocypridina Roth 1933 which he treats as a subgenus of Cypridea. See Sylvester-Bradley, P. C. 1949. Proc. Geol. Assoc., vol. lx, pp.125-53.

p. 129. FIGURE 28 : Amend as follows :—1. Cypridea (Pseudocypridina) setina (Anderson) : 2. Ulwellia ventrosa (Jones) : 3. Cypridea cf. propunctata Sylvester-Bradley : 4. Cypridea fasciculata (Forbes) : 5. Cypridea granulosa (J. de C Sowerby) : 6. Metacypris forbesii Jones var. verrucosa Jones : 7. " Cypris " purbeckensis Forbes : 8. " Candona " bononiensis Jones : 9. " Candona " ansata Jones.

p 130. FOSSIL NOMENCLATURE : Amendments are necessary to accord with those given for p. 129, Fig. 28 above

p. 133. FOR AN ACCOUNT OF Chara see Harris, T. M. 1939. British Purbeck Charophyta. British Museum (Natural History).

p. 143. POXWELL ROAD CUTTING : For more detailed section of this road cutting, see Sylvester-Bradley, P. C. 1949. Proc. Geol. Assoc. vol. lx, pp. 151-153.

p. 166. IN TABLE, BED 8, DORSET ; p. 172, FOSSIL LIST (CEPHALOPODS) ; and p. 173, BED 8, PUNFIELD MARINE BAND : delete " Parahoplites ".

p. 181. TABLE OF ZONES : The subzone of Hoplites benettianus should be bracketed with the Zone of Hoplites dentatus.

p. 182. FIRST LIST OF AMMONITES, LINES 8, 9 AND 10 : The first three genera should read :—Beudanticeras, Anahoplites, and Dimorphoplites.

p. 184. LIST OF AMMONITES FROM THE DISPAR SUBZONE : Delete " Dischoplites varicosus (Spath) " : for " Lechites baudini " read " Lechites gaudini "

p. 196. TABLE OF ZONES OF THE CHALK : After " Actinocamax quadratus " insert " (now Gonioteuthis quadrata) ".

p. 197. LAST PARAGRAPH ; and p. 204, LINE 11 : for " Cyrtocheilus baculoides " read " Sciponoceras baculoide ".

p. 197. LAST PARAGRAPH ; p. 199, FIGURE 41 (4) ; p. 206 LINE 33 ; and p. 212, 2ND LINE FROM BOTTOM : for " Scaphites aequalis " read " Scaphites equalis ".

p. 211. LOWER CHALK AT RINGSTEAD : A larger ammonite fauna including the genera Scaphites, Turrilites, Schloenbachia, Acanthoceras and others has been recorded. See Arkell, W. J. 1949. Proc. Dorset Nat. Hist. Arch. Soc., vol lxx, p. 125, and 1951, vol. lxxii, p. 187.

p. 248. TECTONIC STRUCTURE—UNDERLYING CAUSES : As a possible explanation of the local erosion of the Upper Greensand during the formation of the Chalk Rock described by Mr. J. A. Robbie, Messrs. Falcon and Kent have postulated a salt plug under Compton Valence. See Robbie, J. A. 1950. Geol. Mag. vol. lxxxvii, p. 209. Falcon N. L. and P.E. Kent. 1950. Ibid., vol. lxxxvii, p. 302.

p. 260. UPPER GREENSAND AT BINCOMBE : Mr. B. H. Mottram has recorded Upper Greensand on the south (upthrow) side of the Ridgeway fault at Bincombe railway cutting See Mottram, B. H. 1949. Proc. Dorset Nat. Hist. Arch. Soc., vol. lxxi, p. 182.

p 275. LINE 15 : For " 800 yds. N. of Holworth " read " 800 yds. N.W. of Holworth ": It has been shown that the Cretaceous-Jurassic junction N.W. of Holworth Farm is an unconformity, not a fault. See Mottram, B. H. 1949. Proc. Dorset Nat. Hist. Arch. Soc., vol. lxxi, p. 176, and fig. 1.

p. 277. SECOND LAST LINE : For " 50° N." read " 5° N."

p. 280. FIGURE 62: For "+500" on closed contour 1 mile E.S.E. of Osmington read "+300". (This has been amended in the 1953 reprint).

p. 281. SPRING BOTTOM SYNCLINE: The Chalk at Spring Bottom Hill pit is now thought to have been faulted, not slipped.

p. 315. LINE 26 : For " White Horse Hill 551 ft." read " White Horse Hill 515 ft."

p. 324. LINES 9 AND 10 : It is now considered that no outlier of Reading Beds is present, but that the mottled clay is Clay-with-flints. See Arkell, W. J. 1951. *Proc. Geol. Assoc.*, vol. lxii, p. 29.

pp. 324- TERRACED RIVER GRAVELS : River terraces of the River Frome have been
327 described in particular by J. F. N. Green. 1946. *Proc. Geol. Assoc.*, vol. lvii, p. 82 ; 1947, *ibid*, vol. lviii, p. 128.

p. 341. ERRATICS IN SHINGLE BEACHES: For further notes, see Lang, W. D. 1948. *Proc. Dorset Nat. Hist. Arch. Soc.*, vol. lxviii, p. 90 ; *ibid.*, vol. lxix, p. 121; Arkell, W. J. *Ibid.*, vol. lxx, p. 125.

p. 353. MUD SLIDES, OSMINGTON : These occur along a fault line parallel to the coast, which has been breached by the sea. The fault has a downthrow to the north. See Arkell, W. J. 1951. *Proc. Geol. Assoc.*, vol. lxii, p. 27.

Plate COLOURED GEOLOGICAL MAP: Bincombe village. The outcrops of Forest
XIX. Marble (g^8) should be coloured red and the outcrop of Cornbrash (g^9) orange. The mile long outcrop of Upper Greensand north of the village should be coloured dark green. These errors of colouring have been corrected in the 1953 reprint.

The Geology of the Country around Weymouth, Swanage, Corfe and Lulworth

ADDENDA AND CORRIGENDA, 1976

This list of corrections and additions has two purposes. First, it draws attention to the more important works published since 1950 that present different views of the geology from those expressed in the Memoir, and to those that present additions to knowledge. These works are grouped under chapter headings and their authors' names are printed with an asterisk in the list of references that follows on p. xix. They do not include the hundred or so references listed in Arkell, W. J. 1951b. Secondly, the list provides modern names for the fossils illustrated in the Memoir, taking into account the corrections provided for the 1953 reprint of the Memoir, by the late Dr. Arkell, Mr. C. W. Wright, C.B., M.A. and the writer.

CHAPTERS II–XI. Couper, 1958, and Lantz, 1958, present preliminary studies of Mesozoic miospores and pollen. Delair, 1958–1960, gives a comprehensive revision of Mesozoic reptiles.

CHAPTERS II–VII. Torrens (Editor), 1969, gives a comprehensive revision up to that date of Jurassic stratigraphy. Only 150 roneoed copies of this work were produced.

CHAPTER II. Cifelli, 1959, describes Bathonian foraminifera. Hallam, 1970, describes trace-fossils from the Forest Marble. House, 1957, presents a new map and description of the Fuller's Earth. Martin, 1967, analyses the processes of Bathonian sedimentation. Stinton and Torrens, 1968, describe otoliths of Bathonian fishes. Sylvester–Bradley, 1957, revises the classification of the Forest Marble. Torrens, 1965 and [1974], gives revised zonal schemes for the Bathonian.

p. 16. FIG. 3.—Read (1, 2, 3) *Liostrea hebridica* (Forbes); (1, 2) subsp. *elongata*. (4) *Rhynchonelloidella smithi* (Davidson).

p. 17. FIG. 4.—Read (1) *Digonella* cf. *digona* (J. Sowerby); (2) *Avonothyris langtonensis* (Davidson); (3) *Camptonectes laminatus* (J. Sowerby); (4) *Chlamys (Radulopecten) vagans* (J. de C. Sowerby); (5) *Liostrea hebridica* (Forbes); (6) *Catinula ancliffensis* (Cox and Arkell); (7) *Goniorhynchia boueti* (Davidson).

p. 18. LINE 5. For *Belemnopsis bessina* (d'Orbigny) read *Belemnopsis fusiformis* (Parkinson).

p. 19. LINES 2 and 3. For *Ostrea (Catinula) minuta* (J. Sowerby) read *Catinula ancliffensis* (Cox and Arkell). LINE 9 FROM BOTTOM. For *Oxytoma costata* (J. Sowerby) read *Oxytoma costatum* (Townsend).

p. 20. FIG. 5.—Read (2) *Obovothyris obovata* (J. Sowerby). (3) *Cererithyris intermedia* (J. Sowerby). (4) *Trigonia crucis* Sharp ex Lycett MS. (5) *Vaugonia angulata* (J. de C. Sowerby). (7) *Neocrassina hilpertonensis* (Lycett). (9) *Kallirhynchia yaxleyensis* (Davidson).

p. 22. FIG. 6.—Read (1) *Microthyridina siddingtonensis* (Walker MS. in Davidson). (2) *Microthyridina lagenalis* (Schlotheim). (3) *Rhynchonelloidella cerealis* (Buckman). (4) *Lopha marshii* (J. Sowerby). (5) *Plagiostoma rigidulum* (Phillips).

CHAPTERS III–VII. Norris, 1965, and Sarjeant, 1960 and 1962, describe Upper Jurassic dinoflagellates, hystrichospheres and microplankton, respectively.

CHAPTER III. Barnard, 1953, describes Oxford Clay foraminifera. Rood and others, 1971, describe Oxford Clay coccoliths.

p. 26. KELLAWAYS BEDS: It is now known that these beds are not faulted out near East Fleet. See Arkell, W. J. ,1948, *Proc. Dorset Nat. Hist. and Arch. Soc.*, **69**, p. 122.

p. 27. DESCRIPTION OF PUTTON LANE BRICKYARD: Delete *"Erymnoceras"*; for *"Sigaloceras"* read *"Gowericeras"*; for *"braamburiensis* (J. Sowerby)" read *"braamburiensis* (J. de C. Sowerby)".

p. 28. FIG. 7—Read (1) *Dicroloma trifidum* (Phillips); (2) *Catinula alimena* (d'Orbigny); (3) *Nuculoma calliope* (d'Orbigny); (4) *Myophorella scarburgensis* (Lycett); (5) *Modiolus bipartitus* (J. Sowerby); (10) *Gryphaea dilatata* J. Sowerby.

p. 29. DESCRIPTION OF CROOK HILL BRICKYARD: Delete "? Jason Zone" and "*Kosmoceras* cf. *jason* (Reinecke)". Bed 1 is now included in the Coronatum Zone. See Arkell, W. J., 1948, *Proc. Dorset Nat. Hist. and Arch. Soc.*, **69**, p. 124.

CHAPTER IV. Brown, P. R., 1964, discusses the petrography and mode of origin of the Corallian Beds. Fuersich, 1973, describes their trace-fossils and Gordon, 1965, their foraminifera. Talbot, 1973. considers that the beds were formed in four sedimentary cycles. Wilson, R. C. L., 1968a, 1968b, discusses the various carbonate facies and the diagenetic processes that have affected the sediments.

p. 39. FIG. 8.—Read (1) *Myophorella clavellata* (Parkinson). (2) *Myophorella hudlestoni* (Lycett). (3) *Chlamys (Radulopecten) fibrosa* (J. Sowerby). (4) *Chlamys midas* (Dollfus). (5) *Chlamys splendens* (Dollfus).

p. 40. FIG. 9.—Read (4) *Nanogyra nana* (J. Sowerby). (5) *Lopha gregarea* (J. Sowerby). (7) *Chlamys qualicosta* (Etallon). (9) Radiole of *Paracidaris florigemma* (Phillips).

p. 46. BED 16, Limestone, for "10 ft" read "1 ft 10 in".

CHAPTERS V–VII. Norris, 1969, describes miospores from the Kimmeridge Clay, Portland Beds and Purbeck Beds.

CHAPTERS V–VI, Casey, 1967, revises the chronostratigraphy of the latest Kimmeridgian stage and the Portlandian stage.

CHAPTER V. Brookfield, 1973, discusses the environment in which the Abbotsbury Ironstone was formed. Cope, 1967, describes the stratigraphy and revises the ammonites and the zoning of the lower part of the Upper Kimmeridge Clay. Downie, 1957, gives a brief note on the microplankton. Kilenyi, 1969, and Lloyd, 1959 and 1962, describe ostracods and foraminifera. Ziegler, 1962, revises the ammonites and the zoning of the *Aulacostephanus* zones of the Lower Kimmeridge Clay.

p. 65. FIG. 15.—Read (1) *Laevaptychus latus* (Parkinson). (2) *Torquirhynchia inconstans* (J. Sowerby). (3) *Nanogyra virgula* (Defrance). (4) *Deltoideum delta* (William Smith). (5) *Discinisca latissima* (J. Sowerby).

p. 67. Under "Zones" in the boxed list, for "*Gavesia*" read "*Gravesia*".

pp. 71–72. Measurements of part of the type-section (Beds 9 to 42) have been revised by Cope, 1967.

p. 74, PLATE IV, fig. 6. For "*Aulacostephanus*", read "*Aulacostephanus (Nannocardioceras)*". The bed from which these ammonites come is now known as the *Nannocardioceras* Bed. It lies 10 ft below The Flats Stone Band.

p. 77. FIG. 17.—Read (1) *Pectinatites (Virgatosphinctoides) pseudoscruposus* (Spath). (2) *Zaraiskites albani* (Arkell).

p. 78, PLATE V, fig. 3, read *Pectinatites (Pectinatites) cornutifer* (Buckman); fig. 4, *Pectinatites (Pectinatites) sp.*; fig. 5, *Pectinatites (Virgatosphinctoides)* cf. *grandis* (Neaverson).

CHAPTER VI. Townson, 1975 (see also Ager, 1976), revises the lithostratigraphic classification and palaeoenvironmental interpretation of the Portland Beds.

CHAPTER VII. Casey, 1963, reclassifies the Purbeck Beds as Lulworth Beds (Jurassic) below and Durlston Beds (Cretaceous) above, with the system boundary at the base of the Cinder Bed. Clements, 1969 (*in* Torrens, Editor), gives a new measured section of the Purbeck Beds of Durlston Bay. Delair, 1963, 1966, 1969, 1974, and Delair and Lander, 1973, examine the reptiles of the Purbeck Beds and their footprints. Huckriede, 1967, revises the non-marine bivalves of the equivalent beds in Germany, with some relevance to the English faunas. Pugh, 1969, describes the algae of the Lower Purbeck. West, 1975 (the latest of several papers) describes the Lower Purbeck Beds, their evaporites, and their mode of formation.

p. 124. The table of zones should be replaced by the following (see Anderson, F. W., 1971, *Bull. Geol. Surv. Gt. Brit.*, No. 34, p. 28):

Upper Purbeck	*Cypridea setina*
Middle Purbeck	{ *Cypridea vidrana*
	Cypridea granulosa fasciculata
	Cypridea granulosa granulosa
Lower Purbeck	*Cypridea dunkeri*

p. 129. FIG. 28.—Read (1) *Cypridea setina* (Anderson) s.l.; (2) *Cypridea ventrosa* Jones; (3) *Cypridea propunctata* Sylvester–Bradley; (4) *Cypridea granulosa* (J. de C. Sowerby) *fasciculata* (Forbes); (5) *Cypridea granulosa protogranulosa* Anderson; (6) *Theriosynoecum forbesii* (Jones) *verrucosum* (Jones); (7) *Mantelliana purbeckensis* (Forbes); (8) *Fabanella boloniensis* (Jones); (9) *F. ansata* (Jones).

p. 133. For an account of *Chara* see Harris, T. M. 1939, *The British Purbeck Charophyta*. British Museum (Natural History), London.

p. 143. For a more detailed section of this road cutting see Sylvester–Bradley, P. C., 1949, *Proc. Geol. Assoc.*, **60**, pp. 151–3.

CHAPTERS VIII–XI. Hancock, 1969, describes the development of the Cretaceous basin of deposition.

CHAPTER VIII. Allen, 1959, offers a new interpretation of the Wealden environment; Hughes and Croxton, 1973, propose a palynological correlation of the Wealden beds.

p. 151. FIG. 34.—Read (11) *Theriosynoecum fittoni* (Mantell). (12) *Cypridea dorsispinata* (Anderson). (13) *Cypridea menevensis* (Anderson).

CHAPTER IX. See Casey, 1961, for a review of the stratigraphy, palaeontology and conditions of deposition of the Lower Greensand.

pp. 166, 172, 173. Delete all references to *Parahoplites*.

p. 170. Fig. 38.—Read (1, 2) *Paranomia laevigata* (J. de C. Sowerby). (3) *Aptolinter aptiensis* (Pictet and Campiche). (4) *Nemocardium (Pratulum) ibbetsoni* (Forbes). (5, 6) *Parmicorbula striatula* (J. de C. Sowerby). (8) *Venilicardia anglica* (Woods). (9) *Ceratostreon tuberculiferum* (Koch and Dunker). (10) *Resatrix (Vectorbis) vectensis* (Forbes). (11) *Freiastarte subcostata* (d'Orbigny). (12) *Linearia subconcentrica* (d'Orbigny).

pp. 180–181. For revised zonal schemes of the Albian compare Owen, 1971, with Wright, C. W. and Collins, J. S. H., 1972, British Cretaceous crabs. *Palaeontogr. Soc. London.*

p. 182. First list of ammonites, lines 8–10: the first three generic names should read *Beudanticeras*, *Anahoplites* and *Dimorphoplites*.

p. 184. In list of ammonites, delete *Discohoplites varicosus* Spath; for *Lechites baudini* read *Lechites gaudini*.

p. 186–187. FIG. 40.—Read (1) *Amphidonte obliqua* (Pulteney). (2) *Merklinia aspera* (Lamarck). (3) *Nanonavis carinatus* (J. Sowerby). (4) *Neithea gibbosa* (Pulteney). (6) *Rotularia concava* (J. Sowerby).

CHAPTERS X–XI. Drummond, 1970, discusses contemporaneous movements in Upper Albian and Cenomanian times. Kennedy, 1970, revises the stratigraphy and correlation of the Upper Greensand and Lower Chalk.

CHAPTER XI. Black, 1953, pioneers new ideas on the constitution of the Chalk. Bromley, 1967, analyses the formation of hardgrounds in the Chalk. Jefferies, 1963, describes the stratigraphy of the *plenus* Marls in detail. Larwood, 1962, revises a large group of Chalk Polyzoa.

p. 196. In zonal table, for *Actinocamax quadratus* read *Gonioteuthis quadrata*; for a new Cenomanian zonal scheme, see Kennedy, 1970.

p. 197, last paragraph, and p. 204, line 11: for *Cyrtocheilus baculoides* read *Sciponoceras baculoide*.

p. 198–199. FIG. 41.—Read (4) *Scaphites equalis* J. Sowerby. (6) *Orbirhynchia cuvieri* (d'Orbigny). (8) *Discoides dixoni* (Forbes). (10) *Sternotaxis planus* (Mantell).

pp. 200–201. FIG. 42.—Read (6) *Uintacrinus socialis* Grinnell. (7) *Isocrania egnabergensis* (Retzius). (9) *Gonioteuthis quadrata* (Defrance).

p. 211. Lower Chalk at Ringstead. For a larger ammonite fauna see Arkell, W. J., 1949, *Proc. Dorset Nat. Hist. and Arch. Soc.*, **70**, p. 125, and Arkell, 1951b, *ibid*, p. 187.

CHAPTER XII. Chandler, 1964, summarises much previous work on the fossil floras and their palaeoclimatic implications. Curry, 1965, revises the stratigraphy of the Eocene formations.

CHAPTER XIII. The following works deal with various aspects of the tectonic structure and its interpretation: Arkell, 1951a; House, 1961; Mottram, 1950; Mottram and House, 1956; Phillips, 1964; Ridd, 1973; West, 1964a.

p. 248. Falcon, N. F. and Kent, P. E., 1950, *Geol. Mag.*, **87**, pp. 302–3, postulate a salt plug under Compton Valence, movement of which might explain local erosion of Upper Greensand during the formation of the Chalk Rock.

p. 260. Mottram, B. H., 1949, *Proc. Dorset Nat. Hist. and Arch. Soc.*, **71**, p. 182, records Upper Greensand on the south (upthrow) side of the Ridgeway fault at Bincombe railway cutting.

p. 275, LINE 16. For "800 yds. N, of Holworth" read "800 yds. N.W. of Holworth".

Mottram, B. H., 1949, *Proc. Dorset Nat. Hist. and Arch. Soc.*, **71**, p. 176 and fig. 1, shows that the Jurassic–Cretaceous junction here is an unconformity, not a fault.

p. 277, penultimate line: for 50° N. read 5° N.

p. 281. The Chalk at Spring Bottom Hill pit is now thought to be faulted not slipped.

CHAPTER XIV. Bird and Ranwell, 1964, May, 1969, and Ranwell and others 1964, discuss the evolution of Poole Harbour. Carr and Blackley, 1969 and 1974 (with references to much earlier work) describe the Chesil Beach. Carreck, 1955b, gives a synopsis of the Quaternary vertebrates. Mottram, 1956a, describes the drainage of the Poxwell and Upton areas and, 1973, the evolution of parts of the Dorset coast. Sparks, 1953, describes the evolution of the Weymouth lowland.

p. 324, LINES 8 AND 9. The mottled clay is now considered to be Clay-with-flints, not Reading Beds; see Arkell, 1951a.

pp. 324–327. The terraces of the River Frome have been described in particular by Green, J. F. N., 1946, *Proc. Geol. Assoc.*, **57**, pp. 82–101; 1947, **58**, pp. 128–43.

p. 341. Erratics in shingle beaches. For further notes see Lang, W.D., 1948, *Proc. Dorset Nat. Hist. and Arch. Soc.*, **68**, p. 90; 1949, **69**, p. 121; Arkell, W. J., 1950, *ibid.*, **70**, p. 125.

p. 353, Osmington mud-slides. These occur along a fault line parallel to the coast, which has been breached by the sea. The fault throws down to the north. See Arkell, 1951a, *Proc. Geol. Assoc.*, **62**, p. 27.

p. 360 (CHAPTER XV). House (1963, pp. 79–80) summarised the log of the BP Kimmeridge No. 1 well and reported the occurrence of oil in the Cornbrash. In 1969 (BP News Bulletin No. 6), BP announced that the well had produced over 100,000 tons of crude oil since 1961 and was then by far the most productive single well ever drilled in Britain. By the end of 1975 it had produced a further 100,000 tons and it is still producing in 1976 (information from the company). Although the Cornbrash is the oil reservoir, it is likely that the source-rock lies somewhat deeper, perhaps in the Bridport Sands.   R.V.M.

ADDITIONAL REFERENCES 1951–1976 (part)

This list contains additional references to the geology of the area covered by the Memoir. They relate to literature published between 1951 and 1976 and do not claim to be complete, particularly for the last year. Works published between 1947 (when the Memoir first appeared) and 1950 are listed in Arkell, 1951b and are not repeated here. References to offshore geology have been added.

In certain references relating to Chapters I to XIV, the authors' names appear with an asterisk. These are the works to which attention is drawn in the Addenda and Corrigenda on pp. xvi–xix. References relating to Chapter XV (Economic Geology) are listed separately.

A. Works relating to Chapters I–XIV

AGER, D. V. 1959. A new inarticulate brachiopod from the Dorset Corallian. *Proc. Geol. Assoc.*, **70**, Pt. 1, pp. 28–30, pl. 1.

—— 1963. Jurassic stages. *Nature*, **198**, No. 4885, pp. 1045–6.

*—— 1976. Discussion of Portlandian faunas. *J. Geol. Soc. London*, **132**, Pt. 3, pp. 335–6.

*ALLEN, P. 1959. The Wealden environment: Anglo-Paris basin. *Phil. Trans. Roy. Soc. London*, (B), **242**, No. 692, pp. 283–346, figs., refs.

——and KEITH, M. L. 1965. Carbon isotope ratios and palaeosalinities of Purbeck–Wealden carbonates. *Nature*, **208**, No. 5017, pp. 1278–80, figs., refs.

ANDERSON, F. W. 1962. Correlation of the Upper Purbeck Beds of England with the German Wealden. *Liv. and Manch. Geol. J.*, **3**, pp. 21–32, figs., pls., refs.

—— 1966. New genera of Purbeck and Wealden Ostracoda. *Bull. Brit. Mus. (Nat. Hist.) Geol.*, **11**, No. 9, pp. 435–46, 485, figs., refs.

—— 1973. The Jurassic–Cretaceous transition: the non-marine ostracod faunas. Pp. 101–10 *in* CASEY, R. and RAWSON, P. F. (Eds.) *The Boreal Lower Cretaceous*. Seel House Press, Liverpool. [viii] + 449 pp., maps, figs., pls., refs.

ANON. 1962. The slow march of a Purbeck *Iguanodon. New Scientist,* **13,** No. 271, p. 186.

*ARKELL, W. J. 1951a. Structure of the Spring Bottom ridge, and the origin of the mud slides, Osmington, Dorset. *Proc. Geol. Assoc.,* **62,** Pt. 1, pp. 21–30, figs., map, refs.

*—— 1951b. Dorset Geology, 1940–50. *Proc. Dorset Nat. Hist. and Arch. Soc.,* **72,** pp. 176–94, pls., refs.

——1951c–1958. A monograph of English Bathonian ammonites. Pts. 1–8, pp. i–viii, 1–264, 33 pls, refs. *Palaeontogr. Soc. London.*

—— 1956b. The effects of storms on the Chesil Beach in November, 1954. *Proc. Dorset Nat. Hist. and Arch. Soc.* **76,** pp. 141–5, refs.

—— 1956c. Geological results of the cloudburst in the Weymouth district, 18th July, 1955. *Ibid.* (for 1955) **77,** pp. 90–6, figs., pls., refs.

BARKER, D. 1966. Ostracods from the Portland Beds of Dorset. *Bull. Brit. Mus. (Nat. Hist.) Geol.,* **11,** No. 9, pp. 447–57, 485, pls. 1–6, refs.

*BARNARD, T. 1953. Foraminifera from the Upper Oxford Clay (Jurassic) of Redcliff Point, near Weymouth, England. *Proc. Geol. Assoc.,* **64,** Pt. 3, pp. 183–97, figs., refs.

*BIRD, E. C. F. and RANWELL, D. S. 1964. *Spartina* salt marshes in southern England, IV. The physiography of Poole Harbour, Dorset. *J. Ecol.,* **52,** pp. 355–66, figs., refs.

*BLACK, M. 1953. [The constitution of the Chalk]. *Proc. Geol. Soc. London,* No. 1499, pp. lxxxi–vi.

BOND, W. R. G. 1952. Theories as to the origin of Chesil Beach. *Proc. Dorset Nat. Hist. and Arch. Soc.,* **73,** pp. 163–70.

*BROMLEY, R. G. 1967. Some observations on burrows of thalassinidean Crustacea in Chalk hardgrounds. *Quart. J. Geol. Soc. London,* **123,** Pt. 2, pp. 157–82, figs., pls., refs.

*BROOKFIELD, M. E. 1973. The palaeoenvironment of the Abbotsbury Ironstone (Upper Jurassic) of Dorset. *Palaeontology,* **16,** Pt. 2, pp. 261–74, figs., refs.

BROWN, E. H. 1960. The building of southern Britain. *Zeitschr. Geomorphol.,* N.F. **4,** Abh., pp. 264–74, figs., refs.

BROWN, P. R. 1963. Algal limestones and associated sediments in the basal Purbeck of Dorset. *Geol. Mag.,* **100,** No. 6, pp. 565–73, figs., pls., refs.

*—— 1964. Petrography and origin of some Upper Jurassic beds from Dorset, England. *J. Sed. Pet.,* **34,** No. 2, pp. 254–69, figs., photos., refs.

BURN, H. 1950. Blashenwell tufa. *Proc. Bournemouth Nat. Sci. Soc.* **39,** pp. 48–51, refs.

CALKIN, J. B. 1968. *Ancient Purbeck: an account of the Geology of the Isle of Purbeck and its early inhabitants.* Friary Press, Dorchester. [vi]+61 pp., figs., photos, refs.

CALLOMON, J. H. 1964. Notes on the Callovian and Oxfordian stages. Cong. Géol. Int. Coll. du Jurassique à Luxembourg. 1962. *Inst. Grd. Duc., Sect. Sci. Nat., Phys. Math.,* pp. 269–91, refs.

CARR, A. P. 1969. Size grading along a pebble beach: Chesil Beach, England. *J. Sed. Pet.,* **39,** No. 1, pp. 297–311, figs., refs.

—— 1971. Experiments on longshore transport and sorting of pebbles: Chesil Beach, England. *Ibid.,* **41,** No. 4, pp. 1084–104, figs., refs.

*—— and BLACKLEY, M. W. L. 1969. Geological composition of the pebbles of Chesil Beach, Dorset. *Proc. Dorset Nat. Hist. and Arch. Soc.,* **90,** pp. 133–40, refs.

*—— —— 1974. Ideas on the origin and development of Chesil Beach, Dorset. *Ibid.,* **95,** pp. 9–17, map, photos, refs.

—— and GLEASON, R. 1972. Chesil Beach, Dorset, and the cartographic evidence of Sir John Coode. *Proc. Dorset Nat. Hist. and Arch. Soc.,* **93,** pp. 125–31, map, figs., refs.

——, GLEASON, R. and KING, A. 1970. Significance of pebble size and shape in sorting by waves. *Sed. Geol.,* **4,** No. 2, pp. 89–101, figs. refs.

*CARRECK, J. N. 1955a (with contributions by DAVIS, A. G.). The Quaternary deposits of Bowleaze Cove, near Weymouth, Dorset. *Proc. Geol. Assoc.,* **66,** Pt. 1, pp. 74–100, fig., map, refs.

*—— 1955b. The Quaternary vertebrates of Dorset, fossil and sub-fossil. *Proc. Dorset Nat. Hist. and Arch. Soc.,* **75,** pp. 164–88, refs.

—— 1960. Whitsun field meeting to Weymouth, Abbotsbury and Dorchester, Dorset. *Proc. Geol. Assoc.,* **71,** pp. 341–7.

CASEY, R. 1960–1966 (incomplete). The Ammonoidea of the Lower Greensand, Pts. 1–7, pp. 1–582, pls. 1–97. *Palaeontogr. Soc. London.*

*—— 1961. The stratigraphical palaeontology of the Lower Greensand. *Palaeontology*, **3**, Pt. 4, pp. 487–621, figs., pls., refs.

*—— 1963. The dawn of the Cretaceous period in Britain. *Bull. of South Eastern Union of Scientific Societies*, **117**, pp. 1–15, figs., refs.

*—— 1967. The position of the Middle Volgian in the English Jurassic. *Proc. Geol. Soc. London*, No. 1640, pp. 128–33, fig., refs.

—— 1971. Facies, faunas and tectonics in late Jurassic–early Cretaceous Britain. 153–72 *in* MIDDLEMISS, F. A., RAWSON, P. F. and NEWALL, G. (Eds.) *Faunal provinces in space and time.* Seel House Press, Liverpool. 236 pp., figs., maps, refs.

*CHANDLER, M. E. J. 1964. *The Lower Tertiary floras of southern England, IV. A summary and survey of findings in the light of recent botanical observations.* Trustees of the British Museum (Natural History), London, xii + 151 pp., map, figs., 4 pls., refs.

CHARIG, A. J. and NEWMAN, B. H. 1962. Footprints in the Purbeck. *New Scientist*, **14**, No. 285, pp. 234–5. fig., photo.

CHURCHER, R. A., BUTLER, B. and BARTLETT, P. D. 1970. A further report on the caves of the Isle of Portland. *Trans. Cave Res. Group Gt. Brit.*, **12**, Pt. 4, pp. 291–8, figs., ref.

*CIFELLI, R. 1959. Bathonian Foraminifera of England. *Bull. Mus. Comp. Zool. Harvard*, **121**, No. 7, pp. 263–368, figs., pls., refs.

—— 1960. Notes on the distribution of English Bathonian Foraminifera. *Geol. Mag.*, **97**, No. 1, pp. 33–42, refs.

CLEMENTS, R. G. 1967. Some notes on the Purbeck Beds. *Proc. Dorset Nat. Hist. and Arch. Soc.*, **88**, pp. 43–4.

COLE, D. I. 1975. Observations on a burning cliff. *Ibid.*, **96**, pp. 16–9, fig., photo, refs.

*COPE, J. C. W. 1967. The palaeontology and stratigraphy of the lower part of the Upper Kimmeridge Clay of Dorset. *Bull. Brit. Mus. (Nat. Hist.) Geol.*, **15**, No. 1, pp. 1–79, figs., 33 pls., refs.

—— 1968a. *Propectinatites*, a new lower Kimmeridgian ammonite genus. *Palaeontology*, **11**, Pt. 1, pp. 16–8, pl., refs.

——1968b. Epizoic oysters on Kimmeridigian ammonites *Ibid.*, **11**, Pt. 1, pp. 19–20, pl., refs.

—— 1971. Geology. *Proc. Dorset Nat. Hist. and Arch. Soc.*, **92**, pp. 41–4, refs.

—— 1972. Geology: [The Natural Sciences, 1971]. *Ibid.*, **93**, pp. 38–40.

—— 1975. Geology. *Ibid.*, **96**, p. 74.

—— and WIMBLEDON, W. A. 1973. Ammonite faunas of the uppermost Kimmeridge Clay, the Portland Sand and the Portland Stone of Dorset. *Proc. Ussher Soc.*, **2**, Pt. 6, pp. 593–8, figs. refs.

—— and ZEISS, A. 1964. Zur Parallelisierung des englischen Oberkimmeridge mit dem fränkischen Untertithon (Malm zeta). *Geol. – Bl. Nordost. Bayern*, **14**, Heft 1, pp. 5–14, figs., refs.

——, SARJEANT, W. A. S., SPALDING, D. A. E. and ZEISS, A. 1964. The Kimmeridgian–Portlandian boundary. Cong. Géol. Int. Coll. du Jurassique à Luxembourg, 1962. *Inst. Grd. Duc., Sect. Sci. Nat., Phys. Math.*, pp. 933–6, refs.

CORBYN, P. R. 1967. The size and shape of pebbles on Chesil Beach. *Geog. J.*, **133**, Pt. 1, pp. 54–5, table, refs.

COSGROVE, M. E. 1970. Iodine in the bituminous Kimmeridge shales of the Dorset coast, England. *Geochim. Cosmochim. Acta.*, **34**, No. 7, pp. 830–6, refs.

—— and HEARN, E. W. 1966. Structures in the Upper Purbeck Beds at Peveril Point, Swanage, Dorset. *Geol. Mag.*, **103**, No. 6, pp. 498–507, figs, maps, pl., refs.

*COUPER, R. A. 1958. British Mesozoic microspores and pollen grains. A systematic and stratigraphic study. *Palaeontogr.*, **103**, Abt.B, Lief. 4–6, pp. 75–179, figs., pls., refs.

COX, L. R. 1958. William Joscelyn Arkell, 1904–1958. *Biog. Mem. Fellows Roy. Soc. London*, **4**, pp. 1–14, photo., refs.

CROSS, T. 1972. A piece of Purbeck rock, or aspects of Dorset geological history. *Petros.*, **10**, pp. 4–7, fig.

CURRY, D. *In* PRUVOST, P. (Ed.) 1958. Cong. Géol. Int. Lexique Stratigraphique International, Europe. Fasc. 3a, England, Wales and Scotland, Pt. 3a XII, Palaeogene. Centre National de la Recherche Scientifique, Paris. 82 pp.

CURRY, D. 1963. Age determinations of some rocks from the floor of the English Channel. *Proc. Ussher Soc.*, **1**, Pt. 1, pp. 5–6.

*—— 1965. The Palaeogene Beds of South-East England. *Proc. Geol. Assoc.*, **76**, Pt. 2, pp. 151–73, map, figs., refs.

DAVIDSSON, J. 1957. Scolt Head Island och Chesil Beach. *Svensk. Geog. Aarsbok*, **33**, pp. 166–71, figs., photos., refs.

DAVIS, A. G. and CARRECK, J. N. 1958. Further observations on a Quaternary deposit at Bowleaze Cove, near Weymouth, Dorset. *Proc. Geol. Assoc.*, **69**, Pt. 2, pp. 120–2, refs.

*DELAIR, J. B. 1958–1960. The Mesozoic Reptiles of Dorset. *Proc. Dorset Nat. Hist. and Arch. Soc.*, Pt. 1, **79**, pp. 47–72, refs.; Pt. 2, **80**, pp. 52–90, refs.; Pt. 3, **81**, pp. 59–85, refs.

*—— 1963. Notes on Purbeck fossil footprints, with descriptions of two hitherto unknown forms from Dorset. *Ibid.*, **84**, pp. 92–100, figs., photos., refs.

*—— 1966. New records of Dinosaurs and other fossil Reptiles from Dorset. *Ibid.*, **87**, pp. 57–66, photos., refs.

*—— 1969. The first record of the occurrence of Ichthyosaurs in the Purbeck. *Ibid.*, **90**, pp. 128–52, photos., figs., refs.

*—— 1975. Worbarrow Bay footprints. *Ibid.*, **96**, pp. 14–6, refs.

*—— and LANDER, A. B. 1973. A short history of the discovery of reptilian footprints in the Purbeck Beds of Dorset, with notes on their stratigraphical distribution. *Ibid.*, **94**, pp. 17–20, figs., refs.

DINGWALL, R. G. 1971. The structural and stratigraphical geology of a portion of the eastern English Channel. *Rep.* No. 71/8, *Inst. Geol. Sci.*, 24 pp., figs., maps, refs.

DONOVAN, D. T. and HEMINGWAY, J. E. *in* PRUVOST, P. (Ed.) 1958. Cong. Géol. Int., Lexique Stratigraphique International, Europe, Fasc. 3a, England, Wales and Scotland, Pt. 3a X, Jurassic. Centre National de la Recherche Scientifique, Paris. 394 pp.

—— and STRIDE, A. H. 1961. An acoustic survey of the sea floor south of Dorset and its geological interpretation. *Phil. Trans. Roy. Soc. London*, (B), **244**, pp. 299–330, maps, pls., refs.

DOORNKAMP, J. C. 1964. Subaerial landform development in relation to past sea levels in a part of south Dorset. *Proc. Dorset Nat. Hist. and Arch. Soc.*, **85**, pp. 71–7, figs., refs.

*DOWNIE, C. 1956. Microplankton from the Kimmeridge Clay. *Quart. J. Geol. Soc. London*, **112**, pp. 413–34, figs., pl., refs.

*DRUMMOND. P. V. O. 1979. The mid-Dorset Swell. Evidence of Albanian–Cenomanian movements in Wessex. *Proc. Geol. Assoc.* **81**, Pt. 4, pp. 679–714, figs., refs.

FALCON, N. L. and KENT, P. E. 1960. Geological results of petroleum exploration in Britain 1945–1957. *Mem. Geol. Soc. London.* No. 2, 56 pp., pls., figs., refs.

FORD, T. D. and HOOPER, M. J. 1964. The caves of the Isle of Portland. *Trans. Cave Res. Group Gt. Brit.*, **7**, No. 1, pp. 13–37, figs., pls.

*FUERSICH, F. T. 1973. Fossil-Diagenese, Nr. 2: *Thalassinoides* and the origin of nodular limestone in the Corallian Beds (Upper Jurassic) of southern England. *Neues Jahrb. Geol. Paläont. Monatshafte*, Jahrg. 1973, Heft 3, pp. 136–56, figs., photos., refs.

*GORDON, W. A. 1965. Foraminifera from the Corallian Beds, Upper Jurassic, of Dorset, England. *J. Paleont.*, **39**, No. 5, pp. 828–63, figs., refs.

GREEN, J. F. N. 1949. The breccia of Redcliff, Wareham. *Proc. Bournemouth Nat. Sci. Soc.*, **38**, pp. 52–3, photo., fig.

HALLAM, A. 1969. Faunal realms and facies in the Jurassic. *Palaeontology*, **12**, Pt. 1, pp. 1–18, figs., refs.

*—— 1970. *Gyrochorte* and other trace fossils in the Forest Marble (Bathonian) of Dorset, England. Pp. 189–200 *in* CRIMES, T. P. and HARPER, J. C. (Eds.) *Trace Fossils*. Seel House Press, Liverpool. 547 pp., figs., photos., pls.

HAMPTON, J. S. 1957. Some holothurian spicules from the upper Bathonian of the Dorset coast. *Geol. Mag.*, **94**, No. 6, pp. 507–10, figs., refs.

—— 1958. *Frizzellus irregularis*, a new holothurian sclerite from the Upper Bathonian of the Dorset coast, England. *Micropaleont.*, **4**, No. 3, pp. 309–16, pl., figs., refs.

—— 1960. A statistical analysis of *Rhabdotites dorsetensis* Hodson, Harris and Lawson, 1956. *Micropaleont.*, **6**, No. 3, pp. 307–14, pl., refs.

*HANCOCK, J. M. 1969. Transgression of the Cretaceous sea in south-west England. *Proc. Ussher Soc.*, **2**, Pt. 2, pp. 61–83.

HEAP, W. 1957. The Mammal Bed of Durlston Bay. *Dorset Year Book* 1957–1958, pp. 83–5, photos.

HODSON, F., HARRIS, B. and LAWSON, L. 1956. Holothurian spicules from the Oxford Clay of Redcliff, near Weymouth (Dorset). *Geol. Mag.*, **93**, No. 4, pp. 336–44, figs., refs.

HOFSTETTER, R. 1967. Coup d'oeil sur les sauriens (=lacertiliens) des couches du Purbeck (Jurassique supérieur d'Angleterre). Pp. 349–71 in *Problèmes actuels de paléontologie (évolution des vertébrés)*, Coll. Int. No. 163, Centre Nat. Rech. Sci., Paris, figs.

HOOPER, M. J. 1964. A new specimen of *Heterostrophus phillipsi* from the Oxford Clay of the Weymouth district. P. 39 *in* HOUSE, M. R. Geology. *Proc. Dorset. Nat. Hist. and Arch. Soc.*, **85**, pp. 38–39.

HOUSE, M. R. 1955. New records from the Red Nodule Beds near Weymouth. *Ibid.*, **75**, pp. 134–5.

*—— 1957. The Fuller's Earth outcrop in South Dorset. *Ibid.*, **78**, pp. 64–70, fig., refs.

—— 1958a. On the Portlandian zones of the Vale of Wardour and the use of *Titanites giganteus* as an Upper Jurassic zone fossil. *Proc. Geol. Assoc.*, **69**, pp. 17–9.

—— 1958b. The Dorset coast from Poole to the Chesil Beach. *Geol. Assoc. Guide*, No. 22.

*—— 1961. The structure of the Weymouth Anticline. *Proc. Geol. Assoc.*, **72**, Pt. 2, pp. 221–38, maps, figs., refs.

—— 1963. Geology: Dorset Geology, 1950–1960. *Proc. Dorset Nat. Hist. and Arch. Soc.*, **84**, pp. 77–91, figs., refs.

—— 1965. Geology. *Ibid.*, **86**, pp. 38–40.

—— 1966. Geology. *Ibid.*, **87**, pp. 33–4.

—— 1967. Geology. *Ibid.*, **88**, p. 41.

—— 1968. Geology. *Ibid.*, **89**, pp. 41–5.

—— 1969a. Geology. *Ibid.*, **90**, pp. 43–5.

—— 1969b. Geologist's Association Guide. No. 22: *The Dorset coast from Poole to the Chesil Beach*. Geol. Assoc., Colchester. 32 pp., figs., refs. [Revised edition]

—— 1970. Geology. *Proc. Dorset Nat. Hist. and Arch. Soc.*, **91**, pp. 38–9, fig.

*HUCKRIEDE, R. 1967. Molluskenfaunen mit limnischen und brackischen Elementen aus Jura, Serpulit und Wealden NW – Deutchslands und ihre palaeogeographische Bedeutung. *Beihefte Geol. Jahr.*, Heft 67, 263 pp. pls., figs., refs.

*HUGHES, N. F. and CROXTON, C. A. 1973. Palynologic correlation of the Dorset 'Wealden'. *Palaeontology*, **16**, Pt. 3, pp. 567–601, figs., refs.

JEFFERIES, R. P. S. 1962. The palaeoecology of the *Actinocamax plenus* Subzone (lowest Turonian) in the Anglo-Paris basin. *Ibid.*, **4**, Pt. 4, pp. 609–47, figs., pls., refs.

*—— 1963. The stratigraphy of the *Actinocamax plenus* Subzone (Turonian) in the Anglo-Paris basin. *Proc. Geol. Assoc.*, **74**, Pt. 1, pp. 1–33, figs., refs.

JOFFE, J. 1967. The 'dwarf' crocodiles of the Purbeck Formation, Dorset: a re-appraisal. *Palaeontology*, **10**, Pt. 4, pp. 629–39, figs., refs.

KENNEDY, W. J. 1967. Burrows and surface traces from the Lower Chalk of southern England. *Bull. Brit. Mus. (Nat. Hist.) Geol.*, **15**, No. 3, pp. 125–67, figs., pls., refs.

*—— 1970. A correlation of the uppermost Albian and the Cenomanian of south-west England. *Proc. Geol. Assoc.*, **81**, Pt. 4, pp. 613–77, figs., refs.

KENT, P. E. 1959. Drilling for oil in Dorset. *New Scientist*, **6**, No. 139, pp. 84–5, photos.

KILENYI, T. I. 1965. *Oertliana*, a new ostracod genus from the Upper Jurassic of north-west Europe. *Palaeontology*, **8**, Pt. 3, pp. 572–6, figs., pls., refs.

*—— 1969. The Ostracoda of the Dorset Kimmeridge Clay. *Ibid.*, **12**, Pt. 1, pp. 112–60, figs., pls., refs.

KING, W. B. R. 1954. The geological history of the English Channel. *Quart. J. Geol. Soc. London*, **110**, Pt. 1, pp. 77–101, figs., map, refs.

LAING, J. F. 1975. Mid-Cretaceous angiosperm pollen from southern England and northern France. *Palaeontology*, **18**, Pt. 4 pp. 775–808 figs., pls., refs.

*LANTZ, J. 1958. Étude palynologique de quelques échantillons Mésozoiques dn Dorset (Grande Bretagne). *Inst. Franc. Pétrole Rev.* **13**, No. 6, pp. 917–43, pls., tables, refs.

*LARWOOD, G. P. 1962. The morphology and systematics of some Cretaceous cribri-morph Polyzoa (Pelmatoporinae). *Bull. Brit. Mus. (Nat. Hist.) Geol.*, **6**, No. 1, pp. 1–285, figs., pls., refs.

*LLOYD, A. J. 1959. Arenaceous foraminifera from the type Kimmeridgian (Upper Jurassic). *Palaeontology*, **1**, Pt. 4, pp. 298–320, figs., pl., refs.

*—— 1962. Polymorphinid, miliolid and rotaliform Foraminifera from the type Kimmeridgian. *Micropalaeont.*, **8**, No. 3, pp. 369–83, figs., pls., refs.

MALZ, H. 1958. Die Gattung *Macrodentina* und einige andere Ostracoden-Arten aus dem Oberen Jura von N.W. Deutschland, England und Frankreich. *Abh. Senckenb. naturforsch. Ges.*, **497**, pp. 1–67, figs., pls., refs.

*MARTIN, A. J. 1967. Bathonian sedimentation in southern England. *Proc. Geol. Assoc.*, **78**, Pt. 3, pp. 473–88, figs., refs.

*MAY, V. J. 1969. Reclamation and shoreline change in Poole Harbour. *Proc. Dorset Nat. Hist. and Arch. Soc.*, **90**, pp. 141–54, figs., refs.

MITRA, K. C. 1958. Variation in *Goniorhynchia boueti* from Normandy and Dorset. *J. Paleont.*, **32**, No. 5, pp. 992–1006, figs., refs.

MORTON, N. (Editor). [1974]. The definition of standard Jurassic stages. *Mém. Bur. Rech. Géol. Minières.*, **75**, 1971, pp. 83–93, refs.

*MOTTRAM, B. H. 1950. Notes on the structure of the Poxwell pericline and the Ridgeway fault at Bincombe Tunnel. *Proc. Dorset Nat. Hist. and Arch. Soc.*, **71**, pp. 175–83, maps, refs.

*—— 1956a. Problems presented by the drainage of the Poxwell pericline and the Upton syncline. *Ibid.* (for 1954), **76**, pp. 136–40, map, refs.

—— 1956b. Some notes on Dorset Geology, 1952–54. I. The inland facies of the Gault, II. Distribution of the superficial Pleistocene deposits near South Holworth. *Ibid.* (for 1955), **77**, pp. 97–101, refs.

—— 1957. The Poxwell wind-gap. *Ibid.*, **78**, pp. 71–2, refs.

*—— 1973. Some aspects of the evolution of parts of the Dorset coast. *Ibid.*, **94**, pp. 21–6, figs., refs.

*—— and HOUSE, M. R. 1956. The structure of the northern margin of the Poxwell pericline. *Ibid.* (for 1954), **76**, pp. 129–35, figs., refs.

NEATE, D. J. M. 1967. Underwater pebble grading of Chesil Bank. *Proc. Geol. Assoc.*, **78**, Pt. 3, pp. 419–26, figs., refs.

NOËL, D. 1965. *Sur les coccolithes du Jurassique européen et d'Afrique du Nord*. Paris.

*NORRIS, G. 1965. Archeopyle structures in Upper Jurassic Dinoflagellates from southern England. *N.Z.J. Geol. Geophys.*, **8**, No. 5, pp. 792–806, figs., pls., refs.

*—— 1969. Miospores from the Purbeck Beds and marine Upper Jurassic of southern England. *Palaeontology*, **12**, Pt. 4, pp. 574–620, figs., pls., refs.

OPPÉ, E. F. 1965. *The Isle of Purbeck: sunny spaces and dinosaur traces*. Bournemouth. 30 pp., pls.

OWEN, H. G. 1961. Discussion on TRESISE, G. R. 1960. *Proc. Geol. Assoc.*, **72**, pp. 266–7.

*—— 1971. Middle Albian stratigraphy in the Anglo-Paris Basin. *Bull. Brit. Mus. (Nat. Hist.) Geol.*, Suppl. 8, 164 pp., figs., pls., maps, refs.

PALMER, S. L. 1964. Prehistoric stone industries of the Fleet, Weymouth. *Proc. Dorset Nat. Hist. and Arch. Soc.*, **85**, pp. 107–15, figs., refs.

—— 1967. Trial excavations in the Fleet area, Weymouth. *Ibid.*, **88**, pp. 152–57, figs., refs.

PARSONS, T. S. and WILLIAMS, E. E. 1961. Two Jurassic turtle skulls: a morphological study. *Bull. Mus. Comp. Zool. Harvard*, **125**, No. 3, pp. 41–107, figs., pls., refs.

PIKE BROS., FAYLE, & Co. 1964. Catalogue of Dorset Ball Clays. Analyses, tables. Wareham.

*PHILLIPS, W. J. 1964. The structures in the Jurassic and Cretaceous rocks on the Dorset coast between White Nothe and Mupe Bay. *Proc. Geol. Assoc.*, **75**, Pt. 4, pp. 373–405, maps, figs., refs.

*PUGH, M. E. 1969. Algae from the Lower Purbeck limestones of Dorset. *Ibid.*, **79**, Pt. 4, pp. 513–23, figs., pls., refs.

—— and SHEARMAN, D. J. 1967. Cryoturbation structures at the south end of the Isle of Portland. *Ibid.*, **78**, Pt. 3, pp. 463–71, figs., refs.

*RANWELL, D. S., BIRD, E. C. F., HUBBARD, J. C. E. and STEBBINGS, R. E. 1964. *Spartina* salt marshes in southern England, V. Tidal submergence and chlorinity in Poole Harbour. *J. Ecol.*, **52**, pp. 627–41, figs., refs.

*Ridd, M. F. 1973. The Sutton Poyntz, Poxwell and Chaldon Herring anticlines, southern England. *Proc. Geol. Assoc.*, **84**, Pt. 1. pp. 1–8, map, figs., refs.

Robinson, A. H. W. 1955. The harbour entrances of Poole, Christchurch and Pagham. *Geog. J.* **121**, Pt. 1, pp. 33–50, map, photo., refs.

*Rood, A. D., Hay, W. H. and Barnard, T. 1971. Electron microscope studies of Oxford Clay coccoliths. *Eclog. Geol. Helv.*, **64**, No. 2, pp. 245–71, figs., photos., refs.

Salter, D. L. and West, I. M. 1965. Calciostrontianite in the basal Purbeck Beds of Durlston Head, Dorset. *Mineralog. Mag.*, **35**, No. 269, pp. 146–50, photos., refs.

Samuel, E. M. 1970. Formations exposed in the trench for the natural gas main in the area south-east of Bincombe. *Proc. Dorset Nat. Hist. and Arch. Soc.*, **91**, pp. 39–41, fig.

*Sarjeant, W. A. S. 1960. New Hystrichospheres from the Upper Jurassic of Dorset. *Geol. Mag.*, **97**, No. 2, pp. 137–44, figs., pls., refs.

*—— 1962. Upper Jurassic microplankton from Dorset, England. *Micropaleont.*, **8**, No. 2, pp. 255–68, map, figs., pls., refs.

Savage, R. J. G. 1958. Pliosaur from Portland. *Proc. Bristol Nat. Soc.*, **29**, Pt. 4, pp. 379–80, refs.

Seagrief, S. C. 1959. Pollen diagrams from southern England, Wareham, Dorset and Nursling, Hampshire. *New Phytol.*, **58**, No. 3, pp. 316–25, figs., refs.

Sidaway, R. 1964. Buried peat deposits at Litton Cheney. *Proc. Dorset Nat. Hist. and Arch. Soc.*, **85**, pp. 78–86, figs., refs.

Smith, A. J. and Curry, D. 1975. The structure and geological evolution of the English Channel. *Phil. Trans. Roy. Soc. London*, (A), **279**, pp. 3–20, maps, figs., refs.

Sparks, B. W. 1951. Two drainage diversions in Dorset. *Geography*, **36**, Pt. 3, pp. 186–93, figs., refs.

*—— 1953. Stages in the physical evolution of the Weymouth lowland. *Trans. Inst. Brit. Geog.*, **18**, pp. 17–29.

*Stinton, F. C. and Torrens, H. S. 1968. Fish otoliths from the Bathonian of southern England. *Palaeontology*, **11**, Pt. 2, pp. 246–58, figs., refs.

Stride, A. H. 1963. Current-swept sea floors near the southern half of Great Britain. *Quart. J. Geol. Soc. London*, **119**, Pt. 2, pp. 175–99, figs., pls., refs.

Swaine, J. 1962. Iguanodon Footprints. *New Scientist*, **13**, No. 276, p. 520.

*Sylvester-Bradley, P. C. 1957. The Forest Marble of Dorset. *Proc. Geol. Soc. London*, No. 1556, pp. 26–8, refs.

—— 1964. Type sections of the Bathonian, Portlandian and Purbeckian stages, and the problem of the Jurassic–Cretaceous boundary. Cong. Géol. Int., Coll. du Jurassique à Luxembourg, 1962. *Inst. Grd. Duc., Sect. Sci. Nat., Phys. Math.*, pp. 259–63.

*Talbot, M. R. 1973. Major sedimentary cycles in the Corallian Beds (Oxfordian) of southern England. *Palaeogeog., Palaeoclimatol., Palaeoecol.*, **14**, pp. 293–317, figs., photos., refs.

Taylor, C. 1970. *Dorset. The making of the English landscape.* Hodder and Stoughton, London. 215 pp., pls., maps, refs.

*Torrens, H. S. 1965. Revised zonal scheme for the Bathonian Stage of Europe. *Rep. VII Cong. Carpato-Balkan Geol. Assoc.*, **I**, Pt. 2, pp. 47–55, figs., refs.

*—— (Ed.) 1969. *International field symposium on the British Jurassic. Excursion No. 1. Guide for Dorset and south Somerset.* Pp. A1–71, maps, figs., refs. (Roneoed. Limited edition.)

*—— [1974]. Standard zones of the Bathonian; Coll. du Jurassique à Luxembourg, 1967. *Mem. Bur. Rech. Géol. Minières*, **75**, pp. 581–604, refs.

Townson, W. G. 1974. Geology of Coombe Valley. *Proc. Dorset Nat. Hist. and Arch. Soc.*, **95**, pp. 7–8, map, refs.

*—— 1975. Lithostratigraphy and deposition of the type Portlandian. *J. Geol. Soc. London*, **131**, Pt. 4, pp. 619–38, figs., refs. (see also Ager, D. V., 1976).

Tresise, G. R. 1960. Aspects of the lithology of the Wessex Upper Greensand. *Proc. Geol. Assoc.*, **71**, Pt. 3, pp. 316–39, figs., refs. (see also **72**, Pt. 2, pp. 26–70).

—— 1961. The nature and origin of chert in the Upper Greensand of Wessex. *Ibid.*, **72**, Pt. 3, pp. 333–56, figs., pl., refs.

Walkden, C. and Oppé, E. F. 1969. In the footsteps of dinosaurs. *Amateur Geol.*, **3**, Pt. 2, pp. 19–35, figs., refs.

West, I. M. 1960. On the occurrence of Celestine in the Caps and Broken Beds at Durlston Head, Dorset. *Proc. Geol. Assoc.*, **71**, Pt. 4, pp. 391–401, figs., refs.

WEST, I. M. 1961. Lower Purbeck beds of the Swindon facies in Dorset. *Nature*, **190**, No. 4775, p. 526, refs.

* —— 1964a. Age of the Alpine folds of southern England. *Geol. Mag.*, **101**, No. 2, pp. 190–1, refs.

—— 1964b. Evaporite diagenesis in the Lower Purbeck Beds of Dorset. *Proc. Yorks. Geol. Soc.*, **34**, Pt. 3, pp. 315–30, figs., pl., refs.

—— 1964c. Deformation of the incompetent beds in the Purbeck anticline. *Geol. Mag.*, **101**, No. 4, p. 373, refs.

—— 1965. Macrocell structure and enterolithic veins in British Purbeck gypsum and anhydrite. *Proc. Yorks. Geol. Soc.*, **35**, Pt. 1, pp. 47–58, figs., refs.

—— 1973. Vanished evaporites: significance of strontium minerals. *J. Sed. Pet.*, **43**, No. 1, pp. 278–9, photos., refs.

* —— 1975. Evaporites and associated sediments of the basal Purbeck Formation (Upper Jurassic) of Dorset. *Proc. Geol. Assoc.*, **86**, Pt. 2, pp. 205–25, figs., refs.

—— SHEARMAN, D. J. and PUGH, M. E. 1969. Whitsun field meeting in the Weymouth area, 1966. *Ibid.*, **80**, Pt. 3, pp. 331–40, figs., pl., refs.

WHATLEY, R. C. 1964. The Ostracod genus *Progonocythere* in the English Oxfordian. *Rev. de Micropaléont.*, **7**, Pt. 3, pp. 188–94, pl., refs.

WILSON, R. C. L. 1961. Some aspects of the geology of central Dorset. *J. Univ. Sheffield Geol. Soc.*, **4**, No. 1, pp. 16–9, figs., refs.

—— 1966. Silica diagenesis in Upper Jurassic limestones of southern England. *J. Sed. Pet.*, **36**, No. 4, pp. 1036–49, figs., photos., refs.

* —— 1968a. Carbonate facies variation within the Osmington Oolite Series in southern U.K. *Palaeogeog., Palaeoclimatol., Palaeoecol.*, **4**, No. 2, pp. 89–123, figs., photos., refs.

* —— 1968b. Diagenetic carbonate fabric variations in Jurassic limestones of southern England. *Proc. Geol. Assoc.*, **78**, Pt. 4, pp. 535–53, figs., pls., refs.

—— 1969. Field meeting in south Dorset. *Ibid.*, **80**, pp. 341–51, figs., refs.

WILSON, V., WELCH, F. B. A., ROBBIE, J. A. and GREEN, G. W. 1958. Geology of the Country around Bridport and Yeovil, *Mem. Geol. Surv. Gt. Brit.*

* ZIEGLER, B. 1962. Die Ammoniten – Gattung *Aulacostephanus* in Oberjura (Taxionomie, Stratigraphie, Biologie). *Palaeontographica*, (A), **119**, pp. 1–172, figs., photos., pls., refs.

—— 1964. Das Untere Kimeridgien in Europa. Cong. Géol. Int., Coll. du Jurassique, Luxembourg 1962. *Inst. Grd. Duc., Sect. Sci. Nat., Phys. Math.*, pp. 345–54, refs.

B. Works relating to Chapter XV (Economic Geology)

ALDRED, M. G. 1957. Portland quarrying. *Mine and Quarry Engineering*, **23**, pp. 311–2.

ANON. 1949. Report of the Mineral Development Committee. *Cmd. 7732, Ministry Fuel Power*, 106 pp., figs., refs. H.M.S.O. ,London.

—— 1957. Quarrying building stone in Dorset. *Mining Equipment*, **8**, No. 12, pp. 35–6, photos.

—— 1960. Dorset Ball Clay production: two hundredth anniversary. *Refractories J.*, **36**, No. 11, pp. 344–5, 348, photos.

—— 1962a. Automation and diamonds modernise an old craft. *Indust. Diamond Rev.*, **22**, No. 255, pp. 52–8, photos.

—— 1962b. The quarrying of Portland Stone. *Quarry Managers' J.* **46**, No. 6, pp. 223–30, photos., fig.

—— [1974]. *Report of the Ball Clay working party, Russell Quay, Arne, mineral project pilot study.* (Roneoed). Dorset County Planning Dept. and E.C.C. Ball Clays Ltd. 47 pp., photos., maps, plans, appendices.

—— 1975. *Development of the oil and gas resources of the United Kingdom*. 38 pp., tables, map. Dept. Energy. H.M.S.O., London.

ARCHER, A. A. (Comp.) 1972. Sand and Gravel. *Mineral Resources Consultative Committee* Mineral Dossier No. 4. 29 pp., figs., tables, map, refs.

ARKELL, W. J. 1950. The future of English building-stones. *Endeavour*, **9**, No. 33, pp. 40–4, photos., ref.

BERKIN, L.V.I. and HOLDRIDGE, D. A. 1967. Physico-chemical properties for the characterization and control of Dorset Ball Clays. *Trans. Brit. Ceram. Soc.*, **66**, No. 4, pp. 189–215, figs., tables, refs.

BROWN, P. R., RUDKINS, G. F. and WHEELDON, P. E. 1954. Portland Stone. *Chart. Civ. Eng.*, 1954, pp. 25–6.

CADMAN, W. H. 1948. The oil shale deposits of the world and recent developments in their exploitation and utilization, reviewed to May 1947. *J. Inst. Petrol.*, **34**, No. 290, pp. 109–32, photos., refs.

COLE, D. I. 1974. A recent example of spontaneous combustion of oil-shale. *Geol. Mag.*, **111**, No. 4, pp. 355–56, refs.

—— 1976. Velocity/porosity relationships in limestones from the Portland Group of southern England. *Geoexploration*, **14**, No. 1, pp. 37–50, figs., photos., refs.

GRODZINSKI, P. 1955. Diamond sawing revolutionizes production at Portland Stone quarry. *Indust. Diamond Rev.*, **15**, No. 100, pp. 199–209, photos., figs.

HARDCASTLE, P. J. and KING, A. C. 1972. Sea wave records from Chesil Beach, Dorset. *Civ. Eng. and Public Works Rev.*, **67**, pp. 299 –300, figs., refs.

HIGHLEY, D. E. (Comp.) 1975. Ball Clay. *Mineral Resources Consultative Committee* Mineral Dossier No. 11. 32 pp., figs., tables, map, refs. H.M.S.O., London.

HODGES, F. O. C. 1970. *Survey of water resources and future demands.* Report under Section 14 of the Water Resources Act, 1963. Avon and Dorset River Authority. 61 pp., figs., tables, maps.

HOLDRIDGE, D. A. 1959. Ball clays and their properties. *Trans. Brit. Ceram. Soc.*, **55**, No. 6, pp. 369–440, figs., refs.

HOUNSELL, S. S. B. 1952a. Portland and its stone. *Mine and Quarry Engineering*, **18**, No. 4, pp. 107–14, photos., figs.

—— 1952b. The fabrication of Portland Stone. *Ibid.*, **18**, No. 5, pp. 143–7, photos.

KEELING, P. S. 1970. Nature and appraisal of clay deposits. Pp. 475–93, figs., refs. *in* JONES, M. J. (Ed.) *Mining and petroleum geology.* Proc. 9th Commonwealth Min. Metall. Cong. 1969, **2**. Institution of Mining and Metallurgy, London.

LOWSON, M. H. 1963. Oil exploration at Lulworth. *Petroleum*, **26**, No. 9, pp. 345–6, photos.

MACLEOD MATTHEWS, A. F., 1975. *United Kingdom oil shales: past and possible future exploitation.* Dept. of Energy. H.M.S.O., London. 30 pp., map.

RENDLE, R. S. 1950. Some notes regarding the water-bearing properties of the Chalk in S.E. Dorset. *J. Inst. Water Engineers*, **4**, No. 7, pp. 552–64, map, figs.

WILLIAMSON, W. O. 1954. The changing face of the British pottery industry. Part 1 : the technical control of raw materials. *Clay Products J. Australia*, **21**, No. 12, pp. 23–31.

YOUNG, D. 1972. Brickmaking in Dorset. *Proc. Dorset Nat. Hist. and Arch. Soc.*, **93**, pp. 212–42, figs., refs.

PLATES

(A 1338)

(For explanation, *see* pp. viii, 139, 140, 301)

VIEW EASTWARDS OVER BACON HOLE AND MUPE ROCKS

PLATE I

(Photos by W.J.A.)

AMMONITES FROM TIDMOOR POINT

PLATE III   GEOLOGY OF WEYMOUTH, SWANAGE, &C. *(Mem. Geol. Surv.)*

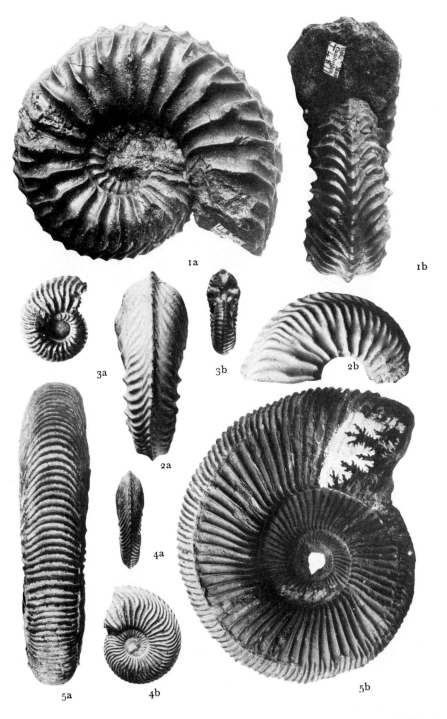

1a

1b

3a

3b

2b

2a

4a

5a

4b

5b

(Photos by W.J.A.)

UPPER OXFORD CLAY AND CORALLIAN AMMONITES

LOWER KIMMERIDGE CLAY AMMONITES

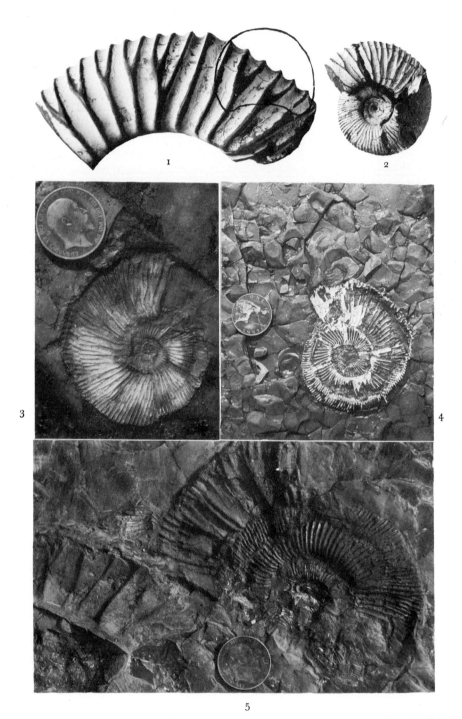

(Photos by W.J.A.)

UPPER KIMMERIDGE CLAY AMMONITES

(For explanation, *see* pp. viii, 79)   (Photo. by W.J.A.)

A. Hounstout Cliff from Freshwater Steps

Plate VI

B. Rope Lake Head; Kimmeridge Shales

(For explanation, *see* pp. viii, 78)   (Photo. by W.J.A.)

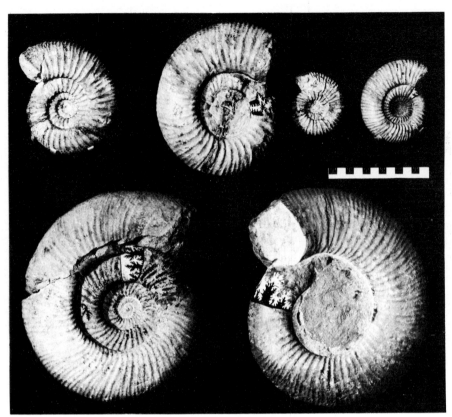

(For explanation, *see* pp. viii, 94)

A. AMMONITES FROM THE PORTLAND STONE QUARRIES

PLATE VII

B. DURLSTON HEAD FROM TILLY WHIM CAVES; PORTLAND STONE CLIFFS

(For explanation, *see* pp. ix, 97)

(For explanation, *see* pp. ix, 105, 301)   (Photo. by S.H.R.)

A. Gad Cliff from the south-east

PLATE VIII

B. Durdle Door

(For explanation, *see* pp. ix, 292, 293)   (A 1326)

(A 1335) (For explanation, *see* pp. ix, 125–6)

A. Silicified Trees and Burrs, the Fossil Forest, Lulworth

Plate IX

B. Purbeck Dirt Bed with stones, Bacon Hole

(Photo. by S.H.R.) (For explanation, *see* pp. ix, 125, 140)

(For explanation, *see* pp. ix, 135, 304)   (A 1291)

A. Durlston Bay, Peveril Point, and Ballard Down

Plate X

B. Swanage Bay in 1883; dressed stone awaiting shipment

(For explanation, *see* pp. ix, 133)   (Photo. by Powells', Swanage)

(For explanation, *see* pp. ix, 111)

A. Portland Beds – Gault unconformity, Holworth House, Ringstead

Plate XI

B. Albian – Cenomanian – Turonian section, White Nothe

(Photo. by W.J.A.) (For explanation, *see* pp. x, 191)

(For explanation, *see* pp. x, 205) (A 12237)

A. Chalk stacks, Handfast Point; Old Harry

Plate XII

B. The Pinnacle, a Chalk stack at the Foreland

(For explanation, *see* pp. x, 205) (A 12238)

(Photo. by W.J.A.) (For explanation, *see* pp. x, 224)

A. PUCKSTONE AND AGGLESTONE, STUDLAND HEATH

PLATE XIII

B. CREECHBARROW HILL FROM THE SOUTH-EAST

(Photo. by W.J.A.) (For explanation, *see* pp. x, 234)

(For explanation, *see* pp. x, 287)   (A 12571)

A. VIEW OF THE PURBECK ANTICLINE FROM EAST OF WHITE NOTHE

PLATE XIV

B. STAIR HOLE, LULWORTH; SHOWING CRUMPLED PURBECK BEDS

(For explanation, *see* pp. xi, 296)   (A 12223)

(Photo. by H.E.A.)

(For explanation, *see* pp. xi, 304–306)

THE BALLARD DOWN FAULT

PLATE XV

(For explanation, *see* pp. xi, 318)   (A 1308)

A. CORFE CASTLE FROM THE WEST, LOOKING ACROSS THE CORFE RIVER GAP

PLATE XVI

B. PLATEAU GRAVEL OF LOWER PALÆOLITHIC TERRACE FILLING A CHANNEL
ERODED IN BAGSHOT SAND. WARMWELL PITS (1938)

(For explanation, *see* pp. xi, 325)   (Photo. by W.J.A.)

(Photo. by 'The Times')   (For explanation, see pp. xi, 337)

A. CHESIL BEACH AND PORTLAND ISLAND, FROM THE AIR

PLATE XVII

B. CLIFFS AT PORTLAND BILL CAPPED BY THE RAISED BEACH

(Photo. by Kestin's, Weymouth)   (For explanation, see pp. xi, 331)

(For explanation, *see* pp. xi, 274, 361) (Photo. by W.F.P.McL.)

A. BORING FOR OIL AT POXWELL CIRCUS, 1937

PLATE XVIII

B.   A STONE QUARRY ON PORTLAND ISLAND; ONE OF WREN'S CHURCHES BEHIND

(For explanation, *see* pp. xii, 354) (A 4957)

THE GEOLOGY OF THE COUNTRY AROUND WEYMOUTH, SWANAGE, CORFE AND LULWORTH

CHAPTER I

INTRODUCTION

Geology and Scenery

DORSET, to its many admirers, is the fairest county in England. The cream of Dorset is the coastline from Abbotsbury to Poole Harbour and its immediate hinterland, with which this volume is privileged to deal.   Nowhere else in 30 miles as the crow flies can be found such a variety of scenery, of floras and faunas and, in the realm of geology, of formations, fossils, structures, and erosion features.   And on its geological variety, as the geologist knows, depend all the other qualities of this favoured region.

The variety of scenery to be found in a small compass is best appreciated by a traveller who crosses Purbeck from north to south, coming from Bournemouth or Wareham.   He enters the so-called " island " across the Egdon Heath of the Wessex novels, a bleak region whose marked features are due to the limeless Tertiary sands and gravels which floor the Hampshire Basin.   Here are to be found all the English species of heath and heather.   The depressions are bogs, where asphodel and gentian flourish. Around the plantations, in some of which the *Osmunda regalis* grows, June brings a blaze of rhododendrons.   The coastline of this region is equally characteristic.   Along the much-indented shores of Poole Harbour the heaths taper off almost imperceptibly into salt-marsh and mud-flat; facing the open sea is a fringe of dunes and a broad sandy beach, the three mile strand of Shell Bay.

The heaths end to the south against a narrow belt of mixed woodland and pasture, denoting the more fertile soils of the Reading Beds and London Clay.   Along this belt are Studland and the parks of Rempstone Hall, Creech Grange, and Lulworth Castle, sheltered under the ridge of the Purbeck Hills.

The Purbeck Hills, the hog's-back ridge running east and west from Ballard Cliff and Handfast Point to Worbarrow Bay, which effectively shuts off the main part of Purbeck to the south, provide a specimen of the high chalk country.   The ridge widens

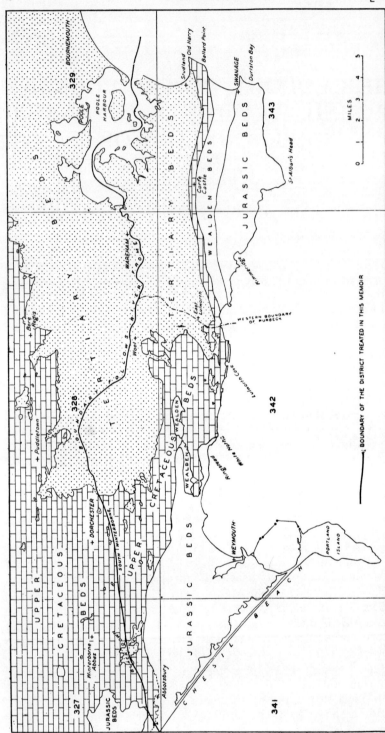

FIG. 1.—Sketch-map showing boundary of the district dealt with in this memoir, the general geology, and sheet-lines of the one-inch Geological Survey colour-printed maps.

about Lulworth and spreads north-westwards round the western end of the Tertiary beds of the Dorset-Hampshire Basin. Here is the land of harebells and many butterflies, of rolling grassy uplands and dry coombs, ridgeways, barrows and earthworks. The cliff scenery in the chalk near Swanage and Lulworth is the equal of any in the land.

South of the ridge of the Purbeck Hills is another contrast, a rich and wooded valley, full of farms and oak spinneys, an outlying fragment, as it were, of the Weald of Kent, and likewise a product of the Wealden Beds. Here the villages cluster thickly—Corfe, Knowle, Steeple and Tyneham; and there are signs of several more, marked by ancient manor houses now become farms, such as Godlingston, Woodyhyde and Barnston. The building material for walls and roofs is the beautiful grey Purbeck stone. To this tract belong the lovely semicircular bays of Swanage, Worbarrow, and Mupe, and the round cove of Lulworth, with their sandy beaches and multicoloured cliffs of orange, yellow and red sands and mottled clays.

A fourth type of scenery is developed in south-eastern Purbeck, in response to the more barren subsoil formed by the hard limestones of the Purbeck and Portland formations. There results from these a Cotswold upland, a treeless and stony tableland intersected by drystone walls and scarred by the tip-heaps and shafts of many quarries, ancient and recent. Seaward the stone presents a mural face falling into deep water. From Durlston Head to St. Alban's Head it builds five miles of nearly vertical cliffs, and the sea can be reached only at four points, at the truncated valleys and quarries of Tilly Whim, Dancing Ledge, Seacombe and Winspit. Here in winter the surf boils in an unbroken line of foam, and many ships were lost before Anvil Point lighthouse was built. In summer this region is a scene of calm beauty, when the hills are clad with orchids and a multitude of meadow flowers and the cliffs and old quarries are gay with thrift, horned poppy, samphire and sea-aster.

Finally, Purbeck offers a fifth province along its south-western coast, where the Kimmeridge Clay comes to the surface in a tract four or five miles long and a mile wide. It is shut off from the other coasts by the crags of Gad Cliff, where the same stone runs into the sea tilted at an angle of 40°. Here the cliffs are all of crumbling black shale and the sea is muddy from lapping at talus slopes, perpetually renewed by subaerial waste. In hot weather the smell of oil from the bituminous shale pervades the beach, and generally there are heaps of rotting seaweed, of which the shallow cementstone ledges grow prolific crops. Agriculture on the clay lands about Kimmeridge wages war ceaselessly against thistles and ragwort, for ever spreading inland from the cliff edge and down from the slopes of Swyre Head and Hounstout.

In the Weymouth district some of the features of Purbeck are repeated, notably in Portland Island, which resembles the fourth district of Purbeck, the stony upland. Its original features, however, have been greatly modified by quarrying and settlement. On the mainland the Jurassic rocks of formations earlier than any seen in Purbeck, from Corallian Beds down to Fuller's Earth, form a country with less marked characteristics. In the marshes of Lodmoor and Abbotsbury Swannery, the Oxford Clay gives rise to some of the fenny country so conspicuously associated with it elsewhere. North of this, from Broadwey to Abbotsbury and Portisham, the scenery is dominated by two parallel ridges formed by the outcrops of the Corallian and Portland limestones, tilted steeply in the northern limb of the Weymouth Anticline. The ridges are separated by a narrow valley lying along the outcrop of the Kimmeridge Clay, as usual a dairy country.

The Coastline

The Weymouth district and Purbeck are unusually rich in different types of coastline. Everything is represented, from the rugged precipices of Portland Stone, sometimes with curtains of landslips, or chalk headlands with sea stacks and caves, to the sand dunes of Studland, and the salt marsh and landlocked mud-flats of Poole Harbour.

The outstanding feature is the Chesil Beach, one of the wonders of the world. (*See* Chapter XIV). In its unbroken sweep of 18 miles from Portland Island to Bridport Harbour, the height of its even crest-line, which rises to over 40 ft. above high-water level, and the extraordinary symmetry of its constituent pebbles, this shingle bank is unique in Europe. Against it is exhausted the fury of the gales in West Bay. The soft clays behind receive instead for nine miles only the lappings of a tidal backwater, the Fleet, which by their gentle action work out many fossils for the collector. Were it not for the protective action of the Chesil Beach, there can be no doubt the site of Weymouth would long since have been destroyed and the coast would strike eastwards from Abbotsbury to White Nothe.

In the region where the formations are tilted in the steep northern limb of the Purbeck Anticline (*see* Chapter XIII) the coastline displays to perfection the effects of the sea upon combinations of rocks of varying hardness. The resistant limestones present a series of barriers to the sea, and the soft marls, clays and sands between are readily hollowed out into bays and coves. Various stages in the formation of these coastal types can be seen. At Stair Hole, Lulworth, and at Pondfield near Worbarrow, the sea has newly found its way through the rampart of Portland Stone, and is at present hollowing out the Purbeck beds behind. At Lulworth Cove the process has proceeded farther, and the soft Wealden beds have been penetrated, but the Chalk has temporarily arrested the advance. At its present stage the breach is almost perfectly circular, and the original doorway through which the sea gained entry through the Portland Stone has not yet been greatly widened. The next stage is exemplified by the gap between Worbarrow and Mupe Bays. Here the Chalk ridge has resisted so long that a gap a mile and a half wide has been cut in the Portland Stone rampart, relics of which are left in Worbarrow Tout and the Mupe Rocks. Once this barrier was broken down over so long a stretch the Purbeck and Wealden beds were quickly consumed. Finally the sea has penetrated the Chalk ridge also, forming the miniature inner cove called Arish Mell. If this breach were farther east the soft Tertiary beds behind would soon be destroyed; but here horizontal Chalk forms the hinterland and rapid advance is arrested. What happens when the hinterland is not of Chalk but of soft Tertiary beds is well illustrated between Purbeck and the Isle of Wight. There the process is far advanced. Nearly 20 miles of the narrow Chalk ridge have been consumed and the sea has flooded far into the basin of the old Frome River, converting its lower reaches into the Solent and Spithead and sending ramifications many miles inland in Poole Harbour.

A peculiar coastal feature has developed in the last 20 years between Black Head and Osmington Mills. Collapse has occurred at three centres along a cliff 200 feet high, composed of Kimmeridge Clay capped with unconformable Gault, Upper Greensand and Chalk. When saturated the Greensand and Chalk have slipped on the clay formation and flowed down the cliff like lava. Fresh movement occurs after every period of heavy rains. The resulting phenomena resemble glaciers, with collecting ground (névé), ice-fall, and terminal fan of boulders.

Contribution of the Area to Stratigraphy and Palaeontology

The importance of the part played by the area in the development of stratigraphical geology and palaeontology is sufficiently illustrated by the names that it has contributed to the subject. The stratigraphical stages Kimmeridgian, Portlandian, and Purbeckian are used the world over, and this is the type region. Nowhere else are they so fully developed and so ideally exposed to view, or are their faunas so completely preserved. The Oxford Clay, Corallian Beds and Upper Chalk are also more fully developed and better exposed than at any other place in England.

The elucidation of the geology, stratigraphy and palaeontology of the district has occupied some of the leading figures in the subject. Research began with Thomas Webster, who in 1811-12 made the pioneer survey of Purbeck and the coast westward and produced a remarkably accurate geological map.[1] The next advances were mainly due to Buckland and De la Beche, Sedgwick, Conybeare, Fitton, Owen and Edward Forbes. Later came Bristow, Osmond Fisher, J. F. Blake, Hudleston, Barrois, Waagen, T. Rupert Jones, and the local author and geologist, R. Damon, who published a " Geology of Weymouth, Portland and the Coast of Dorset " in 1860, which appeared in a second edition in 1884.

The official revision of Bristow's Geological Survey Map of 1850 and the systematic re-examination of the district were undertaken in 1888 to 1890 by A. (later Sir Aubrey) Strahan, assisted by H. B. Woodward for the Jurassic rocks and Clement Reid for the Tertiary beds. Their work resulted in Strahan's classic memoir " The Geology of the Isle of Purbeck and Weymouth," published in 1898. This work has been indispensable to all subsequent students of the district, and on it of necessity the present memoir is largely based. Despite all the changes that the accelerated researches of 40 years have rendered necessary, it remains a contribution of permanent value.

In the early part of the present century A. W. Rowe and C. D. Sherborn examined more minutely the White Chalk, from the point of view of palaeontological zones (1901); H. Salfeld re-studied the Kimmeridge Clay from the same standpoint and recast the zonal classification of the Upper Jurassic (1913-14); and Oligocene deposits were discovered on Creechbarrow (W. H. Hudleston, 1902, and H. Keeping, 1910).

Since the war of 1914-18 research has proceeded at trebled pace on almost every aspect of the geology. Recent contributions are too many to enumerate.

In the sphere of palaeontology perhaps the most interesting and important of the many treasures of the district are the Jurassic freshwater and terrestrial fauna and flora of the Purbeck Beds. (*See* Chapter VII). The marine formations have contributed some of the best material to monographs on Jurassic reptiles, fishes, crustacea, ammonites, gastropods, lamellibranchs, and brachiopods.

TECTONICS

The tectonics of the area are more interesting than those of any other part of the Mesozoic and Tertiary tract in the British Isles. Acute folds, overfolds, overthrusts, and faults of peculiar and complicated type, traverse the area and are well exposed in the cliffs. The more conspicuous examples first attracted the attention of Webster, Buckland, and De la Beche. Strahan's mapping showed the movements to have occurred in at least two major epochs, one Cretaceous, the other Tertiary. Strahan

---

[1] *In* Sir H. C. Englefield. *Picturesque Beauties of the Isle of Wight*, 1816. London.

invoked great overthrusts of a kind unknown elsewhere in Britain or the adjoining parts of the Continent to explain the structures that he found. His hypotheses were exceedingly bold for the time at which they were put forward, and they remained unquestioned for nearly 40 years. Some of the problems are still unsolved, and will provide food for thought for many years to come.

TOPOGRAPHY AND PLACE-NAMES

The area here described affords an exceptionally good example of the connexion, direct or indirect, between the geology and the place-names. As usual, the oldest names in the district, of British origin and surviving from before the Anglo-Saxon occupation in the middle of the fifth century A.D., are those of important natural features, such as the principal rivers, some of the hills, and the marsh called Lodmoor. Wey (from which are derived Upwey, Broadway or Broadwey, Weymouth), Frome and Winfrith are all British river names. On the other hand, the various streams called Lake (*e.g.*, Luckford Lake, the western boundary of Purbeck) were named in Anglo-Saxon times. Creech comes from the British *cruc*, a hill. Lodmoor may be from British *luta*, mud. Broadmayne and Little Mayne may be British names (cf. Welsh *maen*, stone), perhaps from the big sarsens lying there and believed to have formed part of a stone circle. Almost all the other names of which the derivations can be traced are Anglo-Saxon (Old English).

Since Old English ceased to be spoken by the middle of the twelfth century, it is interesting to find that many physical features have retained the names given them at least 800, more probably over 1,000 years ago. The most conspicuous example is the arched rock, Durdle Door. This name is derived from an Old English word ' *thirl*,' meaning to pierce (cf. the cognate ' nostril '), and has its counterpart in Thurlestone in South Devon, where there is an arched rock like Durdle Door. It is obvious that Durlston (formerly sometimes written Durdlestone) is of the same origin, and we may conclude that in Saxon times a similar natural arch existed here, but has since been removed by marine erosion.

Such conspicuous features as Chesil Bank (*cisel*, shingle) and the Fleet behind it (*fleot*, creek or estuary), and Radipole Back-water (" reedy pool ') have retained their names almost unaltered. The passes or defiles at Corfe, Corton, Coryates and Corfe Hill, Radipole, all embody the Anglo-Saxon word *corf* (a pass), from *ceorfan* (to cut). Another interesting group are the Touts or look-out places, from *totian* to look out or protrude : Worbarrow Tout, Hambury Tout, (" the fortified look-out place by the village ", i.e., Lulworth), and Hounstout (*Hund's* tout). These are all prominent cliffs on the coast. Springs are indicated by such names as Wool (*wella*, springs), Warmwell (warm springs),

Ulwell (perhaps from *ule,* owl), Elwell (formerly Helewell), heal-
ing spring, in reference to Upwey Wishing Well.

The three Swyre Heads (Kingston, Lulworth, Puncknowle)
probably derive their names from *swira,* a col. Ballard Down
may come from *bealg,* rounded, smooth, as in Ballingdon, Suffolk,
Balgandun. Rodden is Red Down, from the Abbotsbury Ironstone. Agglestone is probably *hagolstan* (hailstone); Puckstone, near it, is *puca's* stone (goblin's stone). Either *puca* or a
personal name *Poca,* combined with *swelle* (hill), accounts for
Poxwell. *Cnoll* (little hill) occurs in The Knoll, Church Knowle,
Bucknowle; *cnaepp* (top) in Windwill Knap, and Ballast Knap;
hlaew (burial mound) in Winslow near Preston. The common
hope, a small enclosed valley, is represented by Church Hope,
Portland. *Cumb,* narrow valley, is more usual (Coombe Keynes,
Bincombe).

Names containing the Old English -ton (*tun*) (homestead,
village) -worth (enclosure, homestead), -ham (village, estate,
manor, homestead) are common. The puzzling element in many
is due to a personal name. Thus Osmington (home of *Osmund's*
people), Nottington (home of *Hnotta's* people), Tatton (*Tata's*
home), Povington (*Peofa's* home), Holworth (*Hola's* enclosure),
Lulworth (*Lulla's* enclosure). Two are due to the Church : Abbotsbury (manor of the abbot), and Preston (priest's village or home).

A surprising number of names refer to farming or animals.
Examples are everywhere : Wyke Regis (*wic,* dairy farm),
Hewish Hill (*hiwisc,* family holding), Melcombe Regis (" valley
where milk was got "), Bincombe (" coomb where beans grow ")
—but Bindon is " the place within the downs " (*binnan dune*)—,
Studland (" land where horses were kept "), Swanage ("dairy
farm with swans or swine " ?), Elworth (" elder enclosure "),
Waddon (" woad hill "), Chaldon (" hill where calves grazed ").
In the same category are Arne (*aern,* house) and Shilvinghampton
(" home on shelving ground "—the dip-slope of the Corallian
ridge).

The cliffs and headlands bear some of the most interesting
names. Gad Cliff seems to be named after the miner's gad or
wedge, from its silhouette when seen from the east. Winspit
probably embodies the dialect word whinstone or whin, applied to
the black chert beds of which the spit or little headland is
composed ; the Greensand cherts were formerly called whin in
Sussex. Tilly Whim probably contains the miner's whim or
windlass ; the place is an old stone mine. The Nothe (Weymouth)
and White Nothe (Ringstead) probably preserve an old English
word for a head, cognate with Norwegian *nod, noda,* lump (cf.
' noddle '). Emmit Hill, the cliffed western face of St. Alban's
Head, is the dialect pocket-word *emmut,* used of the wind, a

contraction of ' even-might '. It means ' Facing into the wind ' (i.e. to the south-west).

Other features on the coast contain in their names a great variety of more or less hidden meanings. Stair Hole, Bacon Hole, Blackers Hole, Rope Lake Hole, are hollows in the cliffs ranging in size from a cave (Blackers Hole) to small bays. Stair is a dialect word meaning ' steep ', ' sheer '. Rope Lake (lake= stream) may mean much the same as Freshwater Steps. Pondfield and Punfield are recesses, the former almost circular, which probably derive from Old English *pundfald*, ' pinfold ' or pound for stray cattle, in reference to their shape. Gaulter Gap is presumably a place where the Kimmeridge shales were dug in the cliff for ' gaulting ', i.e. marling, the land; the men who dug ' gault ' were called ' gaulters '. ' Hard ', in Clavell's Hard, means ' landing place '.

The many small wooded glens with steep sides, through which a diminutive stream runs down to the shore, are called gwyles. Similar features are called goyls in Devon and gills in Sussex. It is debatable whether this was an independent Anglo-Saxon word or whether it was the Norse *geil, gil,* introduced from the North of England.

THE FUTURE

What will be the future of this 30 miles of coastline, so richly endowed as a training ground and museum of geology? Few tracts of equal size could raise so many claims, scientific, aesthetic and literary, for preservation as a national park. At present, however, it seems that little can be done to save it falling piece-meal before the builder. Weymouth and Swanage are expanding apace and must continue to do so. In the past five years the rural road to Portland Ferry has become a street. Wyke Regis has been engulfed. The villas are marching out to Chickerell and round the back of Lodmoor. They have captured Jordan Hill. The next to fall will be Redcliff. A new building estate with unlimited possibilities has appeared at Ringstead: a red-roofed villa has sprung up on the skyline of the White Nothe itself. If the English of the present generation allow this heritage of the community to be irreparably spoilt for private gain they will be held by posterity to have been unworthy to possess it. To all geologists who have enjoyed and profited by this coast, an appeal is made to do their utmost to preserve it.

TABLE OF STRATA REPRESENTED IN THE DISTRICT

FORMATIONS	STAGES AS USED IN THIS MEMOIR	SYSTEMS	
Blown sand; sand and shingle beaches Alluvium and peat Tufa (Mesolithic)		Holocene or Recent	QUATERNARY
Head and Coombe Rock, with loam Raised beach of Portland Plateau Gravel (high terraces) Angular Flint Gravel		Pleistocene	
Bembridge Limestone of Creechbarrow	Lattorfian	Oligocene	CAINOZOIC or TERTIARY
Bagshot Beds	Cuisian	Eocene	
London Clay	Ypresian		
Reading Beds	Landenian		
Upper Chalk	Senonian	Upper Cretaceous	MESOZOIC or SECONDARY
Middle Chalk	Turonian		
Lower Chalk	Cenomanian		
Upper Greensand Gault	Albian		
Lower Greensand with Atherfield Clay	Aptian	Lower Cretaceous	
Wealden Beds	Neocomian		
Purbeck Beds	Purbeckian	Upper Jurassic	
Portland Stone Portland Sand	Portlandian		
Kimmeridge Clay Abbotsbury Iron Ore	Kimmeridgian		
Corallian Beds Oxford (Upper clays)	Oxfordian		
Clay (Lower shales) Kellaways Beds Upper Cornbrash	Callovian		
Lower Cornbrash Forest Marble Fuller's Earth	Bathonian	Middle Jurassic	

EXPLANATORY NOTE ON THE TABLE OF STRATA

The strata out of which the district is built were deposited during the Mesozoic or Secondary and Cainozoic or Tertiary eras of geological time. The earliest strata exposed at the surface at the present day, belonging to the Middle Jurassic (Bathonian Stage), were laid down at the bottom of the sea, probably about 130-140 million years ago. Farther west along the coast of Dorset the earlier Jurassic rocks come to the surface, followed in Devonshire by the Permo-Triassic, laid down perhaps 160-200 million years ago, and near Torquay these can be seen to rest with a great unconformity upon older members of the Palaeozoic or Primary rocks, laid down in seas peopled with an altogether earlier order of life and dating to something like 200-400 million years ago.

The Mesozoic or Secondary rocks, with which we are here mainly concerned, are very fully developed in South Dorset, and subsequent tilting and folding has brought them up from their original positions several thousands of feet below sea level in such a way that they are displayed with almost unrivalled clarity at the surface.

The strata from the Fuller's Earth up to the Portland Stone inclusive consist entirely of marine sediments, in the aggregate 2,700 ft. thick, laid down at the bottom of an ever-changing and subsiding but never very deep sea, at a time when the climate was subtropical. At the end of the Jurassic period the sea bed was either raised or, more likely, filled up with sediment and almost ceased to subside, and a vast swamp, sometimes land, sometimes brackish lake, sometimes freshwater lake, covered the South of England. This was the Purbeck epoch, which ended about 120 million years ago, after about 400 ft. of sediments had been laid down.

The Wealden Beds which follow consist of up to 2,300 ft. of clays and sands with only a few freshwater and land fossils. They comprise the delta of a large river or rivers with shifting lakes and testify to a bottom once more subsiding rather rapidly.

This lacustrine period was brought to an end by earth movements of compressive type, of the kind that, when intensified, builds mountains. The Jurassic and Wealden rocks were broken (faulted) and folded, some parts subsiding along a break near Weymouth nearly 2,000 ft. relative to another part, and some areas being arched up into regions in which they were attacked by erosion and worn down to the Oxford Clay and even Forest Marble. For the most part this took place early in or before the epoch represented by the Lower Greensand, probably before the formation of the well-known sponge gravels of Faringdon, but the movements were probably spread over a long period of time. They heralded the new epoch of the Upper Cretaceous, during which for a further 30 million years or so the region became the bottom of the sea and subsided steadily while about 1,200 ft. of sediments were laid down over the earlier eroded folds and faults. Most of this thickness is represented by the Chalk, largely a deposit of nearly pure calcium carbonate, which stretches from Antrim and the Hebrides to the Crimea and the Caucasus. The purity of the deposits and the presence of wind-blown sand grains here and there suggest that the land behind the shores of the Chalk seas may have been deserts.

The Chalk epoch came to an end about 60 million years ago. North-west Europe was gently and irregularly upheaved to form land areas interspersed with shallow basins, in which a tropical life flourished. The most characteristic forms of Mesozoic life, the giant land and sea reptiles and the teeming ammonites, had become extinct, and the Tertiary fauna which took their place was modelled more along the lines of the life which we ourselves know. North Britain at this time (Eocene period) was a land area with active volcanoes, but the south, including Dorset, was occupied by one of the shallow sea basins. Into it poured great quantities of granitic debris derived from the erosion of the granite intrusions of the West Country and Brittany, now cleared of their sedimentary covering and undergoing denudation. The white sands and kaolin pipe-clays of the Dorset heaths are derived from this source, and the flint cobbles underneath and above them represent the destruction of Chalk nearer at hand. Only about 1,500 ft. of sands and clays represent the Tertiary era in the Hampshire Basin, but that it was of very considerable duration is shown by the many thousands of feet of limestones and other strata which cover a great part of the Near East and encircle the Mediterranean.

The stratigraphical record was virtually brought to an end in our area in the Middle Tertiary, perhaps 25 million years ago, by movements contemporary with the great earth storm or orogenic revolution which built the Alps, Pyrenees, Carpathians and the other mountain ranges of Southern Europe. Some time during the long period in which these processes were enacted, the South of England was subjected to pressure from the south, which ruckled the Mesozoic and Eocene strata to produce a series of parallel folds running east and west across the country. Examples of these folds in the Chalk areas of England are the Weald Anticline, and the anticlines of the Vale of Wardour and the Vale of Pewsey. The most acute fold and the one best exposed in northern Europe is the Purbeck Anticline, which runs through our district and the Isle of Wight. To the effects of this, Chapter XIII is mainly devoted.

As the folds grew the rising land, made of the consolidated sediments of earlier sea beds, was attacked by the rain and carried down again in streams to the sea. How far the forces of uplift may have prevailed in the earlier stages we do not know, for we cannot tell at what level the folding took place. The great arches produced in the Chalk and Jurassic limestones cannot have been cut through by erosion until after their present form was attained, otherwise they could not have transmitted the stresses necessary for their completion, but would have buckled and collapsed. This does not mean, however, that the Purbeck fold necessarily attained an elevation of some thousands of feet above sea-level. More probably the formative stages were passed through largely a little above or below sea level, and the completed fold was then gradually elevated at such a rate that the forces of erosion were able to keep pace with it.

Probably at some period in the Upper Tertiary the whole area was reduced to a plain of marine erosion, perfectly level and covered by shallow coastal sea. Since then it has been re-elevated *en bloc* and the sea is once more planing down the same structures at a new level. Some account of the processes since the Tertiary folding, so far as they are legible from the evidence of Pleistocene deposits in our area, will be found in Chapter XIV.

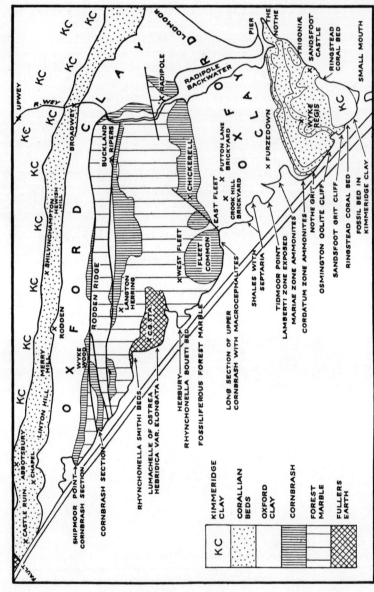

Fig. 2.—*Locality-map of the shores and hinterland of The Fleet, to illustrate Chapters 2 and 8.*

CHAPTER II

BATHONIAN AND BASAL CALLOVIAN STAGES:

FULLER'S EARTH

The Fuller's Earth in Dorset may exceed 250 ft. in thickness. Inland, where it crops out more fully than on the coast, it consists of three divisions, a Lower Clay and an Upper, separated by a highly fossiliferous division of rubbly and argillaceous lime-stones, the Fuller's Earth Rock. That there is some representative of the Rock on the coast would seem from about 25 ft. of argillaceous limestones and clays in a fault-breccia at Watton Cliff, between Bridport and Eypesmouth; but the brachiopods prove these beds to lie on a higher horizon. East of Bridport only the Upper Fuller's Earth Clay comes to the surface. It is only inter-mittently exposed in the area covered by this memoir, and consequently a description of the highest 50-60 ft. as it is seen at Cliff End, Burton Bradstock,[1] is added here, although the locality lies about three miles to the west.

UPPER FULLER'S EARTH, CLIFF END, BURTON BRADSTOCK

[Boueti Bed above]

		Ft.
4.	Prominent band of hard white cementstone	2 - 3
3.	Unfossiliferous grey clay	20
2.	Unfossiliferous grey clay with two thin bands of red claystone 4ft. apart	4
1.	Fossiliferous grey clay with numerous pale crumbling con-cretions and nests of fossils: abundant small gastropods— 'Eulima' sp., Nucula waltoni Morris and Lycett, and other lamellibranchs; seen to about	30

In the centre of the Weymouth Anticline the Upper Fuller's Earth crops out in an ellipse 1 mile long and $\frac{1}{4}$ to $\frac{1}{2}$ a mile wide and can be seen here and there in small sections along the shores

---

[1] W. J. Arkell, *Jurassic System in Great Britain*, 1933, p. 253. Oxford.

of the West Fleet south and south-west of Langton Herring (Fig. 2). The junction with the overlying Boueti Bed and Forest Marble is exposed on the north-west extremity of the little promontory of Herbury (or Herbeyleigh), about a mile south of Langton Herring Church. Bed 4 at Burton Bradstock (which is also prominent at Watton Cliff) is here represented by several bands. The section is only about 25 ft. deep, and does not extend below bed 3 of the Burton section.

The greater part of the Upper Fuller's Earth is concealed in the low grassy shore around the little bay of Herbury, but on the

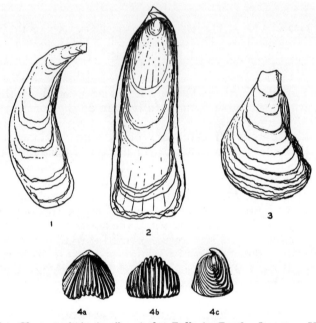

FIG. 3.—*Characteristic fossils of the Fuller's Earth, Langton Herring.* 1, 2, 3, *Ostrea hebridica* Forbes; 1, 2 var. *elongata* Dutertre, 3 normal; 4a, b, c, *Rhynchonella (Rhynchonelloidella) smithi* Davidson.

north side the banks begin to show small sections intermittently for a mile. Nearly the lowest horizon seen is a remarkable oyster-bank ("lumachelle ") composed of an elongated variety of the common oyster of the upper part of the Great Oolite Series and Forest Marble all over the British Isles, *Ostrea hebridica* Forbes (=*sowerbyi* Morris and Lycett), var. *elongata* Dutertre.[1] West of the coastguard station the oysters form a mass at least 12 ft.

---

[1] *See* W. J. Arkell, *op. cit.*, 1933, pp. 251-2 ; and ' The Oysters of the Fuller's Earth,' *Proc. Cotteswold Nat. Field Club*, vol. xxv, 1934, p. 9, pl. iv. In earlier publications this oyster was erroneously identified as *Ostrea acuminata* J. Sowerby, which does not occur above the Lower Fuller's Earth. Good figures were published under that name in R. Damon's *Geology of Weymouth*, 2nd ed., 1884, p. 12, fig. 3. London.

thick. A mile to the north-west the bed is only 3 ft. thick, but it extends at least as far as Watton Cliff, where blocks of it are caught up in two of the faults. The same variety of this oyster is abundant in the Hampen Marly Beds of the Cotswolds and Oxfordshire.

The lowest beds exposed in the Weymouth Anticline are some

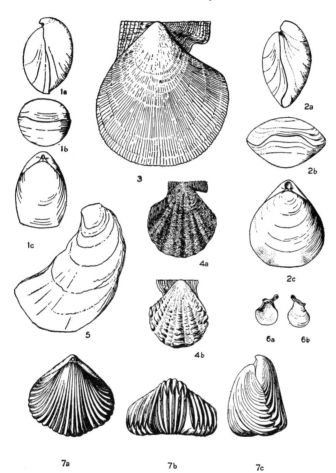

FIG. 4.—*Characteristic fossils of the Forest Marble on the shores of the Fleet.* 1a, b, c. *Ornithella (Digonella)* cf. *digona* (J. Sowerby); 2a, b, c. *Terebratula (Avonothyris) langtonensis* Davidson; 3. *Pecten (Camptonectes) laminatus* J. Sowerby, right valve; 4a, b. *Pecten (Chlamys) vagans* J. de C. Sowerby, right and left valves; 5, *Ostrea hebridica* Forbes, right valve; 6a, b. *Ostrea (Catinula) minuta* (J. de C. Sowerby), left valve; 7a, b, c. *Rhynchonella (Goniorhynchia) boueti* Davidson.

3 ft. of clay containing nodules of argillaceous limestone, which appear beneath the oyster bed one mile west of Langton Herring. They contain numerous *Rhynchonella (Rhynchonelloidella)*

smithi Davidson, including var. *crassa* Muir-Wood, and *Rugitela powerstockensis* Muir-Wood, both characteristic of the Brachiopod Beds of Watton Cliff, Bridport. With them are crushed large perisphinctid ammonites of the genus *Procerites,* also *Hecticoceras, Belemnopsis bessina* (d'Orbigny), and well-preserved large oysters and *Trigoniae.* The last are identified as *Trigonia scarburgensis* Lycett, *T. elongata* var. *lata* Lycett, and *Ostrea undosa* Phillips, all found elsewhere in Upper Cornbrash. In the past they have given rise to suggestions that Oxford Clay or Kellaways Clay exists at Langton Herring.[1]

FOREST MARBLE

The Forest Marble has been estimated to be 80-90 ft. thick by Woodward and 130-140 ft. thick by Strahan, between Herbury and Fleet Common. It falls into three divisions of approximately equal thickness : a block of hard, flaggy, false-bedded, broken-shell limestone, blue-centred and oolitic, between two predominantly argillaceous divisions. The clays are very different from those of the Fuller's Earth, for they are usually greenish or brown, sandy, shaly, or micaceous, with numerous thin impersistent laminae of hard, fissile shale or broken-shell limestone. The limestones are largely made up of broken valves of *Ostrea hebridica* (*sowerbyi*), etc., but there are also many unbroken shells, of which the most conspicuous are *Camptonectes laminatus* (J. Sowerby), *Chlamys obscura* (J. Sowerby), *Lima cardiiformis* (J. Sowerby). The shells of *Gervillia*, or *Isognomon*, have usually been dissolved away, leaving cavities. There are also Rhynchonellids and many other shells, with more rarely an *Epithyris* (? *marmorea* Oppel). The limestone slabs are often ripple-marked and contain clay-galls and vermiform markings and pittings, also rolled and bored pebbles of argillaceous limestone and lignite. The rocks are evidently of very shallow-water origin, and the surfaces of the ripple-marked sandy flagstones appear to point to frequent emergence.

At the base of the Forest Marble is the Boueti Bed. This remarkable bed, only 1 ft. thick, crops out in the beach at the north-west extremity of the little promontory of Herbury, about 1 mile south of Langton Herring, and gradually rises in the low cliff. It is also well seen at Cliff End, Burton Bradstock (p. 15) and can be traced at intervals thence towards Abbotsbury; and there are other exposures at Watton Cliff, near Bridport, and inland. It is a mass of brachiopods, the commonest being *Rhynchonella* (*Goniorhynchia*) *boueti* Davidson and species of *Avonothyris* and *Ornithella*, especially *A. langtonensis* (Davidson) and *O. digona* (J. Sowerby), with which are numerous well-pre-

---

[1] W. J. Arkell, ' Fossils from the Fuller's Earth of the Weymouth Anticline,' *Geol. Mag. vol.* lxxvii, 1940, p. 42.

served valves of *Chlamys vagans* (J. Sowerby), *Placunopsis socialis* Morris and Lycett, and *Ostrea (Catinula) minuta* (J. Sowerby); also ossicles of *Apiocrinus* and occasional *Dictyothyris*. Many of the fossils are encrusted with Polyzoa, *Serpulae* and minute oysters, signs of slow deposition. The fauna is that of the Bradford Clay of Wiltshire, North Somerset, Gloucestershire and Oxford, which rests in those counties upon the Kemble Beds of the Great Oolite limestones. There too the fossils carry the same encrusting organisms. If the Bradford Clay fauna be regarded as exactly synchronous over the whole area of its occurrence, then the Forest Marble of Dorset represents only the Bradfordian and post-Bradfordian Forest Marble inland—namely the Wychwood Beds and, in the lower parts, perhaps the Bradfordian Acton Turville Beds of Gloucestershire.[1] There are thick limestones and marls of Acton Turville facies and containing the fauna of the Boueti Bed in Normandy.

Exposures of the Forest Marble east of Bridport are poor and monotonous. The Boueti Bed occupies the brow of the cliff at Cliff End and the Forest Marble can be seen outcropping in the grass-grown bank above. There have been numerous quarries about Puncknowle and Swyre, and especially Bothenhampton, where the large excavations for road stones and building stones (now long abandoned) were said by Woodward to be some of the best sections of the formation in the country. Small outcrops are numerous thence to Abbotsbury, where the white marls and greenish clays, slabs of stone, and *Rhynchonellae* can be traced along the Abbotsbury Fault, from not far above the shore up to the point where they disappear under the Greensand behind Ferny Hole.

In the Weymouth Anticline the outcrop is arranged in parallel E.-W. ridges, due to faulting. There are numerous small and discontinuous exposures along the banks of the West Fleet. The most interesting is on the west end of Herbury promontory, where what appears to be the lower middle part of the formation crops out, containing some highly fossiliferous bands reminiscent of the Oolithe Blanche de Langrune on the Normandy coast. The most abundant fossils are *Oxytoma costata* (J. Sowerby), nests of a small Rhynchonellid, sponges, and ossicles of *Apiocrinus*. The Boueti Bed descends to water-level a short distance farther north.

Damon described typical sections of Forest Marble, flaggy limestones and shaly clays, of no special interest (none exceeding 21 ft. in depth) and yielding the usual fossils, at Nottington, Radipole Mill, Cold Harbour Lane at Radipole, and between Langton Herring village and the coastguard station.

Small inliers occur at Bincombe and Sutton Poyntz.

---

[1] S. H. Reynolds and A. Vaughan, ' On the Jurassic Strata . . . between Filton and Wootton Bassett,' *Quart. Journ. Geol. Soc.*, vol. lviii, 1902, pp. 742-6; and W. J. Arkell, *Jurassic System in Great Britain*, 1933, p. 271. Oxford.

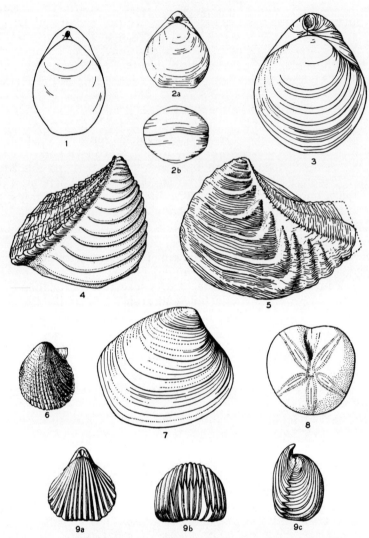

FIG. 5.—*Characteristic fossils of the Lower Cornbrash.*

1. *Ornithella classis* Douglas and Arkell.
2a, b. *Ornithella (Obovothyris) obovata* (J. Sowerby).
3. *Terebratula (Cererithyris) intermedia* J. Sowerby.
4. *Trigonia rolandi* Cross.
5. *Trigonia angulata* J. de C. Sowerby.
6. *Meleagrinella echinata* (William Smith).
7. *Astarte hilpertonensis* Lycett.
8. *Nucleolites clunicularis* (Phillips).
9a, b, c. *Rhynchonella (Kallirhynchia) yaxleyensis* Davidson.

CORNBRASH

GENERAL

The Cornbrash has a narrow outcrop (Fig. 2), but owing to its relative hardness, between the clays of the upper Forest Marble and the Kellaways Beds, it is well exposed near Abbotsbury Swannery and at East Fleet, in the banks of the Backwater; and it has been opened for roadstone and lime burning in a number of old shallow pits.

In most parts of England the thickness of the Cornbrash seldom exceeds 10 ft., but in Dorset it reaches a thickness of 30 ft. Of this one-third belongs to the Lower and two-thirds to the Upper Cornbrash. The two divisions are readily distinguished by both lithic and palaeontological criteria, the fauna of the lower division being Bathonian and that of the upper division principally Callovian.

The Lower Cornbrash consists of rubbly limestone and marl, yielding the ammonite *Clydoniceras discus* (J. Sowerby), and allied species, and crowded with *Meleagrinella echinata* (Wm. Smith), *Chlamys vagans* (J. Sowerby), *Chl. hemicostata* (Morris and Lycett), *Pholadomya deltoidea* (J. Sowerby), *Pleuromya uniformis* (J. Sowerby), *Nucleolites clunicularis* (Phillips), etc., and especially the brachiopod *Ornithella obovata* (J. Sowerby). At the base is generally about 1 ft. of harder cream-coloured limestone crowded with *Terebratula* (*Cererithyris*) *intermedia* (J. Sowerby). This constitutes the Intermedia Zone, and the higher rubble the Obovata Zone.

The Upper Cornbrash consists of alternate bands of cream-coloured argillaceous marl and hard, concretionary, doggery limestone, weathering sandy. It yields ammonites of the genus *Macrocephalites*, usually of large size with massive smooth body-chambers, and the brachiopod *Ornithella* (? *Microthyridina*) *siddingtonensis* (Walker).[1] This indicates the Siddingtonensis Zone; but the uppermost part of the formation yields *Ornithella* (*Microthyridina*) *lagenalis* (Schlotheim) and allied forms (Lagenalis Zone).

Other brachiopods occur more rarely and some are of interest for their extremely localized distribution. For example, *Ornithella classis* Douglas and Arkell is common in a quarry at East Fleet, and has been found on the neighbouring shore, but nowhere else.

DETAILS

The most complete section is at Shipmoor Point, the extremity of Chester's Hill, Abbotsbury Swannery.[2]

---

[1] *Microthyridina* Schuchert and Le Vene is a replacement name for *Microthyris*, preoccupied.

[2] This and subsequent sections from J. A. Douglas and W. J. Arkell, ' The Stratigraphical Distribution of the Cornbrash,' *Quart. Journ. Geol. Soc.*, vol. lxxxiv, 1928, pp. 152-5, where fuller lists of fossils will be found.

FIG. 6.—*Characteristic fossils of the Upper Cornbrash.*

1.   *Ornithella* (? *Microthyridina*) *siddingtonensis* (Walker).
2.   *Ornithella* (*Microthyridina*) *lagenalis* (Schlotheim).
3a, b, c.   *Rhynchonella* (*Rhynchonelloidea*) *cerealis* Buckman.
4.   *Ostrea* (*Lopha*) *marshii* J. Sowerby.
5.   *Lima* (*Plagiostoma*) *rigidula* Phillips.
6.   *Goniomya literata* (J. Sowerby).

CORNBRASH AT SHIPMOOR POINT, CHESTER'S HILL, ABBOTSBURY

Upper Cornbrash (14 ft. 6 ins.)

		Ft.	ins.
14.	Tough laminated limestone	1	0
13.	Hard, nodular limestone with hummocky surface, forming a long shore-platform	1	0
12.	Cream-coloured argillaceous marl, laminated at top... ...	1	3
11.	Hard concretionary limestone	1	0
10.	Cream-coloured argillaceous marl	1	0
9.	Hard limestone		9
8.	Tough laminated marl, with *Ornithella siddingtonensis*, fish-teeth, and tetragonal *Serpulae*	1	0
7.	Sandy marl, with numerous *Exogyra nana* and *Ostrea hebridica* (*sowerbyi*). Crushed *O. siddingtonensis*	2	0
6.	Hard concretionary limestone yielding abundant *Rhynchonella cerealis* and a few *O. siddingtonensis*	1	0
5.	Rubbly, sandy marl, with *O. siddingtonensis*	1	0
4.	Clay and ferruginous sand	1	0
3.	Hard, nodular, concretionary limestone, containing *Pholadomya deltoidea*	2	6

Lower Cornbrash (7 ft.)

		Ft.	ins.
2.	Rubbly limestone, yielding *Ornithella obovata, Rhynchonella* (*Kallirhynchia*) *yaxleyensis, M. echinata, Pholadomya deltoidea, Ph. lyrata, Chlamys vagans, Gresslya peregrina, Ctenostreon proboscideum, Ostrea hebridica*, etc.	4	0
1.	Hard pinkish limestone with *Cererithyris intermedia, Nautilus truncatus, M. echinata, Pygurus michelini*	3	0

The section is repeated by a fault about ¾ mile to the south-east. There the Lower Cornbrash has increased in thickness to at least 11 ft., of which 10 ft. are assigned to the Obovata Zone and yielded, in addition to the fossils found at Shipmoor Point, *Ornithella grandobovata* Buckman, *O. classis* Douglas and Arkell, and a Perisphinctid, *Homœoplanulites*. The Upper Cornbrash is the same as at Shipmoor Point, but it yielded two complete specimens of *O. lagenalis* near the top, and also a large Macrocephalitid ammonite.

West of East Fleet the pale, sandy, hummocky limestone with marl partings of the Upper Cornbrash protrudes from low banks for a considerable distance along the shore. Fossils are scarce, but the usual giant Macrocephalitid ammonites have been found, with gerontic laevigation of the last whorl.

Inland the Lower Cornbrash is exposed in two quarries recently in work. One lies on Fleet Common, west of the road from East Fleet to Chickerell, and is remarkable for the abundance of *Ornithella classis* Douglas & Arkell, a brachiopod of which only one specimen has been found elsewhere, in the Obovata Zone of the shore west of Rodden Ridge. The rest of the fauna is that of the Lower Cornbrash (Obovata Zone). The section shows a bed of fossiliferous marl and rubbly limestone (3 ft. 3 ins.), over-lying hard grey-centred limestone (2 ft. 8 ins.), weathering to a cream colour, and yielding *Clydoniceras*.

The other quarry, a mile away rather north of east, shows 12 ft. of beds in the Obovata Zone. It is situated at East Chickerell, ½ mile east of Chickerell Church.

EAST CHICKERELL QUARRY

Lower Cornbrash   Ft. ins.
4. Hard platy and rubbly limestone. *Ornithella obovata, Aniso-cardia minima, Pygurus michelini*, etc.   3   6
3. Compact marl passing down into a hard nodular band, contain-ing all the fossils of bed 4 plus *Rhynchonella (Kallirhynchia) yaxleyensis, R. (K.) spp., Ornithella rugosa, O. magnobovata, Pholadomya deltoidea*, etc.   1   6
2. Laminated argillaceous marl. *O. magnobovata, O. rugosa, Pholadomya lyrata, Ceratomya concentrica*, etc.   1   3
1. Hard, compact, blue-hearted limestone, becoming concre-tionary towards the base. *M. echinata* abundant, but other fossils scarce and difficult to extract   5   0

From the coast-sections it may be inferred that the Intermedia Bed here occurs immediately beneath the floor of the quarry. A large *Clydoniceras* was found on an adjoining wall in a hard lime-stone matrix, similar to bed 1. Capping the same wall are big spheroidal concretions of sandy limestone, like those of the Siddingtonensis Zone in the coast-sections.

Formerly there were good sections at the north end of Radipole Backwater, where the Cornbrash was dug for lime-burning and for ballasting the railway;[1] but only a few feet of rubbly Obovata Beds are now exposed on the shore. *Clydoniceras* was obtained from the bank of the backwater in 1926,[2] apparently from the spot figured by Woodward in Strahan's memoir.[3] Numerous small and more or less temporary quarries have been opened from time to time on the different outcrops due to repetition by faults, but the sections described above display specimens of all that is of importance now visible in the area.

Three small inliers occur along the fault line at the foot of the Chalk downs at Bincombe and Sutton Poyntz. The Cornbrash strikes roughly east and west and dips to the north under Oxford Clay. Both Lower and Upper Cornbrash are present and have been worked in at least one old pit, from which stone for several walls was obtained. A nearly complete suite of Lower Cornbrash fossils has been collected from field rubble near Sutton Poyntz, and in small exposures at Bincombe. For details see pp. 260-268, and Pl. XIX.

---

[1] R. Damon, *op. cit.*, 2nd ed., 1884, pp. 19-20; A. Strahan, *op. cit.*, 1898, p. 13.

[2] J. A. Douglas and W. J. Arkell, *op. cit.*, 1928, p. 155.

[3] *Purbeck Memoir*, 1898, p. 13. Much hard blue Lower Cornbrash, poor in fossils, was excavated from a sewer trench along the north shore of the Backwater in 1936-7.

CHAPTER III

CALLOVIAN AND LOWER OXFORDIAN STAGES:
KELLAWAYS BEDS AND OXFORD CLAY

I. GENERAL

The core of Middle Jurassic rocks (Lower Oolites) in the Weymouth Anticline is surrounded on three sides by the horseshoe-shaped outcrop of the Oxford Clay (Fig. 2, p. 14). That formation has been estimated to reach 500 ft. in thickness, but it is nowhere fully exposed for direct measurement and it may not exceed 400 feet. The outcrop forms low ground which, at the closed eastern end of the horseshoe, in Lodmoor and Radipole Backwater, degenerates into marshland reminiscent of the Fens. Into this low-lying eastern tract the sea has eaten the regular curve of Weymouth Bay. Most of the outcrop is unexposed on the coast, owing to the town and marshes, which are protected by a shingle bank. Only at the northern end, at Furzy Cliff, Jordan Hill, can any of the clay be seen; there the uppermost zone is exposed. An old section at the south end of the bay has been obliterated by the fortification of The Nothe, and another at Greenhill Gardens, where Damon collected, was long since engulfed by the town.

The two free ends of the horseshoe run into the shores of the Fleet Backwater, where the clays are all much slipped and overgrown, owing to the protective action of the Chesil Beach. The more northerly end, in the West Fleet at Abbotsbury, shows nothing. The more southerly and broader, in the East Fleet, affords some indistinct but highly fossiliferous sections.

Better than any of these exposures are two short stretches of sea cliffs in two detached outcrops at the tip of Redcliff Point and between Redcliff Point and Shortlake, and others in brickyards at Chickerell.

By piecing together the information, the following sequence is obtained for the Oxford Clay and Kellaways Beds near Weymouth :—

Oppel's Divisions			Zones	Strata and Exposures	
OXFORD CLAY	LOWER OXFORDIAN	*biarmatus*	*Cardioceras cordatum*	Red Nodule Beds Jordan Cliff Clays (*pars*)	} of Redcliff-Shortlake and Lynch Farm Bay.
			Quenstedtoceras mariae	Furzedown Clays, with pyritic fossils, of Ham Cliff, Shortlake and Furzedown.	
			Quenstedtoceras lamberti	Tidmoor Point Clays, with pyritic fossils	
	CALLOVIAN	*ath-leta*	*Peltoceras athleta*	Clays with septaria	} Crook Hill Brickyard, Chickerell.
KELLAWAYS BEDS		*anceps*	*Erymnoceras coronatum*	Bituminous Shales with crushed Kosmocerates and large septaria	
			Kosmoceras jason		
		macro-cephalus	*Sigaloceras calloviense*	Sandy clays with doggers and septaria	} Putton Lane Brickyard, Chickerell.
			Proplanulites kornigi	Clay with nodules	

The top of the Oxford Clay here, as in the Oxford district, seems to fall within the Zone of *Cardioceras cordatum* (J. Sowerby) (= *C. cardia* Buckman[1]). On the coast there is a fairly sharp lithic change from the Oxford Clay to the Lower Calcareous Grit in the only clear section, Ham Cliff, and this change seems to take place at about the same level on the Fleet at Wyke Regis. Farther west, towards Abbotsbury, however, the grits either thin out or are largely replaced by clay.

II. DETAILS

(a) SHORES OF THE FLEET AND CHICKERELL BRICKWORKS

Although all parts of the Oxford Clay are represented in the series of low exposures along the shore of the Fleet Backwater from East Fleet village to west of Wyke Regis, the Kellaways Beds appear to be faulted out. At present, however, one of the best

---

[1] W. J. Arkell, ' The Ammonite Zones of the Upper Oxfordian of Oxford,' *Quart. Journ. Geol. Soc.*, vol. xcii, 1936, p. 152 ; and *Geol. Mag.*, 1941, p. 170.

sections of the Kellaways Beds in the South of England is displayed in the Dorset Brick and Tile Co.'s pit at Putton Lane, Chickerell (the more easterly of the two brickyards).[1]

PUTTON LANE BRICKYARD, ½ MILE S.E. OF CHICKERELL CHURCH

Ft.

4. Yellowish to khaki-coloured clay   6

3. Septaria, large and flattened, forming almost a continuous floor in the N.W. part of the pit, becoming less septarian and more like sandstone towards the S. Quantities of selenite. Smooth-whorled ammonite, *Erymnoceras*? (*indet.*) up to 1ft. 9 ins. in diameter; *Modiola bipartita* (J. Sowerby), *Thracia depressa* J. Sowerby...   1

2. Sandy clay and sand with abundant *Gryphaea bilobata* J. Sowerby, and at the base an impersistent band of hard laminated sand-stone, up to 4 ins. thick. Locally some large cementstone concretions in this bed show a rich fauna: crowds of small *Gryphaea bilobata* and *G.* aff. *alimena* (d'Orbigny), small *Astarte spp.*, *Chlamys fibrosa* (J. Sowerby), *Meleagrin-ella braamburiensis* (J. Sowerby), *Trigonia* cf. *irregularis* Seebach, *Sigaloceras* ... ...(?) 1 to 1½

1. Blue clay with two or more lines of small round cementstone nodules, some of which are full of well-preserved *Oxytoma*. Associated with and often partly embedded in the nodules are body-chambers of *Proplanulites spp.*, *Sigaloceras spp.*, *Cadoceras sublaeve* (J. Sowerby), *Cadoceras tolype* Buckman, *Reineckeia sp.* Locally near the base there is a shell-bed full of *Ostrea* (*Gryphaea*?) *alimena*, with *Oxytoma*, etc., which has caused the central and south-westerly parts of the pit to be abandoned. Seen to about   8

The Kosmoceras Shales of the Lower Oxford Clay are exposed intermittently for ¾ mile south-east of East Fleet village, dipping at 5° about south-east. The best exposures on the coast are at the first promontory south of East Fleet and in the middle of the next bay to the south. The shales are highly bituminous and contain numerous layers of 'turtle stones,' or large flattened-spheroidal septarian concretions of hard cementstone, from 1 to 2 ft. in diameter. In former times they were collected, more especially from the shore of Radipole Backwater, for cutting and polishing to make ornamental table-tops.

A far better section of the Lower Oxford Clay is at present afforded by Webb, Major & Co.'s Brickyard, ½ mile south of Chickerell Church, which displays the top of the Jason Zone and the whole of the Coronatum and Athleta Zones.

---

[1] W. J. Arkell, *Jurassic System in Great Britain*, 1933, p. 344. Oxford.

FIG. 7.—*Characteristic fossils of the Oxford and Kellaways Clays.*

1. *Dicroloma trifida* (Phillips); 2. *Ostrea (Catinula) alimena* d'Orbigny, left valve, Kellaways Clay, Chickerell; 3. *Nucula calliope* d'Orbigny; 4. *Trigonia sp.* cf. *irregularis* Seebach; 5. *Modiola bipartita* J. Sowerby; 6. *Oxytoma sp.* (*inequivalve* group), Kellaways Clay; 7. *Hibolites hastatus* (Blainville); 8. *Procerithium damonis* (Lycett); 9a, b. *Pentacrinus sp.*; 10. *Ostrea (Gryphaea) dilatata* J. Sowerby.

CROOK HILL BRICKYARD, CHICKERELL

Ft.

ATHLETA ZONE.

5. Yellowish-brown clays with yellow-coated septaria and well-
    preserved body-chambers, and more rarely inner whorls, of
    ammonites. *Peltoceras athleta* (Phillips) (abundant, large), *P.*
    cf. *athletoides* Lahusen, *P.* (*Rursiceras*) *pseudotorosum* Prieser,
    P. (*R.*) *pratti* Spath, *Kosmoceras transitionis* Nikitin (*non*
    Lahusen), *K. proniae* Teisseyre, *K. bigoti* Douvillé   15
4. Blue clay with grey septaria and similarly preserved ammonites,
    mainly body-chambers, but more often inner-whorls. *Pseudo-*
    peltoceras chauvinianum (d'Orbigny), *Kosmoceras lithuanicum*
    Siemiradzki, *K. couffoni* Douvillé, *Reineckeia* (*Reineckeites*)
    stuebeli (Steinmann) (= *duplex* Buckman), *R.* (*Kellawaysites*)
    multicostata Petitclerc (*non* Buckman), *Hecticoceras* cf.
    pseudopunctatum (Lahusen) (large body-chamber)   10
3. Shales, greenish-brown, bituminous, the surfaces covered with
    crushed *Meleagrinella*. Crushed *Kosmoceras transitionis*
    Nikitin (*non* Lahusen, *non* Krenkel) (*K. proniae-duncani*
    Krenkel, var. β), small crushed *K. proniae* Teisseyre and
    crushed *Lunuloceras* (indet.)   15

CORONATUM ZONE.

2. Shales, greenish and chocolate brown, bituminous, with strong
    odour like Kimmeridge shales, and lines of turtle stones.
    The turtle stones sometimes (rarely) contain large badly-
    preserved *Erymnoceras spp.* In the shales the fossils are
    abundant but crushed flat. The ammonites are chiefly
    Kosmoceras castor (Reinecke) and *K. grossouvrei* Douvillé,
    with less commonly *K. pollux* (Reinecke). One large cement-
    stone mass believed to have come from this zone was crowded
    with *Erymnoceras coronatum* (Bruguière) and other species
    (Spath recorded seven species, presumably from this block,
    which the present writer observed loose in the pit in 1931)[1]
    There are also abundant crushed *Meleagrinella* (*sp. nov.*,
    as at Calvert, Bucks.), *Protocardia*, *Nucula*, *Procerithium*,
    fossil wood, etc. To foot of present working face on west
    side of pit   30

? JASON ZONE

1. Shales, bituminous, with large septaria, seen in north-east side
    of pit only and not worked recently. Forms floor of present
    working pit. Abundant crushed *Kosmoceras* cf. *jason* (Reinecke),
    K. stutchburii (Pratt), and perhaps *K. obductum* (Buckman),
    with crushed lamellibranchs as in Bed 2, especially a small
    Astarte   10

                                                    Total   80

Bed 1 is so bituminous that in emergencies it is mixed with other
fuel and helps to fire the bricks. Bed 4 is said to have properties
resembling those of Fuller's Earth.

The only ammonites found in bed 1 are flattened and difficult
to identify, but at Radipole Backwater uncrushed ammonites of
the Jason Zone were formerly obtained in perfect preservation.[2]

[1] L. F. Spath, ' Revision of the Jurassic Cephalopod Fauna of Kachh,' *Pal. Indica,*
N.S., vol. ix, Mem. 2, 1933, p. 857.
[2] See photograph in S. S. Buckman, *Type Ammonites*, vol. iv, 1923, pl. cdxviii (*K.*
jason). London

The fauna of the Athleta Zone is particularly interesting on account of the Reineckeids, which are very rare in this country. In addition to the two species mentioned, a third, a large tuberculated form of the subgenus *Collotia*, is represented from the district (' lamberti bed, Weymouth pottery ') by a single fragment in the British Museum (No. C.30393). Reineckeids are also known (one fragmentary specimen from each place) from Oxford (Lamberti Zone), Woodham Brick-pit, Bucks. (Lamberti Zone), and Scarborough (Hackness Rock).

The succession is taken up from this brickyard to the top of the Oxford Clay by the low cliff-sections along the Fleet. One of the most celebrated fossil localities in England is Tidmoor Point, long renowned for its pyritous and limonitic casts of small ammonites of the Lamberti Zone. The locality is $1\frac{1}{4}$ miles south of Chickerell Church, behind the rifle-range (*see* Fig. 2, p. 14). The cliff is low and much slipped, but well-preserved small brown ammonites may still be collected in abundance on and just above the beach, especially after a stormy winter (Pl. II). This is the type locality of *Quenstedtoceras lamberti* (J. Sowerby),[1] *Q. leachi* (J. Sowerby) and *Kosmoceras spinosum* (J. de C. Sowerby). With them is found a remarkable assemblage of ammonites, correlating on the one hand with the Lamberti Limestone of Buckinghamshire and the Hackness Rock of Yorkshire, and on the other hand with the classic sections of the Lamberti Zone clays in the cliffs of Normandy and the Jura Mountains. For the classification of the Oxford Clay in north-west Europe the importance of this locality could hardly be over-estimated.

The most fossiliferous spot is near the north-west extremity of the Point, but observations spread over several years have not

---

[1] Examples are figured in S. S. Buckman's *Type Ammonites*, 1920, pl. cliv ; 1922, pl. cccxxxix ; 1925, pl. cliv A ; and W. J. Arkell, *Jurassic System in Great Britain*, 1933, pl. xxxvii, fig. 3.

EXPLANATION OF PLATE II

Ammonites from the Lamberti Zone, Tidmoor Point, collected by the author :

1a, b. *Kosmoceras spinosum* (J. de C. Sowerby) (topotype) ;
2a, b. *Kosmoceras compressum* (Quenstedt) ;
3a, b. *Kosmoceras tidmoorense* Arkell (holotype) ;
4a, b. *Distichoceras bicostatum* (Stahl) ;
5. *Hecticoceras* aff. *nodosum* (Quenstedt) ;
6a, b. *Quenstedtoceras leachi* (J. Sowerby) (topotype, neotype) ;
7. *Perisphinctes kobyi* de Loriol ;
8. *Peltoceras ?prespissum* Spath ;
9a, b. *Grossouvria* cf. *miranda* (de Loriol) ;
10. *Quenstedtoceras lamberti* (J. Sowerby) var. *intermissum* (Buckman) (topotype of species and variety) ;
11a, b. *Quenstedtoceras lamberti* (J. Sowerby) (topotype) ;
12a, b. *Quenstedtoceras brasili* Douvillé.

(All photographs natural size, by the author).

established any sequence in the distribution of species along the fossiliferous part of the beach. The south end cannot be far from the Mariae Zone.

Other common fossils, besides the preponderating cephalopods, are ossicles and parts of stems of *Pentacrinus*, casts of *Nucula* and *Grammatodon*, and numerous *Procerithium muricatum* (J. Sowerby) and *P. damonis* (Lycett *in* Damon), the last two in a thin hard ferruginous layer.

A long list of cephalopoda was published by Spath.[1] The following list is based on about 500 specimens collected by the present writer and a few more in the Geological Survey Museum. Species followed by (S) are included on the authority of Spath's list.

LIST OF CEPHALOPODA FROM TIDMOOR POINT

Oppelia (Lorioloceras) inconspicua *de Loriol*
Oppelia (Eochetoceras ?) villersense (*d'Orbigny*) (S)
Distichoceras bicostatum (*Stahl*)
Horioceras baugieri (*d'Orbigny*) (S)
Hecticoceras (Putealiceras) puteale (*Leckenby*)
     ,,   ,,   punctatum (*Stahl*)
     ,,   ,,   pseudopunctatum (*Lahusen*)
     ,,   ,,   ombilicatum *de Tsytovitch*
     ,,   (Brightia) svevum *Bonarelli*
     ,,   ,,   *aff.* nodosum (*Quenstedt*) (S)
     ,,   (Lunuloceras) pompeckji *Parona and Bonarelli* (S)
Quenstedtoceras (Quenstedtoceras) leachi (*J. Sowerby*) (= vertumnum
                                                              Leckenby)
     ,,   ,,   *aff.* leachi (*finer ribbed more evolute form*)
     ,,   (Prorsiceras) gregarium (*Leckenby*)
     ,,   (Bourkelamberticeras) lamberti (*J. Sowerby*)
     ,,   ,,   intermissum *Buckman*
     ,,   ,,   brasili *Douvillé* (*including* henrici)
     ,,   ,,   gallicum *Arkell*
     ,,   (Eboraciceras)ordinarium (*Leckenby*)
     ,,   ,,   dissimile (*Brown*) (S)
     ,,   ,,   sutherlandiae (*J. de C. Sowerby*) (S)
     ,,   ,,   cadiforme *Buckman* (S)
     ,,   (Pavloviceras) williamsoni *Buckman*
Kosmoceras (Kosmoceras) spinosum (*J. de C. Sowerby*)
     ,,   ,,   compressum (*Quenstedt*)
     ,,   ,,   tidmoorense *Arkell*
Grossouvria (Grossouvria) *cf.* miranda (*de Loriol*)
     ,,   ,,   *aff.* evexa (*Quenstedt*) (S)
     ,,   (Poculisphinctes) *aff.* poculum (*Leckenby*) (S)
     ,,   ,,   trina (*Buckman*) (?)
Perisphinctes (Alligaticeras) *aff.* alligatus (*Leckenby*) (S)
     ,,   kobyi *de Loriol*
     ,,   (Properisphinctes) bernensis *de Loriol*
Peltoceras (Peltoceras) athleta (*Phillips*) (S)
     ,,   ,,   athletoides (*Lahusen*) *Brasil* (S)
     ,,   ,,   metamorphicum *Spath* (S)
     ,,   (Peltoceratoides) subtense (*Leckenby*)
     ,,   (Rursiceras) pseudotorosum (*Prieser*)

[1] L. F. Spath, *op. cit.*, 1933, pp. 858-9.

Peltoceras (Rursiceras) prespissum *Spath*
,, ,, pratti *Spath* (S)
Aspidoceras (Euaspidoceras)clynelishense *Arkell*
,, ,, armatum *de Loriol* (S)
Nautilus hexagonus *J. de C. Sowerby* (S)
Belemnopsis (Hibolites) hastata (*Blainville*)
,, subhastata (*Zieten*) (S)
,, sulcata (*Miller & Phillips*)
Cylindroteuthis puzosiana (*d'Orbigny*) (= oweni *Pratt*)
Rhopaloteuthis aenigmatica (*d'Orbigny*) *Kilian* (S)
,, ? sauvanausa (*d'Orbigny*)

The Mariae Zone (Furzedown Clay) crops out on the north-west side of the next promontory southwards, west of Furzedown. Here the ammonites are almost as abundant but belong to far fewer species (Pl. III). They are in the same state of preservation as those at Tidmoor Point. With them are *Nuculae*, *Pentacrinus* ossicles, and numerous rather small *Gryphaeae*, mainly *G. lituola* Lamarck, with dwarfed *G. dilatata* J. Sowerby.

LIST OF CEPHALOPODA FROM FURZEDOWN (Author's coll.)

Quenstedtoceras (Pavloviceras) mariae (*d'Orbigny*) (*abundant*)
,, ,, omphaloides (*J. Sowerby*)
Cardioceras (Scarburgiceras) scarburgense (*Young and Bird*)
,, ,, praecordatum *Douvillé*
Hecticoceras *cf.* matheyi *de Loriol*
Taramelliceras (Proscaphites) richei (*de Loriol*)
Perisphinctes (Properisphinctes) bernensis *de Loriol*
Peltoceras spp., *many fragments of small nuclei*
Belemnopsis (Hibolites) hastata (*Blainville*) (*abundant*)
? Rhopaloteuthis sauvanausa (*d'Orbigny*)

This is the fauna of the typical Lower Oxfordian of the Jura Mountains, Normandy, the Boulonnais, and Buckinghamshire, called in France the Marnes à *Creniceras renggeri*. The Weymouth district furnished the type-specimen of *C. renggeri*, figured by Sowerby, but it has not been rediscovered in recent years. The original specimen may have come from Greenhill Gardens or Radipole Backwater or brickyard, where there are now no sections. Possibly the species has a restricted range at the base of the zone, as in Buckinghamshire, in which case the beds containing it would crop out at the head of the little bay between the promontory of Furzedown and Tidmoor Point, not at present subjected to erosion.

The Cordatum Zone follows south of the next and last little bay, south-west of Lynch Farm, and round the promontory where the East Fleet narrows, west of Wyke Regis. The rusty-coloured kidney stones of the Red Nodule Beds weather out of the clays and form a bright coloured platform on the beach, mixed with many large oyster shells (*Gryphaea dilatata* J. Sowerby and occasional *Lopha gregarea* J. Sowerby). Here, among multitudes of red casts of *Modiola bipartita* J. Sowerby, *Thracia depressa* (J. de C.

Sowerby) and *Pleuromya alduini* (Brongniart) ($=$ *Mya gibbosa* and *oblata* J. de C. Sowerby), are to be found (usually broken) the ammonites of the Cordatum Zone (Pl. III). The assemblage reproduces faithfully that of the clays of Studley Brickyard, near Oxford, the ironshot clays below the Elsworth Rock at Elsworth, Cambridgeshire, and the ironshot Oolithe ferrugineuse of the Normandy coast.[1]

LIST OF CEPHALOPODA FROM THE RED NODULE BEDS,

WEST OF WYKE REGIS (Author's collection).

Cardioceras (Cardioceras) costellatum *Buckman*
 ,,   ,,   costicardia *Buckman*
 ,,   (Vertebriceras) quadrarium *Buckman*
 ,,   ,,   sagitta (*Buckman*)
Goliathiceras goliathum (*d'Orbigny*)
 ,,   sidericum (*Buckman*)
 ,,   (Pachycardioceras) anacanthum (*Buckman*)
Aspidoceras (Euaspidoceras) nikitini *Borissjak*.

South of this, not many feet above the Red Nodule Beds, follow on the Nothe Grits; but the junction with the Corallian Beds is better seen in Ham Cliff, north of Weymouth.

(b) SECTIONS AT AND NORTH OF WEYMOUTH

The old Weymouth brick-pit was situated close to the west shore of Radipole Backwater, about $\frac{1}{4}$ mile north of Westham Halt Station. No section is visible there now. According to H. B. Woodward,[2] *Quenstedtoceras mariae* occurred on the shore at this point and *Cardioceras cordatum* in the brickpit above. The former statement was confirmed in 1937 when a sewer was laid along the west shore of the Backwater, and the trench, at this point 14 ft. deep, yielded pyritized *Quenstedtoceras mariae*, *Q. omphaloides* and *Cardioceras scarburgense* (see Pl. III).

The lowest clays exposed on the coast north of Weymouth belong to the Lamberti Zone. They are brought up to about 6 ft. above the beach in the core of the anticline east of Ham Cliff, between Redcliff and Shortlake. Above follow clays of the Mariae Zone with pyritized ammonites. In addition to those listed from Furzedown on p. 32, *Grossouvria petitclerci* (de Loriol) has been collected, and shells of *Oxytoma*, *Dicroloma*, etc. The belemnite *Belemnopsis (Hibolites) hastata* (Blainville) is abundant. There must be about 40 ft. of this zone.

Above come the Jordan Cliff Clays (50 ft. or more), containing a fine-ribbed Cardiocerate fauna, crushed flat, as white impressions. These clays are provisionally assigned to the Cordatum Zone, but in part they contain forms of *Cardioceras* intermediate between

---

[1] See W. J. Arkell, ' The Zonal Position of the Elsworth Rock,' *Geol. Mag.,* vol. lxxiv, 1937, pp. 449-450 ; and vol. lxxviii, 1941, pp. 161-172.
[2] *In* A. Strahan, *Purbeck Memoir*, 1898, p. 20.

scarburgense and later forms.   From the Jordan Cliff Clays came
the type specimens of *Cardioceras anacanthum* Buckman and
Peltoceras hoplophorus (Buckman) both Cordatum Zone forms.
The whole of the Cordatum Zone is present and more or less
accessible in the section under Ham Cliff, but it is almost impossible
to measure the thicknesses, owing to the steep dip of the bedding,
the half-foundered state of the cliffs, and repetition by slipping.
The Red Nodule Beds, which must be some 50 ft. in thickness,
are easily recognized.   They consist of grey clays with layers of
very large *Gryphaea dilatata* and some nests of *Lopha gregarea*,
and numerous bands of small red iron-oxide coated cementstone
nodules like those on the shore of the Fleet.   Some are septarian,
and become very striking objects when rounded and polished in
the beach shingle.   The fossils here are the same as recorded on
the shore of the Fleet (p. 33).
The highest 20 ft. of the Oxford Clay (and perhaps another
20 ft. hidden by talus) at Ham Cliff consist of grey blocky clay
with pyrites nodules, and crushed *Modiola*, *Thracia*, *Perna*, *Pinna*,
etc.
The tip of Redcliff Point is formed of Red Nodule Beds with
many giant *Gryphaea dilatata*, faulted against Nothe Clay.   Under
the fault the lowest beds seen on the upthrow (south) side are the
Jordan Cliff Clays, thrown against Nothe Grit.   The total thickness of Cordatum Zone clays exposed on the upthrow side is 80 ft.,
but the base is below sea-level.
Furzy Cliff, Jordan Hill, exhibits a good section of the Jordan
Cliff Clays (about 40 ft.) and Red Nodule Beds (about 45 ft.).

(c)   INLIERS AT RIDGEWAY, BINCOMBE, SUTTON POYNTZ AND

OSMINGTON

On the north side of the intra-Cretaceous Abbotsbury Fault the
Upper Greensand and Chalk were deposited on the Oxford Clay

EXPLANATION OF PLATE III

Ammonites from the Mariae and Cordatum Zones of the Upper Oxford
Clay, and from the Corallian Beds :

1a, b. *Cardioceras* (*Vertebriceras*) *quadrarium* Buckman, Cordatum Zone,
   Red Nodule Beds, near Weymouth (Sedgwick Museum, Cambridge,
   no. J.4811);

2a, b. *Cardioceras costicardia* Buckman, Red Nodule Beds, Wyke Regis
   (author's coll.);

3a, b. *Quenstedtoceras* (*Pavloviceras*) *mariae* (d'Orbigny), Furzedown
   Clay, Weymouth Backwater, sewer trench (author's coll.);

4a, b. *Cardioceras* (*Scarburgiceras*) *praecordatum* Douvillé.   Upper
   Mariae Zone, Furzedown Clay, Furzedown (author's coll.);

5a, b. *Perisphinctes* (*Discosphinctes*) *cautisrufae* Arkell.   *Trigonia*
   clavellata Beds, near Black Head (holotype. Geol. Survey Mus.,
   no. 30664).   (All photographs natural size, by the author.)

in the region of the Downs north of Weymouth. The Oxford Clay comes to the surface in four inliers at Ridgeway railway-cutting, Bincombe, Sutton Poyntz and Osmington (*see* Map, Pl. XIX). The only major section that has been seen is the railway-cutting at Ridgeway. Slipping of the banks of the cutting in 1936, and the removal of the subsided mass, provided a passable section. All the beds exposed belong to the Cordatum Zone, dipping towards the south at 70° or more, and much jumbled.[1]

In the other inliers the Oxford Clay has been proved by pits and trenches, and it has been found possible, with the use of an auger, to map the outcrop by means of the yellow and khaki colour of the Oxford Clay as compared with the blue Kimmeridge Clay. Details of these inliers will be found in the discussion of the structure, in Chapter XIII (pp. 257-268).

---

[1] W. J. Arkell, ' Postscript Notes on the Ballard Down and Ridgeway Faults,' *Geol. Mag.*, vol. lxxiv, 1937, p. 89.

CHAPTER IV

UPPER OXFORDIAN STAGE : CORALLIAN BEDS

I. General

(a) LITHOLOGY AND PALAEONTOLOGY

The Corallian Beds of the Dorset coast are just over 200 ft. thick and the sections in the cliffs are the best in northern Europe. They represent three cycles of deposition, each cycle beginning with clay, continuing with sand, and ending with oolitic limestones. The whole forms a clear- and shallow-water episode in the great period of muddy sedimentation represented by the Oxford and Kimmeridge Clays, together about 2,000 ft. thick in South Dorset.

Twice during Corallian times (indicated by the Nothe Clay and Sandsfoot Clay) the sedimentation reverted to the mud type, with few bottom-dwellers except large oysters. In the Nothe Clay the 'round oyster' of the Oxford Clay (*Gryphaea dilatata*) persisted; in the Sandsfoot Clay the ' flat oyster ' of the Kimmeridge Clay (*Ostrea delta*) appeared. Probably at these times there was a deficiency of oxygen at the sea-bottom, owing to lack of currents adequate to keep it properly aerated.

The sands which succeed the clays (Nothe Grit, Bencliff Grit, Sandsfoot Grit) have each their own individuality and their faunas differ considerably, but they all denote a similar general change in the sedimentation. At these periods currents increased, bringing coarse sediment, producing marked false-bedding in the Bencliff Grit. Aeration of the sea-bottom was improved, but the mechanical conditions of rapid sand-transport were not favourable to a thriving bottom fauna. As usual, shells are not abundant in the sands; though there are certain exceptional bands. A type of rock highly characteristic of the Nothe and Sandsfoot Grits, and found also at various levels in the Corallian Beds, is the so-called fucoid beds. In these beds there is no definite organic structure, but the whole rock is penetrated in all directions by ramifying shapes suggestive of fossilized seaweed-fields. It is uncertain, however, whether the appearances are not due to concretionary action.

The limestones with which the cycles ended are the most characteristic part of the Corallian Beds. They denote periods of shallow contracted seas with good aeration, combined with not-too-coarse or violent sedimentation. At these periods bottom-dwelling faunas flourished. The greatest development of this type of rock in Dorset is the Osmington Oolite Series and Trigonia Beds, altogether 85 ft. thick. Much marl is intercalated, but the pure Osmington Oolite is built up of small ooliths and comminuted shells. The comminution testifies to surf action, and local false bedding shows that currents were sometimes still strong; but in the even-bedded parts of the series (by far the greater proportion) are banks of bivalve shells, whole and exquisitely preserved, sometimes even with the ligament and periostracum. Such are the Trigonia Beds, which are typical " condensed " beds, with many ammonites and phosphatic grey nodules.

Corals are rare in Dorset and nowhere occur in the position of growth. Almost the only horizon at which they occur is the Ringstead Coral Bed, 6 to 8 ins. thick. In the Osmington Oolite Series, however, are several types of rock which are met with inland in close association with coral reefs, and so it is probable that corals were growing not far away from the present exposures of Corallian Beds in Dorset. The Nodular Rubble at the top of the Series, and the Littlemore Clay Beds at several horizons, are especially suggestive of coralline sea-bottoms and alternate with true Coral Rag in the Oxford district and in Wiltshire.

Ammonites are common at certain levels in the Corallian Beds but otherwise usually rare. The Nothe Grits contain a sparse fauna of medium-sized *Cardioceras sensu stricto*, usually found only as indeterminate body-chambers; *Aspidoceras catena* also occurs. This fauna seems to compare best, so far as it is known, with that of the Lower Calcareous Grit of Seend and Calne, Wiltshire, — the Cordatum Zone *sensu stricto*. The Preston Grit or *Trigonia hudlestoni* Bed at the top is rich in species of *Cardioceras*, of which hitherto the following have been identified : *C. excavatum* (J. Sowerby), *C. zenaidae* Ilovaïsky, *C. densiplicatum* Boden and several new species, with *Goliathiceras capax* (Young and Bird), and many *Aspidoceras,—A. catena* (J. de C. Sowerby), *A. akantheen* Buckman, *A. paucituberculatum* Arkell. *Perisphinctes* are rare : *P. (Arisphinctes) helenae* de Riaz and *P. (Kranaosphinctes) sp. indet.* have been collected. This bed therefore correlates with the Trigonia Beds of Wiltshire, Berkshire, and Oxfordshire, and belongs to the lower part of the Plicatilis Zone. The Nothe Clay and Bencliff Grit have not yielded identifiable ammonites.

The Osmington Oolite Series contains some typical forms of

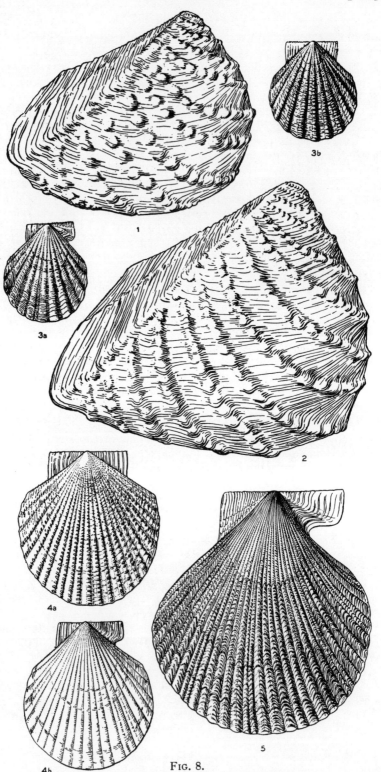

FIG. 8.

the Plicatilis Zone, such as *Perisphinctes (Arisphinctes) maximus* (Young and Bird) and *Cardioceras cawtonense* (Blake and Hudleston).

From the *Trigonia clavellata* Beds, and principally from the Red Beds at the top of that group, has been collected an entirely new fauna of *Perisphinctes*, different from any known in the Plicatilis Zone, and associated with *Amoeboceras spp.*[1] Part of this fauna is met with in the Boxworth Rock of Cambridgeshire and the Ampthill Clay, and again in Normandy and Germany. An example is figured on Plate III, fig. 5.

Finally, in the Sandsfoot Beds and Ringstead Coral Bed is a still more dissimilar fauna, in which the predominant ammonites are the genus *Ringsteadia*, having affinities with the Lower Kimmeridgian *Pictonia*. These beds correlate with strata at Havre which the French often include in the Kimmeridgian.

Occasionally Crustacean remains (*Glyphaea*) are found, and also vertebrae and other bones of *Teleosaurus*. Echinoderms are rare except in the Ringstead Coral Bed; elsewhere only *Nucleolites scutatus* is found. Brachiopods are unknown. Calcareous sponges are probably commoner than usually supposed. Fine examples of U-shaped burrows of marine Polychaete worms occur in the Bencliff Grits at Redcliff Point.[2]

(b) STRATIGRAPHY

Sedgwick in 1826 divided the Corallian Beds of Dorset into 9 groups, without giving them distinctive names.[3] Buckland and De la Beche in 1830 described 31 different beds.[4] It was not till 1877 that Blake and Hudleston[5] established the 8 named sub-

---

[1] W. J. Arkell, ' A Monograph on the Ammonites of the English Corallian Beds,' parts I-III, 1935-7, *Palaeontographical Soc.*

[2] W. J. Arkell, ' U-Shaped Burrows in the Corallian Beds of Dorset,' *Geol. Mag.*, vol. lxxvi, 1939, p. 455.

[3] A. Sedgwick, ' On the classification of the Strata which appear on the Yorkshire Coast,' *Annals of Philosophy*, Ser. 2, vol. xi, 1826, p. 346.

[4] W. Buckland and H. T. De la Beche, ' Geology of Weymouth and the coast of Dorset,' *Trans. Geol. Soc.*, Ser. 2, vol. iv, pt. i, 1836 (read 1830), p. 24.

[5] J. F. Blake and W. H. Hudleston, ' The Corallian Rocks of England,' *Quart. Journ. Geol. Soc.*, vol. xxxiii, 1877, p. 260.

FIG. 8.—*Characteristic bivalves of the Corallian Beds.*

1. *Trigonia clavellata* (Parkinson?) J. Sowerby.
2. *Trigonia hudlestoni* Lycett.
3a. *Pecten (Chlamys) fibrosus* J. Sowerby, right valve.
3b. ,, ,, ,, ,, left valve
4a. *Pecten (Chlamys) midas* Dollfus, left valve
4b. ,, ,, ,, right valve.
5. *Pecten (Chlamys) splendens* Dollfus, right valve.

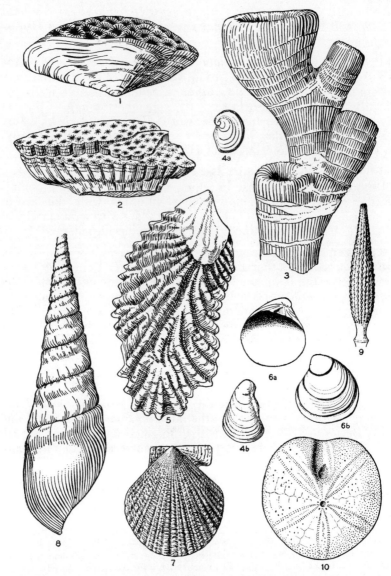

FIG. 9.—*Characteristic fossils of the Corallian Beds.*

1. *Isastraea explanata* (Goldfuss).
2. *Thamnasteria concinna* (Goldfuss).
3. *Thecosmilia annularis* (Fleming).
4a, b. Right and left valves of *Exogyra nana* (J. Sowerby).
5. *Ostrea* (*Lopha*) *gregarea* J. Sowerby (left valve).
6a, b. *Astarte zonata* Roemer (cf. *curvirostris* Roemer).
7. *Pecten* (*Chlamys*) *qualicosta* Etallon (right valve).
8. *Pseudomelania heddingtonensis* (J. Sowerby).
9. Spine of *Cidaris florigemma* Phillips.
10. *Nucleolites scutatus* Lamarck.

divisions that have been adopted by the Survey and all other writers. These subdivisions can be recognized everywhere in the district by lithological and, usually, palaeontological criteria.

The top of the Corallian Beds and so of the Upper Oxfordian Stage is taken by convention since it was fixed by Waagen[1] at the top of the Ringstead Coral Bed; this corresponds with the top of the Zone of *Ringsteadia pseudocordata* and the base of the Zone of *Pictonia baylei*. The bottom falls at an indefinite level, at whatever horizon sand locally began to be deposited. In Dorset, as near Oxford, this line seems to fall in the Zone of *Cardioceras cordatum* [*cardia*].

THE DORSET CORALLIAN BEDS

	AMMONITE ZONES	GENERAL DIVISIONS	DORSET STRATA	BUCKLAND AND DE LA BECHE'S BED NUMBERS
UPPER OXFORDIAN	*Ringsteadia pseudocordata*	Upper Calcareous Grit	Ringstead Coral Bed 1ft.	1
			Ringstead Waxy Clay 10-15ft.	
			Sandsfoot Grits 22-25ft.	2-5
	Perisphinctes cautisnigrae	Glos Oolite Series	Sandsfoot Clay 15-40ft.	6
			Trigonia clavellata Beds 23ft.	7-14
	Perisphinctes plicatilis	Osmington Oolite Series	Osmington Oolite Series (with Little-more Clay facies) 65ft.	15-26
		Berkshire Oolite Series	Bencliff Grit 10-15ft.	27
			Nothe Clay 40ft.	28-30
			Trigonia hudlestoni Bed 6ft.	31
	Cardioceras cordatum (*pars*)	Lower Calcareous Grit	Nothe Grits 27-30ft.	32

II. DETAILS

(a) OSMINGTON MILLS TO RINGSTEAD BAY.

The cliffs east of Osmington Mills reach a height of 160 ft. and expose a continuous section from the top of the Nothe Clay to the base of the Kimmeridge Clay.

---

[1] W. Waagen, *Versuch einer allgemeinen Classifikation der Schichten des Oberen Jura*, 1865, p. 5. München.

Walking eastward along the foot of the cliff one passes first a region of slips due to the Nothe Clay, then a fine vertical cliff composed mainly of the Osmington Oolite Series, with the Bencliff Grit at the base and the Trigonia Beds and Sandsfoot Beds at top. The Trigonia Beds fall to beach-level east of Bran Point (Fig. 10), where they have yielded large *Perisphinctes spp.* and *Amoeboceras*.[1] The Sandsfoot Clay is much obscured by slipping, but the red sandstone of the Sandsfoot Grit can soon be distinguished, and falls to beach-level at the mouth of The Glen. East of The Glen for ¾ mile the low cliffs of Ringstead Bay display an almost continuous section of the Ringstead Waxy Clay, with its flat iron-coated mudstone slabs, and the famous Ringstead Coral Bed with ammonites of the genus *Ringsteadia* associated with the corals *Thecosmilia annularis* (Fleming), *Thamnasteria concinna* (Goldfuss), *Th. arachnoides* (Parkinson), *Protoseris waltoni* Edwards and Haime, many *Serpulae*, *Cidaris* spines, and a host of lamellibranchs, of which the most conspicuous are Pectens (*Chlamys nattheimensis* (de Loriol), *Chl. splendens* (Dollfus), etc.), *Velata hautcoeuri* (Dollfus), and the large *Ctenostreon proboscideum* (J. Sowerby).[2]

Above the Coral Bed the basal beds of the Kimmeridge Clay are well seen. In the lowest bed of the formation the ammonites *Pictonia densicostata* Salfeld, *Pictonia spp.*, and *Prorasenia spp.* are not uncommon. Some are perfectly preserved in the clay (Pl. IV), along with numerous *Rhactorhynchia inconstans* (J. Sowerby) and other fossils, while others are embedded in lenticles of hard mudstone which develop at this horizon, especially on the foreshore below the Smuggler's Cottage. Above the Inconstans Clay with *Pictoniae* is a conspicuous band of small oysters (*Exogyra nana* J. Sowerby sp.), followed by dark shales crowded with layers of exceptionally well-preserved large flat oysters (*Ostrea delta* Wm. Smith). The *Ostrea delta* shales descend to beach level at the promontory east of the Smuggler's Cottage, owing to the axis of the Ringstead Anticline passing a little way inland, but the top beds of the Corallian re-appear again and continue as far as the ' gwyle ' or ravine 635 yds. east of the Smuggler's Cottage and former chapel.

The Bran Point Fault runs partly under and mainly a little distance off from the shore from Bran Point past Ringstead, bringing up the *Trigonia clavellata* Beds and topmost Osmington Oolite as an elongated flat anticline to form the Ringstead Ledges, dry at low tide. The big ledge at Bran Point, which at first sight appears to be a continuation of the Middle White Oolite seen at the same level in the adjoining cliff, consists in reality of the

---

[1] W. J. Arkell, *op. cit.*, 1935-7, *Palaeontographical Soc.*

[2] This bed is the " Kimmeridge Grit " of Damon and the " Upper Coral Rag " of Blake and Hudleston. It is neither a grit nor a rag, but a typical coral bed. For a more complete list of the fauna see W. J. Arkell, ' The Corallian Beds of Dorset,' *Proc. Dorset Nat. Hist. Arch. Soc.*, vol. lvii, 1936, p. 67.

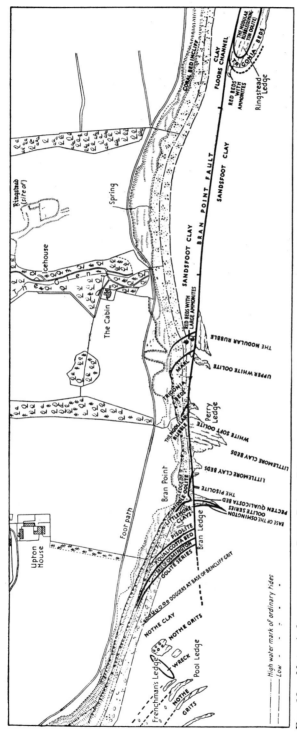

Fig. 10.—*Map of the outcrops at Bran Point, Ringstead, showing the effects of the Bran Point Fault and the locations of the principal horizons and ammonite beds described.* (Topography based on the 25-inch Ordnance map, sheet Dorset LIV, 5; ed. of 1902, with some minor changes in the shapes of the ledges, but the topography not brought up to date). (Reproduced from *Proc. Dorset Nat. Hist. Arch. Soc., vol.* lvii, 1936).

Chlamys qualicosta Bed and basement bed of the Osmington Oolite Series.   The fault therefore to some extent repeats the beds seen in the cliffs, bringing them up again farther east in the ledges between tide marks (*see* Fig. 10).

The section measured in the cliffs from Ringstead to Osmington Mills is as follows :—[1]

SECTION FROM RINGSTEAD TO OSMINGTON MILLS

KIMMERIDGE CLAY

		Ft.	In.
28.	Shaly clay, blue, with layers of *Ostrea delta* seen to	15	0
27.	EXOGYRA NANA BED. A mass of small oysters, locally hardened to a dark limestone like Forest Marble. *Pictonia sp. in situ* (rare). ... ... 8 ins. to	1	0
26.	RHACTORHYNCHIA INCONSTANS BED. Purplish-grey clay, locally hardened, with many large *Serpulae* and some rolled and bored phosphatic pebbles. *Pictonia densicostata* Salfeld, *Rh. inconstans, Exogyra nana, E. praevirgula,* and many casts of other mollusca	2	0

CORALLIAN   BEDS

UPPER CALCAREOUS GRIT

25.	RINGSTEAD CORAL BED. Marly limestone, hard, greenish, a mass of fossils.[2] *Ringsteadia spp.* found *in situ.* 6 ins. to		8

RINGSTEAD WAXY CLAYS

24d.	Clay with *O. delta, Ct. proboscideum*, large *Serpulae*, etc. ...		3
24c.	Prominent band of red claystone nodules (*Ringsteadia anglica in situ* west of Osmington Mills)		3
24b.	Bands of red claystone, less prominent	1	0
24a.	Clay, waxy, mainly unfossiliferous, ferruginous, brown and grey ; seams of laminated claystone nodules ; layers of *O. delta* towards the base ; seen to	9	0

SANDSFOOT GRIT AND CLAY (here not separable ; see Black Head, p. 49)

23b.	Sandstone, bright red, speckled with white ooliths and quartz grains, and pierced by ramifying fucoidal and tubiform markings. *Goniomya literata, Chlamys midas, Pleuromya alduini*, etc. (Blake and Hudleston recorded *Perisphinctes decipiens* J. Sowerby)[3]	2	0
23a.	Sandy marl, tough, brown and greenish, ferruginous ; now seen to 2 ft. ; Woodward recorded 2 ft. to 4 ft. and Blake and Hudleston saw	7	0
22-19.	Clays, blue and brown, with varying amount of ferruginous matter, a band of red sandstone, and nodular cementstones and layers of *Ostrea delta*. Thickness difficult to estimate, owing to slipping ; according to Blake and Hudleston 18 ft. ; to H. B. Woodward 10–12 ft. About 10 to	18	0

---

[1] Condensed from section in W. J. Arkell, ' The Corallian Beds of Dorset,' *Proc. Dorset Nat. Hist. Arch. Soc.*, vol. lvii, 1936, pp. 67-71.

[2] *See* p. 42 ; and for a more complete list *see* W. J. Arkell, 1936, *loc. cit.*

[3] J. F. Blake and W. H. Hudleston, *op. cit.*, 1877, p. 272.

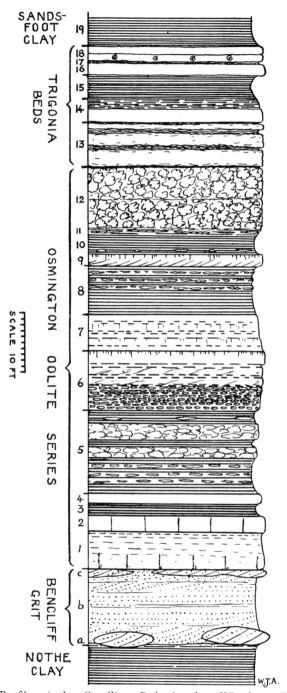

FIG. 11.—*Profile of the Corallian Beds in the cliffs from Bran Point, Ringstead, to near Osmington Mills.* Scale 1 inch = 16 feet. (Reproduced from *Proc. Dorset Nat. Hist. Arch. Soc.*, vol. lvii, 1936, p. 71.)

Ft. In.

TRIGONIA CLAVELLATA BEDS (20 ft.)

THE RED BEDS (OF DAMON [1]) (4 ft. 10 in.)

18. Limestones, red, mottled grey, full of fucoids, the grey parts strongly oolitic, the ooliths large. Roughly divided into 2 courses, with very irregular surfaces. Fossils as in the bed below, but fewer. Large Perisphinctids visible on the surface of the lower course on shore at low tide. *Perisphinctes uptonensis, P. ringsteadensis, P. osmingtonensis, P. boweni, Nautilus hexagonus*   2   6

17. Marl parting ; casts of *Trigonia clavellata*, etc.   3 ins. to   6

16. Limestone, tough, sandy, very shelly, greenish brown to reddish, patchily oolitic. Full of *Trigonia clavellata* etc. *Amoeboceras sp. nov.*   10   0

THE CLAY BAND

15. Marl, greenish grey, oolitic, with some partly-consolidated masses, passing down into clay. Casts of *Pholadomya protei, Pleuromya uniformis*, etc. *Chlamys superfibrosa, Exogyra nana, Ostrea delta*   4   0

THE CHIEF SHELL BEDS

14c. Shelly marl, a mass of well-preserved lamellibranchs : *Trigonia clavellata, T. reticulata, Ostrea delta, O. solitaria, E. nana, Plicatula weymouthiana, Gervillia aviculoides, Isognomon subplana, Pteria pteropernoides, Pteroperna polyodon, Mytilus pectinatus, Chlamys superfibrosa, Chl. qualicosta, Velata anglica, Lima rigida, Entolium demissum, Cucullaea contracta, Isocyprina cyreniformis, I. glabra, Pleuromya uniformis, Pseudomelania, Ampullina, Serpulae* passing down into dark grey shelly limestone with the same fauna ; marl parting at base   3   6

THE SANDY BLOCK

13. Limestones, grey, rough, lenticular, with hummocky surfaces and marl partings ; often sandy and sometimes oolitic, generally more or less fucoidal, locally shelly, but the fossils in most of the bands only as casts. *Trigonia clavellata, Isognomon subplana, Ostrea delta, Modiola, Isocyprina*, gastropods, and abundant casts of *Pleuromya uniformis*   7   6

OSMINGTON OOLITE SERIES (65 ft.)

12. NODULAR RUBBLE LIMESTONE, the nodules hard but with much clay. Mainly composed of small fragments of shells, spines of echinoderms, etc. *Nucleolites scutatus, Exogyra nana*, casts of *Pholadomya, Pseudomelania, Natica*; the lowest foot is oolitic and clayey. In two courses ...   11   0

11. UPPER WHITE OOLITE (upper half) : clay with laminæ of fissile white oolite full of small *Ostrea* cf. *dubiensis*   ...   1   0

10. Clay, grey, the lower part oolitic, with oolitic white nodules in the lowest foot   3   3

9. UPPER WHITE OOLITE (lower half) : false-bedded, upper part solid, with vertical tubular markings   2   0

---

[1] R. Damon, *Geology of Weymouth*, 1860, p. 41 ; 2nd ed., 1884, p. 45. London.

Ft. In.

8. Clay, with three bands of nodular white mudstone in the
   highest 4 ft.   8   3

7. Marl and soft rubbly marlstone, in several bands, strongly
   oolitic, with fucoidal markings ; *Exogyra nana* common ;
   Chlamys qualicosta   5   9

6. MIDDLE WHITE OOLITE.   At the west end of the cliff, towards
   Osmington Mills, there are 7 ft. 6 ins. of solid false-bedded
   white oolite overlying 3 ft. 6 in. of more thinly-bedded
   false-bedded white oolite.   Eastwards the whole becomes
   more marly from the base up, until at Bran Point only the
   highest 2 ft. is solid white oolite.   Vertical tubiform
   markings are a conspicuous feature in the oolites ;   also
   false-bedding, clay partings, and lignite   10   0

5. Littlemore Clay Beds facies.   Clay and bands of nodular
   whitish mudstone. *Perisphinctes spp.*   12   6

4. PISOLITE, coarse, purplish-grey, hard, forming first small
   ledge both west and east of Bran Point (repeated by fault).
   Chlamys qualicosta, Chl. fibrosa Trigonia cf. *hudlestoni,*
   fragmentary *Perisphinctes sp., Cardioceras (Cawtoniceras)*
   sp., etc.   1   6

3. Clay, black, full of fragile compressed shells, especially
   small *Trigonia* (clavellate sp.), *Chl. qualicosta, Cucullaea,*
   Grammatodon, Lucina, etc.   Locally a marl   2   0

2. CHLAMYS QUALICOSTA BED.   Limestone, hard, oolitic,
   sparsely pisolitic, gritty, shelly, dark grey, weathering
   brown :   the highest 6 ins. forming a separate course.
   Crowded with *Chlamys qualicosta, Chl. fibrosa, Exogyra*
   nana, etc.   Forms Bran Ledge at Bran Point, and the
   second ledge to the west   2   6

1. Marl, oolitic, sandy, with *Exogyra nana* (4½ ft.) passing down
   into a westerly-thickening hard band of the same material
   full of fucoid markings.   The latter helps to form Bran
   Ledge and also causes the third and largest ledge on the
   shore west of Bran Point.   Total thickness   6   6

BERKSHIRE OOLITE SERIES

BENCLIFF GRIT (*c.* 13 ft.)

c. Nearly continuous band of indurated gritstone doggers ...   1   4

b. Yellow and white sands, locally false-bedded, with interlaminated clay seams and a few doggers.   The upper
   part is strongly impregnated with oil   10   0

a. Huge doggers of false-bedded blue calcareous gritstone,
   some over 6 ft. in diameter, passing into a more or less
   continuous band of flaggy calcareous gritstone with
   Gryphaea dilatata and *Serpulae.* The doggers weather out
   as a prominent feature on the beach   1   6

NOTHE CLAY

The greater part is obscured by slips or faulting in the gap in
   the cliffs east of the cascade.   Thickness cannot be estimated.

In the small headland between the cascade and the slipway at
Osmington Mills the low cliff provides a good section of the Nothe
Grits and the junction with the Nothe Clay.   The two highest grit-

stone bands are very shelly and correspond with a solid 5 ft. block at Ham Cliff and Redcliff (*see* p. 52), there designated the *Trigonia hudlestoni* Bed.   For the correlation of this bed and remarks on the " cannon balls " in the Nothe Grits, the reader is referred to the description of those more westerly and more complete sections.

SECTION AT OSMINGTON MILLS

NOTHE CLAY

		Ft.	In.
9.	Grey clay with *Gryphaea dilatata*, seen to	3	0

TRIGONIA HUDLESTONI BEDS (*c.* 5½ ft.)

8.	Shelly, flaggy calcareous gritstone, with some of the fossils in the next gritstone band below, but not so plentiful ...	1	6
7.	Sand	1	4
6.	Shelly calcareous gritstone, full of *Pleuromya uniformis, Isognomon subplana* and *Gryphaea dilatata,* with *Chlamys fibrosa, Chl. splendens, Trigonia hudlestoni, Exogyra nana, Lopha gregarea, Gervillia aviculoides, Thracia depressa, Goniomya literata, Pholadomya aequalis, Plicatula weymouth-iana, Lucina lyrata, Serpulae*	2	4

NOTHE GRITS

1–5.	Grey sandy clay with bands of irregular gritstones, some containing cannon-ball concretions and *Gryphaea dilatata*	17	0

On the west side of the headland, near the slipway, a low-angled fault brings down Bencliff Grit against Nothe Grit, and 7 ft. of the base of the Osmington Oolite Series against Nothe Clay. Adjoining this on the north is an isolated wedge of the Osmington Oolite Series (Littlemore Clay facies) with the Pisolite at the base, resting on Kimmeridge Clay (Aulacostephanus Zone).

(b)   OSMINGTON TO BLACK HEAD AND SHORTLAKE

A sharp anticline seen in the beach at Osmington Mills, west of the slipway, is continued westwards along the coast a short distance off-shore.   It causes the strata to dip steeply to the north in Black Head, and the hard bands, picked out by the sea, to run in a series of parallel ridges, like low walls, along the beach between tide marks.   The outermost ledge is formed by the top of the Nothe Grits, the innermost by the Pisolite and White Oolites of the Osmington Oolite Series.

At Black Head, along the foot of the cliff and close above the beach, there is a fine section of the Lower Kimmeridge Clay, Ringstead Coral Bed, Upper Calcareous Grit, Sandsfoot Clay, and *Trigonia clavellata* Beds.   The Osmington Oolite Series is continuously exposed close above the shore from here to Shortlake ravine, where the Bencliff Grit and Nothe Clay come into view also.

As at Ringstead, four divisions of the *Trigonia clavellata* Beds are recognizable. The Red Beds are as at Bran Point, but slightly thicker; *Perisphinctes cautisrufae* Arkell and *P. osmingtonensis* Arkell have been found near the top, and other species of *Perisphinctes* in fallen blocks. The Clay Band is here 2 ft. in thickness, but the Chief Shell Beds are thicker than at Ringstead and the shells better preserved. A feature not met with at Bran

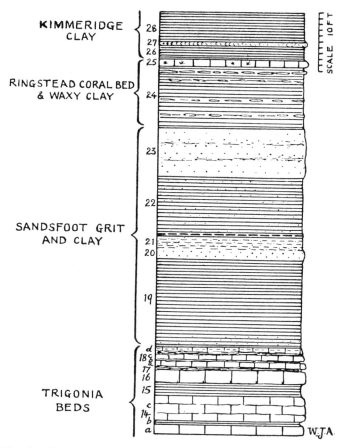

Fig. 12.—*Profile of the uppermost Corallian Beds exposed at Black Head (the upward continuation of Fig. 11, on the same scale).* (Reproduced from *op. cit.*, p. 74).

Point is the masses of small Astartids. Very rarely small fragments of coral (*Thamnasteria*) are found. The Sandy Block comprises 8 or more irregular limestone courses, with fossils (chiefly casts of *Trigonia* and *Pleuromya*) as at Bran Point.

The Sandsfoot Grit and Clay are better differentiated here than at Ringstead. At the top an 8-ft. bed of red, greenish and khaki-coloured sandstone and sand includes some white ooliths and quartz grains and marly layers, with two layers of *Ostrea delta* in the upper part.   Below is grey sandy clay (10 ft.), with a layer of *Ostrea delta* at the base, then grey clay and ferruginous sand (2 ft.), rusty, friable sandstone (1 ft. 9 ins.), and grey clay (15 ft.), sandy towards the base.   These beds can be broadly correlated with beds in the type section at Sandsfoot.   The top bed of sandstone represents the top bed and probably also the lower bed of consolidated sandstone at Sandsfoot.   The next bed (with *Ostrea delta*) represents the brown and blue clay and probably the ferruginous sand into which it passes down.   The lowest three beds may be correlated with three beds in the corresponding position at the type locality.

The Ringstead Waxy Clays, with the band of red claystone nodules near the top, are again generally similar to those at Ringstead.

The Ringstead Coral Bed is here an inconstant band of hard green limestone, locally ironshot and passing locally into black clay.   It includes many of the fossils found at Ringstead, among them *Ringsteadia*.

The basal part of the Kimmeridge Clay is much the same as at Ringstead—the *Rhactorhynchia inconstans* Bed, the *Exogyra nana* Bed, and about 15 ft. of clay with layers of *Ostrea delta*.

The principal changes that will be noticed in the passage of one mile and a half westwards are the following :—

(1)   The Osmington Oolite Series shows a marked augmentation of the white oolite facies at the expense of marls and Littlemore Clay Beds.   A Lower White Oolite, 4 ft. thick, appears where east of the Mills there are only clays and nodules; and above the Middle White Oolite 7 ft. of white oolites replace what was at Bran Point 5 ft. 9 in. of drab oolitic marls and rotten marlstones. The Middle White Oolite itself thickens greatly west of Bran Point.   This tendency reaches a climax in the thick and hard oolitic limestones of Abbotsbury, 30 ft. thick (*see* p. 60), and of North Dorset.

(2)   The *Trigonia clavellata* Beds contain a few fragmentary corals.   In North Dorset corals are locally abundant; and at Steeple Ashton in South Wilts there is a coral reef on this horizon.

(3)   The combined Sandsfoot Grit and Sandsfoot Clay have expanded in thickness and there is an increase in the gritty element. At Weymouth the gritty element becomes much more preponderant and the clay below (Sandsfoot Clay) more than doubles in thickness.

(4)   The Ringstead Coral Bed is locally (on the west side of Black Head) passing laterally into an ironshot oolite almost without corals and less fossiliferous.   This prepares us for Weymouth, where it closely resembles the Westbury Iron Ore.

(c) REDCLIFF, HAM CLIFF AND JORDAN HILL

The tip of Redcliff Point consists of Oxford Clay, but either side of the point there are good sections of Corallian Beds. The Redcliff section, west of the point, extending to Bowleaze Cove, shows Nothe Grits, nearly horizontal, with the *Trigonia hudlestoni* Bed breaking up into huge cubes on the shore, surmounted by a good section of Nothe Clay. Above this is an overgrown under-cliff caused by slipping of the Nothe Clay and Bencliff Grit. The latter is only discernible by the spheroidal doggers which find their way on to the beach, some riddled with U-shaped worm burrows (*see* p. 39). At the back rises an upper cliff, removed from the sea, consisting of the Osmington Oolite Series.

The Ham Cliff section, east of the point,[1] shows the Upper Oxford Clay, and the whole of the Nothe Grits, *T. hudlestoni* Bed, and Nothe Clay, rising steeply northward away from the fault-plane. These sections therefore supply what is lacking in the otherwise fuller exposures farther east.

At Redcliff, in the upper cliff, the following may be seen :

OSMINGTON OOLITE SERIES (43 ft. seen)

		Ft.	In.
8.	Clay with bands of white nodular mudstone, full of *Placunopsis*, *Exogyra nana*, and *Ostrea dubiensis* ... ... [Uneven surface]	6	6
7.	MIDDLE WHITE OOLITE, false-bedded, ripple-marked, with clay galls, sandy streaks, iron and lignite, like Forest Marble ; the middle 6–8 ft. replaced westwards by shaly clays with films of fissile sandy limestone, also much like Forest Marble	13	0
6.	Marl, full of *Exogyra nana*		6
5.	Soft white oolite, weathering pellety ... ... 1 ft. to 2		0
4.	Marl, oolitic, full of small *Exogyra nana*		3
3.	LOWER WHITE OOLITE (?) hard, full of *E. nana*	2	0
2.	Clay, grey, sandy		8
1.	Marl and clay with layers of whitish nodular mudstone (typical Littlemore Clay Beds facies) seen to about ...	12	0

In the lower cliff, rising directly from the beach, and still better in Ham Cliff, east of the point, the following beds are shown :—

BERKSHIRE OOLITE SERIES

		Ft.	In.
	NOTHE CLAY (*c.* 40 ft.)		
20.	Blue clay ... ... about	18	0
19.	Cementstone nodules in two bands, separated by clay ...	1	0
18.	Blue shaly clay	2	3
17.	Limestone, dark brown, ferruginous, rubbly ; *Gryphaea dilatata*, *Pleuromya uniformis*, *Pholadomya aequalis* ...		8

---

[1] On old maps Ham Cliff and Redcliff (or Radcliff) are sometimes used as synonyms ; but it is convenient to reserve the name Ham Cliff for the separate cliff east of the point, as labelled Ham Cliff in the geological map by W. Buckland and H. T. De la Beche (1836, pl. I) and in R. Damon's *Geology of Weymouth* (1884, p. 44, fig. 27).

Ft. In.

16. Blue shaly clay and ferruginous brown marl, *G. dilatata*   2   6
15. Limestone, dark brown, ferruginous, with fucoid markings   10
14. Blue shaly clay with casts of *Pleuromya*, and two impersistent bands of soft, marly, brown, ferruginous, nodular limestone. *Chlamys fibrosa, Gervillia aviculoides, Lima subantiquata, Modiola bipartita*   2   3
13. Limestone, light grey, weathering brown, nodular   ...   1   3
12. Blue clay with *Gryphaea dilatata*   12   0
11. TRIGONIA HUDLESTONI BED. Massive band of hard, brownish grey, gritty, speckled but doubtfully oolitic limestone, full of fucoid markings ; forming a very prom-

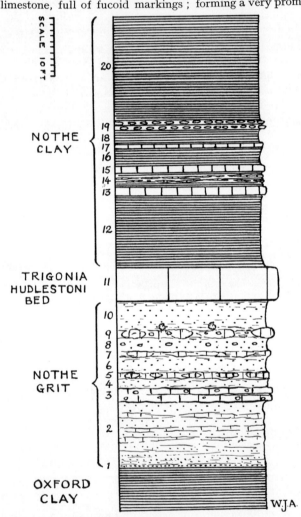

FIG. 13.—*Profile of the Corallian Beds exposed at Redcliff and Ham Cliff* (*combined*). *This profile is the downward continuation of Fig. 11, on the same scale.* (Reproduced from *op. cit.* p. 78.)

Ft. In.

inent feature on both sides of the point. Many fossils,
including *Perisphinctes* (*Arisphinctes*) *helenae* de Riaz,
Cardioceras excavatum (J. Sowerby), *C. densiplicatum*
(Boden), *Goliathiceras capax* (Young & Bird), and
Chlamys fibrosa (abundant), *Trigonia hudlestoni* (large),
Gryphaea dilatata, *Ostrea quadrangularis*, *O. gregarea*,
Exogyra nana, *Lima rigida*, *L. subantiquata*, *Isognomon
subplana*, *Oxytoma expansa*, *Pseudomonotis ovalis*, *Cucullaea
contracta* var. *laura*, *Pholadomya aequalis*, *Pleuromya
uniformis*, *Pseudomelania heddingtonensis*, (*Eocallista
tancrediformis*, *Opis curvirostra*, *Placunopsis radiata*,
Cerithium muricatum, *Pleurotomaria muensteri*, recorded by
Blake and Hudleston from the Nothe Grits, probably
from this bed)   5   6

LOWER CALCAREOUS GRIT

NOTHE GRIT (26 ft. 6 in.)

10. Sand, yellow, becoming grey and yellow mottled towards
     the base. *Cardioceras* cf. *persecans* Buckman *in situ* near
     Bowleaze Cove, 6 ins. from base   ...   4 ft. to   4   6

9. Gritstone, a fairly continuous band, locally hardened into
    intensely hard doggers ; this band also contains smaller
    " cannon ball " concretions   1   6

8. Sand, brown and grey mottled, slightly argillaceous with
    " cannon ball " concretions ...   ...   1 ft. 6 ins. to   2   0

7. Gritstone, locally more hardened to doggers   1   0

6, 5, 4. Sand, soft, bluish-grey, argillaceous, with a line of
    ill-defined doggers   5   0

3. Gritstone, a constant well-marked feature, locally splitting
    into two bands ; " cannon-ball " concretions. *G. dilatata*   2   0

2. Sand and soft gritstone bands : light-coloured bluish and
    mauve argillaceous sands weathering cream-coloured,
    partly consolidated into irregular and impersistent
    gritstone or sandstone bands and occasional small
    " cannon-ball " concretions. *G. dilatata*   10   6

1. Black, sandy clay   6

The hard " cannon-ball " concretions were believed by S. S.
Buckman to be derived blocks and he considered them evidence
for erosion and redeposition.[1] But he only saw them in the top
part of the Grit, whereas they occur at a number of horizons
throughout, and are equally abundant throughout the grits below
the cascade at Osmington Mills. Similar balls are a feature of
the Lower Calcareous Grit at Cayton Bay in Yorkshire, and there
can be no doubt that they are all of concretionary origin.[2] The
bedding, so far as it can be seen, lies always horizontally, never on
end, and sometimes perfect fossils (large Gryphæas, etc.) project
from them in a way they could never do if the rounding were due
to abrasion.

The last exposure hereabouts, worthy of record as an ampli-
fication of the upper cliff at Redcliff, is a quarry on Jordan Hill.

[1] S. S. Buckman, *Type Ammonites*, vol. v. 1925, p. 65. London.
[2] W. J. Arkell, *Jurassic System in Great Britain*, 1933, p. 384. Oxford.

QUARRY   ON   JORDAN   HILL   (1931)

OSMINGTON OOLITE SERIES (20 ft. seen).

		Ft.	In.
9.	Clay	1	0
8.	Marl, oolitic, grey, full of *Placunopsis* and *Ostrea dubiensis*	1	0
7.	Limestone, oolitic, white, rubbly, argillaceous		8
6.	Clay with ooliths		10
5.	Limestone, oolitic, white, rubbly, argillaceous	1	0
4.	Clay, greenish, shaly, with some laminæ of argillaceous shaly limestone ... ... 1 ft. 6 ins. to	2	0
3.	Limestone, rubbly, argillaceous, and marl	1	6
2.	Clay with bands of nodular white mudstone, 4 ft. to ...	5	0
	[Uneven surface]		
1.	MIDDLE WHITE OOLITE. False-bedded white oolite, to ...	8	0

(d)   WEYMOUTH : NOTHE POINT TO SANDSFOOT CASTLE

In the southern limb of the Weymouth Anticline the Corallian Beds are again completely sectioned by the coast between the Nothe Point, forming the southern side of Weymouth Harbour, and the bridge over the Fleet at Small Mouth, south of Sandsfoot Castle.   This is the type section for Dorset, but it is not now nearly so favourable for study as formerly, and more can be learnt in the cliffs on either side of Osmington.

Nothe Point is formed by the Nothe Grits, and on the north side the junction with the Oxford Clay was formerly exposed. The Grits, which are here highly fucoidal and full of large Pernas, and had at the base a layer of *Gryphaea dilatata,* with *Cardioceras cordatum, Ostrea gregarea* and *Serpula tricarinata,* could be seen reposing abruptly upon the Oxford Clay.[1]   This section was long ago destroyed, however, by the fortification of the Nothe.

The Nothe Clay, about 40 ft. thick, was until recently exposed in the low cliff on the south-west side of the promontory, and Blake and Hudleston recorded sixteen species of fossils from it.   This section was obliterated in 1930-31 by the laying out of the cliff as public gardens, with grass slopes and asphalt walks.

At Bincleaves (Bencliff) the cliff shows a considerable part of the Osmington Oolite Series; but most of it is enclosed and inaccessible to the public.   The Bencliff Grit is almost entirely covered up by the banking above the road down to the works. The Osmington Oolite falls rapidly to the beach south of Bincleave Rocks, bringing in the *Trigonia clavellata* Beds, which form the Western Ledges.   These are broad platforms studded with myriads of *Trigoniae* and other fossils; but the stone is hard and extraction difficult.

In Castle Cove the cliffs are composed of the Sandsfoot Clay, said to be as much as 40 ft. thick, which is too slipped and over-grown to admit of continuous examination.   Here and there it

---

[1] J. F. Blake and W. H. Hudleston, ' The Corallian Rocks of England,' *Quart. Journ. Geol. Soc.* vol. xxxiii, 1877, p. 263.

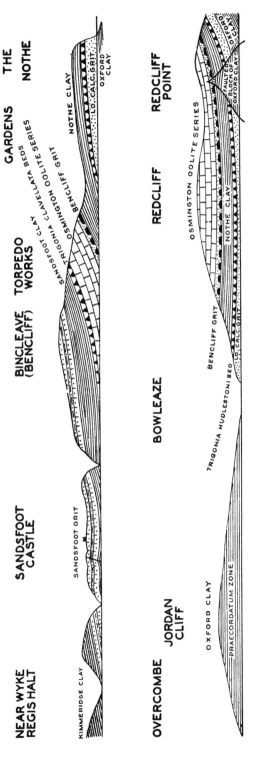

Fig. 14.—*Sections of the Corallian Beds in the cliffs near Weymouth.*

Cliffs south of Weymouth (above). Distance slightly less than 2 miles. (After H. B. Woodward, 'Jurassic Rocks of Britain, vol. v (Mem. Geol. Surv.), p. 83.)

Cliffs north-east of Weymouth (below). Distance 1.1 miles. (Outline from A. Strahan, 'Geology of the Isle of Purbeck and Weymouth' (Mem. Geol. Surv.), pl. ix, 1898.

Both adapted by W. J. Arkell, '*The Jurassic System in Great Britain,*' 1933, p. 382.

yields numerous shells of *Ostrea delta*, on the whole smaller and less senile than those in the basal part of the Kimmeridge Clay. Blake and Hudleston collected a considerable fauna from two indurated bands in the clay.[1] They said that the affinities were all with the Kimmeridge Clay; but except for the problematical '*Ammonites plicatilis* Sow.' the list is most like that from the Sandsfoot Grits. Unfortunately the fossils they collected have not been preserved.

The chief feature of interest in the section is the Sandsfoot Grits, which form the cliffs under and on either side of Sandsfoot Castle, and of which this is still the foremost exposure. As previously mentioned, the Grits are here more in evidence than at Ringstead and Black Head. If the correlation is as suggested on p. 50 above, the Grits, although much more gritty, have only increased in thickness by 2 ft. 6ins.; but if the alleged thickness of the Sandsfoot Clay at Castle Cove is correct, the Clay has more than doubled in thickness. The Ringstead Waxy Clay is half as thick again as at Black Head.

The complete section, measured in the low cliffs on the banks of the Fleet, and checked as far as possible with Sandsfoot Castle, is as follows :—[2]

KIMMERIDGE CLAY

		Ft.	In.
13.	Blue-grey shaly clay with layers of *Ostrea delta*; seen to	6	0
12.	EXOGYRA NANA BED: brown sandy band locally hardened, crowded with small *Exogyra nana* and *E. praevirgula* ...		8
11.	RHACTORHYNCHIA INCONSTANS BED, as at Ringstead ...	1	8

CORALLIAN BEDS

UPPER CALCAREOUS GRIT

WESTBURY IRON ORE BEDS

		Ft.	In.
10.	Prominent band of red claystone nodules	3	
9.	Ironshot oolite: dark ferruginous ooliths in a cream-coloured rubbly argillaceous limestone matrix ; *Ringsteadia anglica*, many large *Serpulae*, *Ctenostreon proboscideum*, *Exogyra nana*, *Goniomya literata*, etc. (=Ringstead Coral Bed)	1	0
8.	RINGSTEAD WAXY CLAYS: Brown and red waxy clay, seen to 3 ft., below which is an unmeasurable gap of perhaps 3-5 ft., and then 6 ft. of blue-grey clay with a few red claystone nodules. Total according to Blake and Hudleston	15	0

SANDSFOOT GRITS

		Ft.	In.
7.	Sand, yellow and ferruginous, full of rubble and fucoid markings, with *Pleuromya* and many broken *O. delta*	4	6
6.	Sand, more consolidated, with some prominent hard bands containing *Pinna sandsfootensis* and full of fucoid markings	3	0

---

[1] J. F. Blake and W. H. Hudleston, *op. cit.*, 1877, pp. 269-70.
[2] J. F. Blake and W. H. Hudleston, *op. cit.* 1877, p. 270; W. J. Arkell, *op. cit.*, pp. 385-6; W. J. Arkell, ' The Corallian Beds of Dorset,' *Proc. Dorset Nat. Hist. Arch. Soc.* vol. lvii, 1936, p. 81.

Ft. In.

5. Clay, blue and brown, passing down into   5   0
4. Sand, impure, ferruginous, with *Pleuromya* and *O. delta* and
   impersistent hard gritstone bands full of fucoid markings.
   Ringsteadia cf. *pseudo-yo* found *in situ* at Sandsfoot   ...   8   6
3. Clay, sandy, passing into sand under Sandsfoot Castle   ...   1   6
2. Fossil Bed : hard ferruginous gritstone, a mass of *Chlamys
   midas, Ctenostreon proboscideum, Ostrea delta*, etc. Large
   Ringsteadia seen *in situ*   2   0

SANDSFOOT CLAY

1. Sandsfoot Clay, much concealed by slips and vegetation,
   seen to about 12 ft. ; total according to authors 38 ft. to   40   0

There was formerly a good section of the Osmington Oolite Series and part of the *Trigonia clavellata* Beds in the railway-cutting at Rodwell, but little is now to be seen there. Strahan wrote of the section in 1898 " The Sandsfoot Clay was formerly dug for brick-making south of the cutting and at the end of the cutting is overlain by a little Sandsfoot Grit. The *Trigonia* Beds rise on the north side of the southern bridge, the Osmington Oolite appears about midway between the two bridges, and the Nothe Clay, surmounted by Bencliff Grit, underlies the northern bridge. The Nothe Grit is not here exposed, but can be seen in a brick-pit 500 yards west of the workhouse . . . overlying the grey, sandy, Oxford Clay." Blake and Hudleston[1] gave a detailed description of the Corallian Beds seen in the railway-cutting, but the impression given by their description, that there are great changes in the succession, and in particular that the Osmington Oolite Series has dwindled to 17 ft. 4 in., is due to erroneous interpretation. As can be seen at Bencliff, near by, the Osmington Oolite Series has not changed greatly in thickness. Blake and Hudleston's errors misled Damon,[2] Woodward,[3] and Strahan,[4] all of whom erroneously transferred a considerable portion of the Osmington Oolite Series to the Bencliff Grit.[5] The section should read as follows :—

Ft. In.

Soil and downwash clay (Bed 1) (No thickness stated)   ...   ...   —
Trigonia clavellata Beds (top not seen) (Bed 2)   12   0
Osmington Oolite Series (base not seen)   ...   .
    Beds 3-15 inclusive, totalling   46   7
    Obscured, of the 22 ft., about   12   0

(e) THE EAST FLEET

The banks of the East Fleet backwater, though presenting a discontinuous and unspectacular section, nevertheless show features of considerable interest. In 1926 it was possible to measure a section from the Kimmeridge Clay through the Ring-

[1] J. F. Blake and W. H. Hudleston, *op. cit.*, 1877, p. 267.
[2] R. Damon, *Geology of Weymouth*, 2nd ed., 1884, p. 38. London.
[3] H. B. Woodward, ' Jurassic Rocks of Britain,' *Mem. Geol. Survey*, 1895, p. 89.
[4] A. Strahan, *Purbeck Memoir*, 1898, p. 42 .
[5] For details see W. J. Arkell, *op. cit.*, 1936, pp. 82-3.

stead Coral Bed, which is here a pale ironshot oolite full of fossils but without corals, down to the top of the Sandsfoot Clay, and the data obtained are incorporated in the description printed in the preceding Section. In 1934 and 1935, however, this part of the exposure had changed out of recognition through slipping and foundering, presumably as the result of the several wet seasons following 1926. Very little can now be seen *in situ* above the Sandsfoot Grits.

The shore for about 100 yds. where the Ringstead Coral Bed crops out is still covered with fossils, mainly *Serpula intestinalis* and fragments of *Ctenostreon proboscideum*, especially the heavy hinges.[1] Occasionally a perfect specimen of a *Ringsteadia* may be found, and broken examples are common.

The Sandsfoot Grits form a little headland with a cliff, and here again fossils abound. The basal fossil-bed is crowded with *Chlamys midas* (Dollfus) and *Ostrea delta* Smith, and out of this and the succeeding grits are washed hundreds of black casts of *Pleuromya uniformis* (J. Sowerby) and *Mactromya aceste* (d'Orbigny), with belemnite fragments. Fragments of *Priono-doceras* cf. *serratum* (J. Sowerby) and *Perisphinctes microbiplex* (Quenstedt) have also been found, in the unmistakable rusty-coloured gritstone matrix.

After another break, caused by the weathering of the Sandsfoot Clay, the following section is seen in a cliff $\frac{1}{4}$ mile long and from 10 to 15 ft. high, south-west of Wyke Regis church. The beds are numbered to correlate with the section at Bran Point.

SECTION IN THE BANK OF THE EAST FLEET, SOUTH-WEST OF WYKE REGIS

TRIGONIA CLAVELLATA BEDS (12 ft. seen)

		Ft.	In.
CHIEF SHELL BEDS			
14. {	Rubbly and flaggy sandy limestone	1	6
	Soft shelly rubble: abundant *Trigonia clavellata, Ostrea delta,* and other shells... ·	1	0
SANDY BLOCK			
13. {	Rubbly and flaggy yellow sandstone. Casts of *Pleuromya* ...	2	6
	Three bands of hummocky and concretionary sandy lime-stone full of fucoid markings, separated by sandy marl and sand with branching concretions	5	0

OSMINGTON OOLITE SERIES

12. NODULAR RUBBLE, softer and shellier than farther west, and pisolitic. Abundant *Nerinea (Nerinella) cyane* de Loriol, with *Bourguetia subelegans* (Hudleston), *Ampullina sp., Dicroloma sp., Littorina muricata* (J. Sowerby), *Procerithium muricatum* (J. de C. Sowerby), and *P. inornatum* (Buvignier), *Isodonta triangularis* ; also *Nucleolites scutatus, Trigonia blakei,* etc. ... ...　4　6

---

[1] Sowerby's type came from here, collected by Dean Buckland.

Ft.In.

11. UPPER WHITE OOLITE (upper half), hard, shelly, pisolitic, crowded with *Isodonta triangularis* ... ... 　1　9

10. { Oolitic marl, full of *Ostrea dubiensis* ... ... 　　　9
　　{ Blue clay and marl ... ... 　3　0

9. UPPER WHITE OOLITE (lower half); locally marly; *Ostrea dubiensis* common ... ... 　　　9

8. Blue clays and marls, with some thin slaty layers (sandy) near top. Unmeasurable, but at least ... ... 　8　0

7. MIDDLE WHITE OOLITE. White oolite, the centre 3 ft. locally replaced by clay ... ... 13　0

6. Oolitic buff marl, false-bedded, with fucoid markings filled with clay ... ... 　3　0

5. Sandy limestone or gritstone, hard, irregular, fucoidal, with honeycomb weathering ... ... 　1　0

4. Marls, rather sandy, with lines of mudstone nodules; seen to ... ... 　6　6

3. Marl and grey-blue clay with lines of white mudstone nodules (typical Littlemore Clay Beds); forms ledges on shore but not measurable; apparently about ... ... 10　0

[Gap]

BENCLIFF GRIT

Sands with enormous lenticular masses of false-bedded gritstone. Unmeasurable, but at least ... ... 10　0

NOTHE CLAY, seen to 2 ft. at top and 8 ft. at bottom ... ... 　—

NOTHE GRIT

Brown marl ... ... 　1　0

Gritstone, intensely hard, with *Gryphaea dilatata* and *Chlamys fibrosa* ... ... 　2　0

Ferruginous sand and marl ... ... 　2　6

[End of section, but gritstone doggers continue for some distance along the shore.]

Here, then, all the Osmington Oolite Series except the basement beds is exposed, and the exposed portion measures over 50 ft. in thickness.

Interesting points are the great development of the Middle White Oolite (about 13 ft.) as at Redcliff; the thinning of the Nodular Rubble and its development into a fossil-bed in which gastropods predominate; and the highly sandy development of the Sandy Block at the base of the *Trigonia clavellata* Beds.

(f) BROADWEY TO ABBOTSBURY

At Bowleaze Cove the Corallian outcrop leaves the coast and runs by Broadwey to Abbotsbury, forming a narrow ridge along the north side of the Weymouth Anticline. At first the Nothe Grits give rise to a small subsidiary escarpment, but, as noted by Blake and Hudleston, they seem to thin away westwards, where they probably become dark and clayey as in Ridgeway railway-cutting (*see* p. 257).

The only large sections until just before Abbotsbury is reached are in the railway-cuttings on the Abbotsbury branch line on either side of Upwey Station (Broadwey). The cutting at and west of the station is mainly overgrown, though bands of limestone crowded with *Trigonia clavellata* protrude here and there. East of the station and the road bridge, below the cemetery wall, there

is still a clean section between 20 and 30 ft. deep, exposing the
whole of the *Trigonia clavellata* Beds with about 6 ft. of marly
oolite and clay at the bottom, belonging to the Osmington Oolite
Series. This cutting was described by Woodward[1] and Strahan.[2]

Another railway-cutting, on the main line 100 yds. south of
Upwey Junction, formerly showed the junction of the Nothe Grit
and Oxford Clay; and Damon collected many fossils from the
Trigonia Beds in a quarry " south of Broadway House."[3]

West of this there are few sections of interest for five miles.

Osmington Oolite of a new type, characteristic of Abbotsbury,
begins to be conspicuous from Rodden westwards. It gives the
ridge a sharp crest at Merry Hill, where quarries near an old lime
kiln show up to 7 ft. of hard, flaggy, densely oolitic white stone
almost devoid of fossils. Poor exposures in the sides of a trackway descending the scarp a little to the west, north of the field
separating Warre Wood from Hodder's Coppice, show that this
stone has a thickness of at least 12 feet. From here westwards,
past Clayhanger to Abbotsbury, it appears to rest directly on clay,
which has been mapped as Oxford Clay. It is more likely,
however, that the Nothe Grits have partly passed into clay, for an
excavation for an electricity pylon west of Corton Dairy House,
on the top of the Corallian escarpment, showed sandy clay with a
little gritstone.

The hard, false-bedded and poorly fossiliferous type of
Osmington Oolite that begins to be conspicuous at Merry Hill is
exposed to 30 ft. in a large quarry on the western extremity of
Linton Hill, south of Odden's Wood, Abbotsbury. Its fine grain,
blue centres, and solid appearance, and the poverty of fossils,
proclaim that we have here already the Marnhull and Todber
Freestone of North Dorset. The only stratum in the cliff sections
comparable with this stone is the Middle White Oolite. At
Redcliff and Wyke (*see* pp. 51, 59) it already reaches a thickness
of 13 ft., but is much less solid, though evidently thickening and
becoming more massive westwards at the expense of the clay. At
Abbotsbury this stone was used for building St. Catherine's
Chapel, the Abbey Barn, and other old buildings.

A softer type of Osmington Oolite, higher in the series and
belonging probably to the even-bedded oolite of North Dorset,
has been quarried recently south of West Shilvinghampton. The
quarry shows 3 ft. of white oolitic marl and marly limestone, with
abundant *Nucleolites scutatus* Lamarck, *Isodonta triangularis*
(Phillips) and some other bivalves. This rock may be correlated
with the Nodular Rubble of the coast sections. At Wyke the
facies is already very similar except that small gastropods are
abundant as well as the *Isodonta* and *Nucleolites*.

---

[1] H. B. Woodward, ' Jurassic Rocks of Britain,' vol. v, *Mem. Geol. Surv.* 1895,
p. 92.
   [2] A. Strahan, *Purbeck Memoir,* 1898, p. 35.
   [3] R. Damon, *Geology of Weymouth,* 2nd ed., 1884, p. 46. London.

The *Trigonia clavellata* Beds have been worked in a chain of shallow pits along the north slope of the ridge, but most of the exposures are overgrown. Sections only 2 or 3 ft. in depth may still be seen in the second field west of the railway bridge near Upwey Station; on the north slope of Hewish Hill; and near Shilvinghampton. Eight feet of highly fossiliferous rock may be seen in a new quarry on the crest of the ridge midway between Linton Barn and Clayhanger. Here *Mytilus pectinatus* J. Sowerby, *Trigoniae* and many other bivalves abound, and *Trichites praealtus* Arkell and *Pygaster semisulcatus* (Phillips) were collected. (For locality map see Fig. 2, p. 14.)

This leads to the well-known locality of Linton Hill, Abbotsbury, described and figured by Blake and Hudleston.[1] The hill terminates the Corallian ridge which stretches uninterruptedly from Rodden, and the truncated edges of the various members of the Corallian Beds have been quarried so as to form conspicuous scars, two of which run up the hill approximately in the direction of dip, like huge steps. The upper step is formed by the Sandsfoot Grits, the lower by the *Trigonia* Beds; and an incipient third step is produced by the quarried Osmington Oolite south of Oddens Wood.

The section of the *Trigonia* Beds seems to have been further cleaned up by quarrying since Blake and Hudleston's visit, for they were able to obtain measurements only intermittently, whereas now there is exposed a continuous section 25 ft. deep. The strata are much ironstained and some are rottenstone. The typical fossils of the *Trigonia clavellata* Beds abound, and in addition the interesting Perisphinctid, *Decipia lintonensis* Arkell, has been found *in situ*.[2] The section is separated by a broad grass platform from the quarries in the Osmington Oolite below, but there are indications that between the massive white oolites seen in the quarries and the bottom of the *Trigonia* Beds there are at least 15 ft. of greyish and white marly or clayey beds, judging by material unearthed by rabbits. These marls would represent the marls at Shilvinghampton and some of the Littlemore Clay Beds and Nodular Rubble of the cliffs; they correspond also with the lowest 6 ft. seen in the Upwey railway-cutting (p. 60).

SECTION OF THE TRIGONIA CLAVELLATA BEDS, LINTON HILL,
ABBOTSBURY

		Ft.	In.
11.	Red clay soil, 3 ft. (Sandsfoot Clay, probably slipped down hill a little)	—	
RED BEDS AND CHIEF SHELL BEDS (not separable)			
10.	Broken, brashy, oolitic limestone; about	2	0
9.	Marl, about	3	0

[1] J. F. Blake and W. H. Hudleston, 'The Corallian Rocks of England,' *Quart. Journ. Geol. Soc.*, vol. xxxiii, 1877, p. 268.

[2] W. J. Arkell, 'A Monograph on the Ammonites of the English Corallian Beds,' Part 3, 1937, p. 45. *Palaeontographical Society*.

Ft. In.

8. Shelly, brashy limestone, a mass of fossils : *Decipia lintonensis, Trigonia clavellata, Plicatula weymouthiana, Chlamys superfibrosa, Chl. qualicosta, Mytilus pectinatus, Trichites sp., Gervillia aviculoides Ostrea solitaria, O. moreana, O. delta, Isognomon subplana, Pholadomya aequalis, Lucina rotundata, Astarte contejeani, Isodonta triangularis*   1   0

7. Marly layer (=The Clay Band of the eastern cliffs ?)   ...   1   0

6. Shelly oolitic limestone as above, but fewer fossils   2   0

5. Shelly, brashy, oolitic limestone, weathering soft, in roughly demarcated irregular courses. *Trigonia clavellata* and most of the fossils in the beds above abundant ; also *Pteria pteropernoides, Cucullaea contracta,* and many *Nucleolites scutatus*   5   0

THE SANDY BLOCK (8 ft. 6. ins. +)

4. Marl, sandy   6

3. Hard sandy limestone, shelly ; projects prominently   ...   1   6

2. Marl, sandy   6

1. Sandstone, in irregular hummocky courses, with casts of *Trigonia, Pleuromya,* etc., and some *Chlamys fibrosa* and other shells, but fossils rather scarce   ...   seen to   6   6

Total of *Trigonia* Beds seen   22   0

It may be observed that, although the upper or shelliest part of the *Trigonia clavellata* Beds of Weymouth and Osmington remains the same (beds 14-18), the lower block, (bed 13) consisting there of courses of already rather gritty, rough, fucoidal limestone with casts of *Trigonia* and *Pleuromya,* has here become even more thoroughly than at Wyke a calcareous sandstone. This again foreshadows North Dorset, where sandstones and sands with the *Trigoniae* as casts occur on the same horizon at Silton, near Bourton.

This section probably shows all but a foot or two of the *Trigonia* Beds at either top or bottom.

The last section of the *Trigonia* Beds, about 6 ft. deep, is in a cutting at the back of Abbotsbury Castle ruins. The Chief Shell Beds are here seen, crowded with *Trigonia clavellata* J. Sowerby, *Cucullaea contracta* Phillips, *Chlamys qualicosta* (Etallon), and all the usual lamellibranchs.

The Sandsfoot Grits, exposed in the upper step on Linton Hill, are a thick mass of ferruginous rusty-coloured sandstones and sand as at Sandsfoot Castle, but poorly fossiliferous. They first begin to make a distinct feature at Rodden. By a coppice one third of a mile north-west of Rodden House a level has at some time been driven into them in the mistaken hope of reaching Abbotsbury Iron Ore. Slabs of rusty calcareous sandstone with *Chlamys midas* (Damon) and *Ostrea delta* W. Smith may still be seen lying in the bracken. From here past Elworth the grits thicken and form an increasingly conspicuous sub-escarpment as they continue towards Abbotsbury. At Linton Barn they break through the soil, and where they run down into the valley, forming the uppermost " step " on Linton Hill, they have undoubtedly been quarried. Much rock still protrudes, but fossils are scarce, and the exposures are protected by dense undergrowth. In these circumstances it is difficult to estimate the thickness, but it cannot be much less than 25 feet. The feature is lost under Abbotsbury but can easily be picked up again round Chapel Hill and Castle Gardens, and it becomes very conspicuous near the extremity of the outcrop, forming Seawell Knap behind Abbotsbury Castle ruins.

The Corallian Beds terminate abruptly west and north-west of Abbotsbury, along the stream which runs into the Chesil Beach between Castle Farm and Lawrence's Cottage. On the east and south bank of the stream are old quarries in Osmington Oolite near the 100-ft. contour, and ferruginous grits and Abbotsbury Iron Ore are traceable up to the top of the beacon, 400 ft. high, which overlooks Countess Coppice. On the west and north bank of the stream there are plentiful small exposures of Forest Marble; against it the Corallian Beds are thrown by the Abbotsbury Fault, which cuts them off from reappearing farther west along the coast.

CHAPTER V

KIMMERIDGIAN STAGE: KIMMERIDGE CLAY

I. GENERAL

(a) THICKNESS AND GENERAL CHARACTERISTICS

After the varied Corallian Beds were laid down a prolonged period of uniformity in bottom conditions recalling those of the Lias set in over the British area. The Kimmeridge Clay consists of a thick succession of black shales, often bituminous, and clays, broken only occasionally by bands of cementstone rarely more than 1 ft. thick.

The thickness in Dorset has been variously stated, but careful remeasurement of the type section in Purbeck (*see* pp. 70-80) shows that the exposed part of the formation has a thickness of about 1,070 ft., measured along the cliffs, while a boring for oil by the D'Arcy Exploration Co. in 1937 at Broad Bench promontory, Kimmeridge, proved a further 581 ft. below sea level at the point, making a total of about 1,650 feet. In the Ringstead district, on the other hand, the thickness does not much exceed half this figure.[1]

The measurement in Purbeck is in a sense composite, for it is spread over an outcrop 3½ miles in length. Since the upper beds are thicker east than west of Kimmeridge, the total thickness under East Purbeck may be greater still.

The famous ' Kimmeridge Coal ' occupies only a minute proportion of the total thickness of the formation and consists of one or more highly special marine layers within the sequence of entirely marine shales. (*See* p. 68.)

---

[1] The total thickness given for the exposed beds is approximate : it may be inaccurate by 3 or 4 per cent.

FIG. 15.—*Characteristic fossils of the Kimmeridge Clay.*

1.   *Aptychus (Trigonellites) latus* Parkinson.
2a, 2b.   *Rhynchonella (Rhactorhynchia) inconstans* J. Sowerby.
3.   *Exogyra virgula* Defrance (= *striata* William Smith sp.).
4.   *Ostrea delta* William Smith (=*deltoidea* J. Sowerby *non* Lamarck). (× ⅔).
5.   *Discina latissima* (J. Sowerby).
6.   *Saccocoma sp.*, a pyritized radial plate from the Oil Shales (× 4).
7.   *Lingula ovalis* J. Sowerby.
8.   *Lucina minuscula* Blake.
9.   *Pleuromya alduini* (Brongniart).

(b) STRATIGRAPHY AND PALAEONTOLOGY

It is customary to divide the formation into a Lower Kimmeridge, which by the new measurements is 834 ft. thick (253 ft. exposed), and an Upper Kimmeridge, 820 ft. thick, the line of division being taken at one of the thin cementstones called the Yellow Ledge Stone Band. This stone band, which is well seen in Hen Cliff, Kimmeridge, and falls to sea-level about half a mile to the east, marks (at least approximately) the upward limit of the small striated oyster, *Exogyra virgula* (Defrance) (= *Chama striata* Wm. Smith).

In the Lower Kimmeridge lamellibranchs abound, the commonest being *Protocardia*, with numerous small *Astarte* and *Lucina*, and *Exogyra virgula*; but like all the fossils they are crushed and difficult to collect. The brachiopods *Lingula ovalis* J. Sowerby and *Discina latissima* (J. Sowerby) occur, but become commoner in the Upper Kimmeridge. Saurian bones are especially characteristic of the Lower Kimmeridge, and of the Aulacostephanus Zones in particular. The ammonites of the Lower Kimmeridge are abundant and varied (Pl. IV). At the bottom for a few feet the Perisphinctid genus *Pictonia* is predominant, with early Rasenids, *Prorasenia*. Then comes a zone of coarse-ribbed *Raseniae* (Cymodoce Zone), followed by fine-ribbed *Raseniae* (Mutabilis Zone), and finally a great thickness of shales rich in a development from the Rasenid stock with a smooth band on the venter, for which the generic name *Aulacostephanus* is universally used.[1] Throughout these beds true Perisphinctids are rare, though they (*Lithacoceras*) occur sporadically, and have been found by the writer as far down as The Flats Stone Band. Cardiocerates (*Amoeboceras*) are common in the Lower Kimmeridge and also *Aspidoceras* and aptychi, especially in the Aulacostephanus Zone.

The highest zone of the Lower Kimmeridge according to the classification hitherto used in England consists at Kimmeridge of 70 ft. of shales in which the ammonites so far mentioned have died out and Perisphinctids have begun to predominate. Besides *Lithacoceras* and its allies there are giant forms which were first discovered by Salfeld and identified as the ammonites of the so-called Portlandkalk and Portlandien inférieur of the Continent. To these he gave the generic name *Gravesia*. Owing to mis-identification of these with the Titanitids of the English Portland Beds by d'Orbigny and his followers, the whole Upper Kimmeridge Clay had come to be classified in the Portlandian. The Portlandkalk of North-West Germany is a white limestone deceptively like Portland Stone, and it rests unconformably upon

---

[1] Though with questionable justification; *see* W. J. Arkell, ' The Lower Kimmeridigian Ammonite Genera *Pictonia, Rasenia, Aulacostephanus* and *Ataxioceras*,' *Geol. Mag.,* vol. lxxii, 1935, p. 252.

black shales of the Aulacostephanus Zone.   D'Orbigny, however, included it in his original definition of the Kimmeridgian Stage.

For the Upper Kimmeridge beds erroneously called Portlandian on the Continent, Blake[1] introduced the term Boulognian or Bolonian.[2]

The Upper Kimmeridge or Bolonian is principally characterised by great abundance of Perisphinctids (Pl. V and Fig. 17). The chief genera are first fine-ribbed forms, *Lithacoceras*, *Subplanites* (including *Virgatosphinctoides*—these show ' virgatotome ' branching of the ribs), and *Pectinatites*; and finally, at the top, the round-whorled, coarse-ribbed *Pavlovia*.   The systematics of these ammonites is extremely complex and they have not yet by any means been worked out.   Collection is difficult owing to crushing of the specimens.   The principal other fossils, likewise crushed, are *Lucina minuscula* Blake, *Protocardia spp.* (both extremely abundant), *Ostrea bononiae* Sauvage, *Discina latissima* (J. Sowerby), and *Lingula ovalis* J. Sowerby; but other lamellibranchs abound at certain horizons.   Fish scales occur in millions in the Pectinatus and Rotundum Zones.

In accordance with the most natural grouping of the ammonite faunas, and in order to equate the Bolonian with the Upper Kimmeridge, the Dorset Kimmeridge Clay is now classified as follows : —

Zones	Divisions	
Pavlovia spp. *Pectinatites pectinatus* *Subplanites spp.* *Gavesia spp.*	Upper Kimmeridge Clay (Bolonian) (=Portlandien inférieur on the Continent)	KIMMERIDGIAN
Aulacostephanus spp. *Rasenia mutabilis* *Rasenia cymodoce* *Pictonia baylei*	Lower Kimmeridge Clay (Kimmeridgian in the Continental sense)	

The sections in Purbeck expose from the top of the formation down to about the middle of the Aulacostephanus Zone.   The rest lies below sea-level in Purbeck but is well exposed in the Weymouth district.

II.   THE ISLE OF PURBECK

(a)   General

The Kimmeridge Clay of the classic area of Purbeck crops out along the south-west side of the peninsula in a strip measuring

---

[1] J. F. Blake, ' On the Portland Rocks of England,' *Quart. Journ. Geol. Soc.*, vol. xxxvi, 1880, p. 196 ; and vol. xxxvii, 1881, p. 581.
[2] Afterwards confused with the Bononian of Pavlow =Portland Beds.

about 6 miles in length and never much exceeding 1 mile in width. Inland it is cut off from the country behind by the escarpment of the Portland Stone. Seaward the clays are laid bare in a line of steep, though never very high, sea cliffs (Pl. VI).

The axis of the Purbeck Anticline runs out to sea in a south-westerly direction on the west side of Broad Bench promontory, which forms the western horn of Kimmeridge Bay. Here, in Hobarrow Bay, the lowest beds in the ' island ' are exposed. The crest of the arch is very flat, but the dip at Broad Bench ledge is gently seaward. Towards the north-west the whole formation is exposed in Hobarrow and Brandy Bays, dipping at up to 20° N.W. in the steep northern limb of the anticline. Eastwards the dip is much more gradual and soon ceases to be controlled by the same subsidiary fold as that seen at Broad Bench, which passes inland towards Kimmeridge village.[1] The fold which replaces it eastwards is arranged *en echelon* and apparently with a somewhat different strike. Numerous faults cause repetitions, but on the whole successively higher parts of the formation come down to sea-level towards the east, until the Portland Beds are reached at Houndstout Cliff. Most of the faults have only a small throw (5 to 20 ft.) but there is one of 32 ft. west of the old lifeboat house near Charnel, and another of 50 ft. in Hobarrow Bay. They tend to counteract the dip, most of those east of Kimmeridge Bay throwing down west and most of those to the west throwing down east.

Erosion of the shales and clays is rapid, the sea keeping the cliffs vertical and free from talus, so that a fresh surface is constantly exposed. Intercalated at intervals, however, are hard cementstone bands, which offer a stubborn resistance to the encroaching sea. They often run out from the shore for more than a mile, forming the notorious Kimmeridge Ledges, marked at low tide by plumes of surf.

Most of the formation is strongly bituminous, and the freshly exposed surfaces along the shore give off a peculiar odour, especially on hot summer days.

(b) KIMMERIDGE OIL-SHALE AND ' COAL '

The famous ' Kimmeridge Coal,' really a bituminous oil-shale with marine fossils, rises from the beach 200 yds. east of the head-

---

[1] The name of this village was CAMERIC in Domesday Book and KYMERICH by 1293 ; by the time of Hutchins' great work on Dorset it had become KIMERIDGE (see J. Hutchins, *History of Dorset,* 2nd ed., 1774, p. 193). The Ordnance map of 1811 (Sheet 16, Old Series) retained one ' m ', and so did Damon in his *Geology of Weymouth* (1860 and 1884-8) and H. B. Woodward in ' *The Jurassic Rocks of Britain,*' (vol. v, 1895), *Mem. Geol. Survey.* In the resurvey of 1892 (Sheet 342, New Series), two ' m 's ' were adopted and the Geological Survey followed suit in 1898.

land marked as Clavell's Hard on the 6-inch ordnance map, and was chiefly mined in adits driven into the cliff on and about the headland, and in surface workings.

It is ' a highly bituminous layer of shaly stone, about 2 ft. 10 ins. thick with its partings, and of a dark brown colour, whence its local name of " blackstone." It breaks with a conchoidal fracture and readily ignites, burning with a bright flame and an offensive smell, and leaving a copious grey ash. When exposed to the weather it is apt to develop a fissile structure, and the laminae curl up so as to imitate layers of brown paper or leather. It is free from pyrites, but contains lenticular masses of calcareous matter.'[1]

The ' coal ' has been in requisition from time immemorial. The earliest traces of its use are the so-called ' coal-money,' and ornaments and vessels found in barrows and with Roman remains in the Weymouth district and as far away as Silchester. The supposed ' money,' which has been found in heaps and scattered under the soil in Purbeck and elsewhere, consists of circular discs of the shale, two or three inches in diameter, which have been turned on a lathe. They are apparently waste pieces produced in turning cups and vases, and the heaps probably indicate the sites where the industry was carried on.[2] An elaborately carved chair leg of this substance has lately been excavated in Roman Dorchester.[3]

As a fuel the ' coal ' may have been used from almost as early times. At the beginning of the 17th century Sir William Clavell, who owned the neighbouring Smedmore House and built the Clavell Tower on Hen Cliff, founded an alum industry, using the blackstone both as source of the alum and as fuel. Coker records[4] that Sir William ' being ingenious in diverse faculties, put in tryall the makeing of allom, which hee had noe sooner, by much cost and travell, brought to a reasonable perfection, but the farmers of the allom workes seized to the king's use; and, being not so skillfull or fortunate as himselfe, were forced with losses to leave it offe, and soe nowe it rests allmost ruined.' But ' Sir William Clavile, who[m] one disaster dismayed not ' set up works for making glass and for boiling the sea-water to extract salt, using the blackstone as fuel. This earned for it the name ' coal,' but Coker records that ' in burning it yields such an offensive savoure and extraordinairie blacknesse, that the people labouring about those fires are more like furies than men.' Notwithstanding the sulphuretted hydrogen and copious ash given off during combustion it has been used down to the present time in the neighbouring cottages as a substitute for coal.

---

[1] A. Strahan, *Purbeck Memoir*, 1898, p. 53. For detailed section at the workings, see *ibid.*, p. 55.

[2] J. C. Mansel-Pleydell, ' Kimmeridge Coal-Money and other Manufactured Articles from the Kimmeridge Shale,' *Proc. Dorset Field Club*, vol. xiii, 1892, p. 178; and vol. v, 1894, p. 172. H. Davies, *Arch. Journ.*, vol. xciii, 1937, p. 200.

[3] Dorchester Museum, Colliton Park excavations.

[4] J. Coker, *A Survey of Dorsetshire*, 1732, p. 46. London.

By the middle of the eighteenth century, Hutchins records, ruins of buildings and heaps of ashes were all that remained of Sir William Clavell's projects. But in the second half of the nineteenth century no less than 8 companies and undertakings (one of them French) were floated for the extraction of oil from the bituminous shale. The residual matter left after distillation of the oil and gas was sold as a deodoriser, decoloriser, disinfectant and manure. A ton of the shale was supposed to produce $7\frac{1}{2}$ gallons of naphtha, 10 gallons of lubricating oil, 1 cwt. of pitch, and some fine white paraffin wax and gas.[1]

Owing to the high content of sulphur (6—7 per cent) and to the thinness of the workable seam, however, the cost of extraction has always been too heavy to allow the projects to become an economic success. No economic process for extracting sulphur having yet been devised, the present century has seen the works totally abandoned. The last activity of the kind in the district occurred in 1917-18, when the Government sank a series of test holes round Kimmeridge and in the Portisham district, to ascertain the total extent of the field in case exploitation should become necessary owing to the shortage of other oils.[2] A company still pays the landowner at Smedmore an annual royalty for the mineral rights.

(c) Description and Measurements of the Type Section

The following table of thicknesses results from a complete re-measurement with an 8-ft. survey rod wherever the beds are directly accessible, supplemented by an Abney level to ascertain the heights of datum-planes on Hounstout Cliff. This was carried out in 1936 and 1937. The result is to show that for the middle parts of the formation, from Hen Cliff to Freshwater Steps, Blake's measurements[3] need little amendment, but that both the upper and the lower parts, in Hounstout Cliff and round Kimmeridge Bay, have hitherto been seriously underestimated.

The classification used, and the names of the subdivisions, embody successive additions and corrections by Salfeld,[4] Buckman,[5] Arkell,[6] and Spath,[7] with subsequent emendations resulting from the remeasurement.

---

[1] A. Strahan, ' Spec. Repts. Mineral Resources,' vol. vii, *Mem. Geol. Survey,* 1918, p. 27.

[2] *See* A. Strahan, *op. cit.,* 1918.

[3] J. F. Blake, ' On the Kimmeridge Clay of England,' *Quart. Journ. Geol. Soc.,* vol. xxxi, 1875, pp. 198-9.

[4] H. Salfeld, ' Die Gliederung des oberen Jura in Nordwesteuropa,' *Neues Jahrb. für Min.* Beil. Bd. xxxvii, 1914, pp. 206-09.

[5] S. S. Buckman, ' *Type Ammonites,*' vol. vi, 1926, pp. 13-14, 29-40. London.

[6] W. J. Arkell, *Jurassic System in Great Britain,* 1933, pp. 440-451. Oxford.

[7] L. F. Spath, ' The Upper Jurassic Invertebrate Faunas of Cape Leslie, Milne Land ; part 2,' *Meddelelser om Grønland,* Bd. 99, no. 3, 1936, pp. 13, 18, 152, 162.

Table of Strata and Thicknesses in the Kimmeridge Clay of Purbeck

Blake's bed numbers, 1875		Thickness East of Broad Bench	Thickness West of Broad Bench
	Pavlovia pallasioides and P. rotunda Zones		
	Hounstout Marl	50	
16	Upper line of seepage		
(1880)	Hounstout Clay	20	
and	Lower line of seepage		
1	*Rhynchonella* and *Lingula* Beds	} 160	
(1875)	*Rotunda* Clays and Nodules		
2 - 4	Crushed Ammonoid Shales[1]	109	
	Total ...	339	
	Pectinatites pectinatus Zone		
	paravirgatites clays (L. F. Spath) ...		
5	Hard shale band	2	
6	Clay	25	
7	Clays with several horizons of large nodules ...	18	
	pectinatites clays (L. F. Spath)		
8	Hard shale band, forms ledge off which the stream pours at Freshwater Steps	2	
9	Shales	20	
	Total ...	67	
	the three white stone bands		
10	Freshwater Steps Stone Band (forms base of headland at cascade)	1½	
11	Shales	28	
12	Middle White Stone Band	2	
13 - 19	Dicey clays and cementstones	24	
20 *pars*	Paper shale	1½	
20	The White Band	3	
	Total ...	60	
	Total to base of the White Band ...	466	
	Subplanites Zone		
	Subplanites (Virgatosphinctoides) wheatleyensis Subzone		
	dicey clays		
21 - 22	Shales and clays	33	30
23	Dicey clays with hard dicey and shaly bands ...	23	16
24	The Basalt Stone. Hard cementstone with cuboidal fracture	3¾	3¾
25	Dicey clay, estimated thickness	55	30
		115	80

[1] The top of Blake's bed 4 reaches beach-level in N.E. corner of Egmont Bay. (Plate VI, A).

Blake's bed numbers, 1875		Thickness East of Broad Bench	Thickness West of Broad Bench
	SUBPLANITES (VIRGATOSPHINCTOIDES) GRANDIS SUBZONE		
	BITUMINOUS SHALES		
26	Shale	4	
	Cementstone	$\frac{1}{2}$	
	Shale and clay	8	
	Rope Lake Head Stone Band	$1\frac{1}{2}$	
	Shales, mainly hard	$5\frac{1}{2}$	
	Hard shale with Blackstone at bottom ...	3	
		$22\frac{1}{2}$	
27	Shales with hard shale bands	27	
28	Dicey clay with abundant *Subplanites* ; forms base of Clavell's Hard promontory	14	
29	Double hard shale band	$5\frac{1}{2}$	
30	Clay with hard band, *Subplanites* common ...	20	
		89	81
	SUBPLANITES VIMINEUS ? SUBZONE		
	CATTLE LEDGE SHALES		
31	Cementstone, formerly worked for cement ; quarried away at Cuddle promontory. Forms Grey Ledge	$2\frac{1}{4}$	3
32	Dicey clay	16	8
33	Laminated clays and hard shaly bands ...	17	17
34	Cementstone, same as 31. Cattle Ledge Stone Band	$1\frac{3}{4}$	$1\frac{3}{4}$
		37	30
35	Shales, bituminous	42	
36	Yellow Ledge Stone Band	$1\frac{1}{2}$	40 ?
		284	
	Total to base of Yellow Ledge ...	750	
	GRAVESIA ZONES		
	HEN CLIFF SHALES, with crushed *Lithacoceras*		
37 - 41	and *Gravesia*	70	
	TOTAL TO TOP OF AULACOSTEPHANUS ZONE	820	
	AULACOSTEPHANUS PSEUDOMUTABILIS ZONE		
	MAPLE LEDGE SHALES		145
42	Laminated shaly cementstone, about 30 ft. above sea-level at the pier under Hen Cliff, and capping cliff 30 ft. above beach in east corner of Kimmeridge Bay	$\frac{3}{4}$	

Blake's bed numbers, 1875		Thickness East of Broad Bench	Thickness West of Broad Bench
43+	Shales with *Lithacoceras* and *Aulacostephanus*, seen in east of Kimmeridge Bay and to about 20 ft. at base of Hen Cliff	68	
	Maple Ledge Stone Band, forming first ledge in Kimmeridge Bay	1	
		70	
	GAULTER'S GAP SHALES		
	Shales seen to 7 ft., cut off by fault of unknown throw. Assuming minimum throw the visible and missing beds amount to some ...	20	
	Shales with abundant *Aulacostephanus* between the fault and Gaulter's Gap	46	
	Shales with abundant *Aulacostephanus* west of Gaulter's Gap	24	
		90	75
	WASHING LEDGE SHALES		
	Washing Ledge Stone Band ; conspicuous double band of cementstone with shale parting : large *Aulacostephanus* common in Brandy Bay	1¼	
	Washing Ledge Shales, with abundant *Aulacostephanus*	40	
	The Flats Stone Band, forms The Flats and Broad Bench, also Long Ebb, the ledge separating Brandy and Hobarrow Bays ...	1½	
		43	45
	Total of Aulacostephanus Zone down to Flats Stone Band	203	
	Shales with *Aulacostephanus*, *Aspidoceras* and *Amoeboceras*, exposed below the Flats Stone Band, down to platform bare at low tide ...	32	50
	Total of Aulacostephanus Zone exposed in Purbeck (203 + 50) ...	253	
	Total (820 + 253) ...	1,073	

Descriptive Notes on the Type Section

Aulacostephanus Zone

Before the boring for oil was started at Broad Bench in 1937 it was thought that the Corallian Beds would be reached within 300 ft. of the surface ; but as already stated, the top of the Corallian was proved to lie 661 ft. below the surface, or 631 ft. below The Flats Stone Band which forms the ledges at Broad Bench promontory. Hence the boring proved 581 ft. of Kimmeridge

Clay below the lowest seen in Hobarrow Bay, where The Flats Stone Band is thrown 50 ft. up in the cliff by a fault. *Aspidoceras longispinum* (J. de C. Sowerby) and *Amoeboceras* were cored from a depth of 240-246 ft., *Rasenia* of the *mutabilis* group from 431-8 ft., *Rasenia evoluta* Salfeld from 540-6 ft., and *Rasenia sp.* from 622-7 ft. below the surface. The site of the boring was at the cliff top about 200 yds. E.S.E. of Black Cottage and rather over 100 yds. W.N.W. of the lifeboat house, at a level about 62 ft. above the top of The Flats Stone Band on the downthrow side of a fault, which was penetrated at sea-level.

The fault penetrated by the boring throws The Flats Stone Band 32 ft. up in the cliff. The shales below the stone band contain *Aulacostephanus spp.* from the base up. At a level 12 ft. below it *Aspidoceras longispinum* abounds, sometimes showing the *Aptychi* within the mouth of the shell (but crushed flat). At 10 ft. below the stone band is a band crowded with small crushed *Amoeboceras spp.* (smooth and faint-ribbed forms).

The surface of the stone band at The Flats and Broad Bench displays a complicated trellis of joints, and meandering ruckles which, when dissected, show slickensiding and appear to be minor thrust faults. The stone band forms the ledge called Long Ebb, dividing Hobarrow and Brandy Bays.

From Broad Bench to the easternmost extremity of Kimmeridge Bay the cliffs display shales of the Aulacostephanus Zone, and the zonal ammonites may be collected in abundance from the talus.

The continuity of the section is interrupted 100 yds. east of Gaulter's Gap by a fault of unknown throw. It throws the Maple Ledge Stone Band up westwards out of the cliff, and there is no datum common to both sides of the fault. Seven feet of shale seen below the stone band on the downthrow side may or may not be present at the top of the upthrow side. The minimum throw necessary to cut out the Maple Ledge Stone Band is 20 ft., and so

---

EXPLANATION OF PLATE IV.

Ammonites from the Lower Kimmeridge Clay (= Kimmeridgian Stage of Continental authors):

1. *Pictonia densicostata* Salfeld, Pictonia Zone, The Glen, Ringstead (author's coll.);
2. *Prorasenia sp.,* Pictonia Zone, Ringstead (author's coll.);
3a, b. *Rasenia* cf. *cymodoce* (d'Orbigny), nucleus, Abbotsbury Iron Ore (Sedgwick Museum, Cambridge);
4. Fine-ribbed *Rasenia* shales of the Mutabilis Zone, Ringstead (author's coll.);
5. Cementstone with *Amoeboceras krausei* (Salfeld) and *Amoeboceras anglicum* (Salfeld), from near top of the Aulacostephanus Zone, Black Head, Osmington (author's coll.);
6. Shale with *Aulacostephanus sp.*, showing lateral and ventral views, Aulacostephanus Zone, Poxwell boring.

(All photographs natural size, by the author).

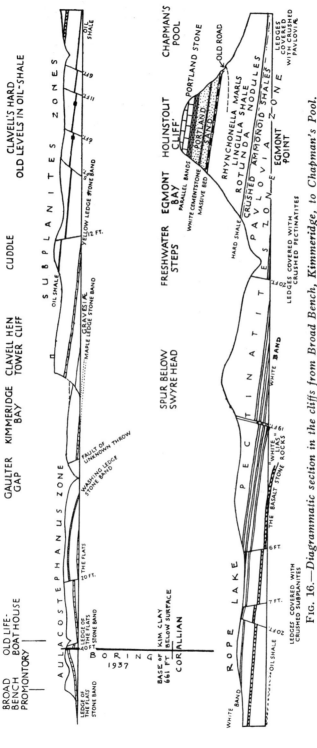

Fig. 16.—*Diagrammatic section in the cliffs from Broad Bench, Kimmeridge, to Chapman's Pool.* (Reproduced with additions from *The Jurassic System in Great Britain*, 1933, p. 444.)

the minimum thickness of missing strata is 13 ft.   Comparison
with Brandy Bay, where the section is continuous between the
Washing Ledge and Maple Ledge Stone Bands and measures only
75 ft., favours the assumption that only the minimum thickness is
faulted out.   Even so, the equivalent beds are 90 ft. thick.

Specimens of *Aulacostephanus* have been found by the writer
on the shore platforms up to the easternmost corner of the bay,
40 ft. above the Maple Ledge Stone Band, and also (*A. pseudomutabilis* de Loriol) at the foot of Hen Cliff, by the old pier, where
Ammonites eudoxus was recorded by Strahan.[1]   The top of the
Aulacostephanus Zone is therefore taken to be the thin cementstone
seen about 30 ft. above the beach at the east end of Kimmeridge
Bay.   The band is not one of the massive cementstones, but is
laminated and weathers shaly.   It is believed to crop out again at
about the same height above sea about 20 ft. above the foot of
Hen Cliff.   If so (and as the two occurrences are on almost the
same line of strike it seems probable), the continuity of the section
is not interrupted, except by the small fault referred to above, to
the top of the Portland Beds.

GRAVESIA ZONES

From the thin cementstone previously referred to (about 20 ft.
above the bottom of Hen Cliff, by the old pier at the east corner of
Kimmeridge Bay) up to the Yellow Ledge Stone Band, are 69-70 ft.
of Hen Cliff Shales.   In these are abundant *Lithacoceras* and,
more rarely, flattened examples of the giant Perisphinctids which
Salfeld was the first to recognize as *Gravesia spp.* of the
Continental ' Portlandkalk.'   He recorded species of the group of
Gravesia irius (d'Orbigny) in the upper part, and of the group of
G. gravesiana (d'Orbigny) in the lower part (*see* p. 66).[2]

SUBPLANITES (INCLUDING VIRGATOSPHINCTOIDES) ZONES

From the Yellow Ledge Stone Band up to the White Band is a
succession of shales and clays 280 ft. thick.   The Blackstone,
rather above the middle, is easily picked up near the old workings
at Clavell's Hard, and still better close to beach-level a short
distance to the east.   Other datum planes are the Basalt Stone
Band (see foregoing table) which forms the ledge bounding the
east side of Rope Lake Hole, and the two cementstone bands
formerly worked for cement, between Clavell's Hard and Cuddle.
All three are easily recognizable also in Brandy Bay.

Ammonites abound at certain levels, but generally are rare, and
they are always crushed.   They are nearly all Perisphinctids with
rather fine biplicate ribbing on the inner whorls, the ribs becoming
irregularly branched and more or less coarsened (virgatotome) on
the outer whorls (Fig. 17).   Neaverson showed[3] that they have no

---

[1] A. Strahan, *Purbeck Memoir*, 1898, p. 55.

[2] Salfeld's original specimens from here are now in the Geological Institute at
Göttingen, where the writer saw them in 1937.

[3] E. Neaverson, ' The Zonal Nomenclature of the Upper Kimmeridge Clay,' *Geol.
Mag.*, 1924, p. 146.

close connexion with the Russian Virgatitids as Salfeld had supposed.[1] Spath has pointed out their resemblance to the Neuberg fauna figured by Schneid from the Upper Danube region, and he assigns them to his genus *Subplanites*, based on *Virgatosphinctes reisi* Schneid.[2] The forms in the upper and greater part of thè succession, down to well below the Blackstone, correspond with species of Neaverson's genus *Virgatosphinctoides*, proposed a few months later, which Spath considers only a subgenus of *Subplanites*, if indeed worth separating at all.

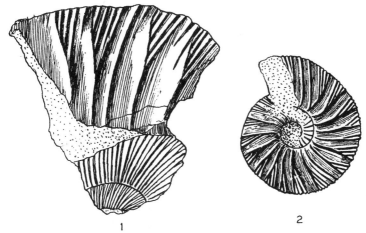

FIG. 17.—*Ammonites with virgatotome ribbing, from the Dorset coast.*

1. *Subplanites pseudoscruposus* Spath, Oil-shales, Grandis Subzone, Corton and Kimmeridge (After Spath, ⅔ nat. size).
2. *Provirgatites albani* Arkell, Portland Sand, Emmit Hill, St. Alban's Head (Holotype, ⅔ nat. size).

As long ago as 1896 W. H. Hudleston[3] remarked on the similarity of the small ammonites in and about the Blackstone to *Am. pectinatus*, and on the strength of this he correlated the Blackstone with the so-called ' Lower Portland Sands ' of Swindon (Shotover Grit Sands). Neaverson considered the Blackstone ammonites indistinguishable from *Pectinatites*, thereby confirming Hudleston's correlation.[4] Buckman, however, named them *Pectiniformites bivius* gen. et sp. nov. and placed them six (supposititious) hemerae earlier than *Pectinatites*.[5] Spath's

[1] H. Salfeld, ' Certain Upper Jurassic Strata of England,' *Quart. Journ. Geol. Soc.*, vol. lxix, 1913, p. 425, and *Neues Jahrb. für Min.*, Beil.-Bd. xxxvii, 1914, p. 208.
[2] T. Schneid, ' Die Geologie der Fränkischen Alb,' *Geognost. Jahresheften*, München, 1914, p. 162; and ' Die Ammonitenfauna der Obertithonischen Kalke von Neuburg-a-D.,' *Geol. u. Pal. Abhandl.*, Bd. xvii, 1915, pp. 305-414.
[3] W. H. Hudleston, *Proc. Geol. Assoc.*, vol. xiv, 1896, p. 322.
[4] E. Neaverson, *Ammonites from the Upper Kimmeridge Clay*, 1925, p. 15, Liverpool.
[5] S. S. Buckman, *Type Ammonites*, 1925, pl. dlxviii. London.

opinion is more in harmony with Buckman's, for he considers them to be 'inner whorls of some group of *Subplanites*, forerunners of *Virgatosphinctoides*, as well as of some Pseudo-virgatitids, but still very close to *Lithacoceras* of the beds immediately below.'[1]

The position at present, therefore, is that the 280 ft. of shales from the Yellow Ledge Stone Band up to the White Band may be considered to belong to one broad zone of *Subplanites spp.* (*sensu lato*, including *Virgatosphinctoides*), in which Spath tentatively recognizes three subzones. The lowest, that of *Subplanites vimineus* (Schneid), is one of Schneid's zones at Neuburg, at the top of the Lower Tithonian.[2]

The vicinity of the Blackstone also yields small pyritized radial plates of the pelagic crinoid *Saccocoma*,[3] which have proved useful as indicators of this horizon in several parts of England. In Dorset their range is said to be 13 ft., and they are most abundant just below the Blackstone.

PECTINATITES ZONE

The Three White Stone Bands rise in the long and ill-accessible stretch of cliff from Freshwater Steps westwards to Rope Lake Head. The most conspicuous datum line is the lowest band, hereafter called The White Band, which persists to Brandy Bay and Gad Cliff and provides a useful datum for correlation with the Ringstead district. It consists of hard white limestone formed of compressed paper-shales with many black seams, and occasionally it contains Saurian vertebrae and bones.[4] On the shore east of Rope Lake Hole it forms the so-called Lias Rocks.

---

[1] L. F. Spath, *Meddelelser om Grønland,* Bd. 99, no. 3, 1936, p. 18. Copenhagen.
[2] T. Schneid, *op. cit.,* 1915, p. 108.
[3] F. A. Bather, ' Note on Crinoid Plates from the Penshurst Boring,' *in* Summary of Progress for 1910,' *Mem. Geol. Surv.,* 1911, p. 78.
[4] In the *Purbeck Memoir* (A. Strahan, 1898) this limestone was misleadingly called the White Septarian Band.

EXPLANATION OF PLATE V.

Ammonites from the Upper Kimmeridge Clay (= Bolonian, = Lower Portlandian stage of Continental authors).

1a, b. *Pavlovia rotunda* (J. Sowerby), Rotunda Nodules, Chapman's Pool (topotype, author's coll.);
2. *Pavlovia sp.,* nucleus, same horizon and locality;
3. *Pectinatites* cf. *nasutus* (Buckman), 100 yards west of Freshwater Steps, 6-10 feet above Freshwater Steps Stone Band;
4. *Subplanites sp.* (typical), Rope Lake Head, 9 yards east of fault, 15 feet above Rope Lake Head Stone Band.
5. *Subplanites* cf. *grandis* (Neaverson), between Clavell's Hard and Rope Lake Head, 6-10 feet below the Blackstone.

(All photographs by the author; figs. 1 and 2 natural size, the rest reduced as shown by the pennies lying by the ammonites, which were photographed on the shore at low tide).

The precipitous cliffs of Egmont Bight show a fine section of beds from the highest of Strahan's Three White Stone Bands, the Freshwater Steps Stone Band, which forms the base of the promontory at Freshwater Steps cascade. In 1933 the occurrence of abundant ' *Keratinites* ' (= *Pectinatites*) was recorded, some identical with species figured from the Oxford district, on the ledges swept clean by the sea in this bay, and down to 6-10 ft. above the Freshwater Steps Stone Band.[1] These are in beds 6-9 of Blake's section. Dr. Spath has since found Swindon forms (*P. aulacophorus* Buckman and *P. eastlecottensis* Salfeld) at levels down to below the Middle White Stone Band.[2] The abundance of *Discina latissima* and fish scales is especially noticeable in Egmont Bight.

PAVLOVIA ZONES.

At the base of this division is a group of shaly clays with crushed *Pavloviae*, seen at the foot of Hounstout Cliff, and named by Buckman the Crushed Ammonoid Shales. *Pavlovia* ranges from the base of Blake's bed 4 (12 ft.) through 109 ft. of these shaly clays to bed 2, and for 100 ft. or more above it, but specific determination of the ammonites is impossible owing to the bad state of preservation. The top of bed 4 is at beach level in the east corner of Egmont Bight, and *Pavloviae* are abundant in this bed here (Pl. VI). The hard top band of the Crushed Ammonoid Shales constitutes the first datum-line in Hounstout Cliff, where it is Blake's bed 2. It descends eastwards and forms a slippery platform on which the waves break, from the stream at the head of Chapman's Pool to the boathouse.

Above the hard shales are the Rotunda Nodules, a bed of calcareous mudstones with well-preserved ammonites (Pl. V, Figs. 1, 2) of a strongly-ribbed Perisphinctid type, long styled *Ammonites biplex* and now assigned to the genus *Pavlovia* Ilovaïsky.[3] The bed dips nearly to beach level at the eastern end of Chapman's Pool near the boathouse. The Rotunda Nodules are succeeded by shales which pass gradually into marls—the *Lingula* Shales and the *Rhynchonella* Marls. Specific determination of the crushed Pavlovids in these beds is impossible on account of the bad state of preservation. Their association with the Pallasioides Zone, first suggested by Neaverson, is still only tentative.[4] In the *Rhynchonella* Marls *Rh*. cf. *subvariabilis* Davidson, *Oxytoma* and small belemnites are not uncommon. The *Lingula* and *Rhynchonella* Beds with the Hounstout Clay and Marl above are well exposed in the face of Hounstout and in the

---

[1] W. J. Arkell, *Jurassic System in Great Britain*, 1933, p. 447. Oxford.

[2] L. F. Spath, *op. cit.*, 1936, pp. 152, 162.

[3] See figures in E. Neaverson, *Ammonites from the Upper Kimmeridge Clay*, 1925 (Liverpool), pl. i, figs. 6-10; and S. S. Buckman, *Type Ammonites*, 1926, pls. dxc, cccliii, dcxxxix. London.

[4] E. Neaverson, ' The Zonal Nomenclature of the Upper Kimmeridge Clay,' *Geol. Mag.*, vol. lxi, 1924, p. 149; and L. F. Spath, *op. cit.*, 1936, p. 161.

ravine at Chapman's Pool; they are also seen between landslips at Pier Bottom and disappear beneath the Massive Bed at the base of the Portland Sand on the west side of St. Alban's Head.

II. OUTCROPS IN THE WEYMOUTH DISTRICT

(a) RINGSTEAD BAY

After a gap of 7 miles the Kimmeridge Clay reappears in Ringstead Bay, where it is thrown into an anticline with approximately E.-W. axis. The Jurassic rocks have been folded and faulted along N.-S. faults and then deeply denuded by intra-Cretaceous erosion, with the result that the Albian (Gault) rests with marked unconformity across the edges of the Purbeck, Portland and Kimmeridge formations.

SECTION AT EAST END OF RINGSTEAD BAY

		Ft.
15.	Slipped clays and shales, containing some cementstones nodules. Obscured	—
14.	Hardened interlaminated black and white shale	1½
13.	Shales, mainly obscured, about	18
12.	THE WHITE BAND. Hard white limestone, up to	2
11.	Dark shales with 3 bands of blackstone	3½
10.	Alternate dark soft and harder light shales, with some pyrites nodules at about the middle. *Lucina, Discina*	20
9.	Black clay with small white shells (*Lucina minuscula*) and small involute densicostate Perisphinctids of 'Pectini-formites' style; also fragments of larger *Subplanites* ...	4
8.	Dark brown bituminous shales; same fossils	3
7.	Brown bituminous limestone overlying blackstone; same fossils	½
6.	Bituminous leathery shales, some surfaces covered with *Lucina minuscula*. *Subplanites*	6
5.	Concretions of hard cementstone, up to 1 ft. thick, with blackstone above and below and replacing them	1
4.	Brown leathery bituminous shales, verging on blackstone ...	3
3.	Shales. Fragments of *Subplanites*	4
2.	Blackstone. Fragments of *Subplanites*, up to	½
1.	Dark shaly clays, seen intermittently to about	8
		——
		75

The Kimmeridge Clay rises from the sea along the west side of White Nothe but is hidden by the slips of Chalk and Greensand as far as the corner of the bay, where the sand and shingle begin. In the lower part of the cliff is the foregoing section, which can be examined in several places. The beds dip here about 6° east, this being the pitch of the anticline, and are cut by a small fault downthrowing to the east. Where the outcrop swings round westward with the curve of the bay the dip changes to 20° and then 35° N., in the northern limb of the anticline, and the Portland Beds come in below the Gault.

There can be little doubt that if these beds were exposed as ledges and platforms along the shore they would appear as fossiliferous as the *Subplanites* zones near Kimmeridge.[1] It seems highly probable that bed 12 is The White Band which forms the ' Lias Rocks ' east of Rope Lake Head (the lowest of Strahan's Three White Stone Bands) and persists at least as far west as Gad Cliff; in appearance it is exactly the same, and there is no other band in the Kimmeridge Clay like it at either place.[2]

At several levels below The White Band there are seams of impure Blackstone, which correspond with those in Brandy Bay and are on higher horizons than the one worked at Kimmeridge. *Saccocoma* has not been found at Ringstead, though it occurred in the Poxwell boring (1937), where all the fossils were much better preserved than at the outcrop.

West of Holworth House an intra-Cretaceous fault with a down-throw east throws up The White Band to the brow of the cliff, against Purbeck Beds. The cliff of Kimmeridge Clay west of this fault is much obscured by slipping. It is called Burning Cliff, owing to spontaneous combustion which broke out in 1826 and continued for several years. The fire is supposed to have been started by heat generated by decomposition of iron pyrites, which ignited the bituminous shale and Blackstone. It was in progress when Buckland and De la Beche visited the district in 1829 for the preparation of their paper on the geology of Weymouth. They state that it had given off flames for many months but by that time was reduced to ' small fumaroles that exhale bituminous and sulphurous vapours, and some of which are lined with a thin sublimation of sulphur.' ' Much of the shale near the central parts has undergone a perfect fusion and is converted to a cellular slag . . . Where the effect of the fire has been less intense, the shale is simply baked and reduced to the condition of red tiles.'[3] The extent of the surface burnt did not exceed 50 ft. square. All traces have now disappeared, excepting an occasional clinker-like pebble on the beach. Buckland saw traces of a similar baked shale at Small Mouth, and a similar fire took place in the Lias of Lyme Regis.

Close to the Burning Cliff fault, on the downthrow side, below the cliff of Portland Stone and Sand, the uppermost part of the Kimmeridge Clay is exposed intermittently. The following section was measured.

---

[1] H Salfeld recorded no ammonites and stated that he was unable to recognize his ' *Virgatites* ' zone or *Gravesia* zones at Ringstead (*op. cit.,* 1914, p. 206).

[2] H. Salfeld, *op. cit.,* 1914, p. 206, seems to have mistaken this bed, misled by Strahan's name ' White Septarian Band ' for he calls it ' eine Geodenlage '. (For further information see W. J. Arkell, 1933, *op. cit.,* p. 449, footnote 3.)

[3] W. Buckland and H. T. De la Beche, *Trans. Geol. Soc.* [2] vol. iv, 1835, p. 23.

SECTION WEST OF HOLWORTH HOUSE

PORTLAND SAND

	Ft.
From base of the *Exogyra* Bed (22½ ft. below the top of the Portland Sands) down to the approximate base of the sands	60

KIMMERIDGE CLAY

From the base of the sands down to the highest visible band of cementstone (nearly all concealed)	75
Cementstone band	½
Black clay with *Pavloviae* (crushed), many large *Protocardia*, also *Ostrea*, *Oxytoma*, etc.	15
Cementstone band	¾
Phosphatic Nodule Bed : grey clay with black and grey phosphatic nodules and phosphatized small Pavlovids as at Swindon, and phosphatic casts of lamellibranchs, especially *Pleuromya alduini* and *Protocardia*. Small belemnites common (*Pachyteuthis explanatus* Phillips sp.)	2
Pavlovia clays : black clay with bituminous smell; *Pavloviae* abundant and well preserved, but mainly flattened ;[1] also many *Astarte*, *Lucina*, *Oxytoma* cf. *expansa*, *Ostrea*, etc.	8
Phosphatic Nodule Bed, similar to above, with same fossils	1
Clays with some large flattened septaria, in which occur occasionally *Paravirgatites pringlei* (Buckman) about	40
Shales and paper shales, sulphurous ; small *Pectinatites* (?)[2] common, *Lucina*, *Discina*, etc., about	30
Whitish paper shale with 2-inch yellow band at top	1¼
Paper shale with *Pectinatites* (?)[2] *Lucina*, *Discina*, etc.	10
THE WHITE BAND ... ... 1½ to	2
Total Kimmeridge Clay above The White Band ...	185

Thus the total thickness of the Kimmeridge Clay above The White Band (about 185 ft.) has diminished by more than half as compared with the Kimmeridge—Hounstout section (where the thickness is 466 ft.). The layers of phosphatic nodules in the Rotunda Zone are reminiscent of the inland outcrop, in Wiltshire and Oxfordshire, and point to condensation.

About 230 yds. west of the fault at Burning Cliff a second north-and-south fault, throwing down east, was inferred by Strahan from the too-close proximity of the base of the Kimmeridge Clay on the upthrow side and from a supposed displacement of the outcrop of the Portland Stone at Holworth Cottages. Nothing can be seen in the cliff owing to vegetation, but judging by the debris in the landslip at the foot, little or nothing seems to be faulted out. Beyond this the cliffs show a good section of the Lower Kimmeridge Clay as far as the ravine about 150 yds. to the

---

[1] *Cf.* E. Neaverson, *op. cit.*, 1925, pl. i, figs. 6-9.

[2] It is not pretended that the small fragments collected can definitely be distinguished from those recorded as *Subplanites* below the White Band in the preceding description, but they are consistent with the most likely identification as *Pectinatites*.

west. The following section was measured below and a little to the east of the naval tripod.[1]

SECTION MIDWAY BETWEEN HOLWORTH HOUSE AND MYRTLE COTTAGE,

RINGSTEAD BAY

Ft.

PSEUDOMUTABILIS ZONE

7. Dark shaly clay crowded with *Exogyra virgula*, *Lingula*, *Nucula*, etc., and crushed *Aulacostephanus spp.*; also *Aptychus (Trigonellites) latus*   25

MUTABILIS ZONE

6. Hard marl band with *Raseniae* and some larger smooth-whorled ammonites (crushed, indet.)[2]   ...   . $\frac{1}{3}$
5. Black clay with *Raseniae* and many shells, as in bed 3   ...   8
4. *Astarte* bed. Shaly clay crowded with small *Astarte* cf. *supracorallina* d'Orbigny and small fine-ribbed *Raseniae* (crushed)   1
3b. Black clay
     [Section discontinuous, but gap probably not more than ...   10]
3a. Black clay, greyer upwards, full of well-preserved but fragile white and iridescent shells, the ammonites much like those from Market Rasen but too fragile to extract whole: *Rasenia mutabilis* (J. Sowerby), *Rasenia spp.*, and many lamellibranchs, including *Exogyra virgula*   22
2. Band of large flattened cementstone septaria, some shelly   ... $\frac{1}{2}$
1. Grey shaly clay with sulphurous sublimation along the partings. Many flattened *Raseniae*, brown in colour, and lamellibranchs. Locally this band becomes black with iridescent shells like bed 3. Seen to...   15
     [slipped ground below]
     [Total of Mutabilis Zone seen   ...   ...   57 ft.]

Bed 2 yields the septaria common among the slips and on the beach; they occur well down in the Mutabilis Zone and therefore not, as Salfeld assumed, on the same horizon as those on the shore at the back of Portland Harbour from which he identified *Aspidoceras longispinum* and 7 species of *Aulacostephanus*.[3]

Beneath the section described above there is a gap of at most 20 ft. (more likely 15 ft.) covered by slips, below which lie the basal clays of the formation, with layers of *Ostrea delta* Wm.

---

[1] W. Waagen gave a brief description of these sections in 1865 (*Versuch einer allgemeinen Classifikation der Schichten des Oberen Jura*, pp. 4-6, footnote ([1]) München), reprinted with notes on Waagen's ammonite collection by H. Salfeld (*Neues Jahrb. für Min.*, Beil.-Bd. xxxvii, 1914, pp. 204-6). Waagen's bed 29, half a metre of ' light yellow limestone with countless casts of *Trigonia voltzi* Ag.', which evidently Salfeld could not find (Diese Bank war in den letzten Jahren überschüttet'), was probably a block of the Portland Roach, of which slipped masses occur at all levels in the cliff and might be taken to be *in situ* by anyone unfamiliar with the sections. That the slipping deceived both Waagen and Salfeld is shown by their stating (W. Waagen, *op. cit.*, p. 6; H. Salfeld *op. cit.*, p. 205) that the *Rasenia mutabilis* Zone was overlain by Greensand—an impossibility here.

[2] Possibly these are ' *Aulacostephanus* ' *yo* (d'Orbigny), made a zonal index by Salfeld, but not recorded from this country and now discarded: *see* K. Beurlen, *Neues Jahrb. für Min., etc.*, Beil.-Band lvi, 1926, pp. 115-16.

[3] H. Salfeld, *op. cit.*, 1914, pp. 203, 206.

Smith, which are exposed intermittently for two thirds of a mile westward. The maximum thickness of these exposed is 15 feet. From them Salfeld recorded *Rasenia cymodoce* (d'Orbigny), *R. uralensis* (d'Orbigny), *Amoeboceras kitchini* (Salfeld) and *A. cricki* (Salfeld).[1] They can be seen to rest upon a 1-ft. bed composed mainly of shells of *Exogyra nana* (J. Sowerby) and *E. praevirgula* (Jourdy), below which is 2 ft. of grey marly clay, locally hardened, with *Pictonia densicostata* Salfeld,[2] *Pictonia spp., Prorasenia spp., Rhactorhynchia inconstans* (J. Sowerby) and many other fossils, also phosphatic nodules. This directly overlies the Ringstead Coral Bed, the top bed of the Corallian, with *Ringsteadiae*, as described above, p. 44.

Hence the *Rasenia* zones, when full allowance is made for discontinuities, cannot much exceed 100 ft. in thickness.

(b) OSMINGTON AND BLACK HEAD

At Osmington Mills, west of the boat-slipway, a wedge of Kimmeridge Clay is let down into Nothe Clay by faulting, as described in Chapter XIII. The structure is sharply anticlinal, but the clay is much slipped and the structure obscure. The Cymodoce and Baylei Zones, with the Ringstead Coral Bed below, appear from time to time near the beach. The main mass of the clay belongs to the Mutabilis and Pseudomutabilis Zones. At the top of the cliff near the footpath down to the slipway the pisolite of the Osmington Oolite Series, with Littlemore Clay facies above, probably a landslip, rests upon shales with *Aulacostephanus pseudomutabilis* (*see* Fig. 63, p. 283).

North of the most northerly E.-W. fault, which throws down south, the sequence begins again, and in the cliff below Goggins Barrow there is a section of the clays of the Baylei, Cymodoce and Mutabilis Zones with *Aptychus* shales of the Pseudomutabilis Zone above, dipping steeply into the cliff. There are lines of large septaria on at least two horizons in the Mutabilis Zone, resembling those at Ringstead.

Westward the cliff is obscured by slipping and the development of glacier-like mud flows, caused by the foundering of the Chalk and Greensand on the Kimmeridge Clay.

On the east side of Black Head there is still a relatively clear section. The strata dip north, into the cliff, at angles of 40° to 60°. Above the Corallian section described on p. 49, can be clearly seen the thin *Rh. inconstans* clay (2 ft.) with *Pictonia*, followed by the *Exogyra nana* Bed (about 1 ft.), here yielding small specimens of *Prorasenia*, and the clays of the Cymodoce Zone with layers of *Ostrea delta* and crushed *Raseniae* of *uralensis* style (about 15 ft.). The cliff then steepens, and the black clays of the Mutabilis Zone succeed, full of iridescent shells as at

---

[1] *Ibid*, p. 205.

[2] See Plate IV, fig. 1 and S. S. Buckman, *Type Ammonites*, 1924, pl. dxxxiii.

Ringstead, among the commonest being fine-ribbed *Raseniae* of *mutabilis* style.   The *Astarte supracorallina* Bed (3 ft. thick) is 100 ft. above the Ringstead Coral Bed, and the first signs of *Aulacostephanus* were not found until 36 ft. higher.   This makes the Mutabilis Zone about 120 ft. thick.

The Aulacostephanus Zone follows, consisting of about 140 ft. of shales crowded with crushed *A. pseudomutabilis* (de Loriol), *A. eudoxus* (d'Orbigny), etc.   Ten feet below the top of the zone the bedding-planes are whitened with crushed shells of small *Amoeboceras krausei* (Salfeld) and *Amoeboceras anglicum* (Salfeld),[1] together with the ubiquitous *Protocardia lotharingica*. On this horizon are occasionally developed lenticles of cement-stone, from which may be obtained great numbers of the small ammonites in good preservation, together with *Dicroloma* and small lamellibranchs, all with the shell intact.[2]

Above the Aulacostephanus Zone follow bituminous shales with numerous harder bands, concretions, and several layers of Blackstone.   The White Band is present but thinner.   If it was not out of place at the only point where it was visible, it lies only 150 ft. above the top of the Aulacostephanus Zone, as compared with 354 ft. at Kimmeridge.

Above The White Band follow 70 ft. of shales and clays to the top of the section.   The clays contain large flattened septaria, from one of which part of a large *Paravirgatites* (?) was obtained. These clays are apparently the same as those which extend from 42 ft. to 82 ft. above The White Band at Ringstead.   The phosphatic nodule beds are not quite reached in the present state of the section, but the continual retreat of the cliff by slipping of the highly-tilted beds may be expected to expose them in a few years.

From the sections described it was inferred in 1936 that the Upper Kimmeridge Clay of the Ringstead Black Head district was not more than half as thick as that of Purbeck.   The D'Arcy Exploration Co.'s boring for oil at Poxwell in 1937 proved the whole Kimmeridge Clay to have a thickness of only about 800 ft., which is almost exactly half the thickness in Purbeck.[3]

(c) PRESTON TO PORTISHAM

At Black Head the outcrop turns inland to run along the north side of the Weymouth Anticline until cut off before it reaches the sea by the Abbotsbury Fault.   There are no sections worth mentioning until Abbotsbury is reached, but round Portisham

---

[1] H. Salfeld, ' Monographie der Gattung Cardioceras,' *Zeitschr. deutsch. geol. Gesellsch.*, Bd. lxvii, 1915, pp. 199-201, pl. xx, figs. 1-10.   The types came from Ringstead or Weymouth.

[2] Fragments of this bed also appear from time to time in the landslip at Ringstead but it has not been detected *in situ*, there being no exposure of the upper part of the zone.

[3] The apparent thickness was 842 ft. with a dip varying from 18° to 30°.

attempts have been made from time to time to work the Blackstone, which was discovered in 1856 at Portisham Dairy and in 1877 in the railway-cutting east of the station.[1] In 1917-18 three borings were made by the Government near Corton and Coryates to prove the oil-shale.[2] The results all showed that the Blackstone is no more remunerative than at Kimmeridge and for the same reasons —low oil and high sulphur content.

The Corton and Coryates Blackstone was proved to be on the same horizon as that at Kimmeridge by the presence in and about it of abundant *Saccocoma* (*see* p. 78 and Fig. 15), together with the characteristic *Subplanites*.[3]   A similar oil-shale formerly exposed in a subway at Abbotsbury Station was presumed to lie on a lower horizon.

(d) THE ABBOTSBURY IRONSTONE

West of Rodden along the junction of the Kimmeridge Clay and Corallian Beds the soil reddens. At first this may be due to the ferruginous Sandsfoot Grits, but from Elworth westwards the Grits form a conspicuous scarp, and ironstone comes in above them, down the dip-slope.   This is the Abbotsbury Iron Ore, which crops out on three sides of the village, dipping under it in a synclinal structure from the north, south, and west. On the north side of Linton Hill ore was found containing 32-36 per cent. metallic iron. Thence Strahan mapped it continuously under the Abbey and Chapel Hill, across Seaway Lane at the junction with Town Lane (where there is a good section), through the north side of Castle Gardens and across Fuller's Way at the garden gate (where there is another section), and thence northward into the fault and along the north side of Countess Coppice.[4]

North of the village there are good sections in Red Lane, leading up the hill north of the Ilchester Hotel (Blake and Hudleston's ' roadway leading over the hill to Gorwell '); in Folly Hollow (the site of old workings and where Blake and Hudleston's section was taken) leading north-west from the school to Ferny Hole; and in several places adjacent to the fault, south-east of Ferny Hole Plantation. The section at Folly Hollow and Red Lane was formerly as follows.   Beds 1 and 2 can now be seen only very imperfectly.

---

[1] For particulars of these abortive attempts see A. Strahan, *Purbeck Memoir,* 1898, pp. 58-9.

[2] Full particulars in ' Special Reports Mineral Resources,' vol. vii, *Mem. Geol. Surv.,* 1918.

[3] F. L. Kitchin and J. Pringle, ' The Concealed Mesozoic Rocks in Kent,' *Mem. Geol. Surv.,* 1923, pp. 222-3 and Table facing p. 224. At Corton was found *Subplanites pseudoscruposus* Spath (L. F. Spath, *op. cit.,* 1936, p. 173, fig. 2) (see above, fig. 17, p. 77).

[4] A. Strahan, *Purbeck Memoir,* 1898, p. 39, and unpublished 6-inch maps.

IRONSTONE AND SANDSFOOT GRIT, ABBOTSBURY[1]

(TOP)

Ft.

6. Sand, yellowish-brown, ferruginous, veined by thin seams of iron ... ... 6 to 8
5. IRON ORE. Crumbling reddish-brown ironshot ore, full of shining millet-seed grains in a matrix of fine quartz sand. A hard band of sandstone near the base, and throughout seams of concretionary iron. Abundant fossils, especially nests of *Ornithella dorsetensis*, abundant *O. lampas* and *Rhynchonella pinguis*, fossil wood, lamellibranchs and some gastropods. *Rasenia spp.* (*uralensis* and *orbignyi* groups), *Prorasenia spp.*, *Rasenioides sp.* 20
4. Sandrock, dark brown, coarse, with ferruginous pellets. Blake and Hudleston stated that the harder bands contain ' numerous *Ammonites decipiens* ' 2½
3. Sand, soft, yellow-weathering 2
2. Sandrock, dark brownish-green, ferruginous 1
1. Sandstones, brown, ferruginous, with variable hard bands, and fossils in the form of casts. Blake and Hudleston recorded ' *Exogyra virgula* ' [*praevirgula* Jourdy ?] About 10

Beds 1, 2 and 3 are presumably Sandsfoot Grits. The ' numerous *Ammonites decipiens* ' in bed 4 may be *Pictoniae* or even *Ringsteadiae*. Bed 6 is possibly only the weathered upper portion of the iron ore; it is variable in thickness, usually much less than the 6-8 ft. of Dr. Pringle's account. The fauna of the iron ore (bed 5) is varied and peculiar, comprising an assemblage not known elsewhere. It includes the ammonites *Rasenia cymodoce* (d'Orbigny), *R. uralensis* (d'Orbigny), *R. involuta* Salfeld, *Rasenioides* cf. *thermarum* (Oppel), *Prorasenia bowerbanki* Spath and *P.* (?) *pseudo-witteana* (Salfeld), the last three having been collected by the author. Among the gastropods are *Pseudomelania pseudolimbata* (Blake and Hudleston), *P. delia* (d'Orbigny) and *P.* (?) *ferruginea* (Blake and Hudleston), *Pleurotomaria reticulata* J. Sowerby, *Natica* (*Ampullina*) *eudora* d'Orbigny, and species of *Dicroloma*, *Cylindrites*, *Nerinea*, and *Trochus*. The lamellibranchs include *Trigonia monilifera* Agassiz, *Protocardia delibata* (de Loriol), and *Velata hautcoeuri* (Dollfus). Four species of brachiopods are common : *Terebratula subsella* Leymerie, *Ornithella dorsetensis* (Davidson), *O. lampas* (J. Sowerby), and *Rhynchonella pinguis* Roemer. Blake and Hudleston also record *Nucleolites scutatus* (Lamarck), *Glyphaea ferruginea* (= G. (?) *rostrata* Phillips sp.), *Serpula royeri* de Loriol, *S. gordialis* Schlotheim, and a tooth of *Ichthyosaurus*; but some of the fossils recorded by these authors are intentionally omitted from this list.

---

[1] J. F. Blake and W. H. Hudleston, ' The Corallian Rocks of England,' *Quart. Journ. Geol. Soc.*, vol. xxxiii, 1877, p. 273 ; emended lithologically by J. Pringle, Special Reports on Mineral Resources, vol. xii, *Mem. Geol. Surv.*, 1920, p. 222 ; and palaeontologically by W. J. Arkell, ' The Corallian Beds of Dorset,' *Proc. Dorset Nat. Hist. Soc.*, vol. lvii, 1936, pp. 90-91.

The ammonites prove that the ironstone belongs to the Zone of *Rasenia cymodoce*, as was first clearly enunciated by Salfeld.[1] Blake and Hudleston described the rock with the Corallian Beds, its natural place being with the ferruginous Sandsfoot Grits with which it is in contact; but that they realized its position is shown by their observing that it overlies the Sandsfoot Grits, and ' we may infer that we are dealing with beds at least on the horizon of the passage-beds to the Kimmeridge Clay.'[2] Definite correlation with the Lower Kimmeridge Clay was made by H. Douvillé four years later.[3]

Although the ironstone contains not less than 30%, and according to old analyses from 32 to 40%, of iron, exploitation has never been profitable on account of the high content of silica.[4]

(e) WEYMOUTH AND PORTLAND

South of Sandsfoot Castle where the Sandsfoot Grits dip below sea-level the cliff becomes low and slipped and is no longer kept free of talus by the sea, owing to the protective action of the harbour breakwaters. The *Rhynchonella inconstans* Clay (1 ft. 8 ins.), with *Pictoniae,* and the *Exogyra* Bed (8 ins.) as at Ringstead, can be recognized, however, followed as usual by shales with layers of *Ostrea delta,* characteristic of the Cymodoce Zone.[5] Similar indifferent sections can be made out in the banks of the Fleet north-west of Small Mouth bridge. Apparently at the base of the Cymodoce Zone is a grey marly sandrock full of well-preserved lamellibranchs.

Some indication of the nature of the clays that floor the isthmus between the mainland and Portland Island is afforded by septaria washed up on the shore of Portland Roads. From them Salfeld recorded seven species of *Aulacostephanus, Aspidoceras longispinum* (J. de C. Sowerby), *Amoeboceras anglicum* (Salfeld), and *A. krausei* (Salfeld).[6]

The lowest horizon to come to the surface on Portland Island is a blackstone, 10 ins. thick, which used to be dug for fuel between tide marks off Castleton and elsewhere.[7] Higher parts of the Kimmeridge Clay form the lower slopes round the north end of the island, but are almost entirely concealed by slips and scree of Portland Stone. Salfeld recorded ammonites of the ' *pallasianus* ' group (i.e., *Pavloviae*) in septaria, and lower down in flattened condition in shaly clays in the railway-cutting.[8]

---

[1] H. Salfeld, *op. cit.,* 1914, p. 200; also *op. cit.,* 1913, p. 426. Salfeld (and later S. S. Buckman, *Type Ammonites,* 1924, p. 35, apparently copying him) wrongly accused Blake and Hudleston of printing their section upside-down.

[2] J. F. Blake and W. H. Hudleston, *op. cit.,* 1877, pp. 273-4.

[3] H. Douvillé, *Bull. Soc. géol. France,* (3) vol. ix, 1881, p. 453.

[4] J. Pringle, *op. cit.,* 1920, for further details.

[5] Details in W. J. Arkell, *Jurassic System in Great Britain,* 1933, pp. 385, 454.

[6] H. Salfeld, *op. cit.,* 1914, p. 203.

[7] A. Strahan, *Purbeck Memoir,* 1898, p. 120. It is mentioned as being dug " especially eastewardes of Her Majesties Castill " in 1594 (William Pitt, quoted in C. H. Vellacott, *Victoria County Histories,* Dorset, vol. ii, 1908, p. 340).

[8] H. Salfeld, *op. cit.,* 1914, p. 203.

CHAPTER VI

PORTLANDIAN STAGE: PORTLAND BEDS

I. GENERAL

(a) LITHOLOGY AND GENERAL CHARACTERISTICS

The Portland Beds mark the last episode of the marine Jurassic. They consist of shallow-water sands and limestones of facies somewhat similar to the Corallian Beds, and though 240 ft. thick in Purbeck they seem to belong to only one cycle of sedimentation. Upon the 1,600 ft. sequence of Kimmeridge Clay the Portland Sand follows like the Lower Calcareous Grit upon the Oxford Clay, and is followed as in the Corallian by limestone, the Portland Stone.

The Portland Sand is highly charged with mud and when unweathered is often black in colour, but it nevertheless indicates shallowing of the sea or uplift of surrounding lands and influx of coarser sediments borne by currents. ' Fucoidal ' structure is conspicuous in the hard bands, as in the Corallian sandstones, and huge doggers are common.

The Portland Stone varies widely. There is the fine white oolite of commerce; hard crystalline shell-limestone; spongy ' Roach ' riddled with hollows from which shells have been dissolved; serpulite; sublithographic stone of china-like appearance; and white chalky rock full of black flints or cherts, easily confused at first sight with Upper Chalk. These deposits were laid down on the quiet, shallow sea-bed which was soon to be upheaved to form a marshy land surface and then to be slowly depressed again beneath the waters of the Purbeckian lake or brackish swamp.

An interesting problem is presented by the abundant chert in the Portland Stone. It occurs in the form of nodules, tabular masses, and veins. The nodules range in size from a thrush's egg to masses 2 ft. in diameter and there is every gradation from discrete nodules to ramifying mesh-works and solid tabular ' floors ' parallel to the bedding. In general, and often in surprising detail, the concentration of chert in certain bands of limestone remains constant for several miles along the outcrop. As will be seen by reference to the drawings of measured sections (Fig. 20), the same courses of stone with approximately the same concentrations of chert nodules can be traced at least from

Seacombe round the point of St. Alban's Head. The appearances of chert of this kind suggest that the silica was a primary constituent of the sediment. On the other hand it is possible that it was of secondary origin, and that the concentration of chert was governed by constitutional differences in the limestone courses. Some of the tabular chert is undoubtedly of secondary origin, for it transgresses the bedding-planes like sills. Instances of this can best be seen at Pondfield and in the face of Gad Cliff, on several horizons. In blocks M. and L. (below, p. 107), numerous parallel veins of black chert cross the bedding at an angle of about 45°. These occurrences are in the west of the Purbeck outcrop, in the region of greatest deformation of the strata, where they are nearest to the steep middle limb of the Purbeck Anticline. It seems that the cracks filled by the secondary chert were probably caused by the Tertiary folding. In the same region the brachiopods are silicified in the Portland Sand.

Even if all the chert proves to be of secondary origin, it is likely that the silica was an original constituent of the sediment but previously existed in some more soluble form. Sponge-spicules of the genus *Pachastrella* have been identified at various points,[1] but although some silicified oolite at St. Alban's Head is largely made of them there is no suggestion that they ever occurred everywhere in sufficient quantities to produce the enormous mass of silica represented by the cherts. It is more likely that their presence was due to a siliceous environment.

(b) THE LINE OF DIVISION BETWEEN KIMMERIDGE CLAY AND

PORTLAND SAND

Lithologically there is an upward gradation from the shales and clays of the Kimmeridge Clay, through a series of sandy clays and marls, into the Portland Sand. The only conspicuous feature in the neighbourhood of the junction in the sections at Hounstout and Emmit Hill is a 6 ft. band of hard cementstone which Buckman called the Massive Bed; and this may have its counterpart in Portland Island. The Geological Survey of 1855 mapped an indefinite line in the sandy clays about 40-50 ft. below the Massive Bed, and in this they were followed by H. B. Woodward, who estimated the thickness of the Portland Sand to be 170 feet.[2] The 40 or 50 ft. of sandy marls (' mottled blue and brown ') below the Massive Bed he designated ' passage beds,' although he included them in the Portland Sand. Blake had adopted a line 126 ft. below the Massive Bed, giving the Portland Sand 244 ft., but with this no authors have agreed.[3]

---

[1] H. B. Woodward, ' Jurassic Rocks of Britain,' vol. v, *Mem. Geol. Surv.*, 1895, p. 187.

[2] H. B. Woodward, ' Jurassic Rocks of Britain,' vol. v, *Mem. Geol. Surv.*, 1895, p. 192 (on p. 180 he says ' 130-170 ft.').

[3] J. F. Blake, ' On the Portland Rocks of England,' *Quart. Journ. Geol. Soc.*, vol. xxxvi, 1880, p. 195.

During the resurvey of 1888-90 the Massive Bed was adopted as the base of the Portland Sand, for the dual reasons that it provided the only recognizable datum-line and accorded closely with Fitton's original classification, in which the Portland Sand was said to be 120-140 ft. thick.[1] This classification is now accepted by most geologists,[2] but there have been some dissentients,[3] and therefore Fitton's original section of the Portland Sand at the type-locality, Emmit Hill, is here reproduced. It can thus be seen to what beds his descriptions correspond. All are agreed that for historical reasons Fitton should be followed, but there is not always clearness on the implications of that agreement.

FITTON'S SECTION OF THE PORTLAND SAND AT EMMIT HILL, ST. ALBAN'S HEAD (1827)

FITTON'S BEDS[4]	MODERN DIVISIONS[5]	
2. Portland Sand. Soft stone, or marly coherent sand, with a rugged external surface of a yellowish grey or brownish colour ; but in the recent fracture, of a dark bluish or greenish grey. It includes concretions of firmer consistence (................) 25 ft. to 30 ft.	The Black Sandstones (Block A) (Beds 26-28)	29 ft.
3. Bluish grey, inclining to green, sandy clay and marl, including ranges of concretions approaching to stone ; the whole effervescing with acids. The more stony portions acquire by exposure a yellowish brown tinge (............) About 60 ft.	Middle and Lower Parallel Bands (Beds 22-25) ... ... St. Alban's Head Marls (Beds 14-21)	15 ft. 45 ft. — 60 ft. —
4a. Soft, dark bluish grey, effervescent sand-rock, or indurated marl, including a band of firmer consistence, which contains casts of [*Thracia*] *depressa* and other bivalves.	The white Cementstone (' of firmer consistence ') full of *Thracia depressa* and other bivalves 2 to Emmit Hill Marls (with stinkstones) (*Thracia depressa* here also) ...	2½ft. 30 ft.
b. Brownish marly sand-rock, softer than a.		
c. A firmer stratum, including, about 20 ft. from the bottom, large sub-globular, but nearly continuous concretions of greater firmness, which also contains casts of [*Thracia*] *depressa* and other fossils. 40 ft. to 50 ft.	The Massive Bed ...	6 ft. — 38 ft. —

[1] A. Strahan, *Purbeck Memoir*, 1898, pp. 60, 62.

[2] *e.g.* M. P. Latter *Proc. Geol. Assoc.*, vol. xxxvii, 1926, p. 76 ; L. R. Cox, *Proc. Dorset. Nat. Hist. Arch. Soc.*, vol. 1, 1929, p. 133 ; W. J. Arkell, *Jurassic System in Great Britain*, 1933, p. 492, and *Proc. Geol. Assoc.*, vol. xlvi, 1935, p. 311.

[3] S. S. Buckman, *Type Ammonites*, vol. vi, 1926, pp. 33-4 ; L. F. Spath, *Medd. om Grønland*, vol. 99, 1936, p. 161.

[4] W. H. Fitton, ' Strata between the Chalk and the Oxford Oolite in the South-east of England,' *Trans. Geol. Soc.* (2) vol. iv, 1836, p. 211.

[5] See below, pp. 102-3.

Fitton added ' Springs break out at the bottom of this group, where the Kimmeridge Clay might be expected.' In the present state of the cliff at Emmit Hill it is not possible to see where those springs might have broken out over a century ago.[1] The ' large subglobular concretions,' which reminded Fitton of the doggers in the Shotover Grit Sands (Upper Kimmeridgian) near Oxford, may have been seen in a very weathered exposure of any of the sandy cementstone bands. Good examples are at present exposed in the decayed eastern end of Gad Cliff.

(c) STRATIGRAPHY AND PALAEONTOLOGY

The Portland Stone and the harder bands of the Portland Sand abound in giant ammonites, but the practical difficulties of a systematic study of them are considerable. Nearly all the specimens in existing collections come from the Portland Freestone Series, only one-fifth part of the formation. Until all the ammonites have been monographed, the vertical ranges of the various genera and species within the formation, and unfortunately also the specific and even generic characters and names of several of the most familiar forms, must remain uncertain and subject to change. Meanwhile it seems best to retain the revised zonal classification shown in the accompanying table.[2]

		ZONES	PURBECK	PORTLAND	RINGSTEAD-PORTISHAM
P O R T L A N D I A N	PORTLAND STONE	*Titanites giganteus*	Freestone Series (50 ft.)	Freestone Series (25 ft.)	Freestone Series (15-24ft.)
		Kerberites okusensis	Cherty Series (with Serpulite) (65 ft.)	Cherty Series (with Serpulite) (50-60 ft.) Basal Shell Bed (6 ft.)	Cherty Series (with Serpulite) (25-35 ft.) Basal Shell Bed
	PORTLAND SAND	*Glaucolithites gorei*	Black Sandstones and Parallel Bands (45 ft.) St. Alban's Head Marls (45 ft.)	Portland Clay (0-14 ft.) West Weare Sandstones and *Exogyra* Bed (30-40 ft.)	West Weare Sandstones (and cementstones with *Serpulae* and *Exogyra* Beds (25-40 ft.)
		Provirgatites albani	Emmit Hill Marls (30 ft.) Massive Bed (6 ft.)	Upper Black Nore Beds (35 ft.) Black Nore Sandstone	Sands of Ringstead and Coryates (*c.* 50 ft.)

[1] Normally Hounstout has 2 conspicuous lines of seepage 20 ft. apart, and others lower down ; but Fitton's type locality was Emmit Hill, a mile away.
[2] W. J. Arkell, *Jurassic System in Great Britain*, 1933, p. 481 ; and ' The Portland Beds of the Dorset Mainland,' *Proc. Geol. Assoc.*, vol. xlvi, 1935, p. 334.

The Lower Portland Sand in Purbeck contains ammonites of exceptional interest which seem to correlate with the lower ' *Virgatites* ' fauna of Russia (*Provirgatites* = *Zaraiskites*). They are characterized by the peculiar sheaf-like ribbing known as virgatotome. No Russian species has yet been found in this country, and although the *Provirgatites scythicus* Zone of Russia, Poland, and Germany is probably represented at this level, it seems advisable to use an English species *P. albani* (Fig. 17, p. 77), as zonal index for this country.[1] The credit for the first discovery of these forms in England and the recognition of their significance is due to S. S. Buckman.[2] Pavlovids also occur, among them *Pavlovia worthensis* Spath;[3] for the most part they are crushed, fragmentary, and usually more or less unrecognizable.

In the upper part of the Portland Sand a large, evolute, round-whorled, biplicate type is characteristic; Salfeld called it *Perisphinctes gorei*. There may be several subgenera, and Buckman invented for them numerous generic names, all except one, however, based on inland specimens. The earliest name is *Glaucolithites*,[4] and since the genotype appears to be a typical member of the fauna of the upper part of the Portland Sand, for which Salfeld used the name *Perisphinctes gorei* in a comprehensive sense, *Glaucolithites* has been adopted for this genus.[5] The largest ammonites in the Upper Portland Sand, which abound for instance at Corton (' *P. pseudo-biplex* ' Pruvost?), probably belong, on Spath's reading, to *Behemoth*.

Most observers have noticed a difference between the giant ammonites of the Cherty Series of the Portland Stone and those of the Freestone Series. Generally those seen in the Cherty Series are more inflated and more evolute, and some show stronger ribbing than those from the Freestone Series; but satisfactory comparison is difficult owing to lack of adequate material from the Cherty Series. Blake distinguished the giants of the Cherty Series as *Ammonites pseudo-gigas*,[6] but unfortunately he designated no type, and subsequently Buckman designated as neotype a specimen from the Freestone Series of the Aylesbury district.[7] Other writers have distinguished them under the name *Am. bononiensis* de Loriol. Buckman's *Behemoth* seemed a likely

---

[1] See W. J. Arkell, *op. cit.*, 1935, pp. 339-42. L. F. Spath (*op. cit.*, 1936, p. 30) has made *P. albani* Arkell genotype of another new genus, *Progalbanites* Spath, but the reasons given—especially that the remarkable virgatotome bundling of the secondary ribs ' is due partly to the compression '—are, in the Author's opinion, unsatisfactory.

[2] S. S. Buckman, *Type Ammonites*, vol. vi, 1926, pl. dclxxv. London.

[3] L. F. Spath, *op. cit.*, 1936, p. 30, pl. xviii, fig. 6.

[4] Type *G. glaucolithus* Buckman, *op. cit.*, 1922, pl. cccvi, A, B.

[5] See W. J. Arkell, *op. cit.*, 1935, pp. 337-8. L. F. Spath (*Meddelelser om Grønland*, vol. 99, 1936, p. 31) prefers the name *Crendonites*, but no further change seems advisable until the group has been monographed.

[6] J. F. Blake, ' On the Portland Rocks of England,' *Quart. Journ. Geol. Soc.*, vol. xxxvi, 1880, pp. 192, 228.

[7] S. S. Buckman, *Type Ammonites*, 1926, p. 26.

generic name;[1] but now Dr. Spath reserves this name for some Portland Sand species, previously included in *Glaucolithites*, and suggests that the giants in the Cherty Series will not be found to be distinguishable subgenerically from the *Titanites* of the over-lying Giganteus Zone.[2] More characteristic of the Cherty Series are smaller, strongly-ribbed triplicate shells formerly known as *Am. triplicatus* (*non* Sowerby),[3] for which Buckman founded the genus *Kerberites*.[4] Badly-preserved specimens which appear to be at least superficially indistinguishable, however, occur at the very top of the Freestone Series (Shrimp Bed) in Purbeck,[5] and Spath inclines to the view that *Kerberites* are merely inner whorls (nuclei) of *Titanites*.[6]

It appears, therefore, that a thorough examination of the Portlandian ammonites may result in establishing that the whole Portland Stone of Dorset belongs to only one major ammonite zone.

The *giganteus* fauna of the Freestone Series is well known from the hundreds of specimens quarried in Portland, Purbeck and inland, many of which find their way into gardens at Weymouth and Swindon. (See Pl. VII.)

The most abundant fossils in the Portland, as in the Corallian, Beds are lamellibranchs. In the Portland Sand they are generally preserved as casts. Some of the commoner forms are cited in the descriptions of sections below. The little oyster, *Exogyra nana* (J. Sowerby) (= *bruntrutana* Thurmann), occurs in great abundance in the upper division over the whole area, and a lumachelle formed by it, with many *Serpulae*, provides a useful datum-plane in correlation and mapping in the inland country north of Weymouth. The rock at this horizon had been mistaken for Portland Stone, with great prejudice to the mapping. Rarer features at certain levels in the Portland Sand are brachiopods—two species of *Rhynchonella* (*R. portlandica* Blake and a new species), various minute *Orbiculoidea*, and the rare *Terebratula bononiensis* Rigaux and Sauvage, found also in the Boulonnais. The *Terebratula* and new *Rhynchonella* are common on a single bedding-plane at Gad Cliff.

In the Portland Stone large heavy-shelled lamellibranchs are conspicuous (Fig. 18). The most abundant are *Isognomon* [*Perna*] *listeri* (Fleming) (= *bouchardi* Oppel), *Chlamys lamellosa* (J. Sowerby), *Protocardia dissimilis* (J. de C. Sowerby), *Ostrea expansa* J. Sowerby, *Trigonia gibbosa* J. Sowerby, *T. incurva*

---

[1] S. S. Buckman, *op. cit.,* 1922, pl. cccv, a, b; and W. J. Arkell, *op. cit.,* 1935, p. 336.

[2] L. F. Spath, *op. cit.,* 1936, p. 32.

[3] See J. F. Blake, *op. cit.,* 1880, pl. x, fig. 7.

[4] Type *K. kerberus* Buckman, from the Vale of Wardour (S. S. Buckman, *Type Ammonites,* 1924, pl. dxx); see also 1926, pls. dxx, a, b, dxxxv. Buckman also stated that *K. okusensis* (Salfeld) was the genotype (*op. cit.,* 1925, pl. dlxx, a).

[5] W. J. Arkell, *op. cit.,* 1935, pp. 335-6.

[6] L. F. Spath, *op. cit.,* 1936, p. 33.

Benett. These and many others range through the Cherty Series and the Freestone Series alike, though there is a special concentration, with many additional species, in the Basal Shell Bed of the Portland Stone in Portland.[1] In the Roach at the very top in Portland the shells are dissolved out, leaving a mass of cavities. Here a turreted gastropod, the Portland Screw *Aptyxiella portlandica* (J. de C. Sowerby) is common, and it occurs at no other horizon (Fig. 18). *Pleurotomaria rugata* (Benett) is commoner at a lower level. In Purbeck no Roach is developed. Its place is taken by a white sublithographic limestone called the Shrimp Bed, from the occurrence of remains of a small Crustacean, *Callianassa*, related to the Hermit Crabs. Below it locally is an oyster bed, peculiar to Tilly Whim.

Serpula gordialis (Schlotheim) is a rock-former in the Cherty Series, especially in Purbeck, and it abounds also in the hard cementstones of the upper part of the Portland Sands farther west, from Poxwell to Portisham.

A calcareous alga, which Mr. W. N. Edwards confirms is *Solenopora sp.* (probably new), occurs in almost reef-building abundance on the horizon of the Roach in the cliffs on the east side of Portland Bill. Corals, contrary to what might be expected from the general lithology, are almost entirely absent; only very rare examples of *Isastraea oblonga* Edwards and Haime, the ' Tisbury Star-coral,' have been recorded in the cherts.

Sponge spicules are referred to on p. 90.

Saurian, chelonian, and fish remains are rare.

II. THE ISLE OF PURBECK

(a) GENERAL

Although the Portland Beds take their name from Portland Island, the formation is thicker, more fully exposed, and more interesting palaeontologically, in Purbeck. At the eastern end of the outcrop, towards which the whole formation thickens, the Portland Stone is 115 ft. thick, the Portland Sand 125-130 ft. thick.

The stone has been quarried from early times along the cliffs, where it is known as Purbeck-Portland. There are two freestones, called the Pond and Under Freestones, both near the top of the series. The stone was reached by means of galleries driven into the face of the cliff or into the sides of the dry coombs which descend to the sea at Anvil Point, Seacombe, and Winspit. Old galleries, which were still being worked at the time of Thomas

---

[1] L. R. Cox, ' The Fauna of the Basal Shell Bed of the Portland Stone, Isle of Portland,' *Proc. Dorset Nat. Hist. and Ant. Field Club*, vol. xlvi, 1925, pp. 113-172; and *idem*, ' Synopsis of the Lamellibranchia of the Portland Beds of England,' *ibid*, vol. 1, 1929, p. 130.

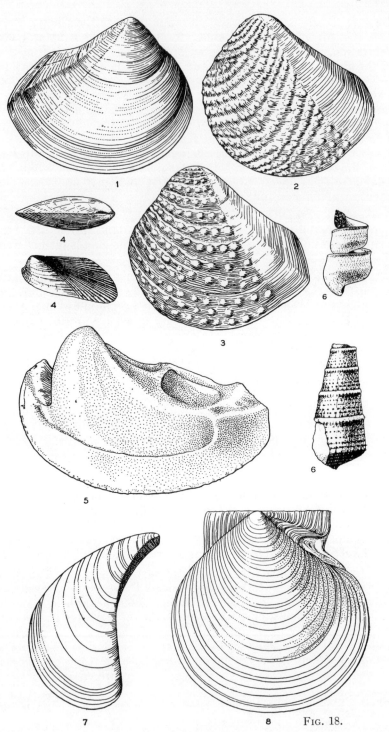

Fig. 18.

Webster's survey in 1811,[1] form the ' caves ' of Tilly Whim (Pl. VII), and many of them were favourite smugglers' resorts. There was a revival after the war of 1914-18 at Seacombe, but the works fell derelict about 1930.   Another attempt was made soon after to quarry the Pond Freestone on St. Alban's Head.   At present the only centres of activity are there and inland, at Sheep-sleights or Worth Quarry, Coomb Bottom, one mile north of Worth Matravers.[2]

West of St. Alban's Head and Worth Quarry, in a south-westerly and westerly direction, the freestones deteriorate by becoming thinner and cherty from below upwards.   In East Purbeck and at Worth the Pond Freestone is 5-7½ ft. thick, the Under or Bottom Freestone 8 ft. thick.   At Seacombe and Winspit the Under Freestone thins down to 3½ ft. in a south-westerly direction through the quarries.   At St. Alban's Head it is replaced altogether by thin limestone bands with chert nodules and is not worth working.   There only the Pond Freestone has been quarried.   By the time Gad Cliff and Pondfield are reached the Pond Freestone also has thinned down to 4 feet.   About Lulworth both freestones have almost disappeared and the only stone that has been considered worth getting is the Shrimp Bed at the top.

(b)   THE EAST PURBECK SECTIONS :

ANVIL POINT TO ST. ALBAN'S HEAD AND HOUNSTOUT[3]

Three good sections of the Portland Sand are provided by the west side of St. Alban's Head with Emmit Hill, Hounstout, and Gad Cliff.   The Parallel Bands and Black Sandstones are also conveniently studied in a slipped mass close to the sea in the under-cliff near the tip of St. Alban's Head.

The Portland Stone forms a vertical wall rising from 100 to 200 ft. straight from the sea for a distance of 4½ miles, from St. Alban's Head to Durlston Head, but deep water nearly everywhere laps the foot of the cliffs (Pl. VII).   Although the strata are nearly horizontal, there is a gentle seaward dip and they undulate slightly

---

[1] In Sir H. C. Englefield, *Picturesque Beauties of the Isle of Wight,* 1816, pl. 33, London.

[2] The quarry is at present (1938) owned by Swanworth Quarries Ltd.

[3] W. J. Arkell, ' The Portland Beds of the Dorset Mainland,' *Proc. Geol. Assoc.,* vol. xlvi, 1935, pp. 304-335.

FIG. 18.—*Characteristic fossils of the Portland Beds.*

1. *Trigonia gibbosa* J. Sowerby.
2. *T. gibbosa* var. *manseli* Lycett.
3. *T. gibbosa* var. *damoniana* de Loriol.
4. *Musculus autissiodorensis* (Cotteau).
5. *Trigonia incurva* Benett, typical cast known as " 'osses 'eads " by quarrymen (" *Hippocephalites* " of Plot).
6. *Aptyxiella portlandica* (J. de C. Sowerby) and cast known as the "Portland Screw " by quarrymen.
7. *Mytilus* (*Falcimytilus*) *suprajurensis* Cox.
8. *Pecten* (*Chlamys*) *lamellosus* J. Sowerby, right valve of double-valved example (× ½).

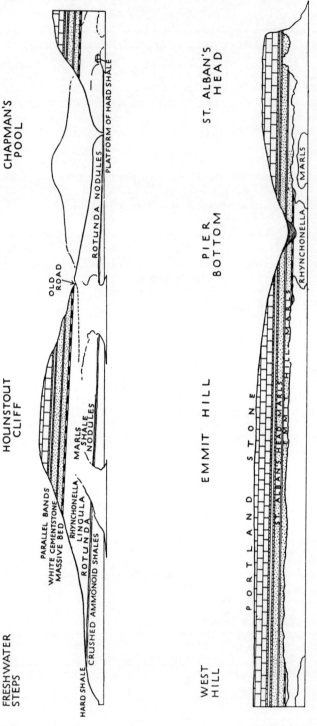

FIG. 19.—*Section along the cliffs from Freshwater Steps, below Encombe to St. Alban's Head. Scale, vertical and horizontal, 7.2 inches = 1 mile.* (Reproduced from *The Jurassic System in Great Britain*, 1933, p. 482.)

and are faulted. Consequently in some places the top of the Portland Sand is brought up not far below sea-level and forms a lodging for huge fallen blocks only approachable from a boat (as at the Ragged Rocks).

The lower half of the Cherty Series can be studied only at St. Alban's Head, where two steep footpaths give access from above and scree fans from below. The east side of the head presents a magnificent precipice of Portland Stone, at the foot of which fallen blocks and disintegrating landslips spread out as a wild undercliff, lodged upon the Kimmeridge Clay. The coastguard's garden is perched upon a detached slice, which has slipped or been faulted down, repeating the section.

The upper half of the Cherty Series, and the Freestone Series, are accessible in the niches in the cliffs, with ancient quarries and galleries, at Tilly Whim, Dancing Ledge, Seacombe, and Winspit. The House Cap forms the roof of the galleries, and the top of the Cherty Series the floor. At Worth Quarry, inland, the method of working is entirely open.

PORTLAND BEDS OF EAST PURBECK
FREESTONE SERIES

The following tabulated section was measured at Seacombe.[1]

Ft.

V.　　SHRIMP BED[2]. White, fine-grained sublithographic lime-stone, constant in appearance from Durlston Head to Lulworth. The ' Shrimp ' is a small Crustacean identified by Mr. H. Woods as probably *Callianassa*. Bivalves abound, especially *Trigonia gibbosa*, mainly var. *damòniana* de Loriol, *Protocardia dissimilis*, *Chlamys* (*Camptochlamys*) *lamellosa*, *Isognomon* [*Perna*] *listeri*, *Pleuromya tellina* (Agassiz), with *Trigonia incurva*, *Isocyprina sp.*, etc. Worth Quarry has yielded from this bed a fairly complete specimen of *Titanites*. There are also fragments of coarsely-ribbed triplicate ammonites suggestive of Buckman's *Glottoptychinites* or *Kerberites* ... ... 　10

U.　　TITANITES BED. Hard, greyish, shelly limestone (' spangle '), as at Worth Quarry, especially shelly in the basal 2 ft. Innumerable *Trigonia gibbosa*, *T. incurva*, *I. listeri*, *Chl. lamellosa*, *P. dissimilis*, *Ostrea expansa*, etc. This bed is the source of nearly all the giant ammonites of various species of *Titanites* (though at Winspit some occur in the House Cap). At Tilly Whim a lenticular oyster bed develops on this horizon. Locally about 8 ft. of the rock is almost entirely composed of *Exogyra nana*, *E. thurmanni* Étallon, *Ostrea expansa* and *Isognomon listeri*, with a smaller proportion of *Lima rustica* (J. Sowerby) and *Plicatula boisdini* de Loriol. Sometimes the fossils are dissolved away, leaving patches of rock like the Roach of Portland ... ... 　10—11

---

[1] W. J. Arkell, *Jurassic System in Great Britain*, 1933, pp. 485-9 ; and *Proc. Geol. Assoc.*, vol. xlvi, 1935, pp. 306 ff.

[2] The thickness of this bed was stated by Hudleston to be 16 ft. at St. Alban's Head, but at all available sections on the head, the thickness does not exceed 11 ft.

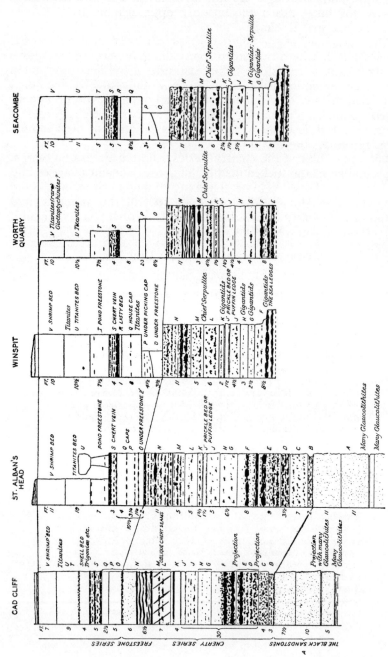

Fig. 20.—*Profiles of the Portland Stone at the principal exposures in Purbeck.* Black denotes chert, dots denote sandstone or sandy limestone. (After Arkell, *Proc. Geol. Assoc.*, vol. xlvi, 1935, p. 301.)

Ft.

T.   POND FREESTONE. Good oolitic freestone. Fossils nearly all comminuted. Occasionally spoilt by lenticles of white silicified oolite. At Worth 7-7½ ft. Here only   5

S.   CHERT VEIN. Limestone with chert, dense and nodular below, sparser above   5

R.   LISTY BED. Grey limestone with a ready vertical and horizontal fracture, strongly marked off above and below.' So called ' because it breaks easily.' Not present at Worth. The ' Lisky ' Bed of Buckman (1926, p. 35) and the ' Nist ' Bed of H. B. Woodward (1895, p. 190)   ...   .   6 ins. to   1

Q.   HOUSE CAP. Hard grey shelly limestone (' spangle '), resembling the *Titanites* Bed, and like it especially shelly in the basal portion. The under surface, which forms the roof of the galleries at all the cliff quarries, is covered with large shells of *O. expansa, I. listeri, L. rustica, Ch. lamellosa,* etc. At Winspit several giant specimens of *Titanites* can be seen embedded in the basal 1-2 ft. About 5 ft. from the bottom of the bed is a band of thin lenticles of white chert and silicified oolite 8½

P.   UNDER PICKING CAP. Hard freestone, locally called spangle. It is cut to waste in order to get at the Under Freestone   3

O.   UNDER OR BOTTOM FREESTONE. Fine cream-coloured oolite, an excellent quality freestone, the shells nearly all comminuted. This was the stone for which all the old cliff quarries were principally worked. Partly false-bedded   8

Total *c.* 50

CHERTY SERIES

From measurements and correlations made at Seacombe, Winspit, Worth and St. Alban's Head :—

N.   Cherty limestones, often sandy, white-weathering ; small   Ft. chert nodules more or less disseminated throughout as well as segregated in bands, and one or two bands of large semi-confluent nodules. The block weathers into different numbers of beds in different places. Total always   11

M.   Cherty and serpulitic limestone. At Worth Quarry and Seacombe 3 ft. thick, with a median band of very large chert nodules up to 1 ft. thick. At Winspit and St. Alban's Head 5 ft. and the nodules smaller. *Isognomon listeri, Chlamys lamellosa, Exogyra nana, Trigonia gibbosa, Serpula gordialis* (Schlotheim), etc.   ...   .   3—5

L.   Highly serpulitic cherty limestone. Often partly a pure serpulite (*S. gordialis*). The upper surface shelly. At Winspit the under surface shows large *Behemoth* (?)[1]. 4½ ft. at Worth, 5 ft. at St. Alban's Head, 6 ft. at Sea-combe and Winspit. Same fossils as M.   ...   ...   4½—6

K.   Persistent band of cherty limestone, sometimes weathering with algal structure. *Behemoth* (?) at Winspit ...   ...   1½—2¼

[1] For interpretation of these records, *see* pp. 93-94.

Ft.

J.   Prickle Bed or Puffin Ledge.[1] The most conspicuous, easily recognised datum in the Cherty Series all along the cliffs. A comparatively soft chertless bed ; weathering reveals a peculiar ropy structure reminiscent of lava and in places of pillow-lava ; and a mass of ramifying forms probably due to algæ. *Behemoth* (?) at Seacombe and Winspit 1½

J.   Limestone, sparsely cherty, cemented on to J′ with an indistinct parting. The two together form the most noticeable and easily recognized block (6-7 ft. thick) in every section   ...   .   4½—5½

H.   Limestone, little chert, locally serpulitic (*S. gordialis*). Large *Behemoth* (?) at Winspit   ...   .   3—4

G.   Limestones with one or more bands of chert nodules. At Seacombe *Behemoth* (?) and many *Lima rustica, Isognomon listeri, Ostrea expansa*. At St. Alban's Head and elsewhere locally in the cliffs G. and H. are fused together or split into three   ...   .   2½—4

F. and E.   The Sea Ledges. Limestones with massive bands of confluent nodular chert (up to 1 ft. thick), usually weathering into two principal blocks, each 6 ft. to 9 ft. thick. These form the ledges at sea-level (Seacombe, Winspit, etc.), and the bottom of Worth Quarry. A few very large *Behemoth* (?). Total thickness at St. Alban's Head   17

From the middle of these beds downwards the rest of the Cherty Series is accessible only at St. Alban's Head.

D,C.   Cherty limestones. Much chert in large nodules...   ...   10½

B.   Soft sandstone weathering to a sand, with bands of chert...   2

         Total thickness of Cherty Series...   65

PORTLAND SAND

THE BLACK SANDSTONES (BLOCK A) AND PARALLEL BANDS   Ft.

A. 28   Hard black sandstones, weathering grey brown, cavernous,
—26   with many of the cavities in the shapes of chert nodules partly filled with black calcite. Honeycombing. In 3 blocks, the lowest (7 ft.) forming the Upper Parallel Band and it and the middle block containing many *Glaucolithites*   29

25.   Shales, chalky, papery, with two white bands   3

24.   Middle Parallel Band : persistent sandy cementstone ; can be followed by the eye from St. Alban's Head to Hounstout 1½

23.   Shales, as above (25)   1

22.   Lower Parallel Band ; hard, grey, sandy cementstone or sandstone, with some cavities containing black calcite (fewer than in Block A)   10

                                   Total   45

---

[1] Quarrymen's names supplied by W. J. Bower of Winspit Cottage. The puffins nest in the recess above it.

ST. ALBAN'S HEAD MARLS[1]　　　　　　　　　　　　　　　　　Ft.

21.　Light grey marls with seven rows of white cementstone
　　　nodules, some rich in lamellibranch casts—*Eocallista
　　　implicata* (de Loriol), *E. pulchella* (de Loriol), *Isocyprina
　　　spp.*, etc., *Glaucolithites* (fragments)　　...　　...　　...　　10

20.　Dark grey bituminous shales and marls with two rows of
　　　nodules.　Layers of *Exogyra nana*, with some *Campto-
　　　nectes* and *Isognomon*　　...　　...　　...　　...　　...　　24

19-14.　Grey shaly marl with two 8-inch bands of hard white
　　　cementstone, and a row of nodules at top with *Thracia
　　　depressa, Buchia mosquensis*, etc. ...　　...　　...　　...　　11

　　　　　　　　　　　　　　　　　　　　　　　Total　　45

　　　　　　　　　　　　　　　　　　　　　　　　　　　Ft.

THE WHITE CEMENTSTONE[2]

13.　Conspicuous band, light grey, with spheroidal fracture and
　　　surfaces often red-stained.　Abundant *Thracia depressa*
　　　(J. de C. Sowerby), *Pleuromya tellina* (Agassiz),
　　　Musculus autissiodorensis (Cotteau), etc....'　　...　　...　　2—2½

EMMIT HILL MARLS[3]

12.　Dark grey to black sandy, shaly marl, with friable marl-
　　　stone bands and bituminous smell　　...　　...　　...　　8

11-7.　Ditto, fossiliferous.　*Provirgatites albani* Arkell *in situ*,
　　　plus lamellibranchs as in bed 13 ...　　...　　...　　...　　9

6-2.　Marls and friable soft marlstone　　...　　...　　...　　...　　13

　　　　　　　　　　　　　　　　　　　　　　　Total　　30

　　　　　　　　　　　　　　　　　　　　　　　　　　　Ft.

THE MASSIVE BED[4]

1.　Prominent band of hard, blue-centred, brown calcareous
　　　sandstone, forming feature on Hounstout and well
　　　exposed also on both sides of Pier Bottom, St. Alban's
　　　Head.　*Oxytoma octavia* (d'Orbigny) and crushed
　　　Rhynchonella portlandica Blake.　Abundant *Exogyra
　　　nana*.　Fragments of *Provirgatites*　　...　　...　　...　　6

　　　　　　　　Total thickness of Portland Sand　　128

As an illustration of the south-westerly deterioration of the
Under Freestone, the following section at St. Alban's Head is of
interest.　It is obtained by combining the information from the
quarry, from the mushroom-shaped monolith left by the quarrymen, and from the top of the cliff path.

　　　　　　SECTION AT ST. ALBAN'S HEAD
　　　　　　　　　PURBECK BEDS
　　　　　　　　　　　　　　　　　　　　　　　　　　Ft.
Grey tufaceous limestone ...　　...　　...　　...　　...　　...　　2

---

[1] Blake's bed, 12, *op. cit.*, 1880, p. 195.
[2] Blake's bed 13.
[3] Blake's bed 14.　For details of beds 1-21 see W. J. Arkell, *op. cit.*, 1935, p. 310.
[4] Blake's bed 15.

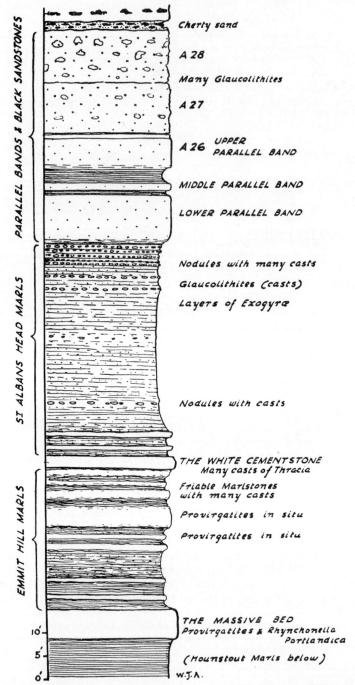

FIG. 21.—*Profile of the Portland Sand in the cliff at Emmit Hill, near St. Alban's Head.* Scale 1 inch = 20 ft. (Reproduced from *Proc. Geol. Assoc.*, vol. xlvi, 1935, p. 309.)

Ft.

FREESTONE SERIES

SHRIMP BED 11

TITANITES BED, in 3 or 4 blocks, very shelly 10

POND FREESTONE, with some white chert lenticles at top and
near base 7

CHERT VEIN. Limestone with three bands of chert lenticles,
one at the top 1 ft. thick 3

	⌈Limestone	4 ft.	⌉
	∣Band of chert nodules		∣
CAPS AND	∣Limestone	3 ft. 3 in.	∣
UNDER	⟨Band of chert nodules		⟩ 10 ft. 6 in.
FREESTONE	∣Limestone	1 ft. 3 in.	∣
	∣Band of chert nodules		∣
	⌊Limestone	2 ft.	⌋

Block N of the Cherty series below (11 ft.)

(c) WEST PURBECK SECTIONS : GAD CLIFF AND WORBARROW

For over a mile the highly inclined Portland Stone and Purbeck
Beds have been carved by the weather into jagged bastions, which
overhang the slope of Portland Sand and Kimmeridge Clay
(Pl. VIII). Gad Cliff owes its grandeur to the fact that, whereas
at St. Alban's Head the beds lie almost horizontally, at Gad Cliff
they dip inland at 25°-35°.

High up in the cliff two conspicuous white bands can be seen.
The higher of these is the Shrimp Bed and marks the top of the
Portland Stone; the lower is about on the horizon of Block M of
the Cherty Series.

In the following description, the measurements and particulars
are taken in Pondfield and Worbarrow Tout down to the 4-foot
block with a constant band of black chert (Block K) and thence
downwards are continued under Gad Cliff. The lettering of the
blocks B to V of the Stone Series is intended to correlate with the
St. Alban's Head section, but the beds of the Portland Sand are
numbered independently, precise correlation being impossible.

FREESTONE SERIES

Ft.

V. SHRIMP BED. The usual white, sublithographic limestone
with the usual fossils. In two blocks 7

U. TITANITES BED. Fossiliferous limestone, with giant
Titanites 1 ft. from the top, and many lamellibranchs
(usual) 9

T. ⌈Band of small chert nodules 1
⟨POND FREESTONE ; a rich shell bed in the middle;
⌊*Trigoniae*, etc. 4

S. CHERT VEIN. Three thick and several thinner bands of
chert in limestone 5

R-O. UNDER FREESTONE AND CAPS. White, oolitic, freestone,
in two blocks 7½

———————

Total of Freestone Series **33 ft.**

———————

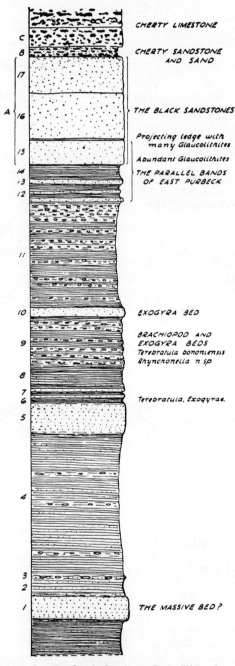

Fig. 22.—*Profile of the Portland Sand at Gad Cliff, showing the junction with the Cherty Series of the Portland Stone* (B, C) *and the position of the brachiopod and Exogyra beds. Scale 1 inch = 20 feet.* (Reproduced from *Proc. Geol. Assoc.*, vol. xlvi, 1935, p. 315.)

Cherty Series

Ft.

N. ⎰ Band of small chert nodules ... ... 1 ft. ⎱
  ⎰ Buff sandy limestone or calcareous sandstone ... 5 ft. ⎱   12½
  ⎰ Buff sandy limestone, with undulating but mainly ⎱
  ⎰ horizontal veins of thick tabular chert, as in N at ⎱
  ⎰ Worth ... ...6½ft. ⎱

M. & L. White limestone with two bands of chert nodules, and crossed by numerous parallel oblique veins of black secondary chert which cut the bedding at an angle of about 45°   7

K. Limestone with a conspicuous and persistent vein of tabular black chert, 6 ins. to 10 ins. thick. Forms good datum for correlating Gad Cliff with Worbarrow Tout   4

J. to E. Cherty limestones, an almost indivisible and inaccessible mass, which forms the chief feature of the precipices of Gad Cliff   30

C. Limestone with much chert, a well-marked block   4

B. Soft sandstone, weathering to a sand, with two or three rows of chert nodules   3

Total thickness of the Cherty Series | 60 ft.

Portland Sand

THE BLACK SANDSTONES (BLOCK A) AND PARALLEL BANDS

A.17 -15. Intensely hard black sandstone, riddled by cavities with shapes like chert nodules, but filled with black calcite; showing fucoidal structure. Honeycomb weathering. In three blocks as at St. Alban's Head, the two lowest with abundant *Glaucolithites*. The lowest bed (5 ft.) is the Upper Parallel Band ... ...   Ft.   22½

14. Soft grey marl and mudstone, hardens on contact with the sea   3

13. Middle Parallel Band : Cementstone   1

12. Lower Parallel Band (equivalent of) : Grey marl with a thin, soft cementstone band in the middle, and a 1-foot cementstone band at the base   4

30 ft.

ST. ALBAN'S HEAD MARLS

11. Grey-blue shaly marls and shales with rows of cementstone nodules, especially in the upper part ... ...   Ft.   22

10. *Exogyra* Bed. Tough pale grey marl full of flattened pellets of white marl, and crowded with small valves of *Exogyra nana*, with abundant *Plicatula boisdini* de Loriol, etc.   2

9. Brachiopod and *Exogyra* Beds. Tough grey sandy marls (hardening on contact with the sea-water) with rows of cementstone nodules and in the bedding-planes impersistent layers of larger *Exogyra nana* crowded together, with abundant *Oxytoma octavia, Ostrea expansa, Plicatula boisdini* and locally (in one seam, 6ft. from top) numerous *Rhynchonella sp.* and *Terebratula bononiensis* Sauvage and Rigaux   10

8. Tough grey sandy marl   5

Ft.

7. Two bands of tough grey marlstone with softer parting ...   2
6. Yellow sandy marl (4in.) overlying grey marl (8 in.) full
   of *Exogyra* ;   also *Oxytoma octavia, Serpulae*, minute
   Terebratulid   1

                                                                    42 ft.

THE WHITE CEMENTSTONE AND EMMIT HILL MARLS
5. Tough, grey-centred, brown-weathering, marly, sandy   Ft.
   cementstone weathering to yellow marly sand   6
4. Grey sandy marls, some bituminous, with three rows of
   cementstone nodules (0-6 in.)   30
3. Marly cementstone band, breaking into nodules (6 in.- ⎫
   9 in.)   ...   .   ⎬   4
2. Grey sandy marls, as above (3 ft. 6 in.)   ...   . ⎭

                                                                    40 ft.

THE MASSIVE BED
1. Tough grey, cream-weathering sandy marl and marlstone,   Ft.
   with obscure nodular structure.   Stands out as a hard
   band, but not so conspicuously as the Massive Bed
   farther east   5

                        Total thickness of Portland Sand   117 ft.

[Top of Hounstout Marls, dark grey-blue marl seen to 15 ft.]

III. LULWORTH : BACON HOLE TO DUNGY HEAD

The development in the two miles of outcrop on either side of
Lulworth Cove is best illustrated by sections at the two extremities :
the Freestone Series at Bacon Hole near the Mupe Rocks (Frontispiece), and the Cherty Series and Portland Sand at Dungy Head.
In Bacon Hole the Freestone Series is well exposed, but the Cherty
Series (cherty limestones, 30 ft.), falls precipitously into the sea all
along the outer side of the outcrop until Dungy Head is
approached, where it becomes accessible and the Portland Sand
rises from beneath.   The Bacon Hole Section is repeated in the
horns of Lulworth Cove, but the rock is too sea-etched to favour
examination.

The Freestone Series in Bacon Hole begins with 10 ft. of
limestone and freestone, false-bedded below; presumably this
represents the Under Freestone and Caps.   The Chert Vein is
represented by a 6-inch band of chert nodules, fused to the base of
the overlying band of shelly limestone.

Apparently the Pond Freestone is absent, and the shelly limestone (6 in.) with 3 ft. 6 ins. of white oolite and a further 6 to 9-inch
band of chert nodules are the equivalents of the *Titanites* Bed.
Above are two beds of white limestone which have been quarried :
the lower (4 ft. 6 ins.) is coarsely oolitic and shelly, and may be part
of the Shrimp Bed; the upper (2 ft.) is the typical development of
the Shrimp Bed, sublithographic limestone full of the usual shells.
A large surface of the top of this bed is exposed.

At Dungy Head there is a complete exposure of the Portland Beds (Fig. 23). The Freestone Series, although evidently well-developed and easily recognizable, does not lend itself to detailed examination and measurement because the exposed surface where accessible is a fault plane. The section begins to be good just

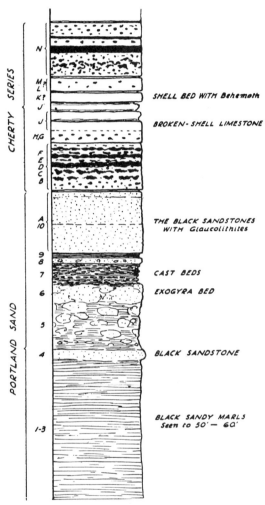

FIG. 23.—*Profile of the Cherty Series and the upper part of the Portland Sand, Dungy Head, Lulworth.* Scale 1 inch = 20 feet. (Reproduced from *Proc. Geol. Assoc.*, vol. xlvi, 1935, p. 321.)

about the junction of the Freestone and Cherty Series, thus forming a continuation of that at Bacon Hole. Probably the whole of the Portland Sand, as defined in Purbeck, was exposed, but much of the section was dangerously steep and has been nearly obliterated by a fall of cliff in the winter 1935-6.

SECTION AT DUNGY HEAD

[Freestone Series—oolitic and shelly limestones with roach bands—above.]

CHERTY SERIES

		Ft.	In.
N.	Limestone, with large masses of chert ... 3 ft. 0 in. Ditto, a band of chert at top ... 2 ft. 0 in. Enormous band of solid chert (connected with disturbance) ... ... 1 ft. 6 in. Limestone, nodular, full of irregular small and large chert nodules ... ... 5 ft. 0 in.	11	6
	[Deeply-weathered parting.]		
M.& L.	White limestone with black chert nodules, forming a conspicuous white band, as at Gad Cliff	3	0
K.	Shelly limestone, no chert. *Behemoth* (?)	2	0
J'.	Relatively soft, easily weathered chertless sandy limestone with the characteristic and peculiar 'ropy', pillowy, fucoidal structure of the Puffin Ledge in Purbeck; irregular surface	1	9
J.	Ditto, shelly, honeycombed, very irregular surface... ...	2	3
	Broken-shell limestone with a few cherts; forming one block with bed below	2	0
H. and G.	Limestone; scattered large nodules of chert ...	2	6
F, E, D, C, B.	Main mass of the Cherty Series: hard limestones, becoming sandy downwards, full of large nodules and bands of chert, especially three thick bands in the upper half, like the Sea Ledges	10	0
	Total thickness of the Cherty Series	35	0

PORTLAND SAND

		Ft.	In.
A.10.	THE BLACK SANDSTONES: Hard black sandstone as at Gad Cliff, the lower part slightly softer, weathering cavernous and honeycombed; the highest 15 inches intensely hard. *Glaucolithites* in the lower half ...	13	6
9.	Clay, black sandy, with some light grey patches	1	0
8.	Black sandy cementstone with intensely hard nodules ...	1	0
7.	CAST BEDS: Black shales with about 10 layers of highly fossiliferous soft cementstone nodules packed with lamellibranch casts. *Glaucolithites* common	4	6
6.	*Exogyra* Bed: Cementstone, hard, grey, sandy, in large irregular, lumpy, semi-coherent masses among marl; crowded with *Exogyra nana*; also *Serpula gordialis* and *Plicatula boisdini*	4	0
5.	Black sandy marls with much nodular, irregular, grey, sandy cementstone like that above but lacking the profusion of oysters	10	0
4.	Grey-black sandstone	2	0
3.	Black sandy marls and sands with occasional more or less indurated bands and a few rows of cementstone nodules *c.*	50	0
2.	Black sandstone	2	0
1.	Black sandy marls, seen to	6	0
	Total Portland Sand seen, *c.*	95	0

Although this section is midway between Gad Cliff and Ringstead (3½ miles from each), the Cherty Series, which is almost identical in thickness with that at Ringstead, shows many more points of resemblance to that at Gad Cliff. Seeing that the total thickness of the Cherty Series has decreased from 60 ft. to 35 ft., the degree of resemblance is surprising. The conspicuous white band near the top (correlated with Blocks M and L of East Purbeck) is still present, and the rest of the cherty beds above (Block N) are still 11½ ft. thick. The scarcity of chert about Blocks G to K and its abundance about the level of the Sea Ledges (Blocks C to F) are still striking, and the peculiar lithological appearance of J and J' the Prickle Bed or Puffin Ledge, is at once recognized by any observer familiar with East Purbeck. Finally, the hard Black Sandstones at the top of the Portland Sand, still with the same ammonites, complete the comparison with Purbeck. Here, however, in conformity with the general attenuation, there are only two blocks of this black sandstone, and the Parallel Bands are no longer recognizable. The upper part of the Portland Sand is also apparently much condensed. Bed 6 is apparently the equivalent of bed 20, and bed 7 that of bed 21 in East Purbeck.

IV. OUTCROPS NORTH OF WEYMOUTH : RINGSTEAD, POXWELL,

PRESTON AND UPWEY TO PORTISHAM

(a)　RINGSTEAD

The east corner of Ringstead Bay, below Holworth House, 3½ miles west by north of Dungy Head, provides a complete key section. The rocks here are lowered by pre-Albian (and perhaps pre-Aptian) faulting, and dip at a high angle into the cliff. The Purbeck and Portland Beds and the Kimmeridge Clay are planed off and directly overlain by the Gault. There are two sections, one immediately below the house (Pl. XI, A), showing Gault at the top, which is difficult of access; the other a short distance farther west. The latter, which has been kept clear by quarrying, shows the following section (Fig. 24) :

SECTION AT HOLWORTH HOUSE, RINGSTEAD

[Lower Purbeck Beds above, see p. 142]

PORTLAND STONE

FREESTONE SERIES

		Ft.	In.
27.	ROACH : White limestone, a mass of casts of *Trigonia gibbosa, Protocardia dissimilis, Pleuromya,* etc., and shells of *Lima rustica* and *Chlamys lamellosa*	1	2
26.	Limestone ; a white, soft freestone, with broken shells, passing down into roach in the lower two-thirds, full of casts as above	3	6

25. Limestone ; a white freestone passing down into roach as
    above ; *Isognomon listeri* common   ...   .

26. Ft. In.
    4   6

24. Gap in section where limestone has been quarried, the place
    now totally concealed by debris ; about...   ...   ...
    12   0

Total about   21   0

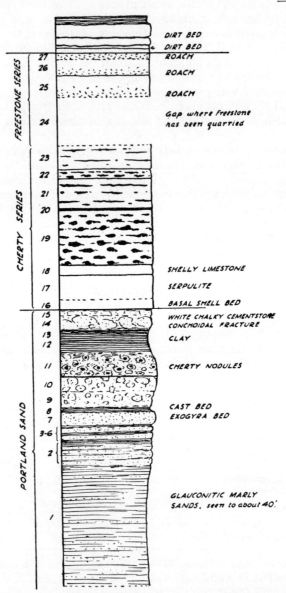

FIG. 24.—*Profile of the Portland Beds at Burning Cliff, west of Holworth House, Ringstead Bay.* Scale 1 inch = 20 feet. (Reproduced from *Proc. Geol. Assoc.*, vol. xlvi, 1935, p. 324.)

CHERTY SERIES

		Ft.	In.
23.	Limestone, oolitic, with a few thin seams of chert ...	5	0
22.	Ditto, more cherty	2	0
21.	Limestone, white, with chert bands...	6	0
20.	Chert band, continuous ... ... 3in. to	1	0
19.	Chalky white limestone with large black chert nodules and broken shells, the lower part with *Serpula gordialis* ...	11	6
18.	Shelly limestone, with large *Isognomon* ; no chert ...	2	0
17.	SERPULITE : white chalky limestone, full of *Serpula gordialis*	5	0
16.	BASAL SHELL BED. Limestone full of calcitic shells, *Trigoniae*, etc., etc. [1]	2	0
	Total ...	34	6

PORTLAND SAND

		Ft.	In.
15.	Cementstone with vertical fracture	1	0
14.	Whitish cementstone with irregular splintery fracture, often spheroidal, weathering red in places	3	0
13.	Black clay	1	6
12.	Marly clay and marl, more or less hardened towards base	2	6
11.	Cementstone, sandy, nodular, the nodules with cherty centres ; the lower part very hard, projecting ... ... [Even bedding-plane]	5	0
10.	Cementstone, sandy, very hard, less nodular and cherty ; forms prominent bluff with the lower part of bed above. *Glaucolithites* (typical), *Ostrea expansa*, *Isognomon*, *Lima* casts, patches of *Serpula gordialis* and *Exogyra nana* ...	2	6
9.	Cementstone, sandy, a strong stinkstone, rubbly, less hard. *Glaucolithites*, *Trigonia incurva* casts, *Modiola autissiodorensis*, *Protocardia calcarea*, *Plicatula*	3	6
8.	Soft rubbly sandstone full of casts of *Trigoniae*	1	0
7.	*Exogyra nana* BED ; Rubbly, sandy cementstone, packed with *Exogyra nana*, also small *Glaucolithites* and clavellate *Trigoniae*	·2	6
	Total to base of *Exogyra* Bed ... 22ft. 6ins.		
1-6.	Sandy marls, soft, greenish-brown, with semi-indurated bands, seen to about	50	0

It will be seen that here the Purbeck subdivisions in both the Stone and the Sand are lost sight of, and affinities are all with the country to the west.   For instance the Freestone Series begins with Roach at the top instead of Shrimp Bed (though the Portland Screw is absent, as noted by Hudleston[2]) ; this rests on freestone (*cf*. Whit Bed of Portland) ; and finally freestone has returned at the bottom and has been quarried (*cf*. the Base Bed Freestone of Portland).

---

[1] The Basal Shell Bed can also be seen, with some of the Cherty Series and a considerable portion of the Portland Sand, dipping north at a high angle, in an old quarry at the back of South Down Farm, half a mile to the north-west.

[2] W. H. Hudleston, *Proc. Geol. Assoc.*, vol. xv, 1898, p. 302.

The Cherty Series has become chalky, and the lowest 9 ft. are without chert, as in Portland; and, most characteristic of all for the Portland section, the Basal Shell Bed has appeared.

In spite of these affinities with Portland and differences from Lulworth, the thicknesses of both the Freestone and the Cherty Series are the same as at Lulworth, as shown by the sections at Bacon Hole and Dungy Head. Thus the stratigraphical changes do not take place *pari passu* with the diminution in thickness from east to west, but independently of it and later. The diminution in thickness occurs in the three miles between Gad Cliff and Dungy Head; the stratigraphical changes occur in the next three and a half miles, between Dungy Head and Ringstead.

In the Portland Sand comparable changes have occurred. There is no sign of the massive block of Black Sandstones at the top, so conspicuous from St. Alban's Head to Dungy Head; and instead we find a few feet of whitish cementstones and clays. The latter (beds 12 and 13) give a suggestion of the Portland Clay. The *Exogyra* Bed is a typical Portland feature, although it has already begun to be developed at Gad Cliff and Dungy Head. Above it at Ringstead come hard sandy cementstones, like the West Weare Sandstones at Portland; below it are mainly soft sands, greenish or mustard-coloured (glauconitic) and marly, with subordinate cementstones (= the Black Nore Beds).

(b) POXWELL, PRESTON AND UPWEY[1]

A quarter of a mile south of Poxwell Church, on the east side of the main road near Poxwell Lodge, a quarry in work shows the highest 12 ft. of the Portland Freestone Series with the same thickness of Purbeck Beds above. *Titanites* and the usual fossils occur here.

The cementstones at the top of the Portland Sand form conspicuous scars showing through the turf all round the Poxwell and Moigns pericline, round the east end of the Sutton Poyntz pericline, at East Hill, Sutton Poyntz, and on the waterworks spur west of Preston. They were seen to a depth of 8 ft., with cast beds full of *Trigonia spp.* and other fossils (cf. Corton, below, p. 116), in excavations for cesspools in the allotments north-east of Preston in 1938. The cementstones were overlain by the Basal Shell Bed of Portland, and cherty limestones. At Chalbury Camp and in Coombe Valley the cementstones form conspicuous scars again, with an oyster bed about 2 ft. thick. The road cutting at Green Hill, where the beds are dragged down into the Ridgeway fault and increase in dip rapidly from 50° at the top end to vertical at the lower end, exposes 18 ft. of greenish sands and marls with irregular bands of cementstone nodules, overlain by 18 ft. of cementstone and marl. The lowest bed of cementstone (6 ft.)

---

[1] For localities see folding map, Pl. xix.

forms a projecting bluff; and the lower and middle parts are an oyster bed—a solid mass of *Exogyra nana*, with *Serpulae* and occasional large shells. The old workings on the north-east side of Chalbury Camp, which expose the cementstone with the *Exogyra* Bed in the middle, likewise give indications of marly strata above and of sandy below.

Two large quarries on the south-west side of Chalbury Camp show a complete section of the Portland Stone with the Basal Shell Bed resting upon the Portland Clay as at the north end of Portland Island.

QUARRIES SOUTH OF CHALBURY CAMP

PURBECK BEDS

			Ft.	In.
16.	Shale and slatt, about...		4	0
15.	Tufa, as at Poxwell, with large trees *in situ*, up to ...		6	0
14.	Dirt Bed, black	1 in. to		2
13.	Tufa	6 in. to	1	6
12.	Dirt Bed, black	1 in. to		2
11.	Laminated white limestone ...		1	4

PORTLAND STONE
FREESTONE SERIES

		Ft.	In.
10.	Shelly limestone, hard, white, full of *Chlamys lamellosa*, *Isognomon*, etc. etc....	3	0
9.	Band of large white chert nodules ...		6
8.	White limestone	10	6
7.	Band of continuous black chert nodules, average about ...	1	0
6.	White limestone in four courses	9	0
	Total ...	24	0

CHERTY SERIES

		Ft.	In.
5.	Hard white limestone with scattered cherts	4	0
4.	Hard white limestone full of big black chert nodules ...	12	0
3.	Hard limestone, a little chert in upper part : large ammonites (*Behemoth* ?), *Isognomon*, casts of *Protocardia dissimilis*, *Serpulae*	8	6
2.	Basal Shell Bed, packed with calcitic fossils : *Trigoniae* ; *Protocardia*, *Isognomon*, *Mytilus*, *Ch. lamellosa*, *Lima*, large ammonite (*Behemoth* ?), *Serpula gordialis*, etc. ...	2	6
	Total ...	27	0

PORTLAND SAND

		Ft.	In.
1.	Greenish clay, becoming sandy downwards (Portland Clay) seen to ...	6	0

West of Bincombe, the *Exogyra* Bed in its thick band of hard cementstone crops out again as a scar, near the top of the escarpment round the head of the coomb on the east side of the ' neck ' of The Knoll.   On the south face of The Knoll there are large masses of the same bed at different levels, all apparently more or less slipped, and a small quarry on the east side shows greatly disturbed beds, a jumble from all levels, but mostly sandy, probably the debris of an ancient landslip.

At Upwey the great quarry in the Portland Stone has deteriorated since it was described by Woodward[1] and Strahan.[2] Beneath thick Purbeck beds, 19 ft. of Portland Stone can still be seen, the whole of it belonging to the Freestone Series, although there are more bands of chert than usual.

(c) UPWEY TO CORTON AND PORTISHAM

The most westerly stretch of the outcrop forms a straight, narrow ridge four miles in length, from the defile at Upwey to Portisham. The dip is steeply to the north in the northern limb of the Weymouth Anticline.

The thick band of hard cementstone, which here marks about the upper-middle part of the Portland Sand, crops out intermittently as a scar low down along the escarpment on the south side of Friar Waddon Hill. It can be followed to Portisham, and the scar formed by it is an easily recognized feature when the ridge is viewed from the south at a distance, from the road or the railway to Abbotsbury. The Portland Stone here again gives rise only to rounded grassy slopes, being apparently more readily soluble, in spite of its massive Cherty Beds and its property of forming angular precipices where cut by the sea. Beside the track over the hill above Friar Waddon Dairy House a lime-kiln quarry exposes about 8 ft. of white chalky limestone (Freestone Series) overlying 12 ft. of the Cherty Series, white chalky limestone with some calcitic shells and many enormous nodules of black chert, many of them two and three feet long. Better sections, however, can be seen farther on.

West of the tumuli on this hill the ridge becomes lower and narrower, and at Corton the road to Corton Farm and Church traverses it by a deep cutting with vertical sides. At first sight the solid rock would be taken for Portland Stone, but the cutting lies entirely in Portland Sand, and the ' scar ' cementstone can be traced into it from both sides. There is here no definite *Exogyra* Bed, but *Exogyrae* are scattered through about 25 ft. of rock, most of which is very hard and much of it serpulitic; but there is no chert. Large ammonites with the round whorl-sections and regular biplicate ribbing of *Glaucolithites* and perhaps also *Behemoth* abound here through at least 30 ft. of rock, and may be seen protruding from the ' scars ' at other places.[3] Below are rubbly mustard-coloured sands as at Green Hill road-cutting.

---

[1] H. B. Woodward, ' Jurassic Rocks of Britain,' vol. v, *Mem. Geol. Surv.*, 1895, p. 195.

[2] A. Strahan, *Purbeck Memoir*, 1898, p. 108.

[3] For detailed description of Corton cutting see W. J. Arkell, *op. cit.*, 1935, pp. 330-1.

Above Coryates there is a second road-cutting. A sand-pit east of the defile exposes about 12 ft. of mustard-coloured glauconitic sands, and discontinuous sections in the bluff on the opposite side show that the sands must be at least 60-70 ft. thick. They lie wholly below the cementstones of the Corton cutting, which here form the crest of the ridge. At Friar Waddon boring, a short distance to the north-east, 80½ ft. of the core were assigned to Portland Sand,[1] and probably about 10 ft. of the supposed basal bed of the Portland Stone should be transferred to the Sand also.

Between Corton and Coryates the Portland Stone retreats off the main ridge for a distance of three quarters of a mile, and its place is occupied by the resistant cementstones of the Portland Sand, which give rise to a remarkably sharp crest.

Beside the track over the hill above Waddon a quarry and an old lime-kiln close together provide a nearly complete section of the Portland Stone. The larger quarry shows beds 1 to 8 and the smaller beds 6 to 10.

WADDON QUARRY AND LIMEKILN

PURBECK BEDS

11. Tufa, in pillowy masses, has been worked two or three feet above the old limekiln, and still protrudes

PORTLAND BEDS

FREESTONE SERIES

	Ft.	In.
10. { Gap　...　...　...　...　...　...　... About	2	6
{ White Chalky limestone　...　...　...　...　...	1	0
9. Line of chert nodules ...　...　...　...　...　...		4
8. White chalky limestone with *Titanites*　...　...　...	3	0
7. Line of chert nodules　...　...　...　...　...		6
6. White chalky limestone, few fossils ; some casts of *Proto-cardia, Natica*, etc. ...　...　...　...　...　...　...	7	0
Total about　...　15ft.0ins.		

CHERTY SERIES

	Ft.	In.
5. Hard white cherty limestone full of enormous black chert nodules 2 and 3 ft. long and more. Some shells　...	10	0
4. Marly parting (chalky)　...　...　...　...　...		3
3. Hard white chalky limestone with scattered chert nodules (common), some fairly large　...　...　...　...	8	6
2. Yellow marly limestone and marl ...　...　...　...		9
1. Serpulite : hard white limestone full of *S. gordialis*, and a few chert nodules ; *Kerberites* (?). Seen to　...　...	4	0
Total seen　...　23ft.6ins.		

---

[1] W. Edwards and J. Pringle, ' Wells and Springs of Dorset,' *Mem. Geol. Surv.*, 1926, pp. **75-6**.

This section affords evidence that the whole Portland Stone is still thinning westwards. The correspondence, bed for bed, with Chalbury Camp and Holworth House is still close, but both divisions are thinner. The Freestone Series has shrunk to 15 ft.; the Cherty Series is a little thinner than at Chalbury, and about 9 ft. thinner than at Holworth. On the other hand the Portland Sand, which crops out with cementstone scars and an *Exogyra* Bed in the bluff overlooking Portisham, still maintains a thickness of at least 60 ft., probably nearer 80 feet.

Portisham Quarries are now derelict and show only the highest 12 ft. of the Freestone Series. The section now visible, so far as it goes, is identical with that at Waddon.

V. The Isle of Portland

(a) GENERAL

The Portland Stone of Portland forms a tilted tableland sloping gently and evenly southward with an average dip of $1\frac{1}{2}°$. At the north end, near Verne Fort, the maximum height is 495 ft. O.D., at the south end or Bill the stone runs down gradually into the sea (Pl. XVII, B).

The island is a fragment of the southern limb of the Weymouth Anticline, which has become almost detached from the mainland by the erosion of the soft Kimmeridge Clay that floors Portland Roads and the isthmus under Chesil Bank. Like the upland plateau of southern Purbeck, around St. Alban's Head, it has suffered little tectonic disturbance as compared with the northern limb of the anticline, and to this is due the unshattered condition of the stone. Nevertheless the plateau is riven by a system of joints forming a roughly rectangular pattern, the largest ones running N.N.E.-S.S.W., smaller ones E.-W., the average interval between them being 60-70 ft. The presence of the joints, which become enlarged by solution to a width of sometimes 2 ft., greatly facilitates the action of landslips. The wreckage of landslips of all ages encumbers the slopes around the north and east sides of the island and produces a natural barrier against further encroachments of the sea.[1]

(b). PORTLAND BUILDING STONE AND QUARRYING INDUSTRY

Before the 17th century Portland Stone was little used except locally, though some is said to have been exported to Exeter and London as early as the 14th century. The earliest known building constructed of it is Rufus Castle, Portland, built about 1080 A.D. Inigo Jones selected it for the Banqueting Hall at Whitehall (1619-22), and from this dates its fame as a building stone in London. Sir Christopher Wren introduced it on a large scale for

---

[1] For particulars of notable landslips and references to their, in some cases, interesting history see A. Strahan, *Purbeck Memoir*, 1898, pp. 112, 114.

rebuilding the London churches after the Great Fire of 1666, and nearly a million cubic feet are said to have been used in St. Paul's Cathedral. Since that time it has been chosen for large public buildings all over the country, and especially in London, where its resistance to the corroding agencies of the smoke-polluted atmosphere renders it particularly valuable. Older buildings constructed of it are the British Museum (1753), Somerset House (1776-92), the General Post Office (1829), the Horseguards and most of the Government offices of Whitehall. The waste stone (roach and cherty beds) were used for Portland breakwater, one of the largest undertakings of its kind in the world, completed by convict labour in 1864.

Among the modern buildings constructed of Portland Stone are Imperial Chemical House, Millbank, Britannic House, Bush House, Selfridge's, London County Hall, the Masonic Memorial Hall, the Bank of England, and the head offices of the Westminster, Midland, and Lloyds Banks. In the provinces conspicuous examples of its use are Leeds Civic Hall, Southampton Municipal Buildings and Manchester Reference Library.

The total output from Portland Island in 1936 was 57,046 tons, and the average since 1899 has been 74,714 tons. Peak years were 1904 with 115,361 tons, during the building of the War Office and other Government buildings, and 1930 with 103,482 tons, in a period of 8 years when much stone was supplied for war memorials and war grave headstones.[1]

When a block of stone is obtained it is given several quarry marks, one of which shows its cubic capacity in feet. Some of these marks are very ancient. The symbols for numerals suggest Roman influence, but it is noteworthy that they are forms suited to cutting with an axe, and so may have been adopted, on Roman lines, at almost any period. Wren used a mark called the wine-glass mark, shaped like a Y with a cross-bar at the bottom. Some of Wren's stones, bearing this mark, can still be seen near the East Weares.[2]

The weathering properties of Portland Stone have been investigated at the Building Research Station. In smoke-polluted atmospheres buildings of Portland Stone acquire a characteristic black and white appearance. The side exposed to the prevailing wind is eroded and washed clean by the rain, and the shell-fragments stand out in low relief. The sheltered side is blackened by a coating of soot, under which a hard skin of calcium sulphate develops. For a time the skin acts as a protection, but eventually it flakes off, carrying a layer of stone with it, and thus disintegration is accelerated. Portland Stone resists this disruptive action

---

[1] Statistics supplied by Bath and Portland Stone Firms Ltd. For statistics from 1840 to 1882 see R. Damon, *Geology of Weymouth*, 2nd ed., 1884, p. 94, London.

[2] F. H. Edmunds and R. J. Schaffer, ' Portland Stone : its Geology and Properties as a Building Stone,' *Proc. Geol. Assoc.*, vol. xliii, 1932, p. 236.

better than most, but it is not immune, and some blocks react more
readily than others.   It was found that by testing good and bad
pieces of stone from old buildings and from the quarries it was
possible to imitate and therefore to forecast the action of the

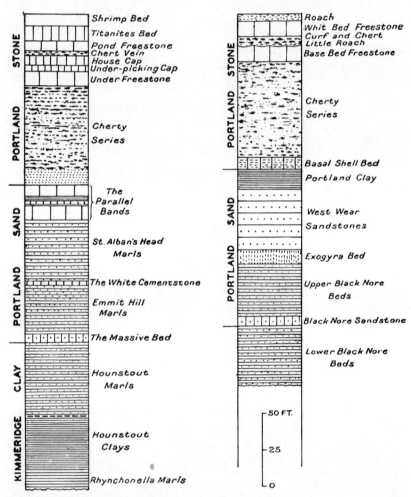

Fɪɢ. 25.—*Comparative sections of the Portland Beds and subjacent strata.*
(After W. J. Arkell, ' *The Jurassic System in Great Britain,*' 1933, p. 495.)

weather.   The test used was the crystallization test.   This
consisted in repeatedly soaking specimens in a 14% solution of
sodium sulphate deca-hydrate and drying them in an oven.
Disintegration took place much more rapidly in some samples

than in others. The differences in behaviour were found to be due to the density or porosity of the oolite grains, which could be measured by a capillary method. On the whole the Whit Bed passed the tests better than the Base Bed, but not invariably.[1]

The crushing strength of Portland Stone is over 200 tons per square foot. In composition it is 95 per cent calcium carbonate.[2]

(c) STRATIGRAPHY AND PALAEONTOLOGY

In a general way the three chief subdivisions of the mainland can be recognized clearly enough in Portland, but detailed correlation has not been established. The following is a résumé of the succession.

PORTLAND SAND

The Portland Sand can only be seen at West Weare Cliffs and Black Nore, where there is a good but somewhat inaccessible exposure. At the north end of the island under Verne Fort temporary exposures have proved 10-20 ft. of clay, the Portland Clay, below the Basal Shell Bed of the Cherty Series,[3] but this feature dies out rapidly southwards. At West Weare Cliffs and Black Nore the highest 35-60 ft. of the Portland Sand consists mainly of muddy-coloured marly sandstones or sandy cement-stones like those seen at Corton cutting, called the West Weare Sandstones. Fallen blocks on the screes below yield fragmentary *Glaucolithites gorei*. At the base is 6-8 ft. of stiff marl packed with *Exogyra nana* (J. Sowerby), which probably correlates with the *Exogyra* Bed in a similar position in Purbeck (Gad Cliff, bed 10) and north of Weymouth (Holworth House, bed 7, and Green Hill).

Below the *Exogyra* Bed are exposed some 80 ft. of black sandy marls, the Black Nore Beds. A 6-foot sandstone in the middle of the visible part may represent the Massive Bed, but almost nothing is known of these beds palaeontologically.[4]

PORTLAND STONE

CHERTY SERIES

The Cherty Series is about 60-70 ft. thick and yields no stone of economic value. It forms imposing cliffs at Black Nore and West Weare Cliffs on the north-west side of the island. Its

[1] R. J. Schaffer, in Edmunds and Schaffer, *op. cit.*, 1932. Fuller treatment with bibliography in R. J. Schaffer, ' The Weathering of Natural Building Stones,' *Special Report No. 18, Building Research, Dept. Sci. & Indust. Research*, H. M. Stationery Office. 1932.

[2] The Department of Scientific and Industrial Research will shortly publish a full account of experiments on the strength and economic properties of Portland Stone, carried out at the Building Research Station.

[3] R. Damon, *Geology of Weymouth*, 2nd edit., 1884, p. 82, London ; A. Strahan, *Purbeck Memoir*, 1898, pp. 119, 121.

[4] For further particulars see W. J. Arkell, *Jurassic System in Great Britain*, 1933, pp. 482-7. Oxford.

principal feature of interest is the Basal Shell Bed (7-8 ft. thick), of which the rich and well-preserved fauna, mainly lamellibranchs, has formed the subject of a special monograph.[1]

FREESTONE SERIES

The details of the Freestone Series differ in different parts of the island but the following succession may be regarded as typical. It is taken from the large Kingbarrow Quarries.

		Ft.	Ins.
6. ROACH. Creamy oolitic limestone, honeycombed by empty moulds of marine fossils, especially *Trigonia gibbosa, Chlamys lamellosa, Protocardia dissimilis,* and other lamellibranchs ; and *Aptyxiella portlandica* (the ' Portland Screw ')		3	0
5. WHIT BED. The best freestone, sometimes with a layer of chert 3 ft. from the base...		8	0
4. FLINTY BED. Limestone full of chert, *Titanites*		2	0
3. CURF. Soft, chalky limestone, seldom oolitic, with much chert	0 to	4	0
2. BASE BED ROACH. Shelly oolitic limestone with numerous casts of *Trigonia, Pecten,* etc.	0 to	2	0
1. BASE BED or BEST BED. Good freestone with few shells ; soft, white, oolitic	6ft. to	8	0
Total usually about ...		25	0

---

[1] L. R. Cox, *Proc. Dorset Nat. Field Club,* vol. xlvi, 1925, pp. 113-172.

CHAPTER VII

PURBECKIAN STAGE: PURBECK BEDS

I. GENERAL

(a) THICKNESS AND GENERAL CHARACTERISTICS

The Purbeck Beds are 396 ft. thick at Durlston Bay, Swanage, and diminish westwards to 290 ft. at Worbarrow. Farther west they thin rapidly in the Lulworth district and then become somewhat thicker again at Ridgeway (189 ft.).

The formation comprises exceptionally varied freshwater and terrestrial strata, with estuarine and marine intercalations. Fossils are numerous and of great variety and interest. There are ostracod beds, pond-snail beds, mussel beds, oyster beds, forest beds, fish beds, insect beds, an isopod bed, and a mammal bed. Lithologically much of the formation resembles the Rhaetic Beds, consisting of thinly laminated limestones, mudstones and shales. with layers of fibrous carbonate of lime ('beef'), gypsum, and slabby calcareous mudstone (' slatt '), sometimes with mammillated surfaces and arborescent markings in the interior, reminiscent of Cotham Marble.

Most famous of all are the ' dirt beds,' and tufas with silicified trees, described below, in section c.

The Broken Beds near the base of the formation, which for many years were interpreted as due to collapse of decayed vegetation in Lower Purbeck times, are now believed to be mainly of tectonic origin and to have been brecciated in the Tertiary folding, although various views are still held by geologists who have seen them. They are described with the tectonics of the area, in Chapter XIII.

Near the middle of the formation there is a white limestone with black chert nodules, both the chert and the matrix containing perfectly preserved thin-shelled freshwater gastropods such as

Valvata and *Physa*. A few feet higher is the Cinder Bed, a mass of oysters, *Ostrea distorta* J. de C. Sowerby, with some other purely marine molluscs and, occasionally, *Hemicidaris purbeckensis* Forbes. These two beds are constant throughout the entire Dorset outcrop, from Swanage to the Weymouth district. There are also some black cherts, mainly in tabular form, in the Upper and Lower Purbeck in various places. Some have been found to consist largely of spicules of *Spongilla* and some of stems of *Chara*.

Ooliths occur sparsely in some of the beds, but there is no true oolite in the Purbeck Beds. The building stones are a compact grey limestone largely detrital in origin.

The well-known ' Marble ' is a greenish or reddish limestone crowded with shells of the freshwater pond-snail *Viviparus* (formerly called *Paludina*).

(b) STRATIGRAPHY

In the absence of ammonites, ostracods have been used with success to divide the formation into three broad zones, which correspond with the Lower, Middle, and Upper Purbeck, as follows :—

	OSTRACOD ZONES	STRATA IN DURLSTON BAY	THICKNESS	
UPPER	*Cypridea punctata* and *C. ventrosa*	*Viviparus* Clays	11 ft.+?	
		Marble Beds & Ostracod Shales	46 ft.	72 ft. +?
		Unio Beds	5 ft.	
		Broken Shell Limestone	10 ft.	
MIDDLE	Subzone of *Cypridea fasciculata* and *Metacypris forbesii*	Chief Beef Beds	30 ft.	
		Corbula Beds	34 ft.	
		Upper Building Stones	50 ft.	157 ft.
		Cinder Bed	8½ ft.	
		Lower Building Stones	34 ft.	
		Mammal Bed	1 ft.	
LOWER	*Cypris purbeckensis* and *Candona ansata*	Marls with Gypsum and Insect Beds	135 ft.	
		Broken Beds and *Cypris* Freestones	15 ft.	169 ft.
		Caps and Dirt Beds	19 ft.	

The Lower Purbeck Beds are strictly conformable with the Portland Stone, but in spite of the perfect parallelism there is always an abrupt lithological and palaeontological change.

The Upper Purbeck Beds pass up into the Wealden, and the vertebrate and freshwater invertebrate faunas of the two formations are almost inseparable. The vertebrate faunas of both are essentially Jurassic, and so are the floras and the invertebrate marine fauna of the Purbeck. Nevertheless the division between the Jurassic and Cretaceous systems has to be drawn arbitrarily between the Purbeck and the Wealden Beds, on grounds which lie outside the scope of this memoir.[1]

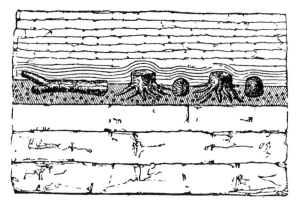

Fig. 26.—*The Great Dirt Bed of the Isle of Portland, showing boles of trees with roots, cycads, and pebbles of limestone.* The Dirt Bed rests on the tufaceous Top Cap limestone and is overlain by the Aish. (After Buckland and De la Beche, *Trans. Geol. Soc.,* ser. 2, vol. iv, 1836, p. 13).

(c) SOILS, FOREST BEDS, AND TUFA

Types of rock peculiar to the Purbeck Beds are the thick tabular or botryoidal masses of tufa, and the fossil soils, with tree stumps in position of growth. These occur mainly near the bottom of the formation. The fossil soils are called Dirt Beds. They consist of thin seams ($\frac{1}{2}$—6 ins.; at Lulworth up to 1 ft.) of a dark brown to black carbonaceous, earthy substance, often containing numerous more or less subangular stones (limestone), such as litter an arable field with a limestone subsoil (Pl. IX). The stones are generally decayed at the surface and have no distinctive characters or fossils, but they have long been said to be in part Portland Stone.[2] Since the Purbeck Beds at all the known exposures are strictly conformable with the Portland Stone, the origin of these stones needs investigating. It often appears that they did not originate from the rock immediately below.

The Dirt Beds are generally believed to be ' seat-earths,' since they contain remains of roots of trees. Above each layer there follows a continuous or impersistent band of calcareous tufa, in which the stumps and fallen trunks of trees, and cycads, are

---

[1] For full discussion of this question, see W. J. Arkell, *Jurassic System in Great Britain,* 1933, chapter xvii. Oxford.

[2] ' Mr. Webster ascertained [them] to be from the lower part of the Portland series '—W. Buckland and H. T. De la Beche, *Trans. Geol. Soc.,* Ser. 2, vol. iv, 1836, p. 13.

embedded (Pl. IX). The tufa generally wraps round the boles and trunks of the trees as a thick sheath, and the upper surface is extremely irregular. Individual masses of tufa, usually containing a cycad or the remains of part of a conifer, are known as Burrs. Occasionally they are gigantic, and have been mistaken by the quarrymen for fossil elephants. One lying in an abandoned quarry at Portisham is 14 feet long. The deposition of the tufa around the plant-remains may have been due to freshwater algae.

The wood within the burrs has generally been silicified, and the structure is beautifully preserved in chalcedony. The tree trunks appear to have been all broken off at about 3 ft. above the ground, only exceptionally as high as 5 or 6 ft., and the wood was much decayed, as well as broken off, before being encased in the tufa envelope. This suggests that the trunks were submerged to that depth in water. The tufa envelope sometimes domes over the stumps but often there is a cup-shaped depression in the centre, marking the position of the stump within the mass.

Fallen trunks have been found as much as 23½ ft. in length, and 20 ft. from the roots to the first bifurcation. The largest seen by Fitton was 2 ft. 10 ins. in diameter.

(d) PALAEONTOLOGY

First place in importance and interest among the Purbeck fossils is taken by the small mammalian jaws and other bones found in the Mammal Bed at the base of the Middle Purbeck Beds. The Mammal Bed is a thin Dirt Bed, suggesting an ancient soil and filling inequalities in the hard marl below. Except for the few mammalian remains found in the Stonesfield Slate and Rhaetic Beds, these are unique in Europe, but there is a comparable assemblage entombed in somewhat similar strata in the Morrison formation of North America. Nearly all the specimens were obtained in a special excavation which struck a rich ' pocket ' (*see below*, p. 135).

The collections, originally described by Owen, have been revised by G. G. Simpson in the light of the American and other material.[1] He rejects the idea that these early mammals belonged to the marsupials. He distributes the nineteen species among thirteen genera and four orders, Multituberculata, Triconodonta, Symmetrodonta, and Pantotheria, and he regards these as derived independently from the Cynodont reptiles. The last two orders may, he thinks, have diverged from the same stock as all the living mammals, but they branched off long before the marsupials and placentals became differentiated.

All the Purbeck mammals were small, but otherwise the four orders differed markedly from one another (Fig. 27). The

---

[1] G. G. Simpson, *Catal. Mesozoic Mammalia Brit. Mus.*, 1928, where full references to the literature are collected. See also G. G. Simpson, ' Palaeobiology of Jurassic Mammals,' *Palaeobiologica*, vol. v, 1933, p. 127.

Multituberculata, the largest of the orders, to which *Plagiaulax becklesii* Falconer belongs, with five other Swanage species, had a longer duration than any other mammalian order, ranging from the Upper Trias to the end of the Paleocene. They possessed highly specialized teeth, unlike those of any other mammals, but showing rodent-like adaptive features. Their food was probably the fruit and bark of cycads and conifers. The skeleton suggests arboreal habits.

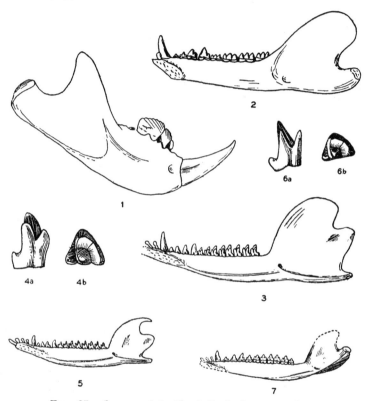

Fig. 27.—*Jaws and teeth of Purbeck mammals.*
1. Jaw of *Plagiaulax* ($\times$ 2); 2. Jaw of *Triconodon* ($\times$ 1$\frac{1}{4}$);
3. Jaw of *Phascolestes* ($\times$ 2); 4a, b. Tooth of *Phascolestes* ($\times$ 10);
5. Jaw of *Amblotherium* ($\times$ 2); 6a, b. Tooth of *Amblotherium* ($\times$ 10);
7. Jaw of *Spalacotherium* ($\times$ 1$\frac{1}{4}$). (After Simpson).

The Pantotheres, no larger than rats, were also possibly arboreal in habit and are thought to have been mainly insectivorous. To this order belonged *Amblotherium* and five other Purbeck genera.

The Triconodonts, about the size of a cat, and the smaller Symmetrodonts, on the other hand, were probably Carnivores. To these belong the well-known Purbeck *Triconodon mordax* Owen, *Trioracodon ferox* (Owen), *Spalacotherium* and *Peralestes*

A few of these species have been found also in the Wealden Beds of Sussex. Simpson states that none is related to Cretaceous or more recent stocks, but that some of the orders are represented in the Stonesfield Slate (Middle Jurassic).

Among the Reptilia the most important are the crocodiles found in the Mammal Bed and at other horizons. Most of them belong to the Goniopholidae, a family akin to the marsh-loving forms of the present day, and the majority, belonging to the genera *Nannosuchus*, *Theriasuchus* and *Oweniasuchus*, are dwarfed; some were only 18 inches in length when full grown. *Goniopholis,* represented by *G. crassidens* Owen, the ' Swanage crocodile,' is full-sized. The Teleosauridae are represented by *Petrosuchus*.[1] There are also the Dinosaurs *Echinodon becklesi* Owen, *Iguanodon hoggii* Owen, and *Nuthetes destructor* Owen.[2] Plates and bones of turtles (Chelonia) are often to be obtained from the quarrymen : they include *Tretosternum*, *Pleurosternum* and an ancestral form of the Cretaceous-Recent *Chelone*.

Fish-remains are abundant in the Building Stones. They have been described by Smith Woodward, who wrote ' So far as known, the fishes of the Wealden and Purbeck formations are essentially Jurassic, and not mingled with any typically Cretaceous forms. Most of them are, indeed, the specialised and evidently final representatives of the Jurassic families to which they belong, and very few can be regarded as possible ancestors of fishes which followed in Cretaceous and later times.'[3] The most striking of the fish-remains to be obtained from the quarrymen are fin-spines of sharks (' ichthyodorulites ') of the genus *Asteracanthus*, but there are at least 24 species of fishes, belonging to 17 genera (mainly ganoids), found at Swanage alone.[4]

Insects are represented by many wings and elytra, found chiefly in the shales of the Lower Purbeck, ' generally detached, rarely collected together in masses, lying in different portions of the stone, and not in particular layers. They are remarkable for their beautiful state of preservation, the elytra usually retaining their elytrine or chitine, and the wings their most delicate nervures and colouring. . . . They are occasionally mingled with *Corbula*, *Cyclas*, and ostracods.'[5] As many as 60 or 70 elytra and several wings and bodies have been counted on a single small slab. They appear to have been drifted from a distance, for whole insects are very rare. The remains include beetles, plant-bugs, cockroaches,

---

[1] A. S. Woodward, ' The History of Fossil Crocodiles,' *Proc. Geol. Assoc.*, vol. ix, 1886, p. 318.

[2] W. E. Swinton, *The Dinosaurs*, 1934, pp. 212, 214, London ; footprints of *Iguanodon* recorded and figured by J. B. Calkin, *Discovery*, vol. xiv, 1933, No. 157.

[3] A. S. Woodward, ' The Fossil Fishes of the English Wealden and Purbeck Formations,' 1916-19, p. 141. *Palaeontographical Soc.*

[4] See A. S. Woodward, *op. cit.*, and listed in W. J. Arkell, *Jurassic System in Great Britain*, 1933, p. 525. Oxford.

[5] P. B. Brodie, ' On the Insect Beds of the Purbeck Formation in Wiltshire and Dorsetshire,' *Quart. Journ. Geol. Soc.*, vol. x, 1854, p. 481.

grasshoppers, primitive hymenopterous saw-flies (*Pseudosirex*), dragonflies, two problematic Lepidoptera (*Cyllonium*), and two-winged flies (Diptera) of many sorts, including St. Mark's flies and daddy-long-legs, and aphides.[1] The insects and mollusca of the Purbeck Beds are all small and suggest a temperate or warm-temperate climate. They are of present day European facies.[2]

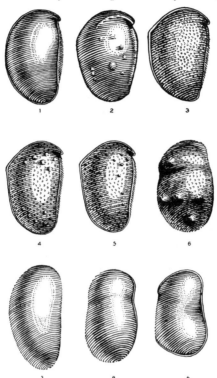

Fig. 28.—*Ostracods of the Purbeck Beds.*
1. *Langtonia setina* Anderson; 2. *Ulwellia ventrosa* (Jones); 3. *Cypridea punctata* (Forbes); 4. *Cypridea fasciculata* (Forbes); 5. *Cypridea pauci-granulata* Jones; 6. *Metacypris forbesii* Jones, var. *verrucosa* Jones; 7. *Cypris purbeckensis* Forbes; 8. *Candona bononiensis* Jones; 9. *Candona ansata* Jones.
The average length of all the above species is between 0.75 mm. and 1.0 mm. (Selected and drawn by F. W. Anderson.)

Another land Arthropod of interest is the Isopod, *Archaeoniscus brodiei* Edwards, a creature resembling and related to the wood-louse (Fig. 29, No. 21). It occurs in the Caps at Ridgeway and in the Lower and Middle Purbeck Beds in Durlston Bay.[3]

---

[1] The Purbeckian insects have been revised by A. Handlirsch, *Die Fossilen Insekten*, 1906-08, Leipzig, pt. 3, ch. 3, pp. 515 ff., where full references will be found.
[2] P. B. Brodie, *A History of the Fossil Insects of the Secondary Rocks of England*, 1845. London.
[3] P. B. Brodie, *op. cit.*, 1854, p. 480; W. J. Arkell, *Proc. Geol. Assoc.*, vol. xlv, 1934, p. 414. For a recent study of the animal see W. Haack, ' Uber einen Isopoden aus dem Serpulit,' *Jahrb. Preuss. Geol. Landesanst.*, vol. xxxix, 1919, p. 75.

The most abundant of all the Purbeck fossils, and the most important stratigraphically, are the Ostracods, minute bivalved Crustaceans, which swarmed in shallow water, whether fresh, brackish or marine. Their vertical ranges are not restricted absolutely within narrow limits, but certain species are abundant in certain zones and very rare outside them, and so they have proved useful in stratigraphy. Of 14 species recognized by T. Rupert Jones in the Purbeck Beds, he found that five occur only in the Lower Purbeck, six occur in both the Middle and Upper Purbeck, and five range from the Middle and Upper Purbeck into the Wealden. *Cypris purbeckensis* Forbes swarms in the Cypris Freestones of the Lower Purbeck, together with *Candona ansata* Jones and *C. bononiensis* Jones; *Cypridea paucigranulata* Jones, *C. fasciculata* (Forbes) and *Metacypris forbesii* Jones are especially characteristic of the Middle Purbeck and do not range above; *Cypridea punctata* (Forbes) and *C. ventrosa* Jones are the zonal forms of the Upper Purbeck, where they swarm in the Ostracod Shales, but they already make their appearance in the Middle Purbeck.[1] These zones have been found to hold also in North-West Germany, and *Cypris purbeckensis* is still the characteristic ostracod of the basal Purbeck Beds in the Jura Mountains.

A revision of the Purbeck ostracods has recently been carried out by F. W. Anderson on the much better preserved material obtained in deep borings for oil at Portsdown and in the Weald.[2] He separates *Cypridea ventrosa* in a new genus *Ulwellia*, on the ground that the right valve is larger than the left, the opposite of *Cypridea*. A smooth form very abundant in the uppermost Purbeck, which may be Dunker's *Cypris laevigata*, he assigns to a new genus and species, *Langtonia setina*. Mr. Anderson has kindly supplied the drawings of Purbeck and Wealden ostracods which illustrate this memoir (Figs. 28, 34).

The mollusca (Fig. 29) are mainly freshwater forms and are mainly small, indicative of a warm-temperate climate, like the insects. Some species are extremely abundant and locally become rock formers. Among freshwater gastropods *Viviparus inflatus* (Sandberger) and *V. cariniferus* (J. de C. Sowerby) are the commonest, their shells massed together forming the Purbeck Marble; they also abound in the Cherty Freshwater Beds in the Middle Purbeck. *Hydrobia chopardiana* (de Loriol) is sometimes almost as common in the Corbula Beds, and *Valvata helicoides* (de Loriol) in the Cherty Freshwater Beds (Middle Purbeck). In

---

[1] T. Rupert Jones, ' On the Ostracoda of the Purbeck Formation, with Notes on the Wealden Species,' *Quart. Journ. Geol. Soc.*, vol. xli, 1885, p. 311 (figures of the zonal forms reproduced in W. J. Arkell, *Jurassic System*, 1933, pl. xli). For further work see F. Chapman, *Proc. Geol. Assoc.*, vol. xv, 1896, p. 96 ; *ibid.*, vol. xvi, 1900, p. 58 ; and *ibid.*, vol. xix, 1906, p. 283 ; E. A. Merrett, *Geol. Mag.*, vol. lxi, 1924, p. 233 ; F. W. Anderson, *Rept. Brit. Assoc.* for 1931, p. 379.

[2] F. W. Anderson, ' Wealden and Purbeck Ostracods,' *Ann. and Mag. Nat. Hist.*, ser. xi, vol. iii, 1939, p. 291. *See also* P. C. S. Bradley, *ibid.*, vol. viii, 1941, p. 1.

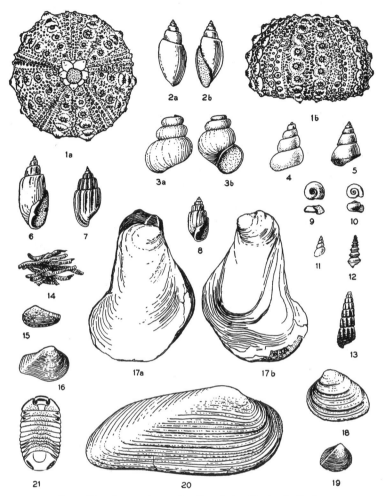

Fig. 29.—*Invertebrate fossils of the Purbeck Beds.*

1a, b. *Hemicidaris purbeckensis* Forbes (after de Loriol); 2a, b. *Physa bristovii* (Forbes MS.) Phillips, Cherty Freshwater Beds, Poxwell cutting; 3a, b. *Viviparus inflatus* (Sandberger); 4. *Viviparus cariniferus* (J. de C. Sowerby), cast; 5. *Viviparus subangulatus* (Roemer); 6. *Ptychostylus philippii* (Dunker); 7. *Ptychostylus harpaeformis* (Koch and Dunker); 8, *Ptychostylus*, intermediate form; 9. *Planorbis fisheri* Arkell; 10. *Valvata helicoides* (Forbes MS.) de Loriol; 11. *Hydrobia chopardiana* (de Loriol); 12. *Promathildia microbinaria* Arkell; 13. *Pachychilus manselli* (de Loriol); 14. *Serpula coacervata* Blumenbach (after Dunker); 15. *Corbula durlstonensis* Maillard; 16. *Corbula alata* J. de C. Sowerby; 17a, b. *Ostrea distorta* J. de C. Sowerby, Cinder Bed, Durlston Bay, holotype; 18. *Neomiodon medium* (J. de C. Sowerby); 19. *Protocardia purbeckensis* (de Loriol); 20. *Unio porrectus* J. de C. Sowerby; 21. *Archaeoniscus brodiei* Milne-Edwards (restoration after Haack). (Figs. 9, 10 and 11 are twice natural size.)

the cherty beds also occur other interesting pond-snails, such as *Planorbis fisheri* Arkell and *Viviparus subangulatus* (Roemer), *Physa bristovii* Phillips and *Ptychostylus harpaeformis* (Koch and Dunker). In the Corbula Beds at a certain level the marine gastropods *Pachychilus manselli* (de Loriol) and *Promathildia microbinaria* abound, and they are associated with *Hydrobia chopardiana* (de Loriol) which lived in marine or brackish water. The commonest freshwater mussels are several species of "*Cyrena*" (*Neomiodon*) and "*Cyclas*" throughout all subdivisions. *Unio spp.* abound chiefly in the Upper Purbeck and *Corbula spp.* in the Corbula Beds (Middle Purbeck). Some beds of the Middle Purbeck also contain marine genera such as *Pecten, Modiola, Mytilus, Trigonia, Pinna, Arca,* and *Protocardia,* but these are for the most part rare, except the little *Protocardia purbeckensis* (de Loriol) which is common in the Corbula Beds. The Cinder Bed is made up of a mass of the oyster, *Ostrea distorta* J. de C. Sowerby, which re-appears in the Wealden Shales in Sussex and the Isle of Wight. In the middle of the Cinder Bed is a band almost entirely composed of flattened *Protocardia,* and it is in this band that *Trigonia* is found.[1]

Among Annelids, *Serpula coacervata* Blumenbach is important (Fig. 29), for it is the species which builds the Serpulite of North-West Germany and it occurs in the Middle Purbeck Beds of Dorset, which are presumably of the same age.[2] It is not to be confused with *S. gordialis* which is so common in the Cherty Series of the Portland Stone.

The only Purbeckian Echinoderm (Fig. 29) is *Hemicidaris purbeckensis* Forbes, which is indistinguishable from specimens found in the 'Portlandien inférieur' (Upper Kimmeridgian) of the Boulonnais.[3] In England it is confined to the Cinder Bed of Durlston Bay, where it is usually very rare, but an extraordinary 'patch' was found by Prof. H. L. Hawkins, containing parts of 35 tests.[4]

---

[1] Figures of Dorset Purbeck mollusca will be found in W. H. Fitton, *Trans. Geol. Soc.,* Ser. 2, vol. iv, 1836, pl. xxi-ii; P. de Loriol and S. A. Jaccard, *Mém. Soc. phys. H.N. Genève,* vol. xviii, 1866, p. 63; C. L. F. Sandberger, *Die Land- u. Süsswasser Conchylien der Vorwelt,* 1870-75, Wiesbaden; G. Maillard, ' Monographie des Invertébrés du Purbeckien du Jura,' *Mém. Soc. pal. Suisse,* vol. xi, 1884, and Suppl., 1886; W. Koert, ' Geol. u. pal. Untersuchung der Grenzschichten zw. Jura u. Kreide auf der Südwestseite des Selter,' *Inaug. Dissert. Göttingen,* 1898. See also W. B. R. H. Dunker, *Monographie der Norddeutschen Wealdenbildungen,* 1846, Braunschweig; and C. E. F. Struckmann, *Die Wealdenbildungen der Umgegend von Hannover,* 1880, Hannover; W. J. Arkell, ' The gastropods of the Purbeck Beds,' *Quart. Journ. Geol. Soc.,* vol. xcvii, 1941, p. 79.

[2] W. Koert, *op. cit.,* 1898, p. 53.

[3] P. de Loriol, ' Mon. pal. et. géol. de l'étage portlandien des environs de Boulogne-sur-Mer,' *Mém Soc. Phys. et Hist. nat. Genève,* vol. xix, 1866, p. 122, pl. xi, figs. 13-15.

[4] H. L. Hawkins, *Quart. Journ. Geol. Soc.,* vol. lxxxi, 1925, p. cxxviii.

Some chert nodules in the Purbeck Beds are largely composed of spicules of *Spongilla purbeckensis* Young, the only known British Jurassic Monactinellid sponge.[1]

Plant remains are of great general interest, as section (c), dealing with their mode of occurrence, will have shown. Of the silicified trees, little else is preserved, however, but the trunks and larger branches, and the stumps with roots. They all seem to be conifers. Of more interest botanically are the cycads which are found in some of the ' burrs.' One species, *Cycadeoidea gigantea* Seward, of which the type came from Portland, measures nearly 4 ft. in length and $3\frac{1}{2}$ ft. in circumference.[2] Usually specimens vary from 9 ins. to 1 ft. in diameter and from 9 to 10 ins. in height. They are known by the quarrymen as "crows' nests."[3] Some of the Purbeck chert nodules abound in well-preserved stems of the ancient stonewort, *Chara*, a group of plants placed between the Algae and the bryophytes and going back to the Palaeozoic era.

II. The Isle of Purbeck

(a) SWANAGE STONE AND PURBECK MARBLE INDUSTRIES

Swanage Stone and Purbeck Marble have been quarried for building and interior decoration from time immemorial. The building stones, which occur in the Middle Purbeck, are quarried mainly south-west of Swanage, at Herston and Acton, but nearly the whole outcrop is riddled with old shafts and much land spoilt with tip-heaps. Formerly the stone was also tunnelled in the cliffs of Durlston Bay, but all traces of these workings have now disappeared.[4]

Swanage originated essentially as a quarrying town, and it was not until the present century that any other building material was seen in its house walls or roofs. Until after the turn of the century masons' yards and piles of stone occupied the sea frontage adjoining the quay and as far north as the mouth of the Swan Brook (Pl. X).[5] The industry was a closed guild and only direct descendants of quarrymen were admitted. Some ancient customs and privileges are still kept up. The best known is the preservation of right of way to Ower on Poole Harbour, where the stone used formerly to be shipped. Right of way there was granted by articles dated 1697-8, in which ' provision is made for a football to be carried to Ower, and a present to be made of one pound of pepper as an acknowledgment.'[6] For many years past

[1] G. J. Hinde, Mon. British Fossil Sponges, vol. i, 1893, p. 212, pl. xiii, fig. 6. *Palaeontographical Soc.*

[2] A. C. Seward, *Quart. Journ. Geol. Soc.,* vol. liii, 1897, p. 22 ; and *Plant Life Through the Ages,* 1933, p. 356. Cambridge.

[3] A. Strahan, *Purbeck Memoir,* 1898, p. 84.

[4] See engravings by T. Webster *in* Sir H. C. Englefield's *Picturesque Beauties of the Isle of Wight.* 1816, plate 29. London.

[5] Interesting engravings by T. Webster, *op. cit.,* pl. 26.

[6] J. Hutchins, *History and Antiquities of the County of Dorset,* 3rd. ed., 1861, p. 464. London.

the stone had been shipped from Swanage quay, but now it all goes by rail and road.

The method of mining the stone is by a steeply inclined shaft to a depth of a hundred feet or more, from which galleries are driven underground along the bedding, in the direction of strike. The blocks of stone are brought to the surface by a winch worked by a horse or pony. The Purbeck Marble was presumably worked in the same way (Fig. 30).

a.QuarryMouth

Fig. 30.—*Mouth of a shaft of a stone mine near Swanage.* (Reproduced from *Picturesque Rambles in the Isle of Purbeck*, 1882, by C. E. Robinson.)

The Purbeck Marble occurs as two thin bands near the top of the Upper Purbeck, composed of a mass of freshwater snail shells set in a green or red matrix. Each band never exceeds 4 ft. in thickness and is seldom more than 1 ft. thick, but it was highly valued because it will take a good polish. When exposed to the weather, however, it decays rapidly, and has suffered from damp in some of the old churches where it was used for interior work. The most effective use of Purbeck Marble is perhaps to be seen in Salisbury Cathedral, where it was used for the many slender piers as well as for the drums of the colonnade. It was set up in 1258 and is still perfectly preserved. Smaller quantities may be seen in churches and cathedrals all over the country and sometimes in Normandy also. The earliest known uses of it are in Roman Silchester and Verulamium. The last building for which it was extensively quarried was the Eldon memorial church at Kingston, in Purbeck, opened in 1880.

According to Hutchins the quarries worked in the thirteenth century were mostly at Quarr and Downshay, but there is a line of old workings, marked by mounds and depressions, at intervals along the outcrop from Swanage to Orchard, south of Church Knowle. The rock persists in an attenuated form to as far west as Stair Hole, Lulworth. About 1895 it was being quarried south-west of Orchard for making into cement.

Although the Purbeck Marble industry has died, Purbeck building stone still enjoys a steady market, and some of the thinner seams, formerly used for roofing, are now sold for crazy paving.[1]

(b)　DURLSTON BAY AND PEVERIL POINT

The coast section round Durlston Bay shows a continuous exposure of the whole formation (Pl. X and Fig. 31). The detail of the beds is so great that the following account, like that in the Purbeck Memoir (1898, p. 91), is only intended as notes for those who wish to dispense with the elaborate sections by Bristow, published in 1857 as *Vertical Sections of the Geological Survey*, Sheet 22. Anyone interested in the minute stratigraphy should consult Bristow's vertical sections.

The Lower Purbeck Beds consist mainly of a long series (about 90 ft.) of pale grey clays and shales, with, at a level of about 20-40 ft. from the bottom, some large masses of gypsum, 10-20 ft. in diameter, which were formerly collected for making plaster-of-Paris. The clays and shales contain insect-remains.[2]

The Mammal Bed, which is regarded as the basal bed of the Middle Purbeck, is a carbonaceous earthy layer or Dirt Bed (0-1 ft.), filling inequalities in the surface of the bed below. Most of the mammal remains were obtained about 1856 by S. H. Beckles, who opened a pit specially for the purpose near the top of the cliff a few yards north of Belle Vue restaurant. The bones lay in a pocket, and prolonged subsequent search produced only one more specimen. White shells of *Planorbis*, etc., abound.

The Lower Building Stones (34 ft.) include a varied series of beds of freshwater origin. In the lower part are shales and marls; the upper part includes workable beds of cream-coloured stone. Sixteen feet from the top is the " Flint Bed " or " Cherty Freshwater Bed," a conspicuous white limestone with black chert nodules, which can be traced into the Weymouth district. In it are exceptionally well preserved freshwater shells, *Viviparus*, *Valvata*, *Physa*, *Planorbis*, and *Cyrena*.

Between this series and an upper series of Building Stones is the Cinder Bed, so called from its appearance when weathered. It is made up of a mass of oyster shells, *Ostrea distorta*, but also contains the important *Hemicidaris purbeckensis* and *Serpula coacervata*. In the middle oysters give place to crushed *Protocardia*.

---

[1] For a full and scholarly account of the quarrying industry in Purbeck, see C. H. Vellacott, *Victoria County Histories,* Dorset, vol. ii, 1908, p. 330. London.

[2] For details of the insect horizons see O. Fisher, ' On the Purbeck Strata of Dorsetshire,' *Trans. Cambridge Phil. Soc.,* vol. ix, 1856, part 4, p. 555; in part quoted in A. Strahan, *Purbeck Memoir,* 1898, p. 95; and P. B. Brodie, *Quart. Journ. Geol. Soc.,* vol. x, 1854, p. 475.

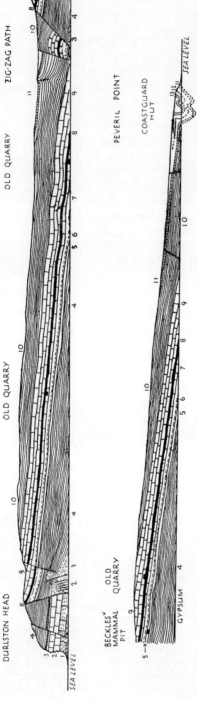

Fig. 31.—*Type-section of the Purbeck Beds, Durlston Bay, Swanage.* Distance 1 mile. After A. Strahan, with modifications.

Upper
Purbeck
{
13. Purbeck Marble Beds
    and Ostracod Shales.
12. *Unio* Beds.
11. Broken Shell Limestone.
}

Middle
Purbeck
{
10. *Corbula* and Beef Beds.
 9. Upper Building Stones.
 8. Cinder Bed.
 7. Lower Building Stones, with
    flint band at base (6).
 5. Mammal Bed.
}

Lower
Purbeck
{
 4. Marls with gypsum and
    Insect Beds.
 3. Broken Beds and Caps.
}

 2. Freestone Series. } Portland Beds
 1. Cherty Series.

The Upper Building Stones, less varied than the lower series, consist of 50 ft. of limestones with shale partings. They have yielded remains of fishes and turtles, but also *Corbula spp.*, *Viviparus*, *Cyrena*, *Ostrea* and plant remains, suggestive of brackish-water estuarine conditions.

Above are the Corbula Beds (33 ft.) comprising layers of shelly limestone, shales, and marls, with ' beef ' and selenite. These are partly of marine origin and contain *Pecten, Protocardia*, etc., as well as abundant *Corbula* of several species, and the diminutive *Hydrobia chopardiana* (de Loriol) associated with the gastropods *Pachychilus manselli* (de Loriol) and *Promathildia microbinaria* in a certain shell-limestone band. Overlying these beds are about 30 feet of shales with thin shaly limestone bands, containing numerous ostracods, and layers of fibrous carbonate of lime, from which they are called the Chief Beef Beds.[1]

The Broken Shell Limestone is a hard massive limestone, 16 ft. in thickness, made up of fragments of *Cyrena*, with *Unio, Viviparus*, and remains of fishes and turtles.

This limestone is succeeded by shales with many *Cypridea punctata* and some thin limestones full of *Unio*.

The highest beds visible are shales, near the base of which is the Purbeck Marble, occurring as two bands of hard limestone 11 ft. apart, almost made up of *Viviparus cariniferus* (J. de C. Sowerby), the lower band red, the upper band grey-green. The junction of the Purbeck and Wealden formations cannot be seen at Swanage.

The coast section is conveniently examined by starting at Swanage and proceeding along the shore round Peveril Point to Durlston Bay. The first rock visible along the shore towards the Point is the Broken Shell Limestone, which makes an inclined platform below the Grosvenor Hotel. The rock dips about 15°-18° N. and its surface is pitted with some large depressions, from 4 ft. to 7½ ft. in diameter and 1 ft. or so deep, first noticed and described by Fitton.[2] They appear to be due to collapse of the limestone after consolidation, owing to the formation of hollows underneath; but the cause of the formation of the hollows can only be conjectured. There are no other passable sections to be seen until Peveril Point is reached.

At Peveril Point the Upper Purbeck Beds, from the Broken Shell Limestone upwards, and including the Marble Beds, are well exposed in contortions within a sharp synclinal fold running W.N.W.-E.S.E. obliquely across the main strike. Sections are therefore afforded on the north side as well as the eastern extremity of the Point.

From the Point to Durlston Head the beds are encountered in descending order. The Broken Shell Limestone, some 25 ft.

---

[1] Cf. W. A. Tarr, ' Origin of the " Beef " in the Lias Shales of the Dorset Coast,' *Geol. Mag.,* 1923, p. 289.

[2] W. H. Fitton, ' . . The Strata between the Chalk and the Oxford Oolite . . .' *Trans. Geol. Soc.,* ser. 2, vol. 4, 1836, p. 209, footnote.

below the Purbeck Marble, crops out at the foot of the north-eastern extremity of the Point and forms the most northerly of the Peveril Ledges.   It dips sharply southwards but rises again about 70 yds. farther south, forming another prominent ledge, and then runs steadily up to the top of the cliff, clear of the tectonic complication at the Point.

The Cinder Bed forms a short ledge jutting into the sea, which cannot be conveniently rounded at high tide.   The Cherty Fresh-water Bed is seen 16 ft. below the Cinder Bed, and four feet below this is a conspicuous black carbonaceous shale (10 ins.), contain-ing insect and fish remains, which serves as a guide to the less conspicuous Mammal Bed, 10 ft. lower still.   The rest of the cliff is occupied by the Lower Purbeck marls to the centre of the bay, where the Broken Beds are the lowest rocks to come to the surface.

At the path leading up to the Belle Vue restaurant the section is cut off and repeated by a double fault, of which the two parts almost meet at beach level and diverge upwards. ' The northern-most branch throws the Cinder Bed from the top nearly to the bottom of the cliff, the second throws it some few feet below the beach, from beneath which it rises again about 180 yds. farther on.   For a time, therefore, we cross over the same strata we have already seen on the north side of the fault, keeping on the *Corbula* Beds if we [scramble] along the cliff, but crossing the Cinder, Mammal and Lower Purbeck strata in succession if we keep to the beach.'[1]

The basal Purbeck Beds are much disturbed and masked at Durlston Head by a fault accompanied by small step-faulting along the junction with the Portland Stone, and a deceptive appear-ance of unconformity is produced.

(c) DURLSTON HEAD TO ST. ALBAN'S HEAD

The basal Purbeck Beds are seen in the brow of the cliff at numerous places along this coast (Pl. VII, B).   They consist of Broken Beds underlain by Caps, or beds of tufa each up to 2 or $2\frac{1}{2}$ ft. thick, sometimes with Burrs, separated by $\frac{1}{2}$ in. of brown Dirt from the Portland Stone.   They can be studied a mile west of Anvil Point and at the quarries of Dancing Ledge, Seacombe, Winspit, and St. Alban's Head.   There are good sections also in the valley sides near the lighthouse.   Here the basal tufas are very thick.

The hills from the lighthouse to Worth are scarred with old quarry tips, and here and there a small outcrop may be seen.   The Cinder Bed is the most easily picked up.   On the surface are fragments of the Cherty Freshwater Bed with *Physa, Valvata, Viviparus,* etc., remarkably weathered out, as first noted by Thomas Webster in 1811.

---

[1] A. Strahan, *Purbeck Memoir,* 1898, p. 95.   The old cliff path is partly destroyed by slips and partly overgrown.

(d) WORBARROW

The next complete sections are on either side of Pondfield Cove and the adjoining Worbarrow Tout. Here the thickness of the Purbeck Beds according to Bristow's measurements is 290 ft. 9 ins. The Lower Purbeck Beds are well displayed in the sides of Pondfield, and almost the entire formation on the west and north sides of the Tout, where the steep northward dip causes the limestone bands to stand up in large wall-like slabs. The beds were measured and drawn with great accuracy and detail by Bristow (Vertical Sections, Sheet 22), and Strahan gave a discontinuous section of the critical uppermost beds saying ' the separation of Purbeck from Wealden, always arbitrary, is here additionally difficult from the obscurity of that part of the section.' He recognized two bands of *Viviparus* [=*Paludina*] limestone separated by 8 ft. of clays (mainly hidden), and more *Viviparus* in nodules in clays and shales as much as 50 ft. higher (the intervening strata mainly concealed).[1] The Unio Beds are especially well seen in the inclined slabs near the beginning of the sandy beach and built into the lifeboat slipway.

The Lower Purbeck of Worbarrow Tout contains large masses of gypsum as at Durlston, and the Broken Beds show puzzling features (see below p. 301).

III. LULWORTH DISTRICT

(a) MUPE BAY, BACON HOLE, AND THE FOSSIL FOREST

Mupe Bay and Bacon Hole afford the most complete section from the Wealden Beds down to the Portland Stone in existence (Frontispiece). The total thickness of the Purbeck Beds is here 250 ft. 8 ins., according to the measurements of Bristow, for whose detailed enumeration of the strata the reader is again referred to Vertical Sections, Sheet 22.

H. B. Woodward and A. Strahan re-examined and re-measured the critical passage-beds between the Purbeck and Wealden Beds, and concluded ' so far from helping in the separation of the Purbeck and Wealden groups, the evidence only confirms the completeness of the passage of the one into the other.'[2] Their section, with their classification, was as follows (somewhat condensed) : —

SECTION AT BACON HOLE, MUPE BAY

WEALDEN BEDS

							Ft.	Ins.
White sand-rock	...	...	...	...	...	...	3	0
Laminated sand and clay	...	...	...	...	...	...	6	0
Clay-ironstone	...	...	...	...	...	...		2
Clay with laminae of sand	...	...	...	...	...	...	1	6

[1] A. Strahan, *Purbeck Memoir*, 1898, p. 99.
[2] *Ibid*, p. 99.

PURBECK BEDS   Ft.   Ins.

	Ft.	Ins.
Ironstone with *Cypridea punctata* (Forbes) and *C. tuberculata* (J. de C. Sowerby) var. *adjuncta* Rup. Jones		1
Clays, marly and greenish, with lignite	9	0
Clay, red, calcareous, with *Viviparus*		8
Clays, reddish and grey ; turtle bones	5	0
Clay, reddish and mottled ; abundant *Viviparus*	2	0
Limestone, green, shelly, fish scales		4
Shell-marl with lignite		6
Clay, mottled, with 3-inch shell-marl at base	2	3
Clay, mottled, with *Viviparus*	2	6
Viviparus-limestone or " Marble," with *Unio*		9

0   1   2 FT

FIG. 32.—*A portion of the top of the Broken Beds at Lulworth Cove (east side ; dip section).* Undisturbed limestone above, with small breccia packed between it and the large tilted block, and also into crevice in the large block. (Reproduced from *Quart. Journ. Geol. Soc.,* vol. xciv, 1938, p. 16.)

The name Bacon Hole presumably refers to the streaky appearance of the cliffs, due to the gently rolling alternations of limestone and clay bands of the Purbeck Beds. All the principal subdivisions and many individual beds developed in Purbeck are easily recognizable. The basal beds are well exposed for study in the west corner of Bacon Hole, where the Dirt Bed with white pebbly stones is conspicuous (Pl. IX, B). This locality also affords the best dip-section of the Broken Beds and leaves little doubt that they owe their chief features to tectonic causes (Fig. 32).

Midway between Bacon Hole and Lulworth Cove the famous Fossil Forest is reached by scrambling down a slope to a ledge half way down the cliff. The ledge consists of the tufa Caps, with the Portland Stone forming a vertical precipice below. Upon the Hard Cap, and well exposed to view, is an unrivalled development of the Dirt Bed, from 6 ins. to 1 ft. thick, consisting of a black gravelly earth full of white stones. Upon it rests the Soft Cap, an irregular band of tufa from 2 to 4 ft. thick, full of great ' burrs ' containing the boles and prostrate trunks of trees (Pl. IX, A). Many of the bosses of tufa covering over stools of trees show the central cup-shaped depression mentioned above. The wood is silicified and there is sometimes black chert mingled with the tufa, as if the tufa had been locally replaced by silica.

A few feet above the Forest Bed begin the Broken Beds, of which this provides the best strike section, contrasting strongly with the dip section near by at Bacon Hole. Here they are up to 25 ft. thick, and higher beds are involved than elsewhere, including the Cypris Freestone and the lowest $3\frac{1}{2}$ ft. of the ' Hard Cockle Beds ' of Bristow.

(b) LULWORTH COVE AND STAIR HOLE

In the east side of Lulworth Cove the tectonic disturbance (drag fold) known as the Lulworth Crumple begins to rise above sea-level and distorts the section, but nearly all the beds can be recognized on both sides of the cove. The thickness is here diminishing rapidly westwards, and has reached 176 ft. 3 ins. Slipping also complicates matters.

The exact sequence and thicknesses of all the beds are shown by Bristow and Whitaker in a vertical section printed on Geological Survey Horizontal Sections, Sheet 56.

On the east side of the cove there is an illuminating section of the Broken Beds (here very well developed) and of small tectonic structures in the overlying Cypris Freestones.

The Lulworth Crumple is best seen at Stair Hole, where all the Upper and Middle Purbeck Beds are involved in it (Pl. XIV, B). Some of the Lower Purbeck Beds are faulted out. These tectonic features will be described in Chapter XIII.

At both Lulworth Cove and Stair Hole thin bands of Purbeck Marble are still present.

(c) DUNGY HEAD AND DURDLE DOOR

The Purbeck Beds at Dungy Head and Durdle Door are mere relics left between powerful strike faults, which have cut out large parts of this and the succeeding formations. At Dungy Head almost all the Lower Purbeck clays and shales are faulted out, leaving the Cinder Bed only 25 ft. from the top of the Portland Stone. This and the other Middle Purbeck Beds are normally developed, but the section is faulted. again at the Beef Beds and Broken Shell Limestone, which latter is impregnated with oil. The total thickness of surviving Purbeck Beds is about 62 ft., including up to 9 ft. of Cap limestones and Dirt Beds.

Durdle provides a good section on each side of the promontory (Pl. VIII, B). In the Lower Purbeck there is a reversed fault which pulls the Cypris Freestones apart for a distance of several yards. The whole Upper Purbeck and most of the Middle, seen at Stair Hole, are faulted out, the highest beds present being Beef Beds in the fault breccia. The strata stand nearly vertical and are as follows : —

PURBECK BEDS AT DURDLE DOOR

		Ft.	Ins.
38.	Marl and beef beds, jumbled. Fault breccia ? ... *c.*	5	
37-34.	Bands of shale, marlstone, mudstone and limestone ...	11	
33.	CINDER BED	3	
32.	Shale and thin laminated limestone	2	6
31.	Cherty white limestone ('Cherty Freshwater Bed ')	1	3
30-24.	Bands of limestone and shale	17	9
23.	Hard cuboidal mudstone	2	6
22-18.	Bands of limestone and shale	4	
17.	Pellety Bed, brown, with flat white pellets	1	6
16-6.	Bands of limestone, mudstone and shale	12	
5.	Cypris Freestones	17	6
4.	Broken Beds, with conspicuous splintered black chert ...	9	
3.	Soft Cap	2	
2.	Dirt Bed, with pebbles, 6″ to		9
1.	Hard Cap, inaccessible ... ... *c.*	8	

Total (about)   98ft. 0ins.

Bed 17 is apparently the ' Hard limestone with pebbles of white marl, 1 ft. 4 ins.' of Bristow and Whitaker's section at Lulworth.[1] It is traceable through all these coast sections and is a useful datum for assisting correlation and elucidation of the tectonics. It suggests that hereabouts, where the Purbeck Beds are abnormally thin (138 ft. calculated at Durdle Door before the faulting, and little more at Stair Hole) there was some penecontemporaneous erosion.

IV. RINGSTEAD, POXWELL, UPWEY AND PORTISHAM[2]

The Lower Purbeck Beds are exposed with the Portland Beds in the fault-block west of Holworth House, Ringstead Bay.[3]

The lowest bed, a thin layer of white splintery limestone, full of hollow moulds of the tiny freshwater gastropods *Hydrobia* and

---

[1] *Horizontal Sections Geol. Survey,* sheet 56, 1859.
[2] For localities see folding map, Pl. XIX.
[3] W. J. Arkell, *Proc. Geol. Assoc.,* vol. xlvi, 1935, p. 323.

Valvata, with *Cyrena,* is cemented tightly to the Portland Roach below (*see* p. 111). It is similarly attached to the overlying tufaceous ostracodal limestone (6 ins.). Above are two beds of tufa, each resting on a thin, laminated Dirt Bed. The succeeding beds are slatt and clay, with a 2-inch chert seam in limestone and two beds of *Cypris* freestone in the lower part. Above the chert seam, for a foot or two, on the level of the base of the Broken Beds of the Lulworth district, the thin-bedded limestones are puckered and obscurely disturbed, locally even brecciated on a small scale. This may indicate expansion of anhydrite, and subsequent removal by solution, causing a plane of weakness, which perhaps determined the level at which the adjustment-sliding took place which produced the Broken Beds in the Purbeck Fold.[1]

Widening the road in 1936 at Poxwell Lodge, ⅓ mile south of Poxwell Church, produced the following section :—

POXWELL ROAD CUTTING (July, 1936).

		Ft.	Ins.
31.	*Unio* Bed		
30.	Clay and slipped stuff		
29.	Two hard bands ... ... *c.*	2	0
28.	Flaggy hard limestone		6
27.	Shales with beef, disturbed, and some *Corbula* limestone ...		
26.	White limy deposit (?), enclosing beef lenticle ; jumbled		
25.	Shales with beef and thin *Corbula* beds		
24.	*Cyrena* beds (well-preserved shells)		
23.	Beef layer...		6
22.	Blue and brown clay, a few feet (4 ft. ?)		
21.	Limestone with *Cyrena*	1	0
20.	Clay (gap in section, a few feet)		
19.	CINDER BED, hard and blue, soft top. *Ostrea distorta* ...	3	0
18.	Marl full of *Ostrea distorta* (lower part of Cinder Bed) ...	1	3
17.	Dark leathery shale		6
16.	Marl with double valved Cyrenas, also *Physa bristovii* ...	1	0
15.	CHERTY LIMESTONE full of *Cyrena* and well-preserved *Physa bristovii, Viviparus inflatus, Valvata helicoides, Viviparus subangulatus*	2	0
14.	Clay parting		6
13.	Porcellanous stone with carbonaceous flecks ... 9 in. to	1	0
12.	Shaly marl and clay with thin stone seams	2	0
11.	Clay, tough, blue	1	0
10.	Limestone, hard, blue hearted lagoonstone, vermiform marks	2	0
9.	Clay, tough, blue and brown	1	2
8.	Limestone, hard, blue hearted	1	3
7.	CYPRID BED. Soft cream marl almost composed of *Cypridea granulosa.* (A similar bed seen in the pit 1 mile east, at Moigns Down Barn)		4
6.	CYRENA BED. A mass of casts		4
5.	Clay, pockety ... ... up to		10
4.	Marlstone	1	3
3.	Clay, brown, and marl ... ... *c.*	2	0
2.	CYPRID LIMESTONE		6
1.	Marls, clays, and thin marlstones, to end of section, about	5	0

[1] S. E. Hollingworth, *Geol. Mag.,* 1938, p. 330.

The beds dip 40-50° towards the south and the highest are exposed at the lower end of the cutting. The stone bands have been left uncovered and provide the best section of the Middle Purbeck Beds now to be seen in the district.

The basal Purbeck Beds (11 ft.) and the junction with the Portland Stone are to be seen in a small quarry on the east side of the road almost opposite the top end of this cutting. At the base of the Purbeck Beds is a bed of white splintery limestone with moulds of small gastropods (*Hydrobia*), as seen at Holworth House; then follow a bed of tufa, resting on a thin laminated Dirt Bed, and slatt and shale. The tufa (4 ft.), in large lenticular pillow-like masses (burrs) includes silicified tree-trunks (one more than 6 ft. in length) and locally thin dirt beds.

A similar section of the basal Purbeck Beds is well exposed in the Portland Stone quarries south of Chalbury Camp (*see* p. 115). The tufa burrs protrude from the turf as a discontinuous scar along the west side of Coomb Valley, across Chalbury Camp, and at intervals farther west. There are small shows of Purbeck Beds steeply inclined to nearly vertical near Green Hill Barton, and much quarry refuse on the plateau summit of the hill west of Chalbury Camp, where limestones were formerly worked underground.[1]

The approach cutting to Bincombe Tunnel (Ridgeway Hill) formerly exposed a complete section of the formation, which was measured and described in great detail by the Rev. Osmond Fisher. His detailed section is incorporated in the Geological Survey Vertical Sections, Sheet 22.[2] He found two groups of insect beds in the Lower Purbeck, and was able to recognize the Cinder and Cherty Freshwater Beds (these are still visible south of the road bridge) and above them much the same divisions of the Middle and Upper Purbeck as farther east :—*Corbula* Beds, Chief Beef Beds (much thinner), Broken Shell Limestone, *Unio* Beds, *Cypris* Clays and Shales, and *Viviparus* Clays. The total thickness was 189½ feet. Two stratigraphical observations are important : the first is that the Upper Purbeck Beds were found to be sandier and coarser than farther east, containing a larger proportion of the spoils of the land, such as lignite and plants; the second is that the Middle Purbeck building stones that are so important commercially in Purbeck are here almost worthless and their place is taken by the Cypris Freestones of the Lower Purbeck.

The basement beds, Caps and Dirt Beds, can still be seen near by in Upwey Quarry about 200 yds. south-west of Upwey Halt Station. There is more chert than usual, but otherwise nothing calling for special remark.[3] The same distance north-

---

[1] A. Strahan, *Purbeck Memoir*, 1898, p. 108.
[2] See also O. Fisher, ' On the Purbeck Strata of Dorsetshire,' *Trans. Cambridge Phil. Soc.*, vol. ix, 1856, p. 566.
[3] For details see A. Strahan, *Purbeck Memoir*, 1898, p. 108.

west of the station other old quarries show a good section of the upper part of the Lower Purbeck. Cypris Freestones and higher beds can also be seen in a quarry on the east side of Gould's Bottom on the Bridport road about 300 yds. S.S.W. of the pumping station. This and a small opening on the opposite side of the Bottom are in the north limb of the Upwey syncline and close to the Ridgeway Fault.[1] The Lower Purbeck Beds of the south limb have been extensively quarried on Windsbatch, south-west of Upwey Church (Pl. XIX, Map).

A quarry south of the Portisham road 500 yds. north-west of Upwey Church has been worked recently in Middle Purbeck flaggy limestones with well-preserved *Cyrena,* near the centre of the syncline, and there is a second quarry south of the same road rather less than $\frac{1}{2}$ mile farther west. The Cinder Bed protrudes in the road-cutting 150 yds. north of Upwey Church, dipping about 18° N.N.W.

The tufa makes a scar feature in several places along the ridge of Friar Waddon Hill and above Little Waddon, and Strahan mapped the Cinder Bed almost to Portisham. The last sections are in the old disused Portisham Quarries, described by Strahan; they show from 11 to 13 ft. of Lower Purbeck beds above 15 ft. of Portland Stone. At the base of the Purbeck beds are two irregular and undulating layers of laminated limestone separated by a thin shaly seam. Above is tufa in great irregular masses up to 4 ft., resting on a thin irregular bed of dirt with lumps of chert and irregular masses of white marl. At the top are 4-6 ft. of laminated limestone (' slatt ').

Strahan observed that the tufa masses were replaced horizontally as well as overlain by laminated limestone, and he saw an erect tree-trunk about 8 ft. high standing with its base in the Dirt Bed and in a slight depression in the laminated limestone below the Dirt Bed. The trunk was embedded in an irregularly cone-shaped mass of structureless tufa. The gigantic tufa sheath of a prostrate tree-trunk, measuring 14 x 4½ ft., figured in Strahan's memoir, can still be seen in the floor of the western extension of the quarry. It has curious annular ribs, difficult to explain.

V. THE ISLE OF PORTLAND

Only Lower Purbeck Beds remain on the Isle of Portland. The greatest thickness survives north and west of Southwell, where little less than 100 ft. are exposed in the cliff.[2] The geological map by Buckland and De la Beche[3] shows that a century ago Purbeck Beds also overspread much of the northern part of the island, whence they have since been completely quarried away.

---

[1] These quarries are figured in W. J. Arkell, ' The Tectonics of the Purbeck and Ridgeway Faults in Dorset,' *Geol. Mag.,* vol. lxxiii, 1936, p. 102, figs. 6 a-c.
[2] A. Strahan, *Purbeck Memoir,* 1898, p. 112.
[3] *Trans. Geol. Soc.,* Ser. 2, vol. iv, 1836, pl. i.

The essential features of the basement-beds, the tufaceous Caps with silicified trees and Dirt Beds, are present, but the details vary from place to place.   The following section may be taken as representative (Fig. 33) :—

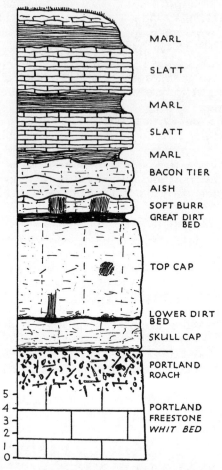

Fig. 33.—*Section of the basement-beds of the Lower Purbeck in the quarries at the south end of West Weare Cliff, north of Black Nore, Isle of Portland.* (Reproduced from *The Jurassic System in Great Britain,* 1933, p. 530).

KINGBARROW QUARRIES

LOWER PURBECK BEDS.

			Ft.	Ins.
	Rubble and clay	...	7	0
13.	Slatt, laminated limestone	...	4	0
12.	Bacon Tier, hard streaked limestone with sandy layers	...	2	0
	Greenish clay	c		2

---

¹ A. Strahan, *op. cit.,* p. 115.

Ft. Ins.

11. Aish, fine-grained argillaceous limestone, drying white   ...   2   0
10. Burr, tufaceous limestone, used for building in the Island,
    chiefly in chimneys   1   4
9. Top or Great Dirt Bed, dark carbonaceous clay with frag-
    ments of limestone and wood, ...   0 to   1   0
8. Top Cap, tufaceous limestone, with nearly horizontal holes
    2 to 8 ins. in diameter and 5 to 6 ft. long, sometimes
    branching and filled with fossil wood   ...   ... 8 to   9   0
    Lower Dirt Bed, carbonaceous clay and gravel   3 ins. to   6
7. Skull Cap, hard brown tufaceous limestone, variable   ...   1   6
    Carbonaceous parting; sometimes a chert band with
    Ostracods   ...   .   3 ins. to   6

PORTLAND STONE

6. Roach   3   0
[For downward continuation see p. 122]

Strahan has published descriptions of 7 other quarries and
cliff-sections, all varying in detail.[1]   He found that the Burr,
Upper Dirt Bed, and Top Cap are not represented at the southern
end of the island.   In all the sections the base of the Purbeck
rests upon the Roach of the Portland Stone (with the ' Portland
Screw,' *Aptyxiella portlandica* J. de C. Sowerby sp.) and the
junction is perfectly even and conformable, but the change from
marine to freshwater fauna is abrupt, as on the mainland.

In the Great Dirt Bed the trees are more perfectly preserved
than in Purbeck, and the Lower Dirt Bed has yielded some of the
best specimens of Cycads known.

[1] *loc. cit.,* 1898

CHAPTER VIII

NEOCOMIAN STAGE: WEALDEN BEDS

I. General

The regime of swamps and still muddy lagoons which characterized the Purbeck epoch was brought to an end by earth-movements which accelerated subsidence and at the same time rejuvenated the effete drainage system of the surrounding land. In consequence there was formed an extensive shallow basin of fresh water over the South of England, from west Dorset to Kent and the Boulonnais and northwards at least to the present edge of the Chalk downs. Into the basin flowed rivers from various directions, but predominantly from the west, bringing vast piles of detritus and floating vegetation, which were spread out on the bottom as false-bedded sands, marls and clays, with bands of coarse grits. In south Dorset the thickness exceeds 2,000 ft. at Swanage but diminishes westward to about 1,400 ft. at Worbarrow and much less in the Weymouth district. West of Worbarrow, however, the formation has been reduced an unknown amount by subsequent Cretaceous erosions and Tertiary faulting. The sediments become noticeably coarser westwards in Dorset. Eastward the Wealden Beds thin to 785 ft. in the Portsdown boring, though they thicken again to nearly three times that amount in the Weald of Kent. Northward they are well developed (though incomplete) in the Vale of Wardour and have been proved by the recent boring to be at least 580 ft. thick in the Vale of Kingsclere, near Newbury. The most northerly occurrences cap some of the hills near Oxford, notably Shotover and around Great Haseley.

In their distribution, therefore, the Wealden Beds are co-extensive with the Purbeck Beds. Moreover, in Dorset and the Weald they are perfectly conformable with the Purbeck Beds and were folded in harmony with them during the intra-Cretaceous earth-movements. Both lithologically and palaeontologically there is a perfect passage upward from one formation into the other. As Strahan wrote in the Purbeck Memoir, " no line can be drawn which does not either include beds of Purbeck type in the

Wealden or beds of Wealden type in the Purbeck, the two formations being absolutely inseparable."

Webster in 1824[1] and Fitton in 1827[2] united the Purbeck and
Wealden Beds as a single formation under the name of Wealden,
and this classification survived until 1850, when Forbes[3] pointed
out that the few marine fossils of the Purbeck have Jurassic affinities which should separate the formation from the Cretaceous
system.   As late as 1885 some authors were retaining Fitton's
Wealden under the name Purbeck-Wealden and regarding the
separation of the two formations as unnatural.[4] If a purely insular
view be taken this contention is correct.   Wider considerations,
however, demand that the boundary between the Jurassic and
Cretaceous systems should be drawn somewhere in the Purbeck-
Wealden, which are only an abnormal facies developed locally.
The classification has to be based on the equivalent marine invertebrate faunas elsewhere; and while the marine fossils of the
Purbeck Beds are Jurassic, in Germany beds of Wealden facies,
likewise overlying Purbeck Beds, pass laterally into marine strata
with Neocomian fossils.   Hence the line is now drawn in this
country at the rather vague lithological change from fossiliferous
limestones and marls (Purbeck Beds) to sands and barren marls
or clays (Wealden Beds).   The earth-movements that produced
this lithological change were probably connected with those which
in other parts of Europe gave rise to the widespread Valanginian
(Lower Neocomian) transgression which ushered in the new Cretaceous fauna.[5]

The area drained by the Wealden rivers must have greatly
exceeded all the existing mountainous regions of the British Isles.
Some of the pebbles in the Weald have been identified as from the
Palaeozoic rocks of the London-Ardennes landmass, but in Purbeck the quartz pebbles increase in size and abundance westwards
and obviously came from the west.   With them came pebbles of
chert containing Radiolaria of the Culm Measures, together with
tourmaline slate and quartzites, all rocks composing the Devon-
Cornwall peninsula.[6]   The heavy minerals were largely derived
from the Dartmoor granite, now freshly laid bare of its sedimentary covering.[7]

[1] T. Webster, ' Observations on the Purbeck and Portland Beds,' *Trans. Geol.
Soc.*, ser. 2, vol. ii, 1826, p. 44.
[2] W. H. Fitton, ' . . The Strata between the Chalk anl the Oxford Oolite . . ,'
ibid., vol. iv, 1836, pp. 105, 159.
[3] E. Forbes, ' On the Succession of Strata and Distribution of Organic Remains
in the Dorsetshire Purbecks,' *Rept. Brit. Assoc.* for 1850, sections, pp. 79-81.
[4] W. Topley and A. J. Jukes-Brown, ' Report of the Sub-Committee on Classification and Nomenclature II. Cretaceous,' *Compte Rendu, Congrès géol. Int.*, 3me
Session, Berlin, 1885, p. 453.
[5] For fuller discussion of this subject see W. J. Arkell, *Jurassic System in
Great Britain*, 1933, chapter XVII.   Oxford.
[6] J. F. Kirkaldy, ' . . the Pebble beds of the Lower Cretaceous rocks of
England . . ,' *Rept., Brit. Assoc. Adv. Sci.* for 1938, p. 424.
[7] A. W. Groves, ' The Unroofing of the Dartmoor Granite,' *Quart. Journ. Geol.
Soc.*, vol. lxxxvii, 1931, pp. 70-72.

II. STRATIGRAPHY

As in the Isle of Wight, the Wealden Beds of Dorset comprise two series of sharply contrasted lithological types, the Variegated Marls and Sandstones below and the much thinner Wealden Shales above. The formation differs from its equivalents in the Isle of Wight by the fact that the Wealden Shales are very much thinner, and by the greater proportion of sandstones and coarse grit or conglomerate bands in the underlying Marls.

In the Isle of Wight the Marls are exposed to a maximum depth of 550 ft. and their total thickness is unknown. In Dorset the division comprises almost the whole of the formation (about 2,300 ft.) at Swanage, and quite the whole of it at Worbarrow (1,400 ft.) where the overlying Shales have disappeared. Attempts to subdivide the series are rendered almost useless by the rapid lateral variation of the strata.   Red, purple, green, grey and mottled clays and marls alternate with variegated white, yellow, purple and pink sandstones.   The sandstones tend to predominate towards the top of the series at Worbarrow.   At varying intervals throughout there are thin bands of coarse quartz grit and conglomerate, usually cemented by iron.   Most of the bands are only from 6 ins. to 2 ft. thick, and some disappear when traced laterally even up the face of Worbarrow cliff.   They denote that subsidence was intermittent, or else that influxes of coarse material came sporadically.   One such pebbly bed is much thicker than all the others and can be traced from Swanage (3 ft. thick) through Purbeck and the Lulworth district to Durdle Door (28 ft. thick).   Since it occurs about the middle of the series it is useful in stratigraphy.

The Wealden Shales in the Isle of Wight are 192 ft. thick at Atherfield and 170 ft. at Sandown, but they diminish rapidly westwards to less than 100 ft. at Compton Bay.   At Punfield Cove, Swanage, they are only 34½ ft. thick, and the westerly attenuation continues through Purbeck, reducing them to 12 ft. at Corfe Castle and to nothing at Worbarrow Bay.   Contrasting markedly with the variegated marls and sandstones beneath, they consist of evenly stratified dark shales with occasional thin bands of shelly limestone, though westward their typical character is lost.   In the Isle of Wight the base of the Shales is the most readily recognized and the most constant horizon in the whole Wealden formation, but at Corfe Castle the distinction between the two was indefinite. " the upper division losing its distinctive character as a shale, and passing westward into the sand and sandy clays ".[1]

The precise position of the Wealden Beds in terms of the Continental marine sequence of Infra-Valanginian, Valanginian, Hauterivian and Barremian is unknown. Comparison with North-West Germany suggests that only the lowest Neocomian is

---

[1] A. Strahan, *Purbeck Memoir*, 1898, p. 127 (a temporary section).

represented, namely the Infra-Valanginian and basal Valanginian.[1] It is possible, however, that there is an important break between the Variegated Marls and Sandstones and the Wealden Shales, and that the latter belong to a much later period of the Neocomian. This is suggested by the occurrence of two characteristic Lower Greensand lamellibranchs in the Wealden Shales of Kent and Surrey : the oyster *Exogyra sinuata* is locally abundant near Ashford,[2] and *Cardium ibbetsoni* Forbes has been found 25 ft. down in the Wealden Shales near Reigate.[3]   As remarked by Cornes and Chatwin, " their occurrence points to a temporary incursion of the sea, before the true Lower Greensand transgression ", but *Exogyra sinuata* occurs in the Valanginian of Lincolnshire and Yorkshire and so has no zonal value.

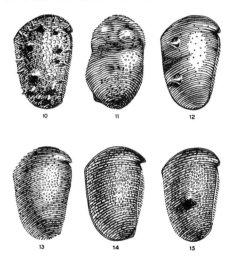

Fig. 34.—*Ostracods of the Wealden Beds.*

10. *Cypridea tuberculata* (J. de C. Sowerby); 11. *Metacypris fittoni* (Mantell); 12. *Morinina dorsispinata* Anderson; 13. *Ulwellia menevensis* Anderson; 14. *Cypridea valdensis* (J. de C. Sowerby); 15. *Cypridea spinigera* (J. de C. Sowerby).
    The average length of all the above species is between 0.75 mm. and 1 mm., excepting *C. valdensis*, which averages 1.5 mm. in length. (Selected and drawn by F. W. Anderson.)

III. Palaeontology

(a) THE VARIEGATED MARLS AND SANDSTONES

Neither the vegetation nor the marine and terrestrial vertebrate faunas of this part of the world underwent the fundamental changes from the Jurassic type to the Tertiary and modern until about the

    [1] For correlation table summarizing Spath's views on the Neocomian see W. J. Arkell, *Jurassic System in Great Britain*, 1933, p. 546. Oxford.
    [2] H. W. Cornes, ' The Geology of the Canterbury District,' *Proc. Geol. Assoc.*, vol. xxxvi, 1925, p. 259.
    [3] C. P. Chatwin, ' Geology of the Country around Reigate and Dorking,' *Mem. Geol. Surv.* 1933, p. 115.

middle of the Cretaceous period. The fish remains of the marine Neocomian on the continent of Europe, and even in Brazil, Mexico, the United States and East Africa, are of as typically Jurassic aspect as their contemporaries in the Wealden lake or estuary.[1] The dinosaurs of the Wealden still have a thoroughly Jurassic appearance, and *Megalosaurus* survived into the Neocomian from at least the Bathonian; but most of them are now assigned to special genera. Some of the Purbeckian mammals have been found in the Wealden of Kent. As to the vegetation, of which copious samples from the land drained by the great Wealden rivers are preserved as lignite in the deltas, " the contrast between the earlier and later Cretaceous floras may be described as a contrast between ancient and modern".[2] As usual in ancient floras, there is a preponderance of trees, mostly conifers. Cycads were still abundant (*Williamsonia, Cycadeoidea,* and the Jurassic *Williamsoniella*), as also were a great variety of ferns, with Equisitales and Lycopodiales. Above all, no sign of flowering plants has been found in temperate regions, although they were already established in Greenland.[3]

Palaeontologically the Variegated Marls and Sandstones of Dorset are disappointing compared with those elsewhere. Bones of *Iguanodon* have been found ½ mile north of Swanage[4] and in Godlingston brickyard, and were said to be common in the base of the formation in Ridgeway cutting;[5] but only one species, *I. hollingtoniensis* Lydekker, has been recognized as compared with 13 genera and 15 species from the Isle of Wight.[6] Casts of large *Unio* occur in ironstone concretions in the upper part of the series in Swanage Bay and at Ridgeway. At Downshay, two bands with *Viviparus* have been recorded near the base of the formation in a small roadside exposure,[7] but by definition such bands generally belong to the Purbeck Beds (*see* p. 156). Ostracods have not yet been systematically searched for.

(b) WEALDEN SHALES

The Wealden Shales provide somewhat greater palaeontological variety. As in the Isle of Wight, they abound with ostracods, of which *Cypridea tuberculata* (J. de C. Sowerby), *C. valdensis*

---

[1] A. S. Woodward, ' The Fossil Fishes of the English Wealden and Purbeck Formations,' 1916-19, pp. 144-5. *Palaeontographical Soc.*

[2] A. C. Seward, *Plant Life through the Ages,* 1933, p. 384. Cambridge.

[3] A. C. Seward, *op. cit.* pp. 385-408. See also A. C. Seward, ' Catalogue of the Mesozoic Plants . .' The Wealden Flora, *Brit. Mus.* (*Nat. Hist.*), 1894; and ' A Contribution to our Knowledge of Wealden Floras,' *Quart. Journ. Geol. Soc.,* vol. lxix, 1913, p. 85.

[4] W. Buckland, ' On the discovery of Fossil Bones of the Iguanodon . .' *Trans. Geol. Soc.,* ser. 2, vol. iii, 1835, p. 428; and W. H. Hudleston, ' Excursion to the Isle of Purbeck,' *Proc. Geol. Assoc.,* vol. vii, 1882, p. 387.

[5] O. Fisher, ' On the Purbeck Strata of Dorsetshire,' *Trans. Camb. Phil. Soc.,* vol. ix, 1856, p. 3.

[6] W. E. Swinton, *The Dinosaurs,* 1934, pp. 210-219. London.

[7] A. Strahan, *Purbeck Memoir,* 1898, p. 126.

(J. de C. Sowerby), *C. spinigera* (J. de C. Sowerby) and *Metacypris fittoni* (Mantell) have been found at Punfield. According to Jones the first occurs commonly in the Purbeck Beds, and the second very rarely in the Middle Purbeck only,[1] but Mr. F. W. Anderson questions the specific identity of both the Purbeck forms with the Wealden species.[2]

Two 6-inch bands of *Viviparus* limestone like Purbeck Marble, with *Viviparus elongatus* (J. de C. Sowerby) and indeterminate *Cyrena* and *Ostrea*, are intercalated in the shales at Punfield. Besides *Viviparus* some larger gastropods have been found both at Punfield[3] and at Corfe Castle,[4] and they are common in the Weal-

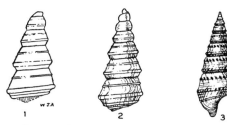

Fig. 35.—*Characteristic gastropods of the Wealden Shales.*
Paraglauconia strombiformis (Schlotheim).

1. var. *tricarinata* (J. de C. Sowerby) (= *bilineata* Goldfuss). Corfe.
2. var. *tricarinata* (J. de C. Sowerby) (= *bilineata* Goldfuss). Hanover.
3. var. *multilineata* Goldfuss. Hanover.

den Shales of the Isle of Wight, where bands of them are noted at levels 1 foot, 12 ft. and 30 ft. below the base of the Lower Greensand.[5] At Corfe, an ironstone 9 ft. below the base of the Lower Greensand is packed with them. Unfortunately the preservation in all these places is poor, but from a considerable quantity of material there is no doubt that this is the same highly variable gastropod as is common in the Wealden of North-West Germany, where it has often been figured as *Melania strombiformis* (Schlotheim) as well as under other synonyms and varietal names.[6] Although this shell has been given several new generic names, of which the valid one is *Paraglauconia* Steinmann,[7] there seems

[1] T. R. Jones, ' On the Ostracoda of the Purbeck Formation . . ,' *Quart. Journ. Geol. Soc.,* vol. xli, 1885, pp. 333, 335.

[2] F. W. Anderson, *in lit.,* 1938.

[3] Fitton coll., Geol. Survey nos. 2346, GSd. 3777.

[4] Geol. Survey coll. no. Rh. 2973.

[5] H. J. O. White, ' Short Account of the Geology of the Isle of Wight,' *Mem. Geol. Surv.,* 1921, pp. 14-17.

[6] W. B. R. H. Dunker, *Mon. norddeutschen Wealdenbildung,* 1846, p. 50, pl. x, figs. 17, 18, 19 Braunschweig; also *M. tricarinata* and *bicarinata* Dunker, *op. cit.;* = *Potamides carbonarius* Roemer et Goldfuss, and vars. *bilineata, trilineata, multilineata* and *nodosa* Goldfuss, *Petrifacta Germaniae,* iii, 1844, p. 30, pl. clxxiii. Düsseldorf.

[7] G. Steinmann, *Geologie von Peru,* 1929, pp. 112, 113. Heidelberg. (= *Pseudoglauconia* Fritzsche, 1924, *non Douvillé,* 1921, = *Glauconia auct. non* Gray 1845 preoccupied for Lizards).

little by which it can be distinguished from the marine Aptian genus *Cassiope* Coquand (*see* below p. 169) and the two are said to occur together in the Aptian of Spain.[1] An intermediate form may be the tuberculate marine Spanish Aptian *C. lujani* (de Verneuil) which occurs in the Dorset Lower Greensand, but *Cassiope* may be a homoeomorph. In North-west Germany countless millions of *P. strombiformis* form thin platy limestones and something of the same sort occurs occasionally in the Wealden of the Isle of Wight.[2] Fitton's names[3] antedate all the German names except the original *strombiformis* (Schlotheim, 1820). The type-form (the commonest in Germany) is that later named var. *nodosa* by Goldfuss, and it does not seem to occur in England (Fig. 35).

IV. Details

(a) SWANAGE BAY

The junction of Purbeck and Wealden Beds at Swanage runs from 100 to 300 ft. north of and approximately parallel with the High Street. The point where it enters the sea, somewhere south of the mouth of the Swan Brook, is concealed by masonry and alluvium. There are no sections for $\frac{1}{2}$ mile until at Beach Restaurant, where Beach Road turns inland to Ulwell, a cliff begins and continues round the rest of the bay.

From the beginning of the cliff to a ravine one mile from Swanage is exposed a continuous section at an average angle of 28° to the direction of dip. The apparent dip of the beds is at first 18°-20° rather east of north, then about 15° for some way, and eventually flattening to 7° about 400 ft. before reaching the ravine. The succession begins with alternating mottled marl and sandstone, followed by green sand with lignite, sandstone with interbedded shale and lignite, red marl (causing slips south of the Grand Hotel) and then 3 ft. of coarse grit with little quartz pebbles. This grit can be traced intermittently through Purbeck as far as Durdle Door, thickening westwards. Above it comes green sandy marl with lignite, followed by a conspicuous red marl band about 10 ft. thick, and then white sand and ferruginous sandstone in which the ravine is cut.

Beyond the ravine the section turns more easterly and runs at 42° to the direction of dip. The apparent dip remains only 7° for at least 500 ft. then increases to 12° in the next 400 ft. and to 20°-21° in the next 600 ft., and reaches 29° at the end of the section,

---

[1] *See* exhaustive treatment in B. Rehbinder, ' Fauna und Alter der cretaceischen Sandsteine in der Umgebung des Salzsees Baskuntschak,' *Mém. Comité Géol.,* vol. xvii, no. 1. 1902, p. 83.

[2] See G. A. Mantell, *Geol. Excursions round the Isle of Wight,* 1847, pl. vi, fig. 5. London.

[3] W. H. Fitton, ' . . Geol. Relations of the Beds between the Chalk and the Purbeck Limestone . . ' *Ann. Phil.* N.S. vol. viii, 1824, p. 376 (nomina nuda) ; see J. de C. Sowerby, *in* W. H. Fitton, ' . . the Strata between the Chalk and the Oxford Oolite . . ' *Trans. Geol. Soc.* Ser. 2, vol. iv, 1836, pl. xxii, fig. 4.

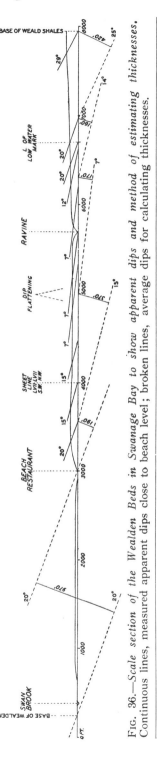

BASE OF WEALD SHALES

L. OF WATER
LOW MARK

RAVINE

DIP
FLATTENING

SHEET
LVII.LVII
S.W. NW

BEACH
RESTAURANT

SWAN
BROOK
BASE OF WEALDEN

FIG. 36.—Scale section of the Wealden Beds in Swanage Bay to show apparent dips and method of estimating thicknesses. Continuous lines, measured apparent dips close to beach level; broken lines, average dips for calculating thicknesses.

where the true dip is about 55° N. From the ravine onwards the following succession is passed :—sands with a thick band of red clay, white sandy clay and purple clay, white sand and selenitiferous clay with lignite and some lumps of ironstone containing large elongate *Unio*, then sandstones, purple clay, red and white clay and sand with broken trunks of trees in the upper part, sandstone, red marl (thick beds), and soft sandstone and white sand with grey clays. At this point, about 2,250 ft. from the ravine, the cliff suddenly turns inland to form the recess known as Punfield Cove. The southern side of the recess is a steep wooded slope formed by the Wealden Shales, dipping 55° N.

Only the upper part of the Wealden Shales is now visible, including a 6-inch band of limestone with *Cypridea tuberculata, Cyrena, Ostrea,* and *Viviparus,* which forms a dip-slope on the ridge on the south side of the path from the beach to the top of the cliff; the path lies on the basal pebble bed of the Lower Greensand (concealed). Strahan measured a total thickness of 34 ft. 6 ins. of Wealden Shales, with *Cypridea* to the base, resting on 70 ft. of white sands, which pass down into grey clays and white sands with brown sandstones; but even his section was interrupted by two gaps totalling 12 ft. 6 ins. of " beds not seen ". Since then the section has deteriorated. Sixteen feet from the base was a hard grit 6 ins. to 1 ft. thick.[1]

Owing to the great thicknesses of irregularly-bedded and rapidly varying marls which form a large proportion of the Wealden Beds of Swanage Bay and cannot be satisfactorily subdivided, it is not easy to obtain direct measurements. The total thickness of the formation can only be estimated by measuring the dip at a number of

[1] A. Strahan, *Purbeck Memoir,* 1898, p. 125.

points and drawing a scale section. The method employed is shown in Fig. 36 (p. 155). Strahan calculated the thickness as 2,350 ft., made up of 1,000 ft. for the half mile south of Beach Restaurant, 1,315 ft. for the rest of the Variegated Marls and Sandstones, and 35 ft. for the Wealden Shales. For the first half mile there are now no exposures, but Strahan stated that the average dip is 20°. In this stretch the section is exactly in the direction of true dip, and the width of outcrop being about 2,700-2,800 ft., the thickness is about 970 feet. Apart from this discrepancy of 30 ft. in a stretch which is in any case doubtful, an independent recalculation, as shown in Fig. 36, produced almost exactly the same result as Strahan's: 1,310 ft. for the rest of the Variegated Marls and Sandstones, to which 35 ft. have to be added for the Shale, making a total of 2,315 ft. The difference of only 5 ft. in the main stretch of 1,310 ft. (less than one-half per cent) shows that this must be very nearly the true thickness.

(b) INLAND SECTIONS, SWANAGE TO WORBARROW

The Wealden Variegated Marls and Sandstones form the rich undulating valley, 10 miles long and averaging 1 mile wide, between the stone hills on the south and the chalk ridge to the north. There are endless small exposures, but few sections of note. The best is at the pit of the Swanage Brick and Tile Co., by the roadside between Godlingston and Ulwell, where red, purple and grey marls have been made into bricks for at least two hundred years. The section at present shows a thin band of ferruginous quartz grit running through the middle. The beds dip 23° N. (*see* p. 355). A smaller section showing sandstones and marls, not now seen in the cliff, is exposed in the road-cutting at Forres School.

At Downshay in small roadside exposures Strahan noted a thin band of green limestone and a seam of clay ironstone, both containing *Viviparus*. These were said to be an indefinite but considerable way up in the Variegated Marls; but the green limestone closely resembles a band near the top of the Upper Purbeck Beds at Mupe Bay (*see* p. 140).

At Corfe railway-station, in the cutting referred to below Strahan saw the highest 106 ft. of the Wealden Beds and the junction with the Lower Greensand. It showed " the upper division of the Wealden losing its distinctive character as a shale and passing westwards into sandy clays ".[1]

WEALDEN BEDS AT CORFE STATION (A. Strahan)

[Lower Greensand above, p. 175]

	Ft.	Ins.
Hard grey sandstone, irregular ; about 1 to		3
Yellow sand	7	0
Yellow loamy clay	2	0

[1] A. Strahan, *op. cit.*, 1898, p. 127.

Ft.　Ins.

Ironstone and ferruginous clay, the ironstone packed with the
　　gastropod *Paraglauconia strombiformis* (Schlotheim),　var.
　　tricarinata J. de C. Sowerby[1]　...　...　...　...　...　　　10
Laminated shale like Cyprid-shale but no Cyprids seen　...　...　　2　0
Yellow loamy clay and sand ...　...　...　...　...　...　20　0
Yellow sand　...　...　...　...　...　...　...　...　20　0
Yellow loam　...　...　...　...　...　...　...　...　54　0

Total　...　106 ft.

About the middle of the Variegated Marls and Sandstones a
coarse quartz grit can be mapped at intervals, forming at times a
subdued strike ridge.　It appears first at Windmill Knap near
Godlingston, crosses the north part of Corfe Common, and runs
for about 3 miles past Steeple and Tyneham.　The grit becomes
markedly coarser and thicker westward.　In a pit 8 ft. deep in a
field on the east side of Steeple church it is worked for gravelling
paths.　Some 12-15 ft. of grit are exposed, dipping 34° N.　The
bulk of the pebbles are the size of a pea but a few of vein-quartz
are up to 2 ins. diameter.　There are other old pits west of the
road to Kimmeridge.　A rather bolder escarpment is usually
formed by a sandstone lower down in the series.　This is
responsible for the higher southern part of Corfe Common and the
strike ridge followed for two miles eastwards by the main road to
Swanage.

(c) WORBARROW BAY

The variegated Wealden marls and sandstones give to this
beautiful bay its brilliant red, orange, yellow and purple cliffs.
Nearly the whole of the formation is well exposed and dips
to the north steeply enough for direct measurement.　Almost
exactly in the middle is the Coarse Quartz Grit, 20 ft. thick.　In
addition there are numerous thinner grit and conglomerate bands
which provide useful datum planes in measuring.

WEALDEN BEDS, WORBARROW

[Lower Greensand above ; *see* p. 175]

Ft.

35.　Sandrock, bright ochre and orange-coloured ;　irregular
　　　surface ; ¼ to ...　...　...　...　...　...　...　2
34.　Sand, white, and some white clay　...　...　...　6½
33.　Ironstone, blood-red and purple, botryoidal.　2-3 inches　...
32.　Red, purple and orange sandrock　...　...　...　...　18
31.　White sands and clays ...　...　...　...　...　...　68
30.　Red sands with blood-red and purple irony bands ...　...　33
29.　Gritstone, coarse, 1 ft. to　...　...　...　...　...　2
28.　Clays, mainly slipped　...　...　...　...　...　...　214
27.　Yellow sand, about　...　...　...　...　...　...　10
26.　Clays, partly dark　...　...　...　...　...　...　70
25.　Yellow false-bedded sand　...　...　...　...　...　6

[1] Geol. Survey Coll. no. Rh. 2973 (see fig. 35).

Ft.

24. Gritstone, coarse, irony 1½
23. Clay, sand and sandrock 60
22. Gritstone, dark, irony, impersistent 1
21. Mottled clays 30
20. Gritstone, coarse, rusty, with lignite 1
19. Mottled clays 30
18. Conglomerate, iron hard, impersistent 2
17. Clays, sandy towards base 60
16. Ironstone 1
15. Sandy clays with sulphur, blackish to pale, passing irregularly into false bedded concretionary sandstone masses ... 65
14. THE COARSE QUARTZ GRIT, false-bedded, conglomeratic ironstone, sand and interbedded clay seams ; maximum ... 20
         Total to the base of the Coarse Quartz Grit   701ft.
13. Pink ,white and orange sandstones and sands, some clay ... 36
12. Clay, sand and thin sandstones, with a thin impersistent grit in middle 115
11. Ironstone, banded, conspicuous 3
10. Clay, largely red 47
9. Sand and grit ,white and yellow 24
8. Clay, red, purple and mottled 59
7. Ironstone, hard, purple ... ... ½
6. Coarse yellow and brown sand and sandrock... 14
5. Ironstone, hard, brown ; in places 1 ft., generally ... ... ½
4. Clays, sulphurous towards base 63
3. Lignite beds 5
2. Clays and subordinate beds of sand to end of exposure ... 190
1. Gap, unexposed at stream, then Wealden clays 135
         Total below the Coarse Grit 692 ft.

Total ... 1,393

The section printed above was measured in 1938 with the help of Mr. C. W. Wright. After careful corrections for the dip and angles of measurement, the beds above the base of the Coarse Quartz Grit (701 ft.) emerge as only 30 ft. thinner than in Strahan's section (allowing for the transference of the highest 6 ft. of Strahan's section to the Lower Greensand; *see below*, p. 176). Below the Coarse Quartz Grit beds 9 to 13 (225 ft.) correspond to Strahan's beds 6 to 11 (253 ft.). Below this, however, Strahan has only 108 ft. of beds seen plus 140 ft. not seen (248 ft. total), whereas it is possible to measure in continuous section 332 ft. of beds, to which have to be added at least 135 ft. of beds not seen, making 465 ft. total. Hence the total thickness of the Wealden Beds emerges as 1,393 ft., some 250 ft. thicker than stated by Strahan.

(d) MUPE BAY

This section, although complete, is only 1½ miles from Worbarrow and so need not be described in detail. Nevertheless in that short distance there has been a great reduction in thickness to not much more than half (about 750 ft.). The Coarse Quartz Grit appears again, still about 20 ft. thick, about 270 ft. from the top, or 100 ft. above the middle instead of at the middle as at Worbarrow. Hence it may be inferred that whereas the whole formation has been reduced by nearly half by original thinning westwards, some 30 per cent of the upper division was removed by erosion before the deposition of the Lower Greensand.

The most interesting feature in this section is a conspicuous oil sand about 80 ft. above the base of the Wealden (95 ft. above the thin band of green limestone with fish scales mentioned on p. 140). At least 16 ft. of sands with some interlaminated shaly layers are impregnated with oil, which colours them brown and emits a strong odour. One band about 1-2 ft. thick near the middle carries coarse soft sandstone pebbles and boulders up to 2 ft. long, black, greasy and pungent with oil. They lie in a finer sand which is less strongly impregnated.

The dip at the base of the Wealden is 40°, at the oil sand 53°, and at the Coarse Quartz Grit 75°.

(e) LULWORTH COVE TO DUNGY HEAD

The east side of Lulworth Cove provides another good section of the Wealden Beds. Long ago the Variegated Marls in the lower half of the formation were made into bricks, and remains of the old kilns still stand by the beach at the mouth of the little dell leading up to Bindon Abbey. The dips range from 90°-100° N. (inverted) in the lower beds to 73° N. at the Coarse Quartz Grit and beyond. Here and westward the influence of the Lulworth Crumple (see p. 296) makes itself felt by oversteepening the dips in the Lower Wealden.

WEALDEN BEDS, LULWORTH COVE, EAST SIDE

[Probable thin Lower Greensand above ; see p. 177]

	Ft.
Variegated marls and sands ...　...　...　...　...　...	85
Four or five bands of soft ironstone　...　...　...　...	5
Variegated marls and ferruginous sands　...　...　...　...	100
Coarse Quartz Grit　...　...　...　...　...　...　...	14
Variegated marls and sandstones, with black oil sand at base (lower beds partly obscured ; formerly worked for bricks)　...	230
Variegated marls and sandstones, exposed intermittently...　...	110
[Purbeck Beds below ; see p. 141].	
Total　...	544

The measurement of 190 ft. for the beds above the Coarse Quartz Grit was obtained in the upper part of the cliff where now they are best exposed. It is possible that Strahan's measurement, some 40 ft. larger, was taken at a lower level, and that the difference may be due to unconformity of the supposed Lower Greensand or the Gault (see p. 177).

On the west side of the cove the section is poor. A conspicuous black sand exposed here does not smell of oil and owes its colour only to carbonaceous matter. The oil sand reappears in the high cliff between Stair Hole and Dungy Head, however, at a point marked by a navigation beacon. It is chocolate coloured and about 12 ft. thick. On the west side of Dungy Head where the oil is fresher, the oil sand is sticky and chocolate brown to black in colour, as at Mupe Bay.[1]

At Dungy Head the Wealden Beds, like the Purbeck, have been reduced an unknown amount by strike faulting. At the same time the upper part is rapidly overstepped southwards and westwards by the Gault. Strahan found the total thickness to be 156 ft. But while both the Gault and the Wealden are inverted, the dip of the Gault is only 100° N. and that of the Wealden 110° N. In consequence of this lack of parallelism there are 35 ft. more Wealden Beds at the foot of the cliff than at the top[2]; a result which doubtless throws light on the similar anomalies in the measurements of the upper part of the section at Lulworth Cove.

(f) DURDLE PROMONTORY

The last coast section is in the promontory of Durdle. The Wealden Beds are fully exposed on both sides and can be followed along the strike from beach level on one side to the crest of the col and down to the beach on the other side. The strata are all inverted and show steep apparent dips to the south. The lower beds dip about 110° N. in the lower part of the cliff and curve upwards to 95° N. near the top; but from about the Coarse Quartz Grit upwards in the succession the dip is only 95° N. at beach level.

The succession is most complete on the east side of the promontory (Man-o'-War Cove) where a thickness of 215 ft. can be measured along the foot of the cliff :—

WEALDEN BEDS, DURDLE (EAST SIDE)

[Pebble Bed at base of Gault above ; *see* p. 190]

	Ft.	
Sands and marls with lignite	39	
Coarse Quartz Grit, with interlaminated sand and clay ...	28	
Variegated marls and white sand	61	⎫
White sandstone	10	⎬ 148 ft.
Variegated marls with an indefinite lignitic quartz grit at 58-64 ft. down	77	⎭

[Fault breccia with Beef Beds below; *see* p. 142].

Total ... 215ft.

The Coarse Quartz Grit is here thicker than at any other exposure in Dorset and contains many pebbles an inch or more in diameter, mainly of white quartz and black lydite. It can be

---

[1] G. M. Lees and P. T. Cox, ' The Geological Basis of the present Search for Oil in Great Britain . . ' *Quart. Journ. Geol. Soc.*, vol. xciii, 1937, p. 166.
[2] A. Strahan, *op. cit.*, 1898, p. 130.

followed up to the crest of the col where it cannot be more than 15 ft. below the base of the Gault (instead of 39 ft. at beach level), although the contact is not at present exposed. Half way down the west side the Grit almost disappears, being apparently represented at the foot of the cliff in Durdle Cove by sandstone with only one bed of pebbles, about 1 ft. thick, and a few much thinner seams such as occur at various other levels in the Wealden Series. The explanation seems to be that there is an oblique strike fault. It brings the surviving part of the Grit almost into contact with the 10 ft. bed of white sandstone, which lies 61 ft. below it on the east side of the promontory. Part of the slickensided fault plane was exposed in 1938 in a small gully between the top of the sandstone and the supposed continuation of part of the Coarse Quartz Grit.

The total thickness of Wealden Beds at beach level in Durdle Cove is about 160 ft.; but true thicknesses are difficult to measure, owing to the varying dip.

Calculations indicate that about 130 ft. of the basal Wealden Beds, probably including the oil sand, are cut out by the strike fault which also cuts out the Upper Purbeck (*see* p. 142), and that probably something like 300 ft. of the upper beds were removed by erosion before the deposition of the Gault.[1]

(g) CHALDON, OSMINGTON AND RIDGEWAY

Wealden beds floor most of the Chaldon pericline, forming an elliptical inlier, in which the beds dip in general to the south at about 20-25° off the small Purbeck dome under the northern chalk escarpment. A band of white and yellow sand and quartz grit forms a ridge north of Chaldon Herring and again south-west of Northground Dairy.

West of the Albian bridge at Holworth a tongue of Wealden extends for nearly 3 miles along the centre of the Upton Syncline, broken only by the gorge at Osmington.[2] This green and oak-studded vale reproduces on a small scale the scenery of the main Wealden outcrop from Swanage to Worbarrow. The meagre exposures show Variegated Marls and Sandstones of the usual type. A quartz grit can be mapped for nearly a mile towards Upton, at a distance of 200 yds. from the top of the Purbeck Beds. That the Wealden Beds do not terminate on the east side of Osmington as indicated on the 1904 edition of Sheet 342, but are continued by a synclinal outlier north and north-west of the church, is proved by the nature of the soil, by hand-augering, by a pond, and by small excavations made in 1938.

---

[1] W. J. Arkell, ' Three Tectonic Problems of the Lulworth District,' *Quart. Journ. Geol. Soc.*, vol. xciv, 1938. pp. 28-9.

[2] See folding map, Pl. XIX.

The auger proves yellow and orange quartz sand along the top of the strike-ridge west of Bincombe, but this is probably in the uppermost Purbeck Beds. True Wealden comes in at Lower Bincombe Farm and was exposed by the Ridgeway railway-cutting. It is pinched in at the overdeepened centre of the Upwey Syncline and faulted on the north against Oxford Clay. The Ridgeway cutting shows little of the Wealden Beds now, except sands in the lower part and the junction of the red and green mottled clays with blue-grey Oxford Clay. Strahan made out a succession of ferruginous clay with lignite and sand, grey and brown clay and sand, quartz grit, white sand, and clay, the dip being 40-50° N. According to Fisher the total thickness seen was 350 ft., but this is not necessarily the full thickness of the formation. He found *Unio* in some hard bands, and abundant bones of *Iguanodon* in a stiff grey clay near the base.[1]

Mottled clay probably belonging to the Wealden Beds comes in again in the centre of the syncline north of Friar Waddon.

---

[1] A. Strahan, *op. cit.,* 1898, p. 132.

CHAPTER IX

APTIAN STAGE: LOWER GREENSAND

I. GENERAL

The Lower Greensand begins the long cycle of marine transgression and sedimentation that continued until the end of the Cretaceous period.

As shown in Chapter VIII, the Aptian sea invaded the tract occupied in Upper Wealden times by a vast estuary, which had previously been a lake, and was by this time choked up almost to the surface with deltaic and fluvio-marine deposits. Since the precise date of the Wealden Shales within the Neocomian is unknown (*see* p. 151), the extent of the gap between the Wealden Beds and the Lower Greensand must remain uncertain. Some time before, during, or after the deposition of the Lower Greensand, or perhaps at several dates in all three periods, but at least between the Wealden and the Gault epochs, the Weymouth district was strongly folded and faulted and the irregularities so formed were planed off (*see* Chapter XIII, pp. 246-7).

The idea that the folding and faulting were brought about by repeated movements spanning the time from Upper Neocomian to Lower Albian, and that after each spasm of earth-movements the sea pared off a fresh layer of the upraised rocks, seems probable when Lower Cretaceous movements in neighbouring areas are considered. In the Teutoburger Wald and other hills near Hanover the so-called Hils phase of the Cimmerian movements caused the Upper Valanginian and later Neocomian to overstep the Jurassic rocks and lie unconformably on their bevelled edges.[1] In Eastern Spain[2] it is the Lower Aptian that is transgressive and in the Ardennes the Upper Aptian,[3] and it was within the Upper Aptian

---

[1] H. Stille, *Grundfragen der Vergleichenden Tektonik,* 1924, ed. 1, pp. 140-1 (where references will be found). **Berlin.**

[2] H. Coquand, *Monographie de l'étage Aptien de l'Espagne,* 1865. Marseille.

[3] K. Hummel, ' Meeresbewegungen und tektonische Erscheinungen im südlichen Ardennenvorland,' *Geol. Rundschau,* vol. xi, 1920, p. 18.

that the most important of the Lower Cretaceous movements took place elsewhere in the south of England and also in the Boulonnais. During the deposition of the Nutfieldensis Zone (*see* table on p. 166), as indicated by lateral changes in the thickness and facies of the Hythe and Sandgate Beds, sedimentation in the western Weald was controlled by both E.-W. folding of the sea bottom and monoclinal warping along N.-S. axes.[1] In many parts of the Weald the deposition of the Sandgate or equivalent Bargate Beds was preceded by a break in deposition, marked by a phosphatic pebble bed, or else they may overstep the Hythe Beds completely, to spread over the Weald Clay, as in the south and east of the Weald.[2] The differential movements accompanying or causing this overstep brought Oxford Clay, Corallian Beds and Kimmeridge Clay within the influence of erosion close to the present Hog's Back, south of which the succession is complete up to Wealden Beds; this is shown by the abundance of well-preserved Jurassic ammonites found in the pebble beds of the Bargate Beds, and it seems explicable only by analogy with the Boulonnais (Cap Gris Nez) and the Ridgeway Fault Zone of the Weymouth district.[3]

The highly transgressive Lower Greensand patches in other parts of the South of England, notably at Seend and Calne in Wiltshire and Faringdon in Berkshire, likewise belong to the Nutfieldensis Zone (=Subnodosocostatum Zone) and are correlated with the Sandgate Beds.[4] Near Calne the beds cross a big fault from Kimmeridge Clay on to Corallian Beds, and at Faringdon the Sponge Gravels overlie eroded folds and faults in the Corallian Beds and Kimmeridge Clay.

That the whole area was subjected to renewed movements and erosions in early Albian times is indicated by the transgressive and somewhat diachronic base of the Upper Gault.[5] In Sussex the Gault rests on a nodule bed containing phosphatized ammonites of the uppermost Lower Albian and basal Middle Albian (Mammillatum Zone).[6]

In East Dorset and the Isle of Wight the Lower Greensand begins with a basal pebble bed containing phosphatic nodules and fish teeth. In the Isle of Wight this is called the Perna Bed, and it rests on a puckered and brecciated surface of the Wealden

---

[1] J. F. Kirkaldy, ' The Tectonic Development of the Western Weald,' *Geol. Mag.*, 1933, pp. 263-5.

[2] J. F. Kirkaldy, ' The Sandgate Beds of the Western Weald,' *Proc. Geol. Assoc.*, vol. xliv, 1933, pp. 302-5; and ' The Overstep of the Sandgate Beds in the Western Weald,' *Quart. Journ. Geol. Soc.*, vol. xciii, 1937, p. 94.

[3] W. J. Arkell, ' Derived Ammonites from the Lower Greensand of Surrey,' *Proc. Geol. Assoc.*, vol. 1, 1939, p. 22.

[4] J. F. Kirkaldy, 1933, *op. cit.*, p. 306.

[5] F. L. Kitchin and J. Pringle, 'The Overlap of the Upper Gault in England . . ,' *Geol. Mag.*, 1922, pp. 156, 194.

[6] J. F. Kirkaldy, ' The Base of the Gault in Sussex,' *Quart. Journ. Geol. Soc.* vol.xci, 1935, p. 524.

Shales.[1]　At Swanage beneath the corresponding bed the surface
of the Wealden Shales was seen to be disturbed.[2]　The pebble
bed at Swanage, however, may be somewhat later than in the
Isle of Wight, and west of Corfe Castle it seems to be overlapped
by still higher beds.　At Worbarrow and Mupe Bays, there is
nothing definite to mark the junction of the Wealden with the
Lower Greensand.

Near the top of the Dorset Lower Greensand there are pebble
beds which can be correlated, via the Isle of Wight, with the
pebbly and transgressive Sandgate and Bargate Beds of the
Weald.　If these beds ever overstepped westwards, as is highly
probable, the evidence has been removed by the subsequent paring
off of the surface by the Albian sea.

II.　Stratigraphy

In order to understand the Lower Greensand of Dorset, it is
essential to compare it with the much thicker and more fossiliferous equivalents in the Isle of Wight.　On the west coast of the
island, in the cliffs from Atherfield Point to Chale, the formation
reaches a thickness of nearly 800 feet.　It thins north-eastwards
to 600 ft. at Sandown Bay (10 miles) and to only 92 ft. in the
Portsdown boring (20 miles).　North-westward it thins to 400 ft.
in Compton Bay (about 8 miles) and westward to 200 ft. at Punfield in Swanage Bay (26 miles).

Where fully developed from Atherfield Point to Chale, the
Lower Greensand comprises the succession of subdivisions listed in the middle column of the table on p. 166.　Most of the
subdivisions were named and defined in 1845-7 by Fitton, whose
names are adopted in the Survey Memoirs on the Isle of Wight[3]
and are reproduced in the accompanying table, with trifling modifications where the palaeontological titles are out of date and
misleading (for instance, *Gryphaea* beds, *Scaphites* group).
Against the groups have been placed the principal ammonites
found in them, according to the revision carried out by Spath[4],
and in the left-hand column is the zonal scheme for the Aptian,
also the work of Spath.[5]　The Dorset equivalents are on the right.

In general, beds I to IV, up to the top of the Lower Exogyra
sinuata Bed, are characterized by abundance of *Deshayesites
deshayesi* (d'Orbigny) and other species of the genus.[6]　This is a

---

[1] H. J. O. White, ' Short Account of the Geology of the Isle of Wight,' *Mem.
Geol. Surv.*, 1921, p. 24.

[2] A. Strahan, *Purbeck Memoir*, 1898, p. 136.　The Wealden-Aptian junction is now
obscured.

[3] *See* H. J. O. White, *op. cit.*, 1921, ch. iii.

[4] L. F. Spath, ' On Some Ammonoidea from the Lower Greensand,' *Ann. Mag.
Nat. Hist.*, ser. 10, vol. v, 1930, p. 417.

[5] L. F. Spath, ' On the Ammonite Horizons of the Gault and Contiguous Deposits,'
Sum. Prog. Geol. Surv. for 1922, 1923, p. 148 ; some emendations in Spath, *op. cit.*,
1930.

[6] *Parahoplitoides* Spath, 1922, is a synonym of *Deshayesites* Kazansky, 1914.

Divisions of the Lower Greensand in the Isle of Wight and Dorest

	Zones	Isle of Wight Strata	Geol. Surv. I.O.W. 1887	Dorset	
				Bed Nos.	Strata at Punfield
ALBIAN ?	?	XVI. Carstone (73ft.) XV. Sandrock Series (184ft.)	Sand-rock Series	15 ?	Top bed at Punfield ? (10ft.)
UPPER APTIAN (GARGASIAN)	*Parahoplites nutfieldensis*	XIV. Blackgang Ferruginous bands ... (20ft.) XIII. Walpen Undercliff Sands (100ft.) XII. Foliated clay and sand (25ft.) XI. Cliff-end Sands (28ft.)	Ferruginous Sands (493ft.)	14 13 12	Ferruginous Sands (undifferent-iated) (138ft.)
	Cheloniceras martini	X. Upper Exogyra sinuata Bed ... (16ft.) IX. Walpen and Ladder Sands (42ft.) V-VIII. Tropaeum Beds (*T. gigas, T. hillsi, T. bowerbanki, Ch. martini*) (170ft.)		11 10 9	
LOWER APTIAN (BEDOULIAN)	*Deshayesites deshayesi*	IV. Lower Exogyra sinuata Bed (*Deshayesites grandis* dominant) ... (33ft.) III. { c. Upper Lobster Bed (*Deshayesites sp.*) (40ft.) b. Crackers (abundant *D. deshayesi* and allied species) ... (20ft.) a. Lower Lobster Bed (abundant *D. deshayesi* and allied species) (25-30ft.) II. Atherfield Clay (rare fragments of *Procheloniceras* ?) (75ft.) I. Perna Bed	Atherfield Clay (105 ft.)	8 7 6 5 4 3 2 1	Punfield Marine Band (*Deshayesites punfieldensis* and *Parahoplites sp.*) Condensed (10 ins.) Atherfield Clay (abundant *Deshayesites deshayesi* and allied species in bed 7 (46ft.) Pebble Bed (3ft.)
	Costidiscus rectecostatus Absent				Absent

Lower Aptian fauna, but not the lowest. Whether the Rectecostatus Zone of the Continental Lower Aptian is represented in the Perna Bed is uncertain, for Spath states that the ammonite records from that bed are doubtful, and that he knows of only two fragments of ammonites (*Procheloniceras?*) from the restricted Atherfield Clay (bed II).

The Upper Aptian begins with the Martini Zone, beds V to X, long noted for the occurrence of large uncoiled ammonoids formerly called *Crioceras* and *Scaphites,* now assigned to the genus *Tropaeum.*   The genus *Cheloniceras* ranges through all three zones, but in beds XI to XIV rare examples of the *Cheloniceras subnodosocostatum* group are the only ammonites found.   In the Sandrock Series ammonites are virtually unknown.   Spath states that " the ammonite fauna of the Lower Greensand as a whole must be considered an impoverished one " ; a verdict which will be readily agreed with when the Aptian faunas of some other regions, such as Georgia, are considered.[1]

Already at Compton Bay, only 6½ miles north-west of Atherfield Point, precise correlation with Atherfield is impossible.   All the beds are much thinner and they have changed in character and, with the exception of the Perna Bed, are less fossiliferous. Here already the Survey were able to employ only their threefold division, Atherfield Clay (extended to include the Lower Lobster Bed), Ferruginous Sands, and Sandrock Series.   The Atherfield Clay (*sensu lato*) of this section is only about 60 ft. thick, but it is much obscured by slipping.   This is unfortunate, for it is with the Compton section that the Dorset Lower Greensand should be most nearly comparable.

III.   PALAEONTOLOGY

In Dorset the Lower Greensand is divided into a predominantly argillaceous division below (Atherfield Clay and Lower Lobster Bed) with a basal pebble bed, and a sandy division above (Ferruginous Sands). The argillaceous lower part of the formation is highly fossiliferous, though the fossils are difficult to collect owing to fragile preservation and slipping of the clays at the only exposure (Punfield, Swanage) where the beds are typically developed.   The most fossiliferous horizon of all, however, is the basement bed, about 1 ft. thick, of the overlying Ferruginous Sands.   It is called the Punfield Marine Band, although the whole sequence is marine (*see* p. 173).   It is a sandy limestone almost composed of shells, of which the commonest are small bivalves, especially *Anomia laevigata, Exogyra tuberculifera, Cardium ibbetsoni, Corbula striatula, Ostrea cunabula.*   Bored fossil wood is common, and also remains of crustaceans.   The rest of the Ferruginous Sands above is unfossiliferous.

---

[1] J. Rouchadzé, ' Les ammonites aptiennes de la Géorgie occidentale,' *Bull. de l'Inst. géol. de Géorgie,* vol. i, fasc. 3, Tiflis, 1933.

The Punfield Marine Band, which persists as a fossil bed as far west as Worbarrow Bay, appears to be the only representative of the Isle of Wight Crackers, Upper Lobster Bed, and Lower

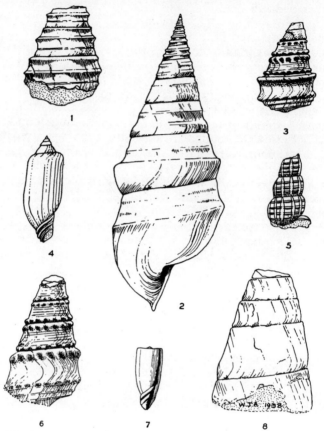

FIG. 37.—*Gastropods from the Lower Greensand of Purbeck.*
1. *Cassiope pizcuetana* (Vilanova) var. cf. *renevieri* Coquand, Corfe Station, G.S. No. 70317; 2. *Cassiope pizcuetana* (Vilanova), the commonest species in Purbeck, drawn from a perfect Atherfield, I.O.W., Crackers specimen, B.M. No. G.7810; 3. *Cassiope lujani* (de Verneuil) var. *crassa* Coquand, Worbarrow, G.S. No. 70314; 4 *Actaeonella* cf. *oliviformis* Coquand, Punfield, C. W. Wright Coll. ($\times$ 1½); 5. *?Dimorphosoma* cf. *calcarata* (J. Sowerby), Punfield, C. W. Wright Coll. ($\times$ 1½); 6. *Cassiope lujani* (de Verneuil), Corfe Station, G.S. No. 70315; 7. *Actaeonella? verneuilli* (Vilanova), Punfield, C. W. Wright Coll. ($\times$ 1½); 8. *Cassiope helvetica* (Pictet and Renevier), Corfe Station, G.S. No. 70316.

Exogyra sinuata Bed. Most of its fossils are found in the Crackers Group, but higher beds appear to be represented, and the crustacean remains suggest that at least the Upper Lobster Bed is included. The most interesting feature of this remarkable bed is an assemblage of gastropods characteristic of the marine Aptian (Trigonia Limestone) of Teruel, eastern Spain, and assembled together nowhere else (Fig. 37). The most characteristic forms of the assemblage belong to the Turritellid genus *Cassiope* Coquand (= *Glauconia* auct., Giebel 1852, preoccupied for a lizard by Gray, 1845).[1] They are ponderous thick-shelled gastropods more than 2 ins. in length, ornamented with coarse spiral ribs and spiral rows of tubercles in various combinations, and they show as great a range of individual variation as the freshwater or brackish *Paraglauconia strombiformis* (Schlotheim) of the Wealden Beds. Rehbinder maintained in an exhaustive study of these forms from all parts of the world that the genus *Cassiope* (*Glauconia* auct.) is distributed indiscriminately in the freshwater Wealden of Europe, the Astrakhan Steppe and the Americas, and the marine Aptian and perhaps even higher beds in Europe and America[2]; but it has not been demonstrated that any one species ever occurs in both freshwater and marine beds. A record in the Purbeck Memoir of *P. strombiformis* from the Punfield Marine Band is erroneous, but specimens of that species from Swanage in a different state of preservation have come from the Wealden Shales (*see* p. 153).

Cassiope is such a striking genus that it is not likely to have been overlooked in France, where, of the Dorset species, only *C. helvetica* has been figured. Therefore a direct marine connexion with Spain, down the Channel, is indicated. The largest and commonest Dorset species, *C. pizcuetana* (Vilanova), occurs also in the Crackers at Atherfield, but none has been recorded elsewhere in Britain. Of the gastropods listed below, almost every one has been figured from Teruel.[3]

Fossils from the Lower Greensand of Purbeck

P=Punfield (the numbers refer to beds on p. 173-4)
C=Corfe Castle　　,,　　　,,　　,,　　,,　　,, 175)
W=Worbarrow, bed 7 (p. 176).

Species from Worbarrow marked * are added on the authority of a list supplied by Mr. J. F. Kirkaldy mainly from his own collection. The rest are in the collections of the Geological Survey and have been revised by the author, except that Punfield species marked * have been seen and identified by the author in his own or Mr. C. W. Wright's collection only. Records marked + are from specimens loaned from the Sedgwick Museum (chiefly Meyer Coll.).

In the Isle of Wight column, P = Perna Beds, A = Atherfield Clay, C = Crackers Group, F. = higher Ferruginous Sands (from

[1] They were wrongly recorded in the *Purbeck Memoir* (1898, pp. 127, 142, and figure on p. 137) and elsewhere as belonging to the Tertiary Cerithiid genus *Vicarya* (d' Archiac, 1853), which is unrelated.
[2] B. Rehbinder, ' Fauna und Alter der cretaceischen Sandsteine in der Umgebung des Salzsees Baskuntschak,' *Mem. Comité géol.*, vol. xvii, no. 1, 1902, p. 83.
[3] See especially H. Coquand, *Monographie de l'étage Aptien de l'Espagne*, 1865. Marseille; and E. de Verneuil and G. de Lorière, *Descr. fossiles Néocomien sup. de Utrillas et ses environs* (*Province de Teruel*), 1868. Le Mans.

Fig. 38.—*Characteristic fossils of the Lower Greensand of Purbeck.*

1, 2. *Anomia laevigata* J. de C. Sowerby; 3. *Barbatia aptiensis* (Pictet and Campiche); 4a, b. *Cardium ibbetsoni* Forbes; 5, 6. *Corbula striatula* J. de C. Sowerby ($\times 2\frac{1}{2}$); 7. *Corbula* aff. *striatula,* form from Punfield ($\times 2\frac{1}{2}$); 8a, b. *Cyprina anglica* Woods; 9. *Exogyra tuberculifera* Koch and Dunker; 10. *Cyprimeria* (*Cyclorisma*) *vectensis* (Forbes); 11. *Astarte subcostata* d'Orbigny; 12. *Tellina* (*Linearia*) *subconcentrica* (d'Orbigny); 13. *Deshayesites punfieldensis* Spath (drawn from the original figure); 14. *Deshayesites deshayesi* (d'Orbigny) (drawn from the original figure).

Woods's Monograph).   The Isle of Wight gastropods have not been worked out.

LAMELLIBRANCHIA	PURBECK			ISLE OF WIGHT			
Nucula planata *Deshayes*	$*P_7$			P		C	
Nucula sp.			W*				
Nuculana scapha (*d'Orbigny*)	P_1				A		
Nuculana sp.	$*P_7$						F
Anomia laevigata *J. de C. Sowerby* (Fig. 38)	P_8						F
Barbatia aptiensis (*Pictet & Campiche*) (Fig. 38)	$P_{1,2,*7,*8}$			P	A	C	F
Cucullaea cornueliana (*d'Orbigny*)	$P_{1,8}$	C†	W			C	F
?Pectunculus marullensis *Leymerie*	P_8						F
Trigonia etheridgei *Lycett* or caudata *Agassiz*		C_1		P		C	
Trigonia vectiana *Lycett*			W*	P			F
Mytilus lanceolatus *J. de C. Sowerby*	$*P_8$	C_1		P		C	F
Modiola subsimplex (*d'Orbigny*)	$?P_8$		W	P		C	
Modiola aequalis *J. Sowerby*			W*	P		C	F
Brachidontes vectiensis *Woods*	P_8		W*	P		C	
?Crenella bella (*J. de C. Sowerby*)	$*P_7$			P		C	
Chlamys robinaldina (*d'Orbigny*)	P_1			P			F
Neithea morrisi (*Pictet & Renevier*)	P_1	C_1		P		C	
Lima (Pseudolimea) parallela (*J. Sowerby*)	P_1			P	A		F
Lima (Limatula) cf. tombeckiana *d'Orbigny*	P_7*						F
Ostrea cunabula *Seeley*	P_8						
Exogyra sinuata (*J. Sowerby*)	P_8				A		F
Exogyra tuberculifera *Koch and Dunker* (Fig. 38)	$P_{1,7,*8}$	C_3		P		C	F
Pteria cottaldina (*d'Orbigny*) var. carteroni (*d'Orbigny*)			W				
Pseudoptera subdepressa (*d'Orbigny*)	$P_{1,7}*$					C	
Gervillia linguloides *Forbes*	$P_8†$	C_3	W*			C	
Astarte subcostata *d'Orbigny* (Fig. 38)	P_7*	C_3	W	?P			
Astarte obovata *J. de C. Sowerby*			W	P			
?Cardita fenestrata (*Forbes*)	P_2			P	A		
Cardita cf. dupiniana *d'Orbigny*	P_7	C_3					
Anthonya cornueliana (*d'Orbigny*)			W			C?	
Cyprina saussuri (*Brongniart*)		C_3		P		C	
Cyprina anglica *Woods* (Fig. 38)	P_7*	C_3	W			C	
Cyprina vectiana (*Forbes*)		C_1				C	
Lucina sp. (*Woods*, pl. xxiv, figs. 4,5)	$P_{2,7}*$						
Mactromya compressa (*Woods*)	P_7*					C	
Thetironia minor (*J. de C. Sowerby*)	$P_7†$	$C_{1,3}$		P		C	F
Tellina (Linearia) subconcentrica (*d'Orb.*) (*Woods* pl. xxvii, fig. 9) (Fig. 38)	$P_{1,7,*8}*$	C_3				C	
Cyprimeria (Cyclorisma) parva (*J. de C. Sowerby*)	P_8		W*	P		C	F
Cyprimeria (Cyclorisma) vectensis (*Forbes*) (Fig. 38)	$P_7*_8†$	C†			A	C	F

Lamellibranchia	Purbeck			Isle of Wight
Cardium ibbetsoni *Forbes* (Fig. 38)	$P_{1,2,8}$	$C_{1,3}$		C
Corbula striatula *J. de C. Sowerby* (Fig. 38)	P_8	C_3	W	P A C F
Corbula aff. striatula (*Woods*, pl. xxxiv, 13) (Fig. 38)	P_8	C_3		
Pharus warburtoni (*Forbes*)	P_7*	C_1	W*	C
Panopea gurgitis (*Brongniart*) (and var. plicata *J. de C. Sowerby*)	$P_{1,2,6}$			P C F
Plectomya anglica *Woods*	P_7*			C
Thracia robinaldina (*d'Orbigny*)		?C	W*	P C
Pholadomya cornueliana (*d'Orbigny*) (& P. martini *Forbes*?)		C_1		P C
Myopholas cf. semicostata (*Agassiz*)	P_8			
?Cuspidaria sp.			W	

Gastropoda

	Purbeck			Isle of Wight
Cassiope pizcuetana (*Vilanova*) (Fig. 37)	P_8	C_3		C
Cassiope pizcuetana var. cf. renevieri *Coquand* (Fig. 37)		C_3		
Cassiope lujani (*de Verneuil*) (Fig. 37)	P_8	C_3		
Cassiope lujani var. crassa *Coquand* (var. verneuilli *Coquand*) (Fig. 37)		C_3	W	
Cassiope helvetica (*Pictet and Renevier*) (Fig. 37)		C_3		
Turritella (Haustator) cf. dupiniana *d'Orbigny*			P_8	
Turritella sp.		W		
Actaeonella (Trochactaeon) cf. oliviformis *Coquand* (Fig. 37)		$P_8 C$†		
Actaeonella (Cylindritella) cf. verneuilli (*Vilanova*) (Fig. 37)		P_8		
Trochus (Proconulus) esqueriae *de Verneuil and de Lorière*		P_8		
Natica pradoana *Vilanova*		P_8		
Natica laevigata (*Deshayes*)		P_8, C_3		
Tylostoma rochatiana (*d'Orbigny*)		P_8		
Cerithium (Gymnocerithium) nostradami *Coquand*		P_8		
?Dimorphosoma cf. calcarata (*de Verneuil and de Lorière*, pl. iii, fig. 1, *non Sowerby*) (Fig. 37)		P_8, W		
Aporrhais (Perissoptera) spartacus *Coquand*		P		
?Aporrhais cf. casullae *Coquand*		P_8		

Cephalopoda

Deshayesites deshayesi (*d'Orbigny*) (Fig. 38)	$P_{7,*8}$
Deshayesites punfieldensis *Spath* (Fig. 38)	P_8, type
Parahoplites sp. juv.	P_8

Miscellaneous

Fish teeth (Pycnodus, Lepidotus, Lamna)	$P_{1,8}$ C_1
Crustacean remains	$P_{7,8}$ common
Serpula	P_8
Multizonopora ramosa (*d'Orbigny*)	P_1
Wood, bored	P_8

IV. Details

(a) PUNFIELD COVE, SWANAGE

The best section of the Lower Greensand in Dorset is to be seen in the recess known as Punfield Cove, at the north corner of Swanage Bay. The true succession and approximate correlation of the lower beds was first elucidated by Meyer, who found the basal pebbly bed resting on estuarine Wealden Shales as in the Isle of Wight, and proved all the beds above it to be marine. He recognized in the clay many fossils of the Atherfield Clay and ' Lobster Clay ' (Lower Lobster Bed).[1] Fifteen years later (1888) special excavations were undertaken by the Survey and the section was measured by Strahan and fossils were collected sytematically by J. Rhodes.[2]

Before Meyer's papers appeared the lower third of what is now known to be Aptian was believed to contain an alternation of marine and freshwater faunas and to be of Upper Wealden age.[3] The mistake was probably due to slipping.

The following description and measurements are taken from Strahan, with slight modifications and fossils added. The Punfield Marine Band, the principal fossil bed, was so named by Judd, who regarded it as part of his Wealden "Punfield Formation.'

LOWER GREENSAND AT PUNFIELD

[Gault above, with traces of thin Carstone at base ; see p. 185]

		Ft.
FERRUGINOUS SANDS (149 ft.)		
15.	Yellow sand, not well seen ; about	10
14.	Clay, dark, sandy, selenitic	15
13.	White sandstone with quartz pebbles	20
12.	Brown sandstone and yellow sandstone with shales ...	15
11.	Interlaminated sand and clay ; worm burrows ?	15
10.	Ferruginous sand and hard irony sandstone with *Nuculana*	12
9.	Interlaminated sand and yellow clay with some thicker beds of yellow and white sand	61
8.	PUNFIELD MARINE BAND. Fossiliferous limestone with wavy seams of lignite. [*Deshayesites deshayesi* and *D. punfieldensis, Parahoplites sp. juv.*, and many lamellibranchs and gastropods, see p. 171] Variable, about ...	1
ATHERFIELD CLAY (46½ ft.)		
7.	Clay, reddish above, becoming blue and very fossiliferous in the lower part [*Deshayesites deshayesi* and many lamellibranchs]	28
6.	Sandstone, soft yellow,, with *Barbatia aptiensis, Panopea gurgitis, Exogyra*	1
5.	Clay, pale red, bluish in parts ; a few fossils	8½

[1] C. J. A. Meyer, ' On the Wealden as a Fluvio-lacustrine Formation, and on the relation of the so-called Punfield Formation to the Wealden and Neocomian,' *Quart. Journ. Geol. Soc.*, vol. xxviii, 1872, p. 250; and ' Further notes on the Punfield Section,' *ibid.*, vol. xxix, 1873, p. 70.

[2] A. Strahan, *Purbeck Memoir*, 1898, pp. 135, 141.

[3] J. W. Judd, 'On the Punfield Formation,' *Quart. Journ. Geol. Soc.*, vol. xxvii, 1871, p. 207.

Ft.
4. Sandstone, in four hard grey bands ; no fossils 3
3. Clay, red ; a few fossils in the lower part 6

PEBBLE BED (3 ft.)
2. Sand, dark green, with small pebbles and grit ; many fossils 1
1. Pebbly clay, pale blue, sandy, with many fossils ; small
   rolled bivalves, ammonites, etc., and larger pebbles of
   sandstone, wood, etc., at the base 2

[Wealden Shales below, see p. 155]

Strahan correlated the Pebble Bed with the Isle of Wight Perna Bed, but there is no palaeontological evidence for contemporaneity, and it is quite possible that the pebbly basement bed is somewhat diachronic, becoming younger westwards. He correlated the Punfield Marine Band with the Crackers, and the bulk of its fossils are most abundant in the Crackers, where also *Cassiope pizcuetana* (Vilanova) occurs ; but as stated above (p. 168), at least the Upper Lobster Bed is probably represented also. Moreover, Spath states that at Atherfield and Blackgang *Deshayesites punfieldensis* is found in the upper part of the Deshayesi Zone and possibly also in the lower Martini Zone[1] (*see* table on p. 166). At Punfield bed 7, from its abundance of *Deshayesites deshayesi* and other fossils, is to be correlated with the Lower Lobster Bed rather than with the Atherfield Clay proper, which is therefore left with a thickness of only 18 feet.

In the Ferruginous Sands, the coarse sandstone with quartz pebbles, bed 13 which persists on the same horizon at Worbarrow though thinner (*see* p. 175) is probably the continuation of the Walpen Undercliff Sands and Blackgang Ferruginous Bands (XIII and XIV), which have been shown to represent the transgressive Sandgate and Bargate Beds of the western Weald, characterized by conspicuous pebble beds with great quantities of derived Jurassic ammonites and oolitic rock detritus.[2] The dark sandy clay above (bed 14), also present at Worbarrow, probably represents the similar clay which is 40 ft. thick at Blackgang and 26 ft. thick at Compton Bay, and was already correlated by Strahan with the Marehill Clay of Pulborough, Sussex. This would leave only bed 15, obscurely exposed sand 10 ft. thick, to represent the Sandrock Series of the Isle of Wight (up to 184 ft. thick), the bulk of it having been presumably eroded before the deposition of the Gault. At Worbarrow, as will be seen below (p. 175), the overlap goes farther and the pebble bed of the Gault rests on the equivalent of bed 14.

(b) CORFE CASTLE

No noteworthy inland sections of the Lower Greensand are to be seen, but Strahan gives the following important section

---

[1] L. F. Spath, ' On some Ammonoidea from the Lower Greensand,' *Ann. Mag. Nat. Hist.*, ser. 10, vol. v, 1930, p. 431.
[2] J. F. Kirkaldy, ' The Sandgate Beds of the Western Weald,' *Proc. Geol. Assoc.*, vol. xliv, 1933, p. 304.

measured and collected by J. Rhodes in a railway-cutting for a siding on the west side of Corfe Station. The section was long ago grassed over. The beds dip 60° N.[1]

CORFE SIDING (A. Strahan)

LOWER GREENSAND (160½ ft. ; top not reached)

FERRUGINOUS SANDS

		Ft.
6.	Sand, white, brown and red, and laminated sandy loam ...	80
5.	Sandy clay, laminated brown and yellow	30
4.	Blue clay	15
3.	Ferruginous shale with nodules of clay-ironstone, the whole bed full of shell-fragments and lignite	13½

ATHERFIELD CLAY AND PEBBLE BED

2.	Clay, blue and buff, fossiliferous, pink at the top	20
1.	Band of ironstone with fossils, black pebbles, fish-teeth ...	2

WEALDEN BEDS (seen to 106 ft. ; *see* p. 156)

The basal portion of bed 3 represents the Punfield Marine Band. It is noteworthy for a rich fauna like that at Punfield, and in particular there is a greater range of Spanish forms of *Cassiope*. The fossils from bed 3 are listed on p. 171. *Cardium ibbetsoni* Forbes is especially abundant, also *Corbula striatula* J. de C. Sowerby and the little *Tellina (Linearia) sp.* figured by Woods from the Crackers of the Isle of Wight.

Brightly coloured ferruginous sands are exposed to a depth of from 5 to 15 ft. in a long section in the banks of a lane east of Challow Farm.

(c) WORBARROW BAY

This fine section was measured in 1937 with the help of Mr. C. W. Wright, with the following results. The thicker beds which could not be measured perpendicularly were corrected for the dip of 50°.

LOWER GREENSAND, WORBARROW BAY

[Gault above, with at the base a 1-foot pebble bed of quartz and lydite pebbles up to ½ inch in diameter. *See* p. 188]

		Ft.
16.	Interlaminated grey sand and black clay	8
15.	Dark green and black sandy clay or loam, the upper part very glauconitic	12
14.	Sandrock, soft, buff, passing down in to sand ; seam of quartz pebbles at the top	4
13.	Sand, grey and silver	12
12.	Purple ironstone in 2 bands, orange sand between ...	2
11.	Sands, pink in upper part, grey and shaly below, with thin seams of ironstone ; partly obscured. About	20
10.	Ironstone with obscure lamellibranchs	½
9.	Sands, laminated grey and black, with thin shaly ironstone bands as above ; seen to	10
8.	Beds obscured under path (by subtraction). Grey sand at base	14

Total of beds above the ironstone ...   82ft.

[1] A. Strahan, *Purbeck Memoir,* 1898, pp. 126, 139, 141-2.

Ft.

7. Fossiliferous ironstone. For list of fossils *see* p. 171   ...   ¼
6. Sand, grey, with yellow streaks   1
5. Clay, grey, with thin ironstone seams, and much lignite ...   18
4. Sandrock, buff, irony in patches   3
3. Clay and irregular lumpy ironstone 1½
2. Clay, grey, with *Cardium ibbetsoni, Corbula striatula,* and
   lignite   2
   ⎧Ironstone band, irregular (one of many) ; average   ...   ¼
1. ⎨Sand, buff and loamy, passing down into sandy grey
   ⎩clay with lignite   7

Total thickness of L.G.S.   ...   115ft.

[Wealden Beds below, *see* p. 157]

The base of the Lower Greensand is here fixed purely on lithological grounds.   Strahan included bed 1 in the Wealden, but it
is indistinguishable (except for the lack of *Cardium* and *Corbula*)
from beds 2 and 3.   Moreover, bed 1 rests upon an uneven surface
of the last bed of typically Wealden appearance, an ochre-yellow
and orange coarse-grained sandrock, varying in thickness from 3
ins. to 2 ft.

Of the scanty fossils in bed 2, *Corbula striatula* is common in
the Marine Band at Punfield and Corfe and throughout the Lower
Greensand of the Isle of Wight, and has not been recorded from
the Wealden; *Cardium ibbetsoni* is common in all the lower part
of the Lower Greensand at Punfield and in the Marine Band at
Corfe, and in the Isle of Wight is recorded only from the Crackers.
In the Wealden area it is recorded from the Atherfield Clay of
Haslemere,[1] and from the Perna Bed and 25 ft. down in the
Wealden Shales at Woodhatch, Reigate.[2]

The fossiliferous ironstone, bed 7, was correlated by Judd and
by Strahan with the Punfield Marine Band, but Meyer considered
it the equivalent of the Punfield Pebble Bed.[3]   The beds below it
now included in the Greensand are 33 ft. thick as compared with
50 ft. below the Marine Band at Punfield, and the inference is that
the Pebble Bed has been overlapped westwards.   There are
differences in the fauna of the Marine Band at Punfield, Corfe and
Worbarrow, but only such as might be expected at localities 5
and 10 miles apart.   A special feature at Worbarrow is the abundance of the small lamellibranch *Anthonya.*

The remaining Ferruginous Sands (83 ft. as compared with
148 ft.) have a strongly Wealden aspect, with their brilliant colours
and ironstone bands.   The band of quartz pebbles at the top of
bed 14 has its counterpart in bed 13 at Punfield.   It is easily
mistaken for the basement bed of the Gault, for the dark green
glauconitic sandy clays of beds 15 and 16 are not unlike Gault.
They represent beds 14 and 15 at Punfield.

[1] J. F. Kirkaldy, *Proc. Geol. Assoc.,* vol. xlix, 1938, p. 139.
[2] C. P. Chatwin, ' Geology of the Country around Reigate and Dorking,' *Mem.
Geol. Surv.,* 1933, pp. 115, 117.
[3] C. J. A. Meyer, *Quart. Journ. Geol. Soc.,* vol. xxviii, 1872, p. 251.

(d) MUPE BAY

At Mupe Bay the section is badly obscured by Chalk talus. No fossils have been recorded, but there are beds closely resembling the bright-coloured strata above the fossiliferous ironstone at Worbarrow, and the lower part of the section is concealed. It has not been found possible to add anything to Strahan's account, which is reproduced below. The section has deteriorated since the description was made.

LOWER GREENSAND, MUPE BAY

[Gault above ; *see* p. 188]

	Ft.
Clay, light grey, with clay-ironstone 3 ft. down	14
Clay, light grey, interlaminated with white sand ; ferruginous concretions and much lignite	$\frac{1}{2}$
Yellow sandy clay or fullers' earth	$\frac{1}{2}$
Sand, bright yellow and white ; black carbonaceous sand lenticle in upper part	18
Clay, blue, with sandy partings and much lignite	4
Sandy clay	9
Beds not seen	20

[Wealden mottled clay below]

66ft.

(e) LULWORTH COVE

On the east side of Lulworth Cove, 1 ft. below the pebble bed at the base of the Gault, from which it is separated by sandy clay, is a 6-inch band of impersistent ironstone, a limestone where unweathered, containing badly preserved fossils. Strahan recorded " *Cyrena*, *Exogyra*, and a few gastropods " and assigned these beds to the Wealden.[1] But there is a strong resemblance to the fossiliferous ironstones of Worbarrow, and Mr. J. F. Kirkaldy[2] believes the *Exogyra* to be *E. tuberculifera* Koch and Dunker, which is common in the Lower Greensand at Punfield and was collected also in the Lower Greensand at Corfe. Below the fossil band are 5 ft. of dark grey shaly clay, resting on white clay and sand (15 ft). The ironstone band appears to be conformable with the base of the Gault rather than with the Wealden, but the section at present is not decisive on this important point.

[1] A. Strahan, *op. cit.*, 1898, p. 129.
[2] *In lit.* 1938, and *Proc. Geol. Assoc.*, vol. l, 1939, p. 417.

CHAPTER X

ALBIAN STAGE: GAULT AND UPPER GREENSAND
By C. W. WRIGHT

I. GENERAL

(a) LITHOLOGY

The Albian beds of Dorset with their black clays below and green sands above form a marked feature in the cliff sections between the red and yellow Wealden and the white Chalk. The highest beds, consisting of resistant glauconitic sandstone and chert bands, often stand out as prominent ledges.

The thickness of the beds varies from 110 ft. at Lulworth and 120 ft. at Durdle to nearly 190 ft. at Worbarrow; but there are few constant lithological features except at the top and bottom. The junction with the Lower Greensand or with earlier rocks is everywhere marked by a band of quartz and lydite pebbles. Usually, a few feet above this there is a ferruginous stone or shaley band, sometimes fossiliferous. The mass of the lower beds contains few diagnostic fossils, and for anything up to 80 ft. there is undifferentiated dark sandy and sometimes micaceous clay with occasional nodules.

About half way through the stage large grey doggers appear, scattered or in continuous bands. In most sections large numbers of them, many exceedingly hard, are to be found on the beach or in mud glaciers.

Gradually the clay and the doggers become more sandy and more glauconitic, until the prevailing colour is green and the argillaceous content small. The doggers persist but generally decrease in size. It is possible to assign loose ones on the beach to their correct relative levels, although they cannot always be found in place.

The stone bands at the top of the Upper Greensand begin everywhere with the *Exogyra* rock, a knobbly sandstone crowded with *Exogyra conica* (J. Sowerby) and *E. columba* (Lamarck). Next above as a rule are two or three blue argillaceous beds with many fossils, mostly ammonites, separated by grey stone bands. Finally there is a thick bed of sandstone containing much chert in nodules or layers, with an eroded and phosphatized upper surface on which rests the Cenomanian.

Exceptions to this general sequence will be noted in the account of the sections.

(b) RELATIONS TO THE BEDS BELOW (W.J.A.)

In Purbeck the Albian has the appearance of conformity with the Aptian, but it is probable that in reality the 180 ft. of the Isle of Wight Sandrock Series are represented by no more than 10 ft. of sand at Swanage, the rest having been removed before the deposition of the Gault. At Worbarrow the Sandrock Series is absent entirely and the Gault has overlapped on to a dark glauconitic clay which can probably be correlated with the Marehill Clay of Sussex (*see* p. 174). At Lulworth the overlap has increased and probably all but about the lowest 6 ft. of the Lower Greensand has disappeared. A short distance inland, at Chaldon Down, a boring has proved the Gault resting on Lower Purbeck Beds. Farther west, as shown below (pp. 249-285), the Albian oversteps a series of small but acute folds and large faults so that it comes to rest on Wealden-Kimmeridgian rocks at Ringstead, Oxford Clay at Sutton Poyntz and Bincombe, and Forest Marble at Abbotsbury. The junction appears to be almost even, though it is possible that the local preservation of Lower Gault clay at Osmington and the disappearance of the Gault or its lithological transformation a mile or two inland may result from irregularities of the platform due to the very different hardness of its constituent rocks. The thin band of quartz and lydite pebbles always present at the base of the Gault sometimes contains larger pebbles of Purbeck and Portland materials at Osmington (*see* p. 192), but there is no accumulation of pebbles or coarse detritus commensurate with the erosion of many hundreds of feet of rocks of varied lithology. Even the larger quartz and lydite pebbles were brought into the area from outside; they cannot be matched in earlier rocks *in situ*, being larger than any in the Wealden Beds.

The transgression of the Gault sea (which as shown in subsection c did not occur until the Middle Albian) seems to have been due to epeirogenic subsidence of a long-since folded and already peneplaned surface.

(c) STRATIGRAPHY

Previous descriptions of the Albian beds of Dorset have been published by Barrois,[1] Strahan,[2] Fordham[3] and Jukes-Browne.[4] The last-named author summarized the results of the previous writers. Since 1900 little has been published on these beds except a short paper on the Osmington Gault by Col. R. H. Cunnington,[5] which includes important fossil-lists; but Dr. Spath's monograph of the Gault Ammonites contains much valuable information, based on the fine collections of ammonites made by Col. Cunnington and T. F. Grimsdale.[6]

Traditionally these beds in Dorset have been divided into " Lower Gault,'' " Zone of *Ammonites rostratus*," and " Zone of *Pecten asper* and *Cardiaster fossarius*." The first name tells little since it is not defined by any fossil species;[7] "*Ammonites rostratus* " *sensu stricto* does not occur in South Dorset; *Pecten asper* and *Cardiaster fossarius* are fairly good guides to their horizon. It is not easy to improve on this scheme, but the most satisfactory procedure is to correlate the beds as far as possible with the zones and subzones of the Albian proposed by Dr. Spath.[8]

Of Dr. Spath's subzones some can be traced and definitely distinguished *in situ* in Dorset, some are suggested by certain species of ammonites found loose on talus, and some are not represented, probably because of scarcity of ammonites rather than a pause in deposition. Thus the following comparative table can be drawn up :

ZONES AND SUBZONES (L. F. Spath).		OCCURRENCES IN DORSET
Stoliczkaia dispar	*Stoliczkaia dispar*	Proved in every section.
	Arrhaphoceras substuderi	No ammonites.
Pervinquieria inflata	*Pervinquieria inflata var. aequatorialis*	Proved at Punfield.
	Callihoplites auritus	Proved at Osmington. Suggested at Punfield and Worbarrow.
	Hysteroceras varicosum	Proved at Punfield and Osmington.
	Hysteroceras orbignyi	Suggested at Punfield, Worbarrow and ? Osmington.

[1] C. Barrois, ' Recherches sur le Terrain Crétacé Supérieur de l'Angleterre et de l'Irlande,' *Mém. Soc. géol. Nord.* 1876. Lille.

[2] A. Strahan, *Purbeck Memoir*, 1898, Ch. XI.

[3] H. G. Fordham, ' On the Section of Chloritic Marl and Upper Greensand on the Northern side of Swanage Bay, Dorset,' *Proc. Geol. Assoc.*, vol. iv, 1876, p. 506.

[4] A. J. Jukes-Browne, ' The Cretaceous Rocks of Britain,' vol. i, Gault and Upper Greensand, *Mem. Geol. Survey.* 1900.

[5] R. H. Cunnington, ' Osmington Gault,' *Proc. Dorset Nat. Hist. Arch. Soc.*, vol. 1, 1929, p. 125.

[6] L. F. Spath, ' Ammonoidea of the Gault,' vols. i, ii. *Palaeont. Soc.*, 1922-1943.

[7] Except by " *Lima parallela* " (= *Pseudolimea gaultina* Woods sp.) by Jukes-Browne (*op. cit.*, p. 146) for the upper part of the lower beds at Worbarrow.

[8] L. F. Spath, *op. cit.*, vol. i, p. 4, as amended *passim*.

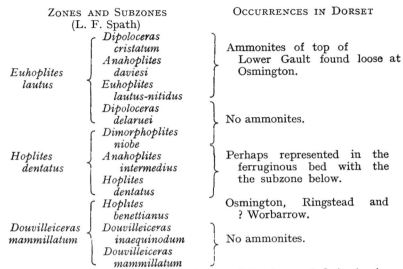

ZONES AND SUBZONES (L. F. Spath)		OCCURRENCES IN DORSET
Euhoplites lautus	*Dipoloceras cristatum* / *Anahoplites daviesi* / *Euhoplites lautus-nitidus*	Ammonites of top of Lower Gault found loose at Osmington.
	Dipoloceras delaruei	No ammonites.
Hoplites dentatus	*Dimorphoplites niobe* / *Anahoplites intermedius* / *Hoplites dentatus*	Perhaps represented in the ferruginous bed with the the subzone below.
Douvilleiceras mammillatum	*Hoplites benettianus*	Osmington, Ringstead and ? Worbarrow.
	Douvilleiceras inaequinodum / *Douvilleiceras mammillatum*	No ammonites.

In this table a zone is called " proved " when a definite horizon in a section can be assigned to that zone, " suggested " when ammonites have been found that usually occur in the zone.

That the upper beds are better worked out than the lower is due both to the greater abundance of ammonites in them and to the dearth of good exposures of the lower beds.

(d) PALAEONTOLOGY

Most of the fossils occur abundantly only in certain bands, but a few species are common throughout, especially the oyster *Exogyra conica* (J. de C. Sowerby) (Fig. 40) and the spirally coiled *Serpula concava* (J. Sowerby) (Fig. 40). The latter is a good guide fossil for the Albian as a whole in Dorset. A number of lamellibranchs have long ranges and can be picked up as phosphatic casts on most talus slopes, especially *Grammatodon carinatus* (J. Sowerby) (Fig. 40), *Cucullaea glabra* Parkinson, *Trigonia aliformis* Parkinson, *Entolium orbiculare* (J. Sowerby), *Chlamys robinaldina* (d'Orbigny) and *Panopea gurgitis* (Brongniart).

The ferruginous band immediately above the base of the Albian is very fossiliferous at Osmington but has yielded few specimens elsewhere. It belongs to the Benettianus Subzone and perhaps includes the Dentatus and Intermedius Subzones of the Middle Albian. It contains magnificent hoplitid ammonites. Individuals are numerous but the number of species is small : they are—

Hoplites devisensis *Spath*
    ,,   aff. benettianus
   (*J. de C. Sowerby*)
    ,,   dorsetensis *Spath* (Fig. 40)
    ,,   canavarii (*Parona and Bonarelli*)
    ,,   obtusus *Spath*
    ,,   mirabiliformis *Spath*

H. pringlei *Spath*
    ,,   pseudodeluci *Spath*
    ,,   rudis (*Parona and Bonarelli*)
    ,,   vectensis *Spath*
    ,,   aff. similis *Spath*
Anahoplites mimeticus *Spath*
    ,,   planus (*Mantell*)

and numerous transitional forms.

Other prominent fossils in this bed are *Camptonectes gaultinus* Woods, *Inoceramus concentricus* Parkinson, *Lima globosa* (J. de C. Sowerby), *Nucula pectinata* J. Sowerby and other Folkestone Lower Gault shells, and small worm-tubes made of quartz grains cemented together as in caddis tubes.

A few ammonites have occurred that are to be referred to the upper part of the Lower Gault :

Aeudanticeras beudanti (*Brongniart*)	Epihoplites metamorphicus
Dnahoplites planus (*Mantell*)	*Spath*
Bimorphoplites biplicatus (*Mantell*)	Euhoplites aff. opalinus *Spath*
,, chloris *Spath*	Dipoloceras bouchardianum
,, parkinsoni *Spath*	*d'Orbigny*

The lowest subzone (Orbignyi) of the Upper Gault is represented by *Hysteroceras orbignyi* Spath and *Epihoplites trifidus* Spath. In the succeeding subzone (Varicosum) numerous ammonites have been found : they include—

Anahoplites picteti *Spath*	Deiradoceras bipunctatum
Dimorphoplites aff. biplicatus (*Mantell*)	*Spath*
Epihoplites deluci (*Brongniart*)	,, cunningtoni *Spath*
,, denarius (*J. de C. Sowerby*)	,, devonense, *Spath*
,, gibbosus *Spath*	Pervinquieria pricei *Spath*
Euhoplites alphalautus *Spath*	Prohysteroceras (Goodhallites)
Hysteroceras binum (*J. Sowerby*)	goodhalli (*J. Sowerby*)
,, subbinum *Spath*	,, delabechei *Spath*
,, varicosum (*J. de C. Sowerby*)	

Anahoplites costosus Spath and some forms of *Pervinquieria inflata* (J. Sowerby) as well as *Callihoplites auritus* (J. Sowerby) are referable to the Auritus Subzone.

The last three horizons mentioned are represented in the Blackdown Greensand and many of the ammonites occur there. Blackdown lamellibranchs also are common in Dorset, especially in this part of the series, though many range up and down ; the commonest or most characteristic of them are :

Modiola reversa *J. de C. Sowerby*	Callista plana (*J. Sowerby*)
Mytilus lanceolatus *J. de C. Sowerby*	Clementia (Flaventia) ovalis
Dosiniopsis caperata (*J. de C. Sowerby*)	(*J. de C. Sowerby*)
Dosiniopsis subrotunda (*J. de C. Sowerby*)	Tellina (Palaeomoera) inaequalis *J. de C. Sowerby*
Cyprimeria (Cyclorisma) faba (*J. de C. Sowerby*)	Panopea gurgitis *Brongniart, and other long ranging species (see list, page 181).*

FIG. 39.—*Characteristic Albian ammonoids from the Dorset coast, collected by C. W. and E. V. Wright.*

1a, b. *Arrhaphoceras studeri* (Pictet and Campiche); 2a, b. *Durnovarites subquadratus* Spath; 3a, b. *Stoliczkaia dispar* (d'Orbigny) (after d'Orbigny); 4a, b. *Callihoplites tetragonus* (Seeley); 5a, b. *Engonoceras grimsdalei* Spath; 6a, b. *Lepthoplites cantabrigiensis* Spath; 7. *Ostlingoceras puzosianum* (d'Orbigny); 8. *Hysteroceras varicosum* (J. de C. Sowerby) (after Spath); 9a, b. *Callihoplites auritus* (J. Sowerby).

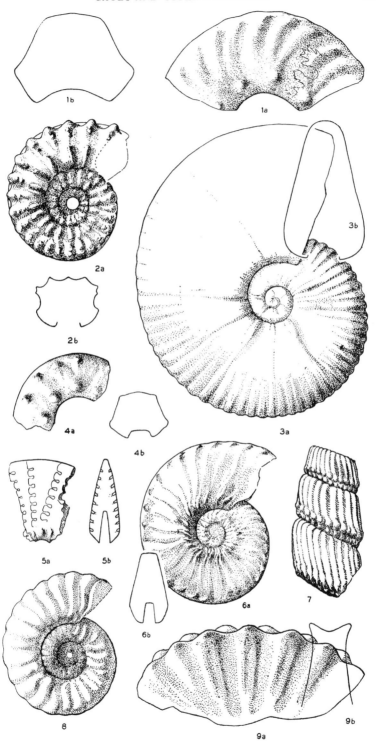

FIG. 39.

The following species of lamellibranchs are particularly abundant in the top beds of the stage in addition to the long ranging species :

Cucullaea mailleana (*d'Orbigny*)
Pectunculus sublaevis *J. de C. Sowerby*
Plicatula gurgitis *Pictet and Roux*
Aequipecten asper (*Lamarck*)

Neithea quadricostata (*J. Sowerby*)
,,   quinquecostata (*J. Sowerby*)
Cardium cf. ventricosum *d'Orbigny*
Cardita cottaldina *d'Orbigny*

Cardiaster fossarius Benett is characteristic of these same beds, replacing *C. latissimus* (Agassiz) which is common at Osmington in the lower part of the Upper Gault.

The Aequatorialis Subzone contains numerous *Pervinquieria inflata* at Punfield. *Arrhaphoceras substuderi* Spath is recorded but probably comes from the Dispar Subzone.

The Dispar Subzone, the highest in the Albian, contains a fauna as varied and interesting as is the lithology of the beds. The most important element is the cephalopods; about fifty species are recorded, with numerous transitional forms, and of these some are confined to Dorset, some are members of the semi-derived Cambridge Greensand fauna, and by their occurrence in Dorset can be placed stratigraphically. The following is a list of the ammonites described from the Dispar Subzone on the Dorset coast :

Puzosia sharpei *Spath*
Callihoplites seeleyi *Spath*
,,   tetragonus (*Seeley*)
Callihoplites vraconnensis (*Pictet and Campiche*)
Pleurohoplites renauxianus (*d'Orbigny*)
,,   subvarians *Spath*
Arrhaphoceras studeri (*Pictet and Campiche*)
Arrhaphoceras substuderi   *Spath*
,,   transitorium *Spath*
Lepthoplites cantabrigiensis *Spath*
,,   falcoides *Spath*
Discohoplites anomalus *Spath*
,,   coelonotus (*Seeley*)
,,   subfalcatus (*Semenow*)
,,   transitorius *Spath*
,,   valbonnensis (*Hébert and Munier-Chalmas*)
,,   varicosus *Spath*
Hyphoplites campichei *Spath*
,,   falcatocoelonotus (*Semenow*)
Schloenbachia nodulosa (*Stieler*)
Stoliczkaia dispar (*d'Orbigny*)
,,   dorsetensis *Spath*
,,   notha (*Seeley*)
,,   rhamnonotus (*Seeley*)
Engonoceras grimsdalei *Spath*
Durnovarites perinflatum (*Spath*)

Durnovarites postinflatum *Spath*
,,   quadratum (*Spath*)
,,   subquadratum *Spath*
Mariella bergeri (*Brongniart*)
,,   miliaris (*Pictet and Campiche*)
Ostlingoceras   puzosianum (*d'Orbigny*)
Scaphites sp. (*Spath, Gault Amm.* vol. 2, p. 498).
Anisoceras armatum (*J. Sowerby*)
,,   campichei *Spath*
,,   exoticum *Spath*
,,   perarmatum *Pictet and Campiche*
,,   picteti *Spath*
,,   pseudoelegans *Pictet and Campiche*
Idiohamites dorsetensis *Spath*
,,   elegantulus *Spath*
Hamites cf. charpentieri *Pictet and Campiche*
,,   duplicatus *Pictet and Campiche*
,,   subvirgulatus *Spath*
,,   cf. venetzianus *Pictet and Campiche*
,,   virgulatus *Pictet and Campiche*
Lechites baudini (*Pictet and Campiche*)
,,   communis *Spath*

Mention may be made of certain important species: *Engonoceras grimsdalei* Spath (represented only by three Dorset specimens) and *E. iris* Spath (one specimen found in the Gault of Folkestone), are the only known British Pseudoceratites. This group was widespread in the Cretaceous, ranging from North America to Persia. The examples of *Schloenbachia* from Punfield are important as the earliest known representatives of this typically Cenomanian genus; at least three species occur at Punfield associated with Albian *Callihoplites, Stoliczkaia*, etc., and forms transitional from *Lepthoplites* and *Pleurohoplites*.

Other fossils are very numerous and include in addition to those previously mentioned from the top beds (p. 184) or the whole stage (p. 181) :—

Neithea cometa (*d'Orbigny*)	Holaster laevis (*de Luc*)
Spondylus striatus (*J. Sowerby*)	Hyposalenia clathrata (*Agassiz*)
Ostrea vesicularis *Lamarck*	Terebratella menardi (*d'Orbigny*)
,, vesiculosa (*J. Sowerby*)	,, pectita
Gyrodes genti (*J. Sowerby*)	(*J. Sowerby*)
Avellana sp.	' Rhynchonella ' spp.
Pleurotomaria spp.	Siphonia tulipa *Zittel*
Discoidea subuculus (*Leske*)	Hallirhoa agariciformis
Catopygus columbarius (*Lamarck*)	(*Benett*)
Caratomus rostratus *Agassiz*	Micrabacia coronula *Goldfuss*

This list is by no means complete but gives an indication of the interest and variety of this fauna.

Some of the species above mentioned are taken from Col. Cunnington's list[1] or from the Grimsdale collection recorded by Spath,[2] but nearly all of them have been collected by the author.

II.   DETAILS OF SECTIONS

(a)   PUNFIELD COVE, SWANAGE

In Swanage bay[3] the base of the Gault can sometimes be traced above the Lower Greensand on the overgrown cliffs of Punfield Cove; it is marked by a bed of quartz pebbles. Little more of the formation can be seen until beds of dark sandy clay with doggers are reached below the chalk cliffs of Ballard Down. Jukes-Browne[4] gives 157 ft. as the overall thickness of the beds, but it is difficult to check the figure.

The section of the Upper Albian as now exposed is :—

[Base of Cenomanian ; *see* p. 204]

HORIZON			Ft.	In.
Dispar	6.	Knobbly sandstone (pale lumps in dark green sand), full of fossils, including subzonal ammonites in the top 2 ft. ; at the bottom crammed with *Exogyra*, representing the *Exogyra* rock (*see* below p. 188)	6	0

---

[1] R. H. Cunnington, ' Osmington Gault,' *Proc. Dorset Nat. Hist. and Arch. Soc.*, vol. 1, 1929, pp. 125-130.
[2] L. F. Spath, *op. cit.*, vols. i and ii, *passim*.
[3] *See* H. G. Fordham, *op. cit.*, for previous description.
[4] A. J. Jukes-Browne, *op. cit.*, p. 145.

		Ft.	In.
	5. Green sand with occasional stone bands and lumps, many *Exogyra*, a few *Cardiaster foss-*		
Aequatorialis (in lower part)	*arius*, occasional *Pervinquieria sp.* in the sand and some *P. inflata* at the base ...	18	0
?Auritus	4. Greenish brown stone band with *P. inflata, Plicatula gurgitis* and *Lima vectensis* ...	1	6
	3. Black argillaceous loam with few fossils ...	13	6
Varicosum	2. Hard blue-grey stone band with *Anahoplites picteti* and *Goodhallites delabechei*	1	0
?Orbignyi	1. Black clay with a stone bed occasionally visible	–	–

Total seen 40 ft.

An example of *Epihoplites trifidus* Spath, probably from the stone band mentioned in bed 1, suggests reference to the Orbignyi Subzone; and with the Varicosum, Aequatorialis and Dispar Subzones attested, the rest fall roughly into place; possibly bed 4 belongs to Aequatorialis and if so Auritus may be represented in the top of bed 3. All the beds of this section are well exposed only under favourable conditions of tide and weather, as they tend to be obscured by chalk downwash. Farther east, however, is a better exposure of the highest 8 ft., the knobbly sandstone crammed with fossils (*see* p. 185); the ammonites include the *Schloenbachia* mentioned (p. 184), several of which have been collected and which show that this bed is at a higher horizon in the Dispar Zone than any ammonitiferous band seen elsewhere.

(b) WORBARROW BAY AND MUPE BAY

The formation comes to the surface at the southern foot of the downs that extend westwards from Swanage, but there are no important exposures till the coast is again reached at Worbarrow Bay, where there is a fine section of the whole formation in the cliffs below Flower's Barrow. With some effort it is nearly all accessible.

The total thickness here is nearly 190 ft., the greatest recorded on the coast, and the section is :—

[Base of the Cenomanian, p. 206]

		Ft.	In.
	13. Knobbly sandstone, not very fossiliferous, with polished and phosphatized top ...	4	6
	12. Ammonite bed, green and blue argillaceous sand with phosphatic lamellibranchs and		
Dispar	a few ammonites	2	3

FIG. 40.—*Characteristic fossils of the Gault and Upper Greensand.*

1. *Exogyra conica* (J. Sowerby); 2. *Pecten* (*Aequipecten*) *asper* (Lamarck); 3. *Grammatodon carinatum* (J. Sowerby); 4. *Neithea quadricostata* (J. Sowerby); 5. *Cardiaster fossarius* Benett; 6. *Serpula concava* (J. Sowerby); 7a, b. *Hoplites dorsetensis* Spath (Dentatus Zone, Osmington) ($\times \frac{2}{3}$).

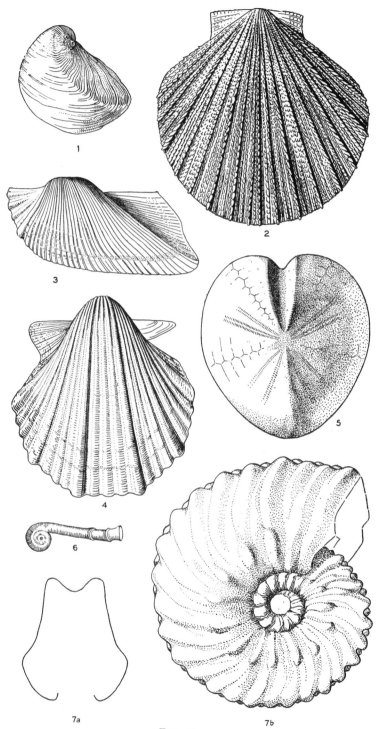

Fig. 40.

HORIZON		Ft.	In.
	11. Irregular pale grey stone band		9
	10. Argillaceous sand, with lamellibranchs ...	2	6
	9. *Exogyra* rock, knobbly sandstone crammed with *Exogyra conica, E. columba* and other fossils	6	0
	8. Sand with *Exogyra* and sandstone nodules ...	3	0
Probably represents Aequatorialis (cf. Punfield section)	7. Green sand with two thin stone bands and layer of phosphatic lamellibranchs (one sulcate *Anahoplites planus* found near top)	13	0
? Auritus	6. Layer of almost continuous grey doggers ...	1	0
? Orbignyi in phosphate band	5. Clayey green sand with doggers and a band of scattered black phosphatic lamellibranchs 13 ft. from the top	40	0
	4. Layer of large grey doggers roughly marking change from black (below) to green (above)	1	0
	3. Black and dark green glauconitic loam ...	36	0
	2. Black loams, ferruginous at base, with layer of doggers at top	76	0
Benettianus	1. Soft ferruginous clayey stone band (Strahan's " Supposed Carstone ") resting on basal pebble bed	1	0
	Total ...	187 ft.	

[Lower Greensand below, *see* p. 175]

The ferruginous bed at the base is equivalent to the Benettianus Beds at Osmington (*see* p. 192). Spath records from Worbarrow a specimen of *Hoplites devisensis* Spath, which came from Bed 2. Few fossils are found in the mass of the clays except the usual long-ranging lamellibranchs and the ubiquitous *Serpula concava;* but the doggers in the slips produce a more varied fauna, including our easternmost *Cardiaster latissimus*. The single specimen found of *Hysteroceras orbignyi* Spath was probably from bed 5. In a boulder probably from the top dogger bed (6) *Callihoplites auritus* of the Auritus Subzone was found. No recognizable *Pervinquieria* occurred and except for the sulcate *Anahoplites planus* (Mantell) mentioned from bed 7 (the highest record of the sulcate form) no more ammonites were met with until bed 12 was reached. This is the most easterly exposure of the Ammonite bed in its typical form. Ammonites are scarce here and comprise chiefly *Durnovarites* and occasional *Stoliczkaia*.

The lithology of these upper beds exposed in the main cliff at Worbarrow is much the same as that which prevails from Lulworth to Osmington, but at the west end of Worbarrow Bay (Cow Corner), and at Mupe Bay too, the lithology is entirely different. Unfortunately, very little of the Albian is visible at either point, but there can be seen a layer of brown phosphatic nodules, with a few ammonites. Albian ammonites (*Durnovarites* and *Callihoplites*) occur up to 2 ft. above the phosphate band, in the featureless dark grey glauconitic sand that passes up into normal Lower Chalk with no " basement bed " of the Cenomanian. Further elucidation of this problem must await drastic alterations in the shingle level at Cow Corner or removal of the talus between that point and the main Greensand cliff.

In Mupe Bay little is visible now, but in 1901 Strahan saw the nodule bed, at the base of the dark, sandy, glauconitic bed, resting on sandy glauconitic clay, presumably of lower Upper Albian age. Thus there must have been erosion of the top of the Albian before the end of Dispar time and peculiar conditions of deposition at the beginning of the Cenomanian.[1]

(c) LULWORTH COVE

At Lulworth Cove the formation crops out in the cliff at the east side and again on the west, near the remains of the old lime kiln; the latter section exposes little but the *Exogyra* rock.

The base is marked by the usual pebble bed resting on Wealden, and a total thickness of 110 ft. can be measured. Of this the black beds account for 37 ft. and the predominantly green upper beds for 73 ft., as at Worbarrow; thus the lower part has been reduced by 77 feet.

The lower clays are poorly exposed and the only fossils noted are lamellibranchs from boulders on the talus. The beds above, up to the *Exogyra* rock, are exposed at the east side, but owing to a landslip (1937-8), are inaccessible at present. In the one mile from Mupe Bay the lithology of the top beds has reverted to the type of the main Worbarrow cliff section, with the addition of one more argillaceous bed. Since this is regular from here to Osmington, a section is included :—

[Base of Cenomanian]

		Ft.	Ins
7. Knobbly sandstone, sand and chert		11	0
6. Blue argillaceous bed with ammonites (Ammonite bed) ...		3	3
5. Irregular band of masses of grey stone		1	0
4. Blue argillaceous bed		3	0
3. Stone band			9
2. Green argillaceous bed		2	0
1. *Exogyra* rock		3	0

The relative thickness of these bands varies, but they are distinct in all western sections. Bed 6 contains *Durnovarites*, *Callihoplites*, *Stoliczkaia* and *Discohoplites*. It is here that chert becomes noticeable for the first time, in the top sandstone.

Barrois gives detailed measurements of the beds and lists of fossils, but as the totals and details given by him, Strahan and

---

[1] A. Strahan, ' An abnormal section of Chloritic Marl at Mupe Bay, Dorset,' *Geol. Mag.*, 1901, p. 319.

Jukes-Browne are usually irreconcilable with present observations it is preferable to describe this and other sections as they now appear.

(d) ST. OSWALD'S BAY AND MAN-O'-WAR COVE

In St. Oswald's Bay little but the uppermost sandstone is visible, about 10 ft. thick, in a vertical bluff on the shore. It is weathered into separate layers of hard and soft sandstone and chert, and on the exposed surface small echinoids are extremely abundant, *Holaster laevis* (de Luc), *Caratomus rostratus* Agassiz and *Discoidea subuculus* (Leske) being the commonest. Ossicles of *Lophidiaster ornatus* Spencer (a shallow-water starfish) and of *Calliderma* type also occur. By the path down from Lulworth the base of the Gault can be seen, with pebbles of white quartz and black lydite.

Man-o'-War Cove shows a poor section, at beach level and in bluffs in the cliff, of the beds from the main green sand to the top of the formation, including the Ammonite bed with a few fossils. A fragment of *Deiradoceras cunningtoni* Spath was picked up on the beach.

(e) DURDLE COVE

Here the formation measures 122 ft. 6 ins., a slight increase since Lulworth, but unfortunately the middle beds are grassed over. At the base is the usual pebble bed, here associated with a 3-inch band of hard white sandstone. About 20 ft. higher is a 1-foot bed of hard ferruginous sandstone, and the intervening clay is sandy and ferruginous; there is a bluff near the path to the shore showing this sequence. Casts of lamellibranchs and gastropods occur in the irony clay and in phosphatic nodules contained in it; though no ammonites have been found, it can safely be referred to the Benettianus Subzone.

There are no good sections before we reach the *Exogyra* rock, which is exposed in a large and well-weathered vertical face projecting from the base of the cliff. Behind it the hard bands appear as ridges and the argillaceous beds as gullies, made by torrents of rain water, which expose numerous fossils. Pectens abound here in the *Exogyra* rock and small echinoids (*Caratomus, Salenia, Hyposalenia, Discoidea*) are fairly common. The Dispar Subzone ammonites occur in profusion in the top argillaceous bed. Besides the common *Durnovarites subquadratus, Lepthoplites cantabrigiensis* and *L. falcoides, Callihoplites tetragonus, Ostlingoceras puzosianum* and *Anisoceras,* this section produces unusually large *Arrhaphoceras studeri* and *Pleurohoplites renauxianus.*

A few ammonites occur in the middle argillaceous band as at White Nothe, and another feature recalling White Nothe is the

presence of many large *Nautili*, a foot or more in diameter, in the
stone band dividing the top two argillaceous beds.

(f) WHITE NOTHE

In the cliffs stretching from Holworth House in the west to
the point of White Nothe in the east, there is the finest section
of the top beds in the county, and they are here most fully
developed (Pl. XI). Unfortunately the rest of the stage is by
no means so well exposed.

The base, however, is shown in a bluff immediately to the east
of the main slip, and is indicated by the lowest pointer in Pl. XIB.
The following beds are seen : —

		Ft.	Ins.
3.	Sandy clay seen to	30	0
2.	Soft ferruginous stone band with phosphatic nodules (=*benet-tianus* beds)	1	3
1.	Dark grey micaceous and sulphurous clay with scattered quartz pebbles	5	6
	[Kimmeridge paper shales]		

36ft. 9 ins.

The same sequence is seen below and slightly to the east of
Holworth House at the top of the Kimmeridge Clay cliff, where
the Albian rests on Hounstout Marls.

In the main cliff only the top of the predominantly black beds
is exposed and it is impossible to estimate the gap between this
and the top of the section given below. The cliff exposure is : —

[Base of Cenomanian, *see* p. 209]

		Ft.	Ins.
12.	Layers of sandstone, sand and tabular and finger-like nodules of chert : the bottom 6 ins. slightly argillaceous and forming a green laminated bed with very regular bedding planes	14	0
11.	Ammonite bed : blue and green streaky argillaceous sand with calcareous lumps and many phosphatic fossils ...	2	0
10.	Grey calcareous stone band : large *Nautili*	2	0
9.	Bluish argillaceous sand : a few ammonites	2	9
8.	Grey calcareous stone band		9
7.	Argillaceous band	2	6
6.	*Exogyra* rock : knobbly fossiliferous sandstone	9	0
5.	Green sand with scattered lumps of stone, full of *Exogyra*, at top and a lumpy stone band at base	6	6
4.	Dark green or brown clayey sand, nearly black when wet, with a line of springs at its base in the east part of the cliff	11	6
3.	Greenish grey clayey sands	22	0
2.	Layer of large grey doggers with many lamellibranchs ...	1	6
1.	Dark clayey sand seen to	3	0

Total seen   ...   77ft. 6ins.

Thus we have a thickness of 114 ft. 3ins. with a gap of unknown extent in the middle. Strahan's measurements total 150 ft., with the same indefinite gap in the middle; but he assigns double the true thickness (24 ft.) to the beds above the *Exogyra* rock.[1]

At the point of White Nothe the chert beds form a prominent ledge at sea level and there is a section down to bed 9.

Few fossils of interest have been found except in the Dispar Subzone, but here the fauna is extraordinarily rich (it is the source of the Grimsdale collection now in the British Museum). Practically all the species mentioned on p. 184 are found and many, including the important *Engonoceras*, only here. None of the other zones has been recognized.

Most of the extent of the Ammonite bed (11) is accessible by climbing up the talus slopes and along the shelves formed by the weathering of the argillaceous beds.

For the tectonic features of this cliff *see* p. 285.

(g) OSMINGTON

The cliffs west of Osmington Mills, where the Albian appears again, are at present largely concealed by mud glaciers. Below and to the east of Goggins Barrow there is an apparently complete though overgrown section from the basal pebble bed to the top, but it is probable that the appearance of completeness is deceptive and that the top has slipped over the lower part and cut out the middle. The section visible is:—

HORIZON		Ft.	Ins.
Dispar	Top sandstone and three argillaceous beds poorly developed		
	Exogyra Rock	4	0
	Sand with stone lumps and *Exogyra*	4	0
	Soft brown and greenish grey stone band	1	0
	[Gap]		
Auritus	Band of detached soft fawn, grey and blue stone lumps with *Idiohamites* and many casts of lamellibranchs	1	0
	[Considerable gap]		
	Alternating blue and fawn sandy micaceous clays and clayey sands	30	0
Benettianus	Ferruginous clay with nodules containing *Hoplites* and other fossils		6
	Pebble bed		
	[Kimmeridge Clay below, *see* p. 84]		

Here, as in all bluffs showing the beds of the Dispar Zone, nearly all the stone has been dissolved out, leaving the chert and phosphatic nodules in a matrix of glauconitic loam.

Farther west the sections are worse but the beds more interesting. The pebble bed is exposed at present in two bluffs at the head of the main 'mud glacier'; it contains many large pebbles including some from the Purbeck and Portland Beds. About six

---

[1] A. Strahan, *op. cit.*, 1898, p. 157.

ft. above it is an irregular ferruginous soft stone band, purplish brown in colour, containing many ammonites and other fossils (*see* pp. 182-183) belonging to the Benettianus Subzone. Collecting is best done from the fallen blocks among the boulders on the beach (for which, as for the other doggers, a sledge hammer is necessary).

The lower Gault ammonites mentioned on p. 182 were picked up on patches of slipped clay and talus. Both the two mud glaciers end on the beach in a spread of boulders, none of which in the present state of the cliff could be traced *in situ*. They are, however, divisible into two main groups. The first consists of very hard rounded grey doggers with flecks of mica, evidently from a bed of dark micaceous sandy clay; they contain numerous large *Cardiaster latissimus*, with *Serpula concava* and a few lamellibranchs; probably they are equivalent to the Cowstones of West Dorset and Devon. Those of the second group are softer, and green, brown and bluish in colour, certainly from a higher horizon; they contain large *Deiradoceras, Goodhallites, Anahoplites picteti*, and other ammonites, with Blackdown lamellibranchs (*see* p. 182); they thus belong to the Varicosum Subzone. To the latter subzone belong also some soft knobbly lumps of black and dark green sandstone yielding *Hysteroceras varicosum* and other species in abundance, with many lamellibranchs (*see* p. 182).

A long stretch of the highest beds is exposed in a low slipped (and probably still slipping) cliff behind the head of the mud glaciers. The stone is dissolved out and the numerous Dispar Subzone ammonites are very fragile.

It is regrettable that the state of the cliffs prevents a more detailed and accurate account being given of these interesting beds.

(h) INLAND OUTCROPS, CHALDON AND RINGSTEAD TO ABBOTSBURY

(W.J.A.)

Although Gault is exposed at Holworth House and Osmington Mills, and can be traced almost all round the Chaldon pericline, it was not found possible to map it as a separate stratum on either side of the intervening ridge of Spring Bottom Hill, or anywhere inland west of Holworth. The base of the formation no doubt remains clayey for some distance west of this, at least intermittently, but surface indications are mainly sandy and the auger nowhere brings up dark micaceous Gault such as is seen in the Osmington and Ringstead cliffs. On the south side of Spring Bottom ridge, near South Down Farm, Ringstead, the Albian outcrop is possibly narrowed by strike faulting, but the absence of the Gault cannot be accounted for in the same way at other localities.

The unconformable junction of the Gault and underlying rocks from Wealden to Kimmeridgian can be readily traced round the

Spring Bottom ridge and its continuation west of Osmington
Mills. It is, perhaps, most spectacularly seen on the road to
Shortlake, or looking east from Sandy Barrow. The relations are
temporarily masked along the Osmington Mills stream by ancient
slips of Gault, Greensand and Chalk, which exaggerate the
synclinal effect. Still more extensive slips have taken place
between Holworth House and South Holworth.

North of the Poxwell pericline the Albian is cut out by a
Tertiary strike fault for nearly 2 miles. It reappears in its proper
position at the foot of the Downs under White Horse Hill and
thence can be traced by many small exposures to beyond
Bincombe. In this stretch it has crossed the intra-Cretaceous
Abbotsbury Fault and rests on Oxford Clay. The mustard-
coloured sands with lines of doggers are exposed for considerable
distances in lanes at East Hill, Sutton Poyntz, and east of
Bincombe Church. At the former place the Ammonite bed and a
band of large *Nautili* occur, as at White Nothe; close above, the
top beds are involved in the remarkable thrust-faulting described
on p. 268-9.

The most conspicuous feature of the Upper Greensand from
Chaldon to Bincombe is an intensely hard coarse quartz grit at the
top. Chert is little in evidence, but the quartz grit is harder and
often shows through the turf continuously for many yards, a boon
in mapping. The best exposures of the grit are in a road-cutting
about 700 yds. north-west of Sutton Poyntz waterworks, and a
quarry in work 300 yds. east-south-east of Bincombe Church
(described on p. 212). The thickness varies from 4 to 10 ft.

In the valley at Lower Bincombe the Greensand is masked
under thick stony hillwash and is sliced from the top downwards
as it gradually comes under the influence of the Ridgeway Fault,
which cuts it out altogether from Ridgeway railway-cutting for
$4\frac{1}{2}$ miles westward. It reappears beyond Portisham on the
opposite side of the fault, resting on Kimmeridge Clay until it oversteps the intra-Cretaceous fault at Abbotsbury on to Forest Marble.
This outcrop is greatly encumbered by landslips and little can be
seen but tumbled chert beds and grit.

CHAPTER XI

CENOMANIAN, TURONIAN AND SENONIAN STAGES: THE CHALK

By C. W. WRIGHT

I. GENERAL

The Chalk comprises a series of white and light grey limestones and subordinate marls, now thought to have been laid down in water not exceeding 200 fathoms in depth.[1] In South Dorset the formation is about 1,300 ft. thick, and contains representatives of the Cenomanian, Turonian and Senonian Stages. The highest chalk preserved is the lower part of the middle sub-division of the Mucronata Zone, at Studland. Higher horizons occur in England only in Norfolk and perhaps the Isle of Wight.[2]

The chalk forms the cliffs of Ballard Head and the Foreland, which display the instructive series of complete and incipient stacks shown in Pl. XII. From Ballard Head to Worbarrow it runs as a hog's-back ridge, broken by the twin gaps at Corfe, on either side of the ruined castle. Westward from Worbarrow there is a wider area of chalk country in the foreland of the Purbeck fold and on the coast some of the most beautiful chalk cliff scenery in England. Plates I, XIV and XVI.

Tectonic movements have made much of the Dorset chalk useless for purposes of stratigraphical and palaeontological study. Vertical shattered rock, often almost crystalline, is not favourable for collecting fossils. However, outside the folded area, and in favourable circumstances within it, there is chalk that repays investigation. Notable instances are the basement bed, which has suffered little all along the coast, the Turonian beds at White Nothe, the Pilula Zone at Cockpit Head, and the Studland

---

[1] K. P. Oakley, 'Cretaceous Sponges: Some Biological and Geological Considerations,' *Proc. Geol. Assoc.*, vol. xlviii, 1937, pp. 340-342.

[2] W. K. Spencer, 'Evolution of the Cretaceous Asteroidea,' *Phil. Trans. Roy. Soc.*, series B, vol. 204, 1913, pp. 104 and 147.

Mucronata beds. In localities where the chalk is inaccessible *in situ*, much information can be gained from weathered fallen boulders.

In spite of the difficulties of this coast, A. W.· Rowe[1] was successful in determining a zonal succession in the White Chalk. Of the few subsequent additions or corrections the most important is Brydone's[2] re-examination of the old Quadratus Zone and his division of it into a Zone of *Offaster pilula* below and a Zone of *A. quadratus* (restricted) above. The account of the White Chalk that follows inevitably owes much to these two authors.

Subdivisions of the Chalk

		STAGES	ZONES	SUBZONES
UPPER CHALK		SENONIAN	*Belemnitella mucronata*	Upper Middle Lower
			Actinocamax quadratus	
			Offaster pilula	{ *Offaster pilula* { *Echinocorys scutata* var. *depressula*
			Marsupites testudinarius *Micraster coranguinum* *Micraster cortestudinarium*	{ *Marsupites testudinarius* { *Uintacrinus westfalicus*
	MID-DLE	TURONIAN	*Holaster planus*[3] *Terebratulina lata*[4] *Inoceramus labiatus*[5]	
LOWER		CENOMANIAN	*Holaster subglobosus* *Schloenbachia varians*	*Actinocamax plenus* at top of zone

II. CENOMANIAN

(a) LITHOLOGY

The Cenomanian in Dorset comprises from 45 to 150 ft. of more or less blocky grey marly chalk with, at the base, a sandy glauconitic bed up to 5 ft. thick. The top of the Albian beds has often a phosphatized and polished surface, pitted and corroded. Nearly everywhere the junction is well marked. Evidently in late

---

[1] A. W. Rowe, ' The Zones of the White Chalk of the English Coast, Part II, Dorset,' *Proc. Geol. Assoc.,* vol. xvii, 1901, pp. 1-76.

[2] R. M. Brydone, ' Zone of *Offaster pilula* in the S. English Chalk, III, Dorset,' *Geol. Mag.,* N.S., Dec. vi, vol. i, 1914, pp. 449-457.

[3] The current generic name *Holaster* is retained in preference to *Sternotaxis*.

[4] Formerly the Gracilis Zone, but *T. gracilis* occurs only in the upper part of the Mucronata Zone.

[5] Formerly the Cuvieri Zone, but *I. labiatus* has priority (Barrois, 1876) and is a much better zone-fossil.

Albian times current action stopped deposition entirely, and this condition continued into the early Cenomanian. Deposition started again only gradually, with the result that the lowest Cenomanian preserved is this sandy glauconitic bed, its base crammed with fossils. Apparently, too, deposition started progressively later towards the west.

Above this basement bed the chalk becomes blocky and marly with prominent bands of pale grey flints in some localities. At Punfield there is a band of green-coated dark phosphatic nodules, probably indicating a pause in deposition. Upwards the amount of marl increases until it reaches a maximum in the Plenus Marls, grey or bluish in colour, with bands of hard marly chalk. These mark the end of the stage.

In most sections the chalk is badly shattered and much of it is faulted out. At Punfield talus-slopes and minor faults prevent an accurate measurement being taken, but the thickness is probably about 150 feet. At White Nothe it is only 45 ft., though there is no disturbance. The difference is possibly accounted for partly by the varying dates at which deposition began.

(b) STRATIGRAPHY

The traditional division of the Cenomanian is into the two zones of *Schloenbachia varians* and *Holaster subglobosus,* but this cannot be applied in Dorset, for fossils are extremely rare except in the basement bed and a few bands above. Ammonites are too scarce in most of the stage for it to be possible to use Dr. Spath's zonal scheme.[1] The accurate determination of the few ammonites must await further work on Cenomanian groups.

M. Collignon (*Annales géologiques du Service des Mines* [of Madagascar], Tananarive, Fasc. viii, 1937, p. 59) has recently proposed the following zonal scheme for the Cenomanian:

Cénomanien supérieur	{	5. Zone à *Mantelliceras vicinale.*
		4. Zone à *Acanthoceras rotomagense.*
		3. Zone à *A. cenomanense et A. cunningtoni.*
Cénomanien inférieur	{	2. Zone à *Mant. mantelli et Eucalycoceras newboldi.*
		1. Zone à *Mant. martimpreyi.*

This scheme is simple enough to meet with general acceptance, provided that it is found to be applicable over a sufficient area. The only Dorset horizon with many ammonites, the basement bed, belongs to Zone 2, of *Mantelliceras mantelli* and *Eucalycoceras newboldi,* of the Lower Cenomanian.

(c) PALAEONTOLOGY

The basement bed, as mentioned above, contains a rich fauna. The cephalopods include several species each of *Schloenbachia, Mantelliceras* and *Calycoceras, Turrilites acutus* Passy, *Scaphites aequalis* J. Sowerby, *S. obliquus* J. Sowerby, *Cyrtocheilus baculoides* (Mantell).

---

[1] 'On the Ammonite Horizons of the Gault and Contiguous Deposits,' *Sum. Prog. Geol. Surv.* for 1922, 1923, p. 139.

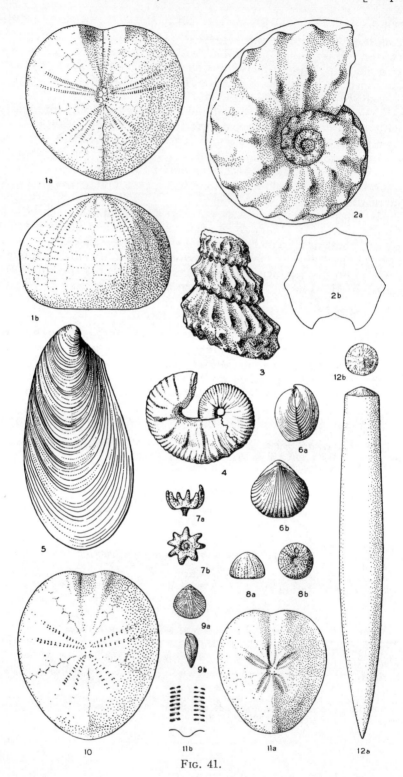

FIG. 41.

Of the other groups casts of small lamellibranchs and gastropods are common. Among Echinoderms *Holaster subglobosus* Leske is so abundant that on split boulders at White Nothe it forms a "*Holaster* pavement." *Glyphocyphus radiatus* Hoeninghaus, *Hemiaster morrisi* Forbes and *Conulus castanea* (Brongniart) are all fairly common. Numerous Terebratulids also occur.

Fossils are rarer above. *Mantelliceras cantianum* Spath from immediately above the basement bed, a few other *Mantelliceras, Calycoceras, Schloenbachia* and uncoiled forms from the lower part, and *Calycoceras,* higher up at Punfield, are the only ammonites noted. Ossicles of the starfish *Lophidiaster ornatus* Spencer occur in the band of phosphatic nodules at Punfield, while *Holaster subglobosus* (Leske) and *H. gregoryi* Lambert are fairly common in bands. The small coral *Micrabacia coronula* (Goldfuss) and the lamellibranch *Lima (Pseudolimea) elongata* (J. de C. Sowerby) are both common throughout the stage. Otherwise the fauna is scanty and uninteresting.

In the Plenus Marl the characteristic belemnite occurs infrequently and on the coast few fossils are found, though Jukes-Browne[1] records a number of species from pits near Corfe. One ammonite was found at Durdle and a few fragments in other localities. They seem to be a species of *Calycoceras,* such as is frequent in the Plenus Marl elsewhere, but apparently undescribed.

III.　Turonian

(a)　lithology

To this stage belong the three zones of *Inoceramus labiatus, Terebratulina lata* and *Holaster planus,* of which the first two form the Middle Chalk. The combined thickness at White Nothe, where the dip is only 12° S., is given by Rowe as 185 ft. (76, 58 and 51); this is reduced to 110 ft. in Man-o'-War Cove, and other localities give intermediate measurements.

The lowest few feet of chalk belonging to the Labiatus Zone are marly and have sometimes been assigned to the Plenus Marl, but they contain Middle Chalk fossils. The rest of the zone con-

---

[1] A. J. Jukes-Browne, ' Cretaceous Rocks of Britain,' vol. ii, *Mem. Geol. Survey,* 1903, pp. 101, 102.

Fig. 41.—*Characteristic fossils of the Cenomanian and Turonian (Lower and Middle Chalk and Planus Zone).*
1a, b. *Holaster subglobosus* (Leske); 2a, b. *Schloenbachia varians* (J. Sowerby); 3. *Turrilites acutus* Passy; 4. *Scaphites aequalis* J. Sowerby; 5. *Inoceramus labiatus* (Schlotheim); 6a, b. *Rhynchonella cuvieri* d'Orbigny; 7a, b. *Bicavea rotaformis* Gregory ($\times 1\frac{1}{2}$); 8a, b. *Discoidea dixoni* Forbes; 9a, b. *Terebratulina lata* Etheridge ($\times 1\frac{1}{2}$); 10. *Holaster planus* (Mantell); 11a, b. *Micraster leskei* (Des Moulins) (11b, detail of ambulacrum); 12a, b. *Actinocamax plenus* (Blainville) (12b, alveolus).

sists of hard white nodular chalk.   The nodules vary from brownish purple blotches in the chalk to extremely hard subangular fragments, almost resembling a breccia.   What little marl there is runs in thin seams.

The Terebratulina Zone consists of much smoother, more marly chalk, which is still very hard.   A sudden increase in current action is suggested by the occurrence, between 12 and 16 ft. from the top of the zone, of 5 ft. of bands of hard yellow and green nodules, once referred to the Chalk Rock.   Flints in this zone are rare.

The Planus Zone is of a distinctive dirty grey colour due to admixture of marl in the body of the chalk.   It is much softer than the Middle Chalk and contains many irregular flint bands, though they are scarcer in the bottom 20 ft. of the zone than higher up.

(b)   STRATIGRAPHY AND PALAEONTOLOGY

The base of the stage is marked by the top of the Plenus Marl, although, as noted above, marly chalk continues for a few feet higher.   Fossils are generally rare in the bottom zone, but *Inoceramus labiatus* (Schlotheim) is abundant, especially in the lower part.   It is not a perfect zonal index for it is common in the zone above, but it is better than *Rhynchonella cuvieri* d'Orbigny which has a still longer range.

The large numbers of *I. labiatus,* however, together with the lithological character, serve to distinguish the zone.

Other common species of the Labiatus Zone are *Typocidaris hirudo* (Sorignet) and *Discoidea dixoni* Forbes. *Hemiaster minimus* Agassiz and *Cardiaster pygmaeus* Forbes are rare.   A single specimen of the ammonite *Metasigaloceras rusticum* (Sharpe) was found, a rare species, of which the type came from Dorset.

Terebratulina lata Etheridge occurs commonly throughout its own zone in Dorset and, in conjunction with the lithological changes, is a good guide to the base of the zone.   The top is shown by the incoming of the Planus Zone species rather than by any

---

FIG. 42.—*Characteristic fossils of the Senonian (Upper Chalk).*

1a, b. *Micraster cortestudinarium* (Goldfuss); 1b, ambulacrum; 2a, b. *Micraster coranguinum* (Leske); 2b. ambulacrum; 3a, b, c. *Magas pumilus* J. Sowerby; 4a, b. *Offaster pilula* (Lamarck); 5. *Marsupites testudinarius* (Schlotheim) (single plate); 6a—d. *Uintacrinus westfalicus* Schlueter (a, b, outer and inner views of plate; c, d, top and side views of arm ossicle); 7a, b. *Crania egnabergensis* Retzius ($\times$ 1½); 8a, b. *Terebratulina rowei* Kitchin ($\times$ 1½); 9a, b. *Actinocamax quadratus* (Defrance); 9b, alveolus; 10. *Belemnitella mucronata* (Schlotheim); 11a—d. *Echinocorys scutata* Leske. Typical profiles; a, gibbous variety from Planus Zone; b, domed variety from Coranguinum Zone; c, pyramidate variety from Marsupites Zone; d, variety *depressula* from the lower part of the Pilula Zone.

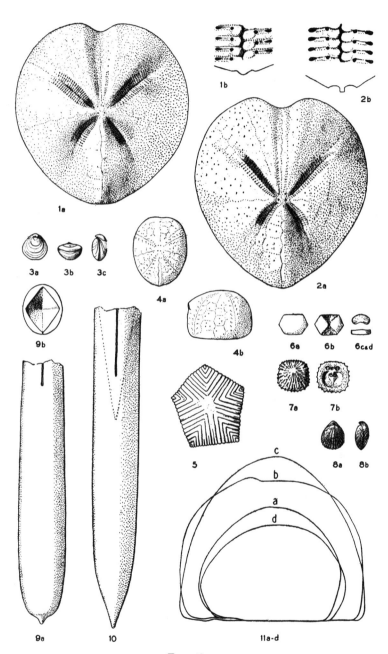

Fig. 42.

marked disappearance of earlier forms. The rest of the fauna of this zone is rather featureless; *Discoidea dixoni* Forbes, *Holaster planus* (Mantell) and *Micraster corbovis* Forbes occur occasionally.

The Planus Zone, compared with the two zones below it, is rich in fossils. In addition to the index fossil *Micraster leskei* (Des Moulins), *M. praecursor* Rowe, *Echinocorys scutata* Leske, *Cidaris serrifera* Forbes, *Tylocidaris clavigera* (Kœnig), and *Isocrinus agassizi* (Hagenow) are abundant. The wealth of these and other species, the characteristic features of the Micrasters[1] and the grey colour of the chalk make this zone easy to distinguish.

Mention must be made of the Bicavea Bed, a 2-foot band near the base of the zone, crowded with the polyzoan *Bicavea rotaformis* Gregory (Fig. 41). At White Nothe the lower part of the zone is characterized by an abundance of a branching cylindrical calcareous sponge, *Pharetrospongia strahani* Sollas. Occasional specimens of this sponge occur at the same horizon elsewhere.

IV. SENONIAN

(a) LITHOLOGY

The following is a summary of the lithology of the Senonian zones :—

The Cortestudinarium Zone consists of rather hard generally discoloured chalk with bands of yellow, nodular chalk and much flint in irregular layers.

The Coranguinum Zone is fairly hard chalk, like that of the zone below at the base but not discoloured higher up. As a rule the flints are in regular even lines.

The Marsupites Zone is very similar with slightly less regular flints; and the same applies to the Pilula and Quadratus Zones, except that they contain many seams of marl.

The lower subzone of the Mucronata Zone is still fairly hard in some localities, but the inland chalk near Wool and the middle subzone at Studland are soft. The chalk contains irregular flint bands and a few yellow stained layers.

(b) STRATIGRAPHY AND PALAEONTOLOGY

The Senonian is here used in the old wide sense, covering all the Upper Chalk above the Planus Zone, although the Quadratus and Mucronata Zones are perhaps better separated as the Campanian, as was shown by Jukes-Browne.[2]

In Dorset most of the Cortestudinarium Zone is poorly fossiliferous, but it is possible to find *Micraster* of the characteristic form (a few with " inflated " and most with " subdivided " ambulacra :

---

[1] A. W. Rowe, ' Analysis of Genus *Micraster*,' *Quart. Journ. Geol. Soc.*, vol. lv, 1899, p. 494.

[2] A. J. Jukes-Browne, ' On the Recognition of Two Stages in the Upper Chalk,' *Geol. Mag.*, vol. xlix, 1912, pp. 304-313, 360-372.

see Fig. 42) and *Echinocorys scutata* of the typical gibbous shape.

The Coranguinum Zone is little better. *Micraster* and *Echinocorys* again provide the only palæontological data for fixing the base of the zone. Other characteristic species are *Conulus albogalerus* Leske and *Cidaris perornata* Forbes. Rowe[1] records (p. 49) an ammonite of the " *leptophyllus* group," i.e., a *Parapuzosia sp.*

The base of the Marsupites Zone is defined by the first appearance of *Uintacrinus westfalicus* Schlueter. This crinoid characterises a lower band, *Marsupites testudinarius* a higher. Prominent characteristic fossils are *Echinocorys scutata* Leske, pyramidate variety (var. *elevata* Brydone) (*see* Fig. 42), nipple-shaped heads of *Bourgueticrinus ellipticus* Miller var. *papilliformis* Brydone and *Terebratulina rowei* Kitchin (Fig. 42).

The old " Zone of *Actinocamax quadratus* " was in 1914 divided by R. M. Brydone into a Zone of *Offaster pilula* below and a Zone of *A. quadratus* above, the former being divided into a Subzone of abundant *O. pilula* above and a Subzone of *Echinocorys scutata* var. *depressula* below. The latter subzone has at its base a band with occasional *Actinocamax granulatus* Blainville. The Pilula Subzone contains large numbers of the typical echinoid in bands. Other characteristic fossils are *Terebratulina rowei* Kitchin, of large size, *Metopaster quadratus* var. *parvus* Spencer, *Crateraster quinqueloba* var. *depressus* Spencer and other typical starfish ossicles.[2]

Actinocamax quadratus (Defrance) occurs rarely in its own zone but there seem to be few other fossils and none of them is characteristic.

The next zone is very different. *Belemnitella mucronata* (Schlotheim) is confined to its zone and is abundant in most of it. Common and characteristic fossils are *Cardiaster ananchytis* (Leske), *Cidaris serrata* Forbes, *Magas pumilus* J. Sowerby (Fig 42) (middle and top of lower subdivisions of the Mucronata Zone), *Kingena lima* (Defrance) (large), *Crania costata* J. Sowerby. Rarer characteristic species include *Cidaris pleracantha* Agassiz, *Aptychus rugosus* Sharpe and *Stephanophyllia michelini* Lonsdale (at junction of lower and middle subzones of the Mucronata Zone). The middle subdivision of the Mucronata Zone can always be distinguished by abundance of ossicles of *Metopaster tumidus* Spencer, *M. undulatus* Spencer and *Teichaster favosus* Spencer.

V. DETAILS OF EXPOSURES.

The sections are taken in order from east to west and the whole of the chalk of each locality is described under that locality.

---

[1] A. W. Rowe, ' The Zones of the White Chalk of the English Coast, Part II, Dorset,' *Proc. Geol. Assoc.,* vol. xvii, 1901, p. 1.

[2] Ossicles of starfish are numerous in most zones of the chalk and are useful for zonal determination. But since they need careful study, only particularly important species are mentioned here.

(a) BALLARD HEAD AND HANDFAST POINT

(including all the chalk from Punfield Cove to Studland)

CENOMANIAN.—Jukes-Browne[1] gives the thickness at Punfield Cove as about 143 feet. At present accurate measurement is impossible but the total was estimated independently as about 160 feet. Immediately above the Albian follows the Cenomanian basement bed or " Chloritic Marl," consisting of about 5 ft. of glauconitic, sandy and marly chalk, with phosphatic nodules and many small fossils. It is usually dark grey or green in colour. The ammonoids include *Schloenbachia spp., Turrilites costatus* Lamarck and *Cyrtocheilus baculoides* (Mantell); the commonest fossils are small Rhynchonellids.

The succeeding chalk is hard and splintery and contains few fossils. Boulders of it are seen to have a blue-grey core and to weather a pale buff on the outside. Between this and the Plenus Marl are alternations of bluish marl and grey chalk. Fossils are rare and no divisions seem justified. Jukes-Browne[2] mentions the fact that no " *Am. varians* " were found higher than 30 ft. from the base. About 40 or 50 ft. from the base there are two layers of phosphatic nodules and among them a number of small *Calycoceras*. Thirty feet from the top there is a band with occasional large *Calycoceras sp*.

The Plenus Marl can be recognized by its light blue colour. It contains here a few examples of the characteristic belemnite and isolated ossicles of *Crateraster quinqueloba* (Goldfuss).

TURONIAN.—The Middle Chalk is well exposed. Airweathered surfaces of the Labiatus Zone and part of the Terebratulina Zone can be reached by walking along the upturned edges of the inclined chalk and climbing a little way up the cliff. The chalk however is extremely hard and contains few fossils of interest. It is impossible to get further than the lower part of the Terebratulina Zone by walking along the base of the cliff. Rowe[3] states that he landed from a boat near Ballard Point and found a small face of the Terebratulina Zone "studded with fossils," and this was "the only exposure in this zone which yielded a good list." The point itself, he says, is in the Planus Zone.

Though the cliff section is disappointing it is worth mentioning that good collecting in these three zones can be had in the slipped masses and fallen boulders along the beach, from Punfield Cove eastward. With a little practice they can readily be zoned and most of the characteristic fossils can be found.

SENONIAN.—Up to the Mucronata Zone this stage is inaccessible except by boat. Rowe[3] landed at various spots and found Cortes-

---

[1] A. J. Jukes-Browne, ' Cretaceous Rocks of Britain,' vol. ii, Lower and Middle Chalk, *Mem. Geol. Survey.* 1903, p. 95.
[2] *loc. cit.*
[3] A. W. Rowe, ' The Zones of the White Chalk of the English Coast. Part II. Dorset,' *Proc. Geol. Assoc.*, vol. xvii, 1901, pp. 34 and 35.

tudinarium beds immediately north of Ballard Point in a small cave and the other zones in succession up to the fault. All the chalk north of this, as well as a little to the south, is in the Mucronata Zone. Rowe[1] gives the total thickness of the zone here as at least 250 feet. According to Spencer[2] the top 50 ft. belong to the middle subdivision of the Mucronata Zone. Until well into Studland Bay the chalk is fairly hard, thus allowing the formation of the magnificent stacks (Old Harry, the Pinnacle and others). Fossils are fairly numerous in the lower subdivision of the Mucronata Zone and more so in the middle, which is mostly very soft.

It is possible to walk from Studland round Handfast Point at low tide, and, provided there is little wind, the Studland Bay part of the section can be worked by wading even when the tide is washing the foot of the cliff.

(b) PITS BETWEEN BALLARD HEAD AND WORBARROW
(C.W.W. and W.J.A.)

There are numerous chalk pits along the narrow ridge from Ballard Head to Worbarrow Bay. Few are worked but there are still a number worth mentioning.

In the gap in the downs immediately west of the Swanage-Studland road at Ulwell a pit, probably in the Cortestudinarium Zone, shows about 20 ft. of very hard chalk dipping 75° N. In contrast with this, a pit on the south side of the Studland-Corfe road near the fork to Swanage shows about 15 ft. of chalk which seems to dip at about 30° N. The rock is comparatively soft chalk of the middle subdivision of the Mucronata Zone, in which over 30 species of fossils were found on a short search.

The next two pits, one up a wooded lane south of Rempstone Hall, the other south of Rollington Farm near Corfe, are both in approximately vertical and extremely hard chalk, the first perhaps in the Planus or Cortestudinarium Zone, the other in the Mucronata Zone. A pit at Corfe, about 100 yds. north of the castle, shows 110 ft. of extremely hard, vertical chalk, much shattered and slickensided; it is almost unfossiliferous, but probably belongs to the Mucronata Zone.

On West Hill, Corfe, on the west bank of the Corfe stream, a pit shows a section from the Plenus Marl to a horizon well up in flinty Upper Chalk (probably top of Planus Zone). The Plenus Marl dips 83° N., the Terebratulina Zone 78° N. with Group 3 shears (see p. 289) dipping 34° S., the base of the Planus Zone dips 90° N. and 60 ft. higher the dip increases to 93°-96° N.

A pit 200 yds west of the highest cottage at Cocknowle, near Church Knowle, shows Lower Chalk at 70° N. with a little upper Greensand below. At the old cement works at Cocknowle there is

---

[1] A. W. Rowe, *op. cit.*, p. 37.
[2] W. K. Spencer, *op. cit.*, p. 146.

a long scar of Labiatus chalk, dipping 75° N. Planus Chalk
dipping 86°-90°, is exposed in the road-cutting at the top. In the
valley north of this, on the same road, there is a pit showing altered
and hardened chalk, dipping 86°-90° N., with Group 3 shears at
30° S. (*see* p. 312). It may be in any zone from Coranguinum to
Mucronata.

Half a mile due south of the summit of Creechbarrow a good
section exposes the junction of Lower and Middle Chalk, with a
conspicuous Plenus Marl bed dipping 45° N. The old lime kilns
near the col of Creechbarrow are in vertical Mucronata chalk,
which is much softer than in neighbouring pits to the east.

Beside the road up the hill leading from Steeple to East
Lulworth two pits and a road-cutting combine to show a nearly
complete section from the uppermost Albian to the Planus Zone
on the crest of the ridge. The base of the Middle Chalk in the pit
dips 55° N., with some Group 3 shears; higher up in the cutting
the Middle Chalk dips 63° N.

Unusually fossiliferous chalk in the Terebratulina Zone is
exposed on the road from Tyneham up Whiteway Hill. On the
other side of the hill there is a roadside pit in highly inclined
Mucronata chalk, fairly soft and with characteristic fossils.

(c) WORBARROW BAY, ARISH MELL AND MUPE BAY
WORBARROW BAY

CENOMANIAN.—Jukes-Browne[1] gives the total thickness of the
Cenomanian in Worbarrow Bay as about 92 ft., and Arkell as
about 90 feet.[2]

The basement bed in the eastern part of the bay consists of 4
feet of soft brownish, slightly glauconitic, sandy chalk, resting on
a pitted and phosphatized surface of the topmost Albian. In the
pockets of this are many white, rather clayey, casts of small
ammonites, including *Calycoceras newboldi* (Kossmat), *Mantelliceras mantelli* (J. Sowerby), *Calycoceras gentoni* (Brongniart),
Scaphites aequalis J. Sowerby, *S. obliquus* J. Sowerby. Above,
the chalk becomes harder, less sandy and grey in colour. About
6 ft. from the base occurs a number of large worn ammonites, the
nuclei of which are determinable as *Mantelliceras cantianum* Spath.

The next 20 ft. or so is hard grey chalk with scattered black
flints, some with a brown cortex, some passing gradually into
the matrix. Fossils are rare. There follow 50 or 60 ft. of blocky
chalk with a little marl and few fossils, and then the Plenus Marl,
6 ft. thick.

In the western part of the bay, near Cow Corner, the base of
the Cenomanian consists of dark glauconitic sand passing down
into similar sand at the top of the Albian.[3] Only a few ammonites

---

[1] A. J. Jukes-Browne, *op. cit.,* p. 96.
[2] W. J. Arkell, ‘ Three Tectonic Problems of the Lulworth District,’ *Quart.
Journ. Geol. Soc.,* vol. xciv, p. 30.
[3] *See above,* p. 186.

were found in the bottom 5 ft. of the Cenomanian and the junction was drawn at the upper limit of Albian forms, 2 ft. above the nodule bed.

TURONIAN.—Only the Middle Chalk is accessible at Cow Corner. The Labiatus and Terebratulina Zones can be examined on the wave-battered ledges at the point. They are not very fossiliferous but characteristic species can be found. Good collecting can be had from the Planus Zone boulders on the beach. Interesting tectonic features of the Middle Chalk here are referred to on p. 301.

ARISH MELL

The Planus Zone is preserved on the tip of the eastern point of the bay.

SENONIAN.—On the eastern side the Cortestudinarium Zone is nearly inaccessible, the Coranguinum Zone accessible but rather barren. The junction with the Marsupites Zone can be determined by finding *Uintacrinus* plates. Rowe found these to occur through a range of 30 ft. and *Marsupites* plates for the next 24 ft., together with other characteristic fossils of the zone. Adding to this 15 ft. in which he found no *Marsupites* and no *Offaster pilula* he had a thickness of 69 feet. The Pilula Zone on this side of the bay is dirty and little is visible.

About 30 ft. of the lower subdivision of the Mucronata Zone is present at the head of the bay on the west side. Beyond this the Quadratus Zone is at least 180 ft. in thickness. Fossils are uncommon but the zonal belemnite can occasionally be found.

On the seaward face of Cockpit Head there is a good exposure of parts of the Pilula Zone. The chalk is hard and wave-beaten but weathered surfaces can easily be reached by climbing up the inclined faces of the chalk. According to Brydone there is a thickness of about 120 ft., but it is hard to fix accurately the junction with the Marsupites Zone.

Rowe[1] found only 12½ ft. of chalk yielding *Marsupites* plates and 17 ft. yielding those of *Uintacrinus*. These crinoids and other typical small fossils are abundant.

According to Rowe there follows about 200 ft. of the Coranguinum Zone, but the exposure is unattractive; then comes 60 ft. of Cortestudinarium Zone, by the headland separating this section from Mupe Bay.

It is advisable to watch the tide carefully when working this section since the eastern corner of Cockpit Head lies low and the tide comes up rapidly; it is possible to get round Black Rock into Mupe Bay, but not easy.

MUPE BAY
(from west to east)

CENOMANIAN.—The bottom of the Cenomanian consists of hard dark-grey and green glauconitic sand presumably resting on similar Albian sand, as in Worbarrow Bay. This bed, together

---

[1] A. W. Rowe, *op. cit.*, p. 25.

with the rest of the stage, is here almost unfossiliferous. Owing to faulting it is not worth measuring. In general there is hard grey chalk with a few flints below and alternations of grey chalk and bluish marl above, capped by about 7 ft. of Plenus Marl.

TURONIAN.—The Labiatus Zone, 49 ft. thick, is hard, nodular, and wave-battered, but characteristic fossils, though scarce, can be found. The Terebratulina Zone, forming long ledges, is still harder, and fossils again are rare.

The next higher zone occupies the rest of the accessible section up to the cave. The chalk is grey and well weathered, yielding a fair list of fossils, including most of the characteristic species. The Bicavea Bed can be seen on the lowest ledge of this zone.

The cave on the west side of Black Rock is cut in the Cortestudinarium Zone.

(d) LULWORTH COVE

CENOMANIAN.—The lower Chalk at Lulworth is so faulted that only about 30 ft. remain. The basement bed is preserved immediately above the Albian as 3 ft. of buff sandy chalk with a few phosphatic nodules and fossils. The Plenus Marl is about 6 ft. thick.

TURONIAN.—The base of the cliff at the back of the cove is cut in Labiatus Zone, from which characteristic fossils can be obtained; a single specimen of *Cardiaster pygmaeus* Forbes was found. Rowe records " *Am. cunningtoni* " (? = *Prionotropis woollgari* Mantell sp.), and large worn ammonites are often visible *in situ*.

It is sometimes possible to reach a face of Terebratulina Zone by climbing up the talus.

Boulders from the Planus Zone are to be found on the beach.

(e) ST. OSWALD'S BAY and MAN-O'-WAR COVE

Much of the Cenomanian is faulted out here and the remainder is uninteresting.

The Middle and Upper Chalk is extensively faulted, stained and hardened and does not merit full description. The back of the bay is cut in Coranguinium Zone and the zones between this and the Cenomanian can be traced on both sides. The tectonic features are of the greatest interest and are referred to on pp. 290-1.

Man-o'-War Cove is a repetition of St. Oswald's Bay, though here the section extends no farther than the Planus Zone.

The basement bed is fairly fossiliferous and comparable with that in Durdle Cove and westwards.

(f) DURDLE COVE—BAT'S HEAD

CENOMANIAN.—Behind the wall of Upper Albian beds there is a good exposure of the basement bed, 4 ft. thick. Fossils are very abundant, especially just above the junction with the Albian.

The small remainder of the Cenomanian is too faulted to be worth examining.

TURONIAN.—The Middle Chalk is battered, very unfossiliferous and not worth examining. The Planus Zone is exposed at intervals above and below the slide-plane, but is, in itself, uninteresting here.

SENONIAN.—Round a small point is a recess leading up to Scratchy Bottom, on the east side of which is a good exposure of Cortestudinarium Zone, 70 ft. thick. Characteristic *Micraster* and *Echinocorys* are fairly common and there is a band of starfish ossicles, of half a dozen species, near the top of the zone.

The rest of this recess, Swyre Head, and the next recess are all in vertical chalk of the Coranguinum Zone, yielding typical fossils but not in abundance. About 140 ft. of the zone are exposed.

All but the tip of Bat's Head itself is cut in vertical chalk of the Cortestudinarium Zone, the tip being in Planus Zone.

(g)   WHITE NOTHE TO BAT'S HEAD

CENOMANIAN.—On the talus slopes below the main Albian section east of Holworth House there are many large blocks of the basement bed, the bottom of which, extraordinarily rich in fossils (mostly ammonites, echinoids and brachiopods), furnishes the best collecting at this horizon in Dorset. Similar blocks occur on the beach towards the point.

There is about 45 ft. of Lower Chalk visible at the point of White Nothe. All below the Plenus Marl is nearly white and smooth, the harder layers weathering into ledges, and there are three prominent flint-bands. Few fossils have been obtained, though *Aequipecten beaveri* (J. Sowerby) is fairly common in fallen blocks.

TURONIAN.—On the undercliff there are several large well-weathered masses fallen from the Labiatus Zone, but they are poor in fossils. The bluffs below the signal on the cliff top are accessible by climbing up the talus slopes. Good collecting can be had here in the Planus Zone, the calcareous sponge *Pharetrospongia strahani* Sollas being particularly prominent in the lower part of the zone.

Higher up the zig-zag path faces of extremely barren Cortestudinarium Zone can be examined, and above these the Coranguinum Zone at the cliff top.

On the shore east of the point the Middle Chalk comes in above the Plenus Marl. The Labiatus Zone is 76 ft. thick, hard, nodular and poorly fossiliferous. Its top is marked by a flint band. Above this there is 58 ft. of the less nodular and more marly chalk of the Terebratulina Zone.

Farther east the grey flinty Planus Zone appears, 51 ft. thick. It is fossiliferous where not too wave-battered.

SENONIAN.—Rowe drew the base of the Cortestudinarium Zone at a nodular flint band at the base of Fountain Rock. The zone is 113 ft. thick and extremely poor in fossils. Its top, as noted by Rowe, is marked by a " strong ferruginous line of crushed and crowded flint."[1]

The Coranguinum Zone is as barren as the last and is about 170 ft. thick.

The chalk of the Marsupites Zone is much battered, but Rowe found enough remains of *Uintacrinus* and *Marsupites* to establish a thickness for the zone of 111 feet.

Above this, in the recess below Middle Bottom, is slightly less than 200 ft. of chalk, referred by Rowe to the Quadratus Zone. Brydone examined it and assigned 52 ft. to the subzone of *E. scutata* var. *depressula,* 84 ft. to the subzone of abundant *O. pilula* and the remainder, about 60 ft., to his Quadratus Zone. Fossils are not very common in this chalk but *O. pilula* is common in its subzone and Rowe found at the back of the recess a band from which he obtained 15 specimens of *Actinocamax quadratus.*

East of Middle Bottom the sequence given above is traversed in descending order through vertical chalk till the Planus Zone is reached on the end of Bat's Head.

(h) EAST LULWORTH, WOOL, and WINFRITH
(W.J.A., based on notes by H. J. O. WHITE, 1936)

Lower and Middle Chalk crop out round the rim of the Chaldon Wealden inlier but the bulk of the downs in this area is composed of the higher zones of the Upper Chalk, especially the Mucronata Zone.

Lower Chalk can be seen 60 yds. south-east of Lords Barrow, dipping 30° N., cut by slide-planes inclined 30°-40° S.; and at the disused limekiln 450 yds. east of Chaldon Vicarage Farm, where the dip is 12° S.E. At the latter place Mr. White found *Acanthoceras* cf. *rhotomagense* (Defrance) and *Mantelliceras* cf. *mantelli* (J. Sowerby).

Middle Chalk (Labiatus Zone) is exposed to a depth of 25 ft. 60 yds. south of Five Marys, dipping 45°-50° N.N.E. and again 300 yds. south-west of Winfrith Rectory Farm, dipping 40°-47° N.N.E.

Of the lower parts of the Upper Chalk, Mr. White recognized the Coranguinum Zone (middle part of the zone) 130 yds. north-west of Lords Barrow, dipping 50°-55° N.; the Marsupites Zone beside Coalhill Drive, 560 yds. west-north-west of Winfrith Church; and the Pilula Zone 700 yds. south-west of Winfrith Church.

For the rest, the chalk pits in the " massif de Lulworth " (as Barrois called it) are nearly all in the Mucronata Zone. Some of the best pits are (1) 500 yds. north-west of Five Marys (very interest-

---

[1] A. W. Rowe, *op. cit.,* p. 10.

ing tectonically ; *see* p. 278) ; (2) Burton Pit, half a mile south-west of Wool ; (3) in the fork of the road a quarter mile north of Coombe Keynes (formerly showed the junction with the Eocene, *see* p. 227) ; (4) North Lodge, Lulworth Park. Fossils from some of these pits were listed in the Purbeck Memoir.[1] The presence of *Magas pumilus* in the Mucronata chalk in certain pits in the Coombe Keynes-Lulworth area[2] and north of Chaldon Herring indicates that chalk up to the middle of the zone is there preserved.[3]

(i) RINGSTEAD AND OSMINGTON MILLS (W.J.A.)

From Holworth the Lower and Middle Chalk extend westward to form the ridge of Spring Bottom Hill, Ringstead, and there are two outliers of Lower Chalk west of the Osmington Mills stream. The Lower Chalk has been worked in nine old pits on both sides of the ridge. One beside the road down to Ringstead is still used for repairing the road and shows a good section of 35-40 ft. of Lower Chalk dipping 12° about N.W. Middle Chalk shows in sections immediately above, and in the brow of the hill above Spring Bottom and overlooking the Mills.[4] The road down to South Down Farm displays the Lower Chalk, including the Plenus Marl, standing vertical. The top of the ridge is thickly mantled with Angular Flint Gravel.

In the outliers west of the Mills, gradually foundering into the mud slides of Black Head, small sections at the top of the cliffs show a leached remnant of the Cenomanian basement bed, full of phosphatic fossils.

(j) NORTH OF THE POXWELL AND RIDGEWAY FAULTS
(W.J.A., based on notes by H. J. O. WHITE, 1936)

In this area the primary interest of the chalk pits is tectonic, and all those near the fault zone were examined from that point of view by Mr. H. J. Osborne White in 1936. The principal results are embodied in Chapter xiii, pp. 264-279. It remains to add a few notes here on the stratigraphical aspect of the exposures.

POXWELL AND SUTTON POYNTZ AREA.—Lower Chalk can be seen in old pits 500 and 800 yds. north-west of Holworth, and again by the cart track 2,000 ft. east of the White Horse.

Middle Chalk (Labiatus Zone) was identified by Mr. White at Moigns Down Barn, with the zonal index-fossil abundant in the highest foot or two of the beds ; and again in a small pit on the east side of Poxwell Drove, 760 yds. west by south of Poxwell Church. The latter exposure shows hard flaggy flintless chalk with scattered small nodules and thin streaky partings of grey marl, dipping about 70° N.

---

[1] A. Strahan, *Purbeck Memoir*, 1898, pp. 183-4.
[2] A. W. Rowe, *op. cit.*, pp. 38, 63.
[3] R. M. Brydone, *Geol. Mag.*, vol. lxxiii, 1936, p. 330.
[4] The whole ridge was wrongly marked as Lower Chalk on the 1904 edition of Sheet 342.

A fresh surface of about 100 ft. of Middle Chalk is displayed in the big chalk pit on the north side of the road 750 yds. north-west of the water-works, Sutton Poyntz. *Inoceramus labiatus* is abundant from about 12-15 ft. above the base and is associated with *Rhynchonella cuvieri*. The higher beds belong to the Terebratulina Zone. The dip is about 30° N.W. In other exposures about 250 yds. farther west the Middle Chalk is much hardened and sheared, and immediately in contact with the fault-plane is converted to low-grade marble (*see* p. 264).

The Upper Chalk shows little of interest. Old pits at Watercombe and 750 yds. to the east-south-east are probably in the Quadratus Zone. Strahan marked dips of 8° and 13° N. in these. A more recent quarry on the north side of the main road 400 yds. south-west of Owermoigne Church shows unfossiliferous chalk of the Mucronata Zone dipping 3° N. Part of the Coranguinum Zone, dipping 30° N., is shown 450 yds. east of Poxwell Church.

The flat-lying thrusts seen in the Upper Greensand and Chloritic Marl of the East Hill Spur, Sutton Poyntz (*see* p. 269) probably lose themselves gradually in the chalk to the north. This may account for a dip of 53° N. marked by Strahan by the track side 300 yds. north-east of the springs of Spring Bottom. Little can be seen there now, but Mr. White thinks the chalk possibly belongs to the Cortestudinarium Zone. About 100 yds. farther north he noted Coranguinum chalk dipping 10° N.W. At West Hill a pipe-trench (*see* p. 265) showed the Upper Chalk dipping about 25° N.E.

BINCOMBE.—A good section of the richly-fossiliferous " Chloritic Marl," with a characteristic basement bed crowded with phosphatized fossils, is displayed in a quarry at Bincombe. The dip is about 35° N.E. The following is abridged from a description by Mr. White, with some additional records of ammonites :—

QUARRY BY CARTWAY 270 YDS. E.S.E. OF BINCOMBE CHURCH

LOWER CHALK.   Ft.

4. Irregularly blocky greyish marly chalk, with a few flints in the upper 10 ft. ; contains small phosphate nodules in the lower part and becomes sandy and glauconitic towards the base. *Plocoscyphia labrosa* T. Smith, *Holaster subglobosus* (Leske), *Inoceramus crippsi* Mantell ...   . c. 20

3. Basement bed (' Chloritic Marl ') : speckled greyish glauconitic and sandy marly chalk, with scattered phosphatic nodules. The lowest 6 to 9 ins. are full of phosphatic nodules and phosphatized fossils, including the ammonoids *Calycoceras newboldi* (Kossmat), *C. spp., Mantelliceras mantelli* (J. Sowerby), *Acanthoceras hippocastanum* (J. Sowerby), *Schloenbachia sharpei* Semenow, *S. spp., Scaphites aequalis* J. Sowerby, etc. Uneven junction ; top of U.G.S. pitted   3

UPPER GREENSAND　　　　　　　　　　　　　　　　　　　　　　　Ft.

2. Quartz grit, glauconitic and calcareous, in a massive bed,
the middle third obscurely nodular : *Cardiaster fossarius*
Benett, *Tetragramma variolare* (Brongniart), *Rhynchonella
grasiana* d'Orbigny, *Aequipecten asper* (Lamarck), *Exogyra
conica, Serpula concava*, etc.　　...　　...　　...　　...　　9

1. Sandstone, brown, with rounded and angular sandy cherts ;
passing down to loose sandstone　　...　　...　　Seen to　　2

　　　　　　　　　　　　　　　　　　　　　　　Total　　...　　34ft.

The upper part of the Lower Chalk, with the equivalent of the
Plenus Marl, and the base of the Middle Chalk, are exposed in a
quarry 100 yds. north of Bincombe Church, dipping about 40°N.E.

QUARRY 100 YDS. N. OF BINCOMBE CHURCH [1]

MIDDLE CHALK　　　　　　　　　　　　　　　　　　　　　　　Ft.

5. Hard nodular chalk (Melbourn Rock?), seen to　　...　　...　　4
4. Hard smooth chalk in lenticular beds with marl partings ...　　14

LOWER CHALK

3. Tough grey marl (Plenus Marl)　　...　　...　　...　　...　　$5\frac{1}{4}$
2. Hard white chalk　　...　　...　　...　　...　　...　　...　　3
1. Firm chalk in thick beds, with flints ...　　...　　...　　...　　9

Mr. White notes that the flints in bed 1 are sparsely distributed
in a band about $1\frac{1}{2}$ ft. thick.　　He found *Aequipecten beaveri*
common in beds 2 and 3, and *Inoceramus labiatus* and *I. crippsi*
in bed 4.

The whole Lower and Middle Chalk and the basal part of the
Upper, dipping at a high angle, are crossed by the lane leading
north from the Upwey road 400 yds. north-west of Bincombe
Church. Flinty Upper Chalk, dipping 40° N. is exposed in a pit
by the tumuli on Bincombe Hill.

RIDGEWAY.—West of the railway at Bincombe Tunnel the
Lower and Middle Chalk are rapidly faulted out by the Ridgeway
Fault. Upper Chalk, with a sharp upward drag at the southern
edge, is brought into contact with the Purbeck Beds.

At the cross-roads north of the summit of Ridgeway Hill, where
the Ridgeway crosses the Roman road from Weymouth to
Dorchester, a pit shows about 10 ft. of soft chalk belonging to the
Marsupites Zone, dipping 4° N. Plates of *Marsupites testudinarius* are common, also the sponges *Porosphaera globularis*
(Phillips) and *P. nuciformis* (Hagenow). The Pilula Zone comes
in a short distance south of this, in the road-cutting, where it dips
3° S. (*see* p. 254). To the north, beds in the Planus and Cortestudinarium Zones are displayed in a 20-foot section 200 yds. north-
north-east of Ashton Cottages, south-west of Maiden Castle.

[1] A. J. Jukes-Browne, ' Cretaceous Rocks of Britain,' vol. ii, *Mem. Geol. Surv.*
1903, p. 99.

Mr. White found the genus *Micraster* well represented here, by a succession of forms that are well preserved and easy to extract; it is, in fact, according to Mr. White, one of the best pits for Micrasters in the south of England.

Small pits, now nearly all abandoned, about Whitcombe and West Knighton, are all in the Mucronata Zone and show nothing noteworthy. The tract north of the South Winterborne lies outside our area.

UPWEY TO PORTISHAM AND ABBOTSBURY.—A synopsis of the pits along the Ridgeway Fault is given in the chapter on tectonics, pp. 252-255.

CHAPTER XII

EOCENE AND OLIGOCENE ROCKS

I. GENERAL

Nowhere in Britain is there any trace of deposits transitional from the Cretaceous to the Eocene, from the Mesozoic to the Cainozoic. In Dorset, as elsewhere, the Chalk ends abruptly with a deeply eroded upper surface upon which the Eocene sands, clays and gravels rest with more or less marked disconformity and contain flints derived from the destruction of the Chalk. After consolidation the Chalk was flexed along a series of gentle anticlines and synclines and tilted up in the west of England so that it began to be eroded. Somewhere to the west of Dorset erosion had penetrated the whole of the Chalk before deposition of the local Eocene rocks began, for the lowest Eocene gravels of the Dorchester area contain pebbles of Upper Greensand.

The Tertiary rocks of the area are as follows : —

4.	Creechbarrow Beds.	Oligocene in part.
3.	Bagshot Beds	
2.	London Clay	Eocene
1.	Reading Beds	

1. READING BEDS. These consist of sand and mottled red and white clay, with bands of concretionary ironstone and a variable amount of flints at the bottom. The sands at Studland are mainly fine, but westward they become coarser and contain small splinters of flint, and in the Dorchester district lenticular masses of sub-angular flint gravel make their appearance at and near the base of the formation, with an increasing amount of Greensand chert with sponge-spicules as the western edge of the outcrop is approached.[1] No fossils have been found and the deposits are probably lacustrine, though the base locally contains glauconite, which is usually considered to indicate deposition in salt water.

---

[1] Clement Reid, ' The Eocene Deposits of Dorset,' *Quart. Journ. Geol. Soc.,* vol. lii, 1896, p. 490.

2. LONDON CLAY. This formation is much thinner and more sandy than in the more typical regions farther east, and no fossils except lignite have been found in it; but hardly any sections are to be seen in the area. It rests upon a bed of well rounded flint pebbles wherever the base has been exposed. In north-east Dorset, around Cranborne, the London Clay locally overlaps the Reading Beds and comes to rest on Chalk,[1] thus indicating a renewal of earth-movements similar to those which preceded deposition of the Reading Beds. The London Clay is probably marine here as elsewhere.

3. BAGSHOT BEDS. Bagshot Beds cover by far the largest area of Tertiary land in Dorset. They consist typically of current-bedded sands, devoid of fossils, and seams of clay, some of which is a pure plastic clay valuable economically and worked for centuries in Purbeck. The clays abound in plant remains. Both the clays and the sands are deltaic in origin and were probably deposited by currents in a shallow subsiding lake fed by a large river flowing from the granitic areas of the west. There is much resemblance to the Wealden Beds, and the conditions under which the two formations originated must have been similar.

The Bagshot Beds of Purbeck comprise three main series, as follows :—

    3.   Agglestone Grit (50 ft. or more)
    2.   Pipe-clay Series (135 ft. to 250 ft.)
    1.   Redend Sandstone (140 ft. ?)

The Redend Sandstone is the brilliant red and yellow soft sandstone of Redend Point, Studland. The Pipe-clay Series is the principal surface-forming rock of the heaths. The Agglestone Grit is an extremely coarse current-bedded and pebbly grit at Studland. Westward it and the upper part of the Pipe-clay Series contain an increasing amount of pebbly seams, composed of flint, Greensand chert, quartz, and far-travelled " Cornish " rocks, with small pieces of silicified Purbeck limestone—in which condition they are " the Bagshot Beds " *par excellence* of the Moreton and Warmwell district—and at the same time they overlap the lower members of the Bagshot Series and the London Clay, until between Warmwell and West Stafford they rest on the Reading Beds. Finally, in the outliers south and south-west of Dorchester they consist mainly of shingle and coarse cobble gravels, in a matrix of typical Agglestone Grit, let into huge solution pipes in the Chalk.[2]

4. CREECHBARROW BEDS.—These beds are known only as a tiny outlier capping Creechbarrow Hill, near Corfe. They consist of sands, followed by buff loamy clay, followed by sands with

---

[1] E. E. L. Dixon, *in* Clement Reid, ' Geology of the Country around Ringwood,' *Mem. Geol. Surv.,* 1902, p. 17.

[2] An outlier much farther west than any in our area is known at Combe Pyne near Lyme Regis : *see* H. B. Woodward, ' Note on the Occurrence of Bagshot Beds at Combe Pyne, near Lyme Regis,' *Geol. Mag.,* 1902, p. 515.

beds of large unrolled flints, culminating in a thin tufaceous limestone with fossils. The sand at the base cannot be distinguished from the Agglestone Grit of Bagshot age; the limestone at the top is dated by its fossils as the equivalent of the Bembridge Limestone in the Isle of Wight, which according to the English

	DORSET AND BOURNEMOUTH	ISLE OF WIGHT	STAGES
OLIGOCENE		Upper Hamstead Beds ⎫ ⎬ 260ft. Lower Hamstead Beds ⎭	RUPELIAN (=STAMPIAN)
	Creechbarrow Limestone Lower Headon Beds	Bembridge Beds 110ft. Osborne Beds 100ft. Headon Beds 150ft.	LATTORFIAN (=TONGRIAN =SANNOISIAN)
EOCENE	Barton Sands 100ft. Barton Clay 100ft. with *Num. orbignyi* at base	Barton Sands 114- (=Headon Hill 221ft. Sands) Barton Clay 147-224ft. with *Num. orbignyi* at base	BARTONIAN (=LUDIAN)
	Highcliff Sands 67ft. Hengistbury Beds 60ft. Boscombe Sands 100ft.	Upper Bracklesham Beds with *Num. variolarius* 211ft. (Whitecliff)	LEDIAN (=AUVERSIAN)
	Bournemouth Marine Beds 150-200ft.	Lower Bracklesham Beds V-VIII with *Num. laevig- atus* 200ft. (Whitecliff)	LUTETIAN
	Bournemouth Freshwater Beds 400ft.	Lower Bracklesham Beds I-IV with *Num. planulatus* 175ft. (Whitecliff)	CUISIAN
	Lower Bagshot Beds Up to 450ft.	Lower Bagshot Beds with Alum Bay leaf bed 76-138ft.	
	London Clay *c.* 100ft.	London Clay 320-405ft.	YPRESIAN
	Reading Beds 40-*c.* 100ft.	Reading Beds 90-150ft.	UPPER LANDENIAN (=SPARNACIAN)
	Thanet Beds wanting		LOWER LANDENIAN (=THANETIAN)
	Wanting		MONTIAN

Note: The customary English method of dividing the Eocene and Oligocene is here retained, but there are good reasons for including the Headon and Osborne Beds (Lattorfian) in the Upper Eocene and beginning the Oligocene with the Hamstead Beds (Rupelian). For full discussion of the point see A. M. Davies, *Tertiary Faunas*, vol. ii, 1934, pp. 128-9. London.

classification is Oligocene. The age of the intervening strata
has not yet been determined.

II. Stratigraphy, Fossil Plants, Climate

(a) stratigraphy

Along the southern shores of Poole Harbour the Agglestone
Grit sinks gently below sea level and is succeeded north-eastward,
outside our area, by the long series of current-bedded deltaic
sands and clays called the Bournemouth Freshwater Series.
They form the cliffs which begin at Poole Head and stretch
towards Bournemouth, and they have yielded a rich tropical
flora.[1]   They are estimated to be about 400 ft. thick and are
probably freshwater equivalents of the lowest 200 ft. of the marine
Lower Bracklesham Beds of Whitecliff Bay in the Isle of Wight,
in which a Cuisian fauna with *Nummulites planulatus* (Lamarck)
is found.[2]

In the type locality of the Cuisian in the Paris Basin
N. planulatus and its associated fauna occur near the top of the
stage, and are rapidly succeeded by *N. laevigatus* (Bruguière),
which is likewise found not far above *N. planulatus* in the upper
part of the Lower Bracklesham at Whitecliff Bay.   Accordingly
Wrigley and Davis assign the underlying Lower Bagshot Beds
to the Cuisian, which is the logical correlation for all strata
between the *N. planulatus* beds and the definitely Ypresian
London Clay.

The table on p. 217 makes clear at a glance the position of the
Dorset strata in the Eocene and Oligocene succession of the Hampshire Basin, and the latest views on correlation with the Continent.
The surfeit of Continental stage names is confusing, and for that
reason the principal synonyms are inserted.

(b) fossil plants, palaeontology, climate

The Reading Beds and London Clay of the area have yielded
no identifiable fossils or plant-remains, but the pipe-clays of the
Bagshot Beds contain a rich tropical flora, including large fan
palms and ferns. " Splendid specimens used to be obtained
abundantly from the Corfe pits, but time and dust have so obliterated the smaller leaves that have been preserved as to render them
valueless for purposes of identification . . . Repeated search in
these pits of late years has only brought to light a few leaves of
simple form, without distinct venation."[3]   Some striking palm
leaves and other plants can be seen in Dorchester Museum.   Plant
remains were also obtained at Studland, though whether from the

---

[1] H. J. O. White, ' Geology of the country around Bournemouth,' 2nd ed.,
Mem. Geol. Surv. 1917, p. 21.

[2] A. Wrigley and A. G. Davis, ' The Occurrence of *Nummulites planulatus* in
England, with a revised correlation of the strata containing it,' *Proc. Geol. Assoc.*,
vol. xlviii, 1937, p. 203.

[3] J. S. Gardner, ' Monograph of the British Eocene Flora,' *Palaeontographical
Soc.*, 1879, p. 16.

cliff near Redend Point or the old brickyard is not now known. Many of the species in the contemporary Alum Bay leaf bed have been found at Studland, including *Aralia* and *Liquidamber*. " The Studland flora, however, has a somewhat different character; for although all the dicotyledons are identical, they are in the minority, and their leaves are bent and mingled with masses of broken fronds of large Fan-palms and Ferns; whilst many Insect wing-cases and Shells have been met with implying, as I believe, greater proximity to land." [1] The shells were recorded as *Unio* by Lyell.[2] At Furzebrook clay pit, between Corfe and Wareham, a " small round oyster " has been recorded.[3] The insect wing-cases belong to beetles.[4]

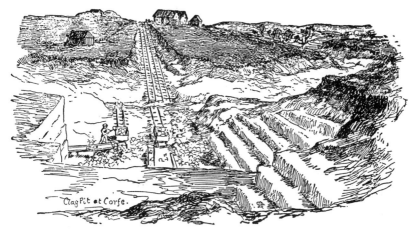

FIG. 43.—*Former open working in the pipe-clay near Corfe.* (Reproduced from *Picturesque Rambles in the Isle of Purbeck*, 1882, by C. E. Robinson.)

The flora of the Paleocene of France and Belgium indicates a warm temperate climate changing to tropical. The floras of the English London Clay, Bagshot Beds and Bracklesham Beds are tropical.[5]

After the Bracklesham period the climate cooled, though the molluscs of the Bartonian were still mainly tropical. English Bracklesham and Barton mollusca show affinity with both tropical and temperate types, this being doubtless due to free communication with the northern as well as the southern oceans.

---

[1] *Ibid.*

[2] C. Lyell, *Students' Elements of Geology,* 1871, p. 238. London. Not repeated in later edition, however.

[3] O. Fisher, ' On the Bracklesham Beds of the Isle of Wight Basin,' *Quart. Journ. Geol. Soc.,* vol. xviii, 1862, p. 83.

[4] P. B. Brodie, ' On the occurrence of the remains of insects in the Tertiary clays of Dorsetshire,' *Quart. Journ. Geol. Soc.,* vol. ix, 1853, p. 53.

[5] E. M. Reid and M. E. J. Chandler, ' The London Clay Flora,' *British Museum (Nat. Hist.)* 1933, p. 59.

III. The Ball-Clay or Pipe-Clay Industry

The plastic clays of the Bagshot Beds are the centre of an industry in Purbeck going back for hundreds of years[1] and second in importance only to the Portland Stone industry. The Purbeck clay, like those of Bovey Tracey and Petrockstow in Devon, is of the kind known as 'transported,' as opposed to the 'residual' kaolin clays of the Cornish granite areas. Its constituents are mainly derived from the decomposition of the Dartmoor and perhaps also Cornish granites, but during transportation to their present position by a river they underwent sorting. The quartz of the parent rock forms the Bagshot sands, and the fine materials, of which by far the greatest part consists of the compound of hydrated alumina and silica, called " clay substance," have been separated to form beds of pure clay. The best beds are from 8 ft. to 14 ft. thick, but there are often several thinner ones separated by shaly or carbonaceous " rubbish clay " or sand.

The principal clay field lies close to the north side of the Purbeck Hills, on the heaths near Corfe, between West Creech and Rempstone Hall. In a belt about five miles long and a mile broad the ground is scarred with a labyrinth of old surface workings. The hollows are filled with lakes, pools and marshes, and the tip-heaps are sparsely overgrown with heather and firs. The famous Blue Pool at Furzebrook is the best known of the lakes in an old surface working. It owes its colour to the great depth of clear water and the white clay bottom. These huge surface pits were excavated in stages entirely by hand (see Fig. 43) and often great thicknesses of over-burden were removed, labour then being cheap. The clay was dug with a special kind of spade in 10-inch cubes weighing 30-35 lbs., called ' balls,' from which the clay gets its trade name. The alternative name is derived from its excellence for making tobacco pipes, a use now almost forgotten. At present open workings are few and comparatively small; in 1938 examples were to be seen in work in Creech Bottom, midway between Furzebrook and Messrs. Pike's office, and south of Norden Farm.

Nowadays by far the greater proportion of the clay is mined. Shafts are sunk vertically, often to depths of 90 to 120 ft.[2] and galleries are driven off in various directions. The galleries are about 6 ft. high and two men work at the end with picks by candle or gas light. The clay is taken to the shaft by hand barrows or rail trucks. After a gallery has been driven a sufficient distance the timbering is recovered or ' drawn ' and the roof and sides cave in, causing subsidence at the surface. The mines in Creechbarrow Hill are rather different. Two levels with tram lines enter the side of the hill at the outcrop 200 yds apart. One level is about

---

[1] It is said to have been started by the Romans (*Victoria County Histories,* Dorset, vol. ii, 1908, p. 363. London).

[2] Pike Bros.' Cotness Shaft is 120 ft. below the floor of an old open working and 160 ft. below the surface.

100 ft. higher than the other and a network of galleries connect up the two inside the hill, following the clay bed on a dip of 10° N. An advantage of these mines is that the clay does not have to be lifted. It is simply put in trucks and trammed out at the surface. There it is tipped to form long embankments for weathering and storage.

Formerly most of the clay was shipped from Wareham and Poole, but now much goes away by train. There are, however, still private lines down to Ridge, Slepe, and Goathorn on Poole Harbour, whence the clay is put on barges and taken across to Poole.

Most of the industry is carried on by two firms of over a century's standing : Messrs. Pike Bros., of Wareham, whose past and present workings extend over ten square miles, with head-quarters at Creech; and Messrs. B. Fayle & Co., who have been working almost as large an area in the Corfe district. The latter firm's present workings are chiefly at Norden, but until recently they were mainly on either side of the Southern Railway line, and earlier still were farther north-east, about Newton and Clay-well, close to the southern shore of Poole Harbour. The combined output of the two firms has been known to exceed 100,000 tons in a year.

The uses to which the Dorset clay is put are innumerable. Its principal value is for mixing with residual kaolin or china-clay to impart to it plasticity and bonding power for the manufacture of white ware. It has high plasticity, high tensile strength, and a nearly pure white colour, owing to freedom from iron oxide; also it is highly refractory. Thus it is an important constituent in the manufacture of sanitary ware, fire cements, crucibles, glazed tiles, electric insulators and iron-enamel. Some of it is worked up in the neighbourhood of Poole and Wareham to make the painted " Poole pottery " displayed in most Dorset china and hardware shops.[1]

III.　READING BEDS, LONDON CLAY AND BAGSHOT BEDS ; DETAILS

(a)　STUDLAND

At the south corner of Studland Bay is displayed a good section of the junction of Chalk and Reading Beds. The Chalk dips at 9° in a direction N. 6° W. Its upper surface is undecayed but undulates deeply owing to erosion before the Reading Beds were laid upon it. At present a hummock of Chalk rises above the beach some yards to the north of the main outcrop, surrounded by Eocene beds. The hollows are filled with up to 4 ft. of dark brown ironstone and black flints, forming the basement bed of the Reading Beds. Between the hollows the same band extends more or less continuously but is thinner. In places it consists of

[1] See A. Scott, ‘ Special Reports on Mineral Resources,’ vol. xxxi, Ball Clays, Mem. Geol. Survey. 1929.

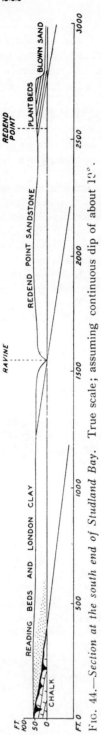

FIG. 44.—*Section at the south end of Studland Bay.* True scale; assuming continuous dip of about 12°.

an 8-inch band of black flints in a irony matrix overlain by about 8 ins. of boxy ironstone with a few flints. Above comes about 6 ft. of buff and greyish mottled clay, passing up into false-bedded red, yellow and white sand. The sand is at present (1938) well exposed in a clean section 40 ft. deep, due to a landslip, after being overgrown for many years. The general dip of the sands is approximately 10° rather west of north.

Besides the erosion-hollows in the Chalk described above there are some big solution pipes of subsequent date, which should be distinguished from the pre-Tertiary phenomena. One pipe 5 ft. wide is seen to pass through the basement bed and the Chalk alike and is filled with the mottled clay and sand to a visible depth of 8ft., when it disappears below the beach, undiminished in width.

The upper part of the Reading Beds and the whole of the London Clay are concealed by slips and vegetation. A clean section begins again north of the small glen which leads the stream and footpath from the village to the beach, where the Bagshot Sands come into the cliff. The rock, midway between a sand and a sandstone, forms a vertical cliff 30 to 55 ft. high; it is bright yellow, streaked and blotched with crimson, often concentrically stained so as to imitate transverse and oblique sections of tree trunks, fantastically false-bedded, and jointed in a criss-cross pattern by joints inclined on the average about 30° N. and 20° S. Although the sand looks friable, some of the dates carved in it are 35 years old. At Redend Point it is hardened on contact with the sea and forms a sandstone ledge. On the north side of the Point hollow pipes a few inches in diameter and lined with ironstone go down 15 ft. from the top of the sand into the beach. They appear to be tilted with the rocks and so may antedate the folding.

Between Redend Point and the beginning of the blown sand of Studland Bay the cliff shows up to 20 ft. of interlaminated grey sandy clay and sand with many carbonaceous plant-remains, resting on the Bagshot Sand. The junction is irregular but dips about 12° rather west of north.

The thicknesses of the Eocene rocks at Studland are as difficult to measure as those of the Wealden Beds at Swanage. The direction of true dip is about N. 6° W., whereas the cliff section runs N. 43° W. Measured parallel to the dip, the width of the combined outcrops of the Reading Beds and London Clay is about 820 ft., which with a dip of 10° means a thickness of about 145 feet. Of this about the basal 50 ft. at least can be seen to be Reading Beds; but it is impossible to apportion the rest even approximately. The Redend Sandstone undulates near the Point, but must be about 140 ft. thick if the dip of 5° to 10° seen at various points is true dip.[1] The exact position of the base cannot at present be determined.

The Redend Sandstone on passing inland forms the prominent bluffs or escarpments of Woodhouse Hill (where it is exposed in the roadside) and Dean Hill where it rises just above the 400-foot contour at the golf-links. Northward it is succeeded by the Pipe-clay Series, a variable belt of sands and clays. The plant-bearing clay of Redend Point is absent at the golf-links, where the top of the Redend Sandstone and the base of the Pipe-clays are exposed in a sand-pit on the north side of the Studland-Corfe road about 300 yds. north-east of Currendon :—

SANDPIT AT SWANAGE GOLF-LINKS

		Ft.	Ins.
3.	Pale grey and white pipe-clay	8	0
2.	Botryoidal ironstone band, very constant, indicating a dip of 13° N.		2
1.	False-bedded yellow and white sandstone	15	0

Two hundred yards north of this is another sand-pit which displays the upper part of the Pipe-clay Series overlain by an exceedingly coarse grit :—

SANDPIT 200 YDS. NORTH OF THE LAST

		Ft.
2.	Coarse quartz grit like the Wealden, the pebbles mainly the size of small peas, but many up to $\frac{1}{2}$in. long ; also many small pebbles of dark ' Cornish ' rocks and flint ; a regular false dip of 20° about N.E.	14
	Irregular but well-defined junction with general dip of 10° N.	
1.	Coarse sand, false bedded, with some seams as in the bed above, but on the whole less coarse, replaced in a few yards by lenticles of mottled pink and white clay up to 8 ft. thick, in places coarsely brecciated	20

Assuming bed 1 to be the top of the Pipe-clay Series, then the total thickness of the series is about 135 ft. hereabouts. A clay belonging to this series was formerly worked for bricks at the old

---

[1] Lyell stated that the Redend Sandstone is only about 25 ft. thick, but it must be at least 50 ft. thick even if it is nearly horizontal in the middle part of the outcrop (C. Lyell, ' On the Strata of the Plastic Clay Formation . . ,' *Trans. Geol. Soc.*, Ser. 2, vol. ii, 1827, p. 284).

kilns by the riding school, 1,000 ft. west of Studland Bay House.

Bed 2 is a very remarkable rock almost indistinguishable from the Wealden quartz grit at Steeple (p. 157). Locally it is cemented to form hard irony sandstone, of which relics in the form of boulders and slabs litter the heaths and have been used for building walls, barns, and houses. The largest isolated mass forms the Agglestone, an anvil-shaped block of about 8,000 cu. ft. weighing 500 tons, perched upon a conical hill which the stone has protected from the weather. A broken smaller mass called the Puckstone crowns another mound 400 yds. to the north-west (Pl. XIII).

Northward as the heaths fall towards Poole Harbour the dip flattens and the Pipe-clay Series continues to form most of the surface. At Newton an open-working $\frac{1}{2}$ mile long and not many years abandoned shows at the west end the following :—

PIPE-CLAY WORKING AT NEWTON

		Ft.	Ins.
5.	Yellow and white sand, locally cemented to form hard irony and red sandstone and gritstone up to 5 ft. thick	10	0
4.	Clay, grey, laminated ... ... 6 ins. to		9
3.	Black sand	2	0
2.	Black dicey clay, passing into grey clay	4	0
1.	Grey pipe-clay, about	12	0

Bed 5 seems to be the Agglestone Grit. It runs down to sea level a short distance farther north and may be seen forming the little promontory at Redhorn Quay. Sections on the motor road to the ferry, on the west side of Little Sea, show false-bedded sands also belonging to this series, and there are numerous small cliffs on the shores of the Harbour.

The Bagshot Beds of Studland may, therefore, be summarized as follows :—Redend Sandstone, perhaps 140 ft.; Pipe-clay Series, 135 ft.; Agglestone Grit, say 35 ft.; total about 300 feet.

(b) CORFE AND WAREHAM

The area worked for centuries for pipeclay shows endless small sections of clay and quartz sands with occasional seams of gritty ironstone. An open working not many years abandoned by Messrs. Fayle & Co., 300 yds. north by east of the Swanage pumping station at Corfe, shows 14 ft. of mottled clay overlain by 25 ft. of almost horizontal yellow sand containing a 3-inch ironstone band. Some distance farther north, in the old Matcham pits on Norden Heath, the dip was 15° S. Hudleston recorded the following section[1] :—

---

[1] W. H. Hudleston, *Proc. Geol. Assoc.*, vol. vii, 1883, p. 378.

MATCHAM PITS[1] (W. H. Hudleston)

		Ft.
1.	Sand, loose, white, with ironstone bands at base	20-40
2.	Clay, stiff, yellowish or variegated ; " pipe-clay " ...	30
3.	Pure " potter's clay,", soft, white, for which the pits were worked	8
4.	Lignite or brown coal, used as fuel at Norden, where it is as much as 7 or 8 ft. thick	2
	Clay	

Cuttings on the clay-railway between Claywell and Bushey, 1 mile north of Rempstone Hall, show interesting exposures, 15 to 20 ft. deep, in strongly disturbed beds. At the west end of the cuttings are grey shales and clays with lines of huge septaria containing plant remains and some lignitiferous ' peaty ' bands, much contorted, and towards the north-east these dip under yellow criss-cross-jointed Bagshot Sands like those exposed at Redend Point, Studland. The junction is transected obliquely by the railway but dips 70-80° N. or N.E. The clay with septaria may be London Clay repeated by a strike fault, but since no authentic London Clay is to be seen in the district, there is nothing with which to compare the beds. Such a fault might also explain the repetition of the outcrop of the pipe-clays, which have been worked in two parallel bands, near the downs and near the harbour. In default of fossils, however, it is best to assume that the strata exposed correspond with beds 1 to 4 in the Matcham pits seen by Hudleston.

An open working south of Norden Farm (B. Fayle & Co.) shows about 15 ft. of typical pipe-clay at present being dug within 200 ft. of the hedge which runs along the foot of the downs and marks approximately the boundary of the Chalk (the actual junction is masked by talus). At the south side of the pit there appears to be a very irregular reversed strike fault which brings up shaly carbonaceous clay, overlain by yellow sand, northwards on to the pipe-clay. The black shaly bands in the hanging wall are dragged down into the fault plane, from a dip of about 40° N. The dip in the pipe-clay is obscure, but probably only a few degrees. Another shallower pit about 20 yds. farther south and within 75 ft. of the hedge shows white sands like the Reading Beds at Studland. Between the two is a shaft which reaches pipe-clay at a depth of 92 feet. The tectonics of this strip at the foot of the downs is complicated and as yet by no means elucidated. The pipe-clay extends much closer to the Chalk than it could without strike faulting, but it may all belong to the Reading Beds.

The sides of the Blue Pool at Furzebrook show how changeable the Bagshot Beds can be in short distances, and how measured

---

[1] The Secretary of B. Fayle and Co. informs me these pits were started in 1875 close to the Corfe River and were worked westward. The Wareham road was reached about 1888. On the west side of the road, the clay seam sank too deep for open workings and was reached for a time by mine shafts varying in depth from 60 to 140 feet.

dips may give little indication of tectonic structures. Here false-bedded sands and quartz grit alternate with " rubbish clay ", and the junction which at the east end is clear cut and emphasized by a band of ironstone rapidly becomes lost towards the west, where the strata undulate in all directions, presumably by original deltaic deposition.

This may be the explanation of a dip of 55° N.W. to be seen in a sandstone—pipe-clay junction in the railway cutting leading to Cotness Shaft in the floor of a large open working (Pike Bros.). The shaft is 120 ft. deep, indicating another pipe-clay 160 ft. below the original surface. A belt of some kind of disturbance is believed by the clay workers to run through Cotness cottages in a west-south-westerly direction; but both the stratigraphy and the tectonics are obscure, allowing neither to be used for the elucidation of the other. Hundreds of exploratory borings have been sunk around Cotness and Creechbarrow by Messrs. Pike Bros., but unfortunately the records are confidential. Study of them by a geologist may one day bring much interesting information to light. Three old ones that have been published, located " on the northern slope of Creechbarrow Hill, near Cotness and Grange Gate,"[1] show two clay series, the upper liable to contain as many as four seams of white clay, separated, underlain, and overlain by sands. The three records may be summarized thus :—

	Ft.
Rubbish clay	14+
Sandy series	56
Clay series, with up to 4 white clay seams	73-105
Second sandy series	60
Second clay series, with 6ft. of good clay	13
Third sandy series	10+
Total ...	226-258 ft.+

It is presumably the rubbish clay and highest sandy series that are exposed in the sides of the Blue Pool and other old open workings. The Cotness shaft probably goes down to the second clay series. Above the whole sequence comes the 80 to 110 ft. of sand and coarse quartz grit classed below as Lower Creechbarrow Beds, but indistinguishable from the Bagshot Beds (see p. 237). If the ' third sandy series ' of the borings is the variegated sand at the base of the formation at Redend Point, Studland, where it may be 140 ft. thick (p. 222), the total thickness of the Bagshot Beds in the Corfe area must be about 450 feet.

Shipstal Point, Arne, provides one of the best and the most accessible of the cliff sections on the south side of Poole Harbour. It shows 25-30 ft. of false-bedded fine and coarse quartz

---

[1] W. Whitaker and W. Edwards, ' Wells and Springs of Dorset,' *Mem. Geol. Surv.* 1926, p. 85.

sand with beds of clay up to 2 ft. thick.   Towards the south it is difficult to distinguish the Bagshot Beds from the Pleistocene sand and gravel (*see* p. 327).

There remains one section to which special attention should be drawn, namely that in the cliff of the River Frome at Redcliff, ½-mile south-east of Wareham church.   The cliff is about 45 ft. high.   The lowest 25 ft. consist of bright red sand containing many thick bands of a remarkable breccia, consisting of mottled white and red loamy clay set at all angles in red sand.   The fragments of clay are mainly from 1 to 3 ins. in diameter, many smaller, and they can be extracted whole.   The highest 20 ft. of the cliff consists of coarse irony sandstone, separated from the red breccia beds below by a conspicuous even bedding-plane, and discordant with the bedding of the breccias.   The section is continued upwards in the road by coarse sands with some pebbles of quartz up to ¾ in. long.   The position of this section in the general sequence is uncertain, but it may be surmised that the upper half and the pebbly beds above represent the Agglestone Grit and that the brecciated beds below are approximately on the horizon of bed 1 in the northern sand-pit at Swanage golf-links (p. 223).

(c)   LULWORTH AND WOOL

The Reading Beds extend westwards in the foresyncline of the Purbeck fold as a long tongue, which is continued by outliers at Newlands Farm and Newlands Warren, and the outliers are connected by scattered blocks of flint conglomerate and sarsen stones. At the base is coarse gravel with unworn flints, above which follow buff sand and bright red and mottled clays.   The best section is in the brickyard at Coombe Keynes, which displays 7 ft. of red and white clay in wavy bands, with an impersistent band (0-1 ft.) of concretionary ironstone in the middle.   Similar ironstone, 3 ft. thick, forms the floor of the pit.   More clay is said to lie beneath, but has never been worked.   The junction of the Reading Beds and Chalk was exposed in Combe chalk-pit a little farther north (1 mile south of Wool), but the section is now overgrown.

In an artesian boring at Bovington Camp, near Wool, the base of the Reading Beds consisted of green sandy clay, 5 ft. thick, with green-coated flints at the bottom.   The total thickness of Reading Beds and London Clay was 115 feet.[1]

The London Clay of this district is little known owing to lack of exposures.   It is said to be sandy and ferruginous and to rest on a pebbly base.[2]

The cliff under Hambury Tout, ¾ mile west of Lulworth Cove, shows large solution pipes in the chalk, filled with rusty sands and ground-up flints, and in places the wider pipes (e.g., Red Hole)

---

[1] W. H. Hudleston, ' Geology in the Field, part 2,' *Geol. Assoc.* 1910, p. 375.
[2] C. Reid, ' Geology of the Country around Dorchester,' *Mem. Geol. Surv.*, 1899, p. 24.

contain in addition masses of grey loamy sand. It is not clear whether these pipes were formed before the Chalk was tilted into the vertical position and have been tilted with it, or whether they post-date the folding. If the deepest ones started from the top of the present hill and the filling be assumed to be Pliocene, they must have penetrated at least 400 ft.; if, as is more probable, the filling is Eocene and they were started from the top of the Chalk, probably as the fold began to rise, they must have penetrated at least 600 feet.

(d) MORETON, WARMWELL AND BROADMAYNE

The Reading Beds are well exposed at Broadmayne, where for many years they have been made into the well-known speckled bricks (*see* p. 355). The last surviving brickyard of a line of six about ½ mile north-east of the village shows the following section :—

BROADMAYNE ; WEBB, MAJOR AND CO'S BRICKYARD

	Ft.	Ins.
Loamy soil full of subangular flints and locally becoming a flint gravel	3-4	0
Red clay, mottled white	6	0
Brown loam with manganese nodules	10	0
Manganese concretionary sandrock ; white quartz grains cemented in small black nodules ; holds up water	2	0
White sand, mottled red (seen to 7 ft.)	8	0
Black flints, sparsely distributed		6
Not seen { White tough clay, from which white bricks have been made	1	0
Rough sand, proved to about	5	0

According to the manager, who supplied particulars of the lowest three beds, the Chalk lies " a good way below."

Thirty or forty years ago bricks were made also at Brick Hill, ¼ mile west of Warmwell church. Clement Reid saw here 10 ft. of sandy loam and red clay, adding " these strata are a few feet above the Chalk."[1] But a boring for water was made in 1929 close to this spot and proved " hard yellow clay all the way, to a total depth of 84 feet."[2] The bottom of the clay was not reached.

Sand in the Reading Beds has been worked recently ¼ mile W.S.W. of Owermoigne Church. A 10 ft. face can be seen, with some ferruginous sandrock bands, dipping at variable angles rather steeply to the south.

A boring at Empool Pumping Station, West Knighton, made in 1936, passed through 32 ft. 9 ins. of Reading Beds, consisting mainly of clay, with a 2-foot band of ironstone about the middle. At the bottom, resting on the Chalk, was 1 ft. of hard sandstone, then 3 ft. of hard gravel, sand, and flints, overlain by 5 ft. of green

---

[1] C. Reid, *op. cit.*, 1899, p. 20.
[2] Lott and Walne, Ltd., The Foundry, Dorchester, *in lit.*

sandy clay, recalling the green sand at Bovington.[1] The Reading Beds here probably do not exceed 40 feet.

The basement bed of the Reading Beds was formerly exposed in the large overgrown chalk pit by the West Knighton road ¼ mile south-east of Lewell Lodge. It was described as consisting of " loam with unworn flints sometimes stained green."[2] Reid also saw a pit ⅓ mile west of the fifth milestone on the Dorchester-Wool road, between Broadmayne and Warmwell, which showed " coarse gravel of subangular flint, flint pebbles, and more rarely quartz, mixed with much hard sandstone and chert from the Greensand. The dip is 45° to the north and the flints are much shattered."[3] Neither he nor Strahan were able to decide whether the tongue of Reading Beds which here extends some distance to the west lies in an eroded channel or owes its position to post-Eocene folding, or to caving in as the result of solution of the Chalk (cf. Bincombe Down, p. 232).

The outliers west of Broadmayne are important because in them takes place the overlap of the London Clay and Reading Beds by the Bagshot Beds, detected and mapped by Clement Reid. At Little Mayne Farm, on the largest outlier, Reid saw the basement bed of green flints and glauconitic sand resting on the Chalk, and higher up, in another pit now overgrown, white sand and red clay. On the opposite (western) side of the hill these beds are all apparently missing and Bagshot Sands rest on the Chalk.[4] Owing to the closing of small sections the evidence for this overlap is now much less clear than it seems to have been forty years ago. It is confirmed, however, by a cutting on a new road from West Knighton to the pumping station at Empool Bottom, on the side of the hill where the map (Sheet 328) shows Reading Beds overlain by Plateau Gravel. The cutting exposed the Reading Beds, brown loam and yellow clay followed by mottled red and white clay, overlain by beds of sandy gravel with the assemblage of pebbles characteristic of the Bagshot Beds—white-coated and black flints with abundant quartz and a very high proportion of black ' Cornish ' material in ¼-inch, ½-inch, and 1-inch pebbles. The Plateau Gravel caps the hill at a higher level. The same relation between the Bagshot and Reading Beds was mapped by Reid all over Warmwell Heath, no London Clay being found. It may be added that by comparison with Studland it is the upper part of the local Bagshot series that passes on to the Reading Beds, namely the equivalents of the uppermost Pipe-clay Series and the Agglestone Grit.

The Bagshot Beds are displayed in many large sand and gravel pits between Warmwell and Moreton Station. The oldest, south

---

[1] Geological Survey record ; information from Weymouth Waterworks Co.
[2] C. Reid, op. cit., 1899, p. 21.
[3] loc. cit.
[4] C. Reid, op. cit., pp. 21, 29 ; and 1 inch map, Sheet 328.

of Moreton Station, cover many acres, and were described by
Reid.[1]   They are now eclipsed by vast·excavations opened in 1932
by Warmwell Pits Ltd., west of the high road 1½ miles north of
Warmwell. The Bagshot Sands, capped by 8 to 10 ft. of Plateau
Gravel, stand in vertical cliffs 30-40 ft. high, displaying to perfection their remarkable current bedding and lateral changes to coarse
grit and bands of pebbles, with here and there a lenticular seam of
clay. (Pl. XVI). At the south end of the section in 1938 the
sands seemed to have cut across and partly destroyed an earlier
deposit formed under disturbed conditions, for at intervals the sands
are channelled and almost appear as if they had been gouged
out, and the hollows so formed are filled with pockets of small
pebbles of quartz, flint, etc., and with breccia and larger blocks
of loamy clay, reminiscent of the breccias at Swanage golf-links
and Redcliff, Wareham (pp. 223, 227). Apart from this, the
Bagshot Sands of these pits are remarkably free from gravel or
clay.

     Both gravel and clay are more strongly developed in a pit half
a mile north of Warmwell on the west side of the road. This pit
was abandoned in 1936 owing to the occurrence of useless clay up
to 8 ft. thick. There are still exposed lenticular masses and beds
of coarse quartz grit and pebbles. A very little collecting serves
to corroborate Clement Reid's important discovery that hereabouts " we can find in unmistakable Bagshot Sands fragments
of all the rocks which occur in the coarser and more abnormal
Bagshot gravels further west."[2] In this pit Reid recorded in
order of abundance Chalk flints (nearly half), Greensand chert
with sponge spicules (about one third), quartz pebbles, silicified
Purbeck limestone with *Cyrena,* etc., radiolarian chert, schorl-
rock, and hard grit. Here too, as Reid noted at Moreton Station,
" fragments of Greensand-chert . . . are often quite soft, so that
they were at first mistaken for pebbles of pipeclay, though they
soon harden on exposure."

     The old brick pit on the north side of Moreton Station was
worked in clay belonging to the Pipe-clay Series, dipping south.
Reid saw 15 ft. of red and white mottled clay, carbonaceous clay,
and lignite.[3] The pit was closed in 1915 (*see* pp. 355-6).

     (e) OUTLIERS OF BINCOMBE DOWN, BLACK DOWN, ETC.

     Important Tertiary outliers cap the crest of the Chalk downs
on the north side of the Ridgeway Fault, extending eight miles
west of the main outcrop and forming the highest points in South
Dorset, culminating in the Hardy Monument on Black Down at
777 ft. above the sea. They were originally mapped as Reading
Beds, but on the identity of the composition of the gravels with
the finer gravels in the Bagshot Sands at Warmwell and Moreton,
Clement Reid correlated them with the Bagshot Beds. They

---

[1] *op. cit.,* pp. 28-9.
[2] C. Reid, *op. cit.,* 1899, p. 28.
[3] *loc. cit.*

consist mainly of coarse cobble gravels, but on Bincombe Down there are also sand and crude pipe clay.

The best exposure now open is a big gravel pit 100 yds. south of the Hardy Monument, which shows a 30-foot vertical section of uniform bedded gravel dipping 25° N.E. The large cobbles of flint are embedded in a matrix of smaller flints, quartz, and ' Cornish ' pebbles (jasper, slate, schorl, etc.) and quartz sand, with a large quantity of Upper Greensand chert and grit of all sizes from medium to fine. There is plenty of silicified Purbeck limestone, containing *Hydrobia* as well as *Cyrena,* but seldom more than 1 in. long, generally ¼ in. or less. I collected also a 2 in. pebble of Purbeck Cinder Bed and a 7 in. pebble of dark chocolate-coloured chert, the outside rounded and much battered, which is probably from the Purbeck Beds. An interesting feature in this pit are small rolled flint flakes with bulbs of percussion. Mr. Reid Moir compared specimens submitted to him with flakes from gravel below the Chalky Boulder Clay, and wrote, " Such things are produced in great numbers in making flint implements and also where nature is engaged in flint flaking."[1] There is a similar but more degraded section 150 yds. south-east of the monument, and close by at a lower level a smaller opening recently worked shows 10 ft. more of the cobble gravel resting on 6 ft. of quartz sand with seams and lenses of shingle, exactly as at Warmwell.

The flints of these and other Bagshot gravels are exceptionally tough, as remarked by Reid. " They seem to have undergone a process of annealing, and are changed to the centre, though at first sight some of them appear still to be almost black and unaltered. This toughness is everywhere characteristic of the flints in the Bagshot gravels and is just as marked in those contained in the gravel of Haldon, in Devon . . . The most common fossils in the Bincombe flints are *Echinocorys vulgaris* and *Terebratula carnea.*"[2] Calcareous rocks of any kind are noticeably absent, and so are quartzite pebbles from the Bunter. " The finer screened material, left after the larger stones are taken away, consists mainly of quartz-pebbles and Palaeozoic rocks, more resembling a Cornish beach than a gravel formed in a country the foundations of which are composed of Secondary and Tertiary strata."[3] The aptness of this observation is evident in the gravel pit now in work near the Hardy Monument.

The source of the materials can only have been the far west, just as in Wealden times. The river that brought them, or a tributary of it, probably passed across West Bay from the neighbourhood of the Haldon Hills and on its way drew supplies of Purbeck pebbles from some outcrop south of the intra-Cretaceous faults, now entirely destroyed by the sea. The pebbles cannot be

[1] *In lit.,* Oct., 1938.
[2] C. Reid, *op. cit.,* 1899, p. 30.
[3] C. Reid, *op. cit.,* 1899, p. 31.

matched with any silicified rock known in the existing outcrops of Purbeck Beds at Portisham or eastwards. This is confirmed by Mr. P. C. S. Bradley, who has made a detailed study of the Purbeck Beds and has kindly examined my pebbles collected from Black Down and Warmwell. The Bunter pebble beds must still have been blanketed by Upper Cretaceous rocks.

The relations of the Bagshot outliers to the Chalk beneath are complicated in the extreme. When the large pits on Bincombe Down were worked for railway ballast and road metal Fisher recorded in 1855 in a 24-ft. section a sequence of subangular flint gravel, sand and clay, gravel of rounded flint pebbles, sand and coarse pipe clay, all standing vertical.[1] Both Fisher and Strahan[2] attributed the verticality to the action of the Ridgeway Fault, but this is highly improbable, and the Chalk beneath almost certainly is nearly horizontal (*see* p. 254). Moreover, Strahan wrote "some pits 100 yds. south-west of the Hardy Monument show stratified pebble gravels dipping at 15°, 45° and even 65°, while in another pit, 600 yds. west of the monument, the gravel is partly vertical and partly horizontal. These dips are none of them due to earth-movements, but merely to the dissolution of the Chalk and the caving-in of the gravels." But he qualified this by the following :—" The Blackdown outliers lie for the most part on nearly horizontal Chalk, but so far from conforming to the bedding of that rock, they run up and down the slopes of the hills, and though as a whole they occupy the high ground, yet at the highest point of all bare Chalk comes to the surface.[3] Part of the irregularity is certainly due to piping . . . but on the other hand the occurrence of banks of shingle low down on the hill-side and of bare Chalk at its highest point can hardly be due to such a cause, unless we suppose that underground solution has proceeded on such an enormous scale as to carve the Chalk into hill and dale and altogether alter the form of the surface on which the Tertiary beds were deposited."[4]

Such wholesale alteration of the Chalk surface by solution in post-Eocene times seems quite possible when the pipes exposed in the cliff at Hambury Tout, Lulworth, are borne in mind. As mentioned on p. 228, if these pipes were formed before the folding they must have penetrated the Chalk a distance of at least 600 feet. Even if the filling were Pliocene and the pipes were formed after the folding and peneplanation, they must be more than 400 ft. deep; but it is more probable that the filling consists of Reading Beds and that they were formed as the fold began to rise, and so have a minimum depth of 600 feet. Their width being in proportion, it is evident that the Eocene strata that lay above them must have suffered as much disturbance as those on Bincombe Down and Black Down.

---

[1] O. Fisher, ' Vertical Tertiaries at Bincombe, Dorset,' *Geol. Mag.,* 1896, p. 246.
[2] A. Strahan, *Purbeck Memoir,* 1898, p. 195.
[3] [Exposed poorly near the road.]
[4] A. Strahan, *op. cit.,* 1898, pp. 195-6.

The basement gravels of the Eocene in the neighbourhood of
Black Down are locally cemented to form an intensely hard conglomerate.   Blocks of the puddingstone lie scattered as greywethers over the surface, especially in the valleys.   They are
sometimes as much as 10 ft. across.   Many may be seen in the
main street of Portisham village.

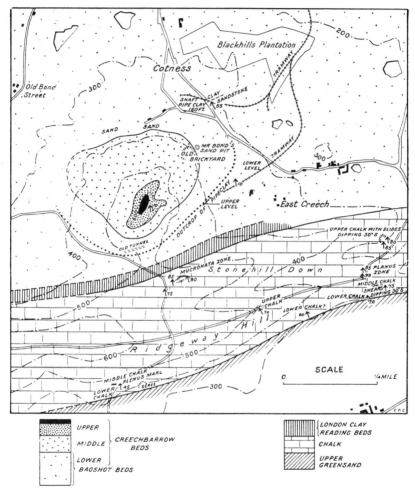

Fig. 45.—*Geological map of Creechbarrow and its surroundings.*
(W. J. Arkell, 1938.)

IV. Creechbarrow Beds

(a) General and historical

Creechbarrow, $2\frac{1}{2}$ miles west of Corfe Castle, was justly
described by W. H. Hudleston as " the most noteworthy hill,
composed exclusively of Tertiary beds, in all England."   It stands

out on the north side of the chalk ridge, isolated and unique, in
form resembling a volcanic cone. Its summit, 637 ft. above O.D.,
dwarfs the ridge behind when viewed from the heaths and peeps
over it when viewed from Purbeck ; for near Corfe Castle the chalk
ridge sinks to its lowest elevation. Half a mile south-east of
Creechbarrow there is a pass well below the 400-foot contour ;
immediately south of the hill the ridge rises between the 500- and
600-foot contours ; and half a mile south-west of it the chalk attains
its highest elevation of 655 ft. in the hog's back of Ridgeway Hill.
Creechbarrow is joined to the chalk ridge by a narrow col which
just overtops the 500-foot contour. (Pl. XIII B).

The Chalk is well exposed in pits near by. Immediately to the
south the top of the Lower Chalk, with the Plenus Marl, is seen
dipping 45° N., with most of the Middle Chalk exposed above it.
The nearest sections are in old lime-kilns in Upper Chalk (presumed
Mucronata Zone) dipping 85° to 90° N., about 100 ft. from the
Tertiary boundary and shown in Pl. XIII. The Reading Beds
and London Clay, vertical or nearly so, must occupy the col.
Creechbarrow itself and all beyond it was mapped by the Survey
as Bagshot Beds. The extensive surface workings in the Bagshot
pipeclay, however, which spread round Creechbarrow on the north,
north-east, and north-west, are confined to the low ground almost
exclusively below the 300-foot contour.

Puzzled by its anomalous position, height and form, W. H.
Hudleston devoted an exhaustive study to the hill.[1] By digging
special pits he established that the summit is capped with hard
tufaceous limestone, up to nearly 10 ft. thick, which gives rise to
the grass turf there and has kept away heather and bracken ; though
the summit has been artificially levelled and still carries the foundations of a keeper's lodge built mainly of Purbeck Stone. Below
the limestone he proved about 15 ft. of sands and layers of large
flints of a peculiar kind (of which more below), dipping rather less
than 11° N. The flinty and sandy series he found to rest upon
a buff clay, now known to be about 60 ft. thick, which was at that
time worked for bricks at Cotness Wood on the north-east side of
the hill (" Mr. Bond's brickyard ") ; and that in turn was proved
to overlie thick sands (probably 100 ft. thick), worked in a sand pit
adjoining the brickyard. This series Hudleston called the
Creechbarrow Beds, in order not to prejudice the question of correlation, and it is advisable to retain the name for the same reason.
He found poorly preserved gastropods in the summit limestone
and identified two species. Although recognizing them as species
of the Bembridge Limestone, and admitting the possibility that
the Creechbarrow Limestone might be of Bembridge age, he
favoured the idea that the Creechbarrow Beds were a peculiar local

---

[1] W. H. Hudleston, ' Creechbarrow in Purbeck,' *Geol. Mag.*, N.S. Dec. IV,
vol. ix, 1902, p. 241, and 1903, pp 149, 197 ; *Proc. Dorset Nat. Hist. Ant. Field
Club*, vol. xxiii, 1902, p. 146 ; ' Geology in the Field,' part 2, *Geol. Assoc.*, 1910,
p. 377.

facies of the Bagshot Beds and in part the lateral equivalents of
the Pipeclay Series.

Keeping, some 7 years later,[1] renewed the investigations.   He
dug a pit 7 ft. deep on the north side of the summit, and in the
lower part of the limestone he found fossils which he considered
proved conclusively that it was to be correlated with the Bembridge
Limestone.   In another pit, on the south side of the cap, he found
a tooth of *Palaeotherium* in a marl band immediately below the
limestone, and on the strength of this considered the Osborne Beds
were present.   He then went on to introduce into Creechbarrow a
full succession of Bracklesham and Barton Beds, Lower, Middle
and Upper Headon Beds, and Osborne and Bembridge Beds.
But his section is almost wholly conjectural.   It is only possible
to introduce all these formations by distorting the scale ; there is no
room for them.   Keeping dismissed the gravels discovered by
Hudleston as Pleistocene Plateau Drift, but he brought forward no
new evidence.

Since these papers were written the pipe-clay workings have
been extended by Pike Bros. ever closer to Creechbarrow and
scores of trial borings have been made round the flanks of the hill.
The borings showed that the clay passes under the hill from the
north and rises in it southward to crop out on the col.   The main
clay seam has been followed by levels driven in from the east side
just above the 300- and 400-foot contours respectively, and these
are united by a meshwork of underground workings which penetrate under the east spur and almost under the summit.   The main
pipe-clay seam is about 12 ft. thick and it rises southwards at an
average angle of 10°, and is therefore exactly parallel to the base of
the limestone cap.   Dips of 20° and more can be measured in the
clay at working faces under the hill, but these are only local, due
partly to oblique bedding (false dip) and partly to minor faults and
undulations.   The general dip of 10° N. is constant.

It would have been better in some ways if Hudleston had drawn
the base of his Creechbarrow Beds at the bottom of the brick clay,
for it would then have coincided with a line easily mapped and
restricted to Creechbarrow Hill.   The thick sand is in part at least
typical Bagshot Sand and it extends over much of the high ground
to the north, its base being difficult if not impossible to map, owing
probably to interdigitation with the Pipe-clay Series. On historical
grounds Hudleston's definition of Creechbarrow Beds is here
retained, but with the understanding that much of the lowest
member of the series, the sand, is indistinguishable from the
Bagshot Beds, and the lower part of it at least is the equivalent of
the Agglestone Grit.   The higher part, exposed in Creech sandpit
(*see* p. 237) is a fine sand which passes up gradually into the clay
and is better grouped with the Creechbarrow Beds that with the
Agglestone Grit.

[1] H. Keeping, ' On the Discovery of Bembridge Limestone Fossils on Creechbarrow
Hill, Isle of Purbeck,' *Geol. Mag.,* N.S., dec. v, vol. vii, 1910, p. 436.

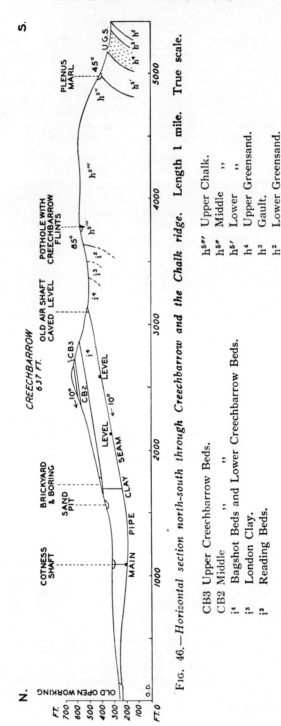

FIG. 46.—*Horizontal section north–south through Creechbarrow and the Chalk ridge. Length 1 mile. True scale.*

CB3 Upper Creechbarrow Beds.
CB2 Middle   ,,   ,,
i⁴   Bagshot Beds and Lower Creechbarrow Beds.
i³   London Clay.
i²   Reading Beds.

h⁵″ Upper Chalk.
h⁵″ Middle   ,,
h⁵′ Lower   ,,
h⁴   Upper Greensand.
h³   Gault.
h²   Lower Greensand.

(b) STRATIGRAPHY

The general succession is:—

			Ft.		
4.	Creechbarrow Limestone	...	7-10	⎫ Upper	⎫
3.	Sand with bands of flints	...	20-30	⎬	⎪
2.	Buff brick clay, flints at base	...	c. 60	Middle	⎬ Creechbarrow Beds
1.	Sand and coarse grit (in part Agglestone Grit)	... ...	80-110	Lower	⎭

170-210ft.

[Pipe-clay Series below]

1. Sand and coarse grit.—The lower part of the sand with the base resting on the " rubbish clay " of the Pipe-clay Series is well exposed in the side of the former open-working at the mouth of the upper level where the tramway line enters the east side of the hill, near the 400-foot contour.   It contains a good deal of coarse quartz grit of Wealden appearance (cf. Swanage golf-links, p. 223), and some interlaminated clay.   The rubbish clay here is about 30 ft. thick.   The sand forms the dry basal part of the slope all round the hill and spreads over the high ground to the north, around Cotness, descending roughly to the 300-foot contour.   It was formerly worked close to the brickyard, for mixing with the bricks. Hudleston saw the following section, showing the junction with the brick clay above :—

CREECH SANDPIT (W. H. Hudleston)

			Ft.	Ins.
The brick clay	⎧ a.	Clay with rootlets	1	6
	⎨ b.	Clay passing into sands ; flints occur, especially towards the base	5	6
	⎩ c.	Bedded sand	1	3
	d.	Yellow clay with large flints at base, and a pink line	1	0
	e.	Yellow variegated sandy clay with a few small flints	1	6
	f.	Sand, salmon-coloured, with a black centre line ...		3
	g.	Fine white sand with little true bedding (base not seen)...	9	0
			20	0

A boring (1938) in the floor of the old brickyard, near the kilns, proved the thickness of strata from the bottom of the brick clay down to the top of the pipe-clay to be 145 ft.   Of this the upper 100 to 110 ft. belongs to the sand of the basal Creechbarrow Beds, the rest is " rubbish " clay of the Pipe-clay Series.

2. Buff brick clay.—This was worked until about 1908 in Mr. Bond's brickyard in Cotness Wood, on the north-east angle of the hill.   The top of the section still shows 15 ft. of yellow marl full of quartz grains, with a spotty black band near the base and overlain by 6 ft. of the same material slumped down the hill-side and mixed with surface flints.   The base, resting on the sands, was described by Hudleston in the adjoining sand pit, and can

also be seen in a ravine or gully at the north-west angle of the
hill.   Some old marl or brick pits between these points are overgrown.   The brick clay forms a long and very wet dip slope
covering most of the north side of the hill and is much slipped.
Hudleston considered it might be a lenticle for " it does not appear
to have any representative if followed in the direction of the eastern
spur.   Hudleston stated that the flints were of Creechbarrow type
ground clay tunnels has exposed small sections which show that
buff marl continues in its expected position round the eastern spur
and to the south slope of the summit hill.   The bands of flints at
the base, observed by Hudleston, are noteworthy, and they have
been confirmed by recent borings in the coombe north of the eastern
spur.   Hudleston stated that the flints were of Creechbarrow type
(*see below*).

   3.   Sand with bands of flints.—The type section of these beds
was obtained by Hudleston in a pit cut in three steps on the south
side of the summit :—

		Ft.	Ins.
1.	Soil with few flints, fragments of pottery, oyster shells, etc.	1	6
2.	Softish tufaceous limestone (passing down into bed 3) ...	2	6
3.	Sand full of calcareous concretions	4	0
4.	Yellow clayey sand		6
5.	Sand, loose, buff-coloured	5	10
6.	Layer of large flints of Creechbarrow type	1	0
7.	Sand, pale buff-coloured (base not seen)	4	0

Total   ...   19ft. 4ins.

Beds 4 and 6 gave a dip of 1 in 5.5, or nearly 11° N.

   Other excavations carried out by Hudleston showed rapid
lateral variation in these beds.   A pit about 33 ft. below the summit
on the west side showed a flint band 2 ft. thick, containing some
very large flints.   Flints were also found occasionally in the sands.
On the east spur a pit showed 6 ins. of flinty soil resting on
3 ft. 6 ins of flint gravel, with 2 ft. 6 ins. of buff ferruginous and
manganiferous sand below.   The thickening of the flint band has
doubtless caused the formation of this spur, as also of the smaller
one to the south-west, on which the tumulus stands.   (Pl. XIII).
There can be no doubt that Hudleston was right in interpreting
these flints as part of the Tertiary strata. They do not cap the hill as
Plateau Gravel would, but crop out in a ring around it, following
the dip of the strata and not the contours; moreover, Plateau
Gravel encircling a hill at a height of 600 ft. above sea-level is
unheard of.   There is also an essential difference in the constituent
flints.   Like those proved to be bedded in the base of the brick
clay, they are for the most part very large (up to 30 lbs. in weight
and often 1 ft. or more long), entirely unrolled, but often (as
Hudleston put it) " split in the bed itself," for they are unusually
brittle.   Keeping, who dismissed these flints as Plateau Gravel,

can hardly have seen them, for Hudleston was obviously right in stating " The peculiar fawn colour of these siliceous masses will help to distinguish them from ordinary plateau gravel or valley gravel flints; and the amount of soft and almost pulverulent material which coats so many of them is a further distinction, as this substance could never endure the wear and tear of the gravel-making process . . . . Their general appearance leads one to suppose that they had been subject to some corrosive action . . . They are much degelatinized and in some the exterior is simply a mass of granular silica."

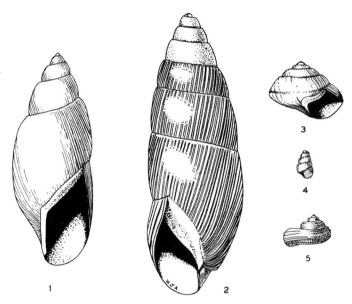

FIG. 47.—*Bembridge Limestone gastropods identified from the Creechbarrow Limestone.*

1. *Palaeoglandina costellata* (J. Sowerby); 2. *Filholia elliptica* (J. Sowerby); 3. *Palaeoxestina occlusa* (Edwards); 4. *Cochlostoma heterostoma* (Edwards); 5. *Bembridgia cincta* (Edwards). (All after F. E. Edwards, ' Monograph of the Eocene Cephalopoda and Univalves of England ', Part 2, 1852, *Palaeontographical Society*).

4. Creechbarrow Limestone.—This was penetrated by Hudleston on the summit to a depth of 7 ft., but below that lies softer limestone passing down into sands, and perhaps also in places a lower bed of limestone, in which Keeping found his fossils. It is possible that the basal part of the limestone passes locally into the 3 ft. of reddish marl found by Keeping on the south side of the hill; Hudleston's and Keeping's accounts are conflicting on this point and suggest rapid lateral variation (as is to be expected in such deposits).

The limestone is essentially tufaceous. It is composed of concretionary nodules built up of concentric tufa layers, and is porous, the cavities often suggestive of stems of plants. It varies from a soft marly deposit which whitens the fingers to a hard compact cream-coloured limestone which takes a polish. Quartz grains are abundant. A variety of the limestone is pisolitic, and some of the pisoliths are egg-shaped and give a curious horse-shoe shaped cross-section. Others are quadrate, and some consist of encrusted snail shells.[1]

(c) PALAEONTOLOGY AND CORRELATION

The question of the correlation of the Creechbarrow Beds has been discussed by Bury.[2] He compares the limestone to the Mesolithic tufa of Blashenwell near Corfe (see p. 351) and suggests that it may likewise have been a local patch deposited in a swamp on a land surface. Accepting the large flints found by Hudleston as interbedded, he points out the implications of this fact : namely, that since they are very large and unrolled flints they cannot have travelled far, and Chalk must have been undergoing erosion in the immediate neighbourhood before the deposition of the tufa. He points out that all the fossils recorded by Keeping are land snails, which are proverbially unreliable for precise dating, and concludes " we know nothing at all about the land and freshwater fauna of England in Miocene times, and it is therefore possible that many of the Oligocene species may have survived to later dates."

The fossils collected by Hudleston cannot be traced, but at my request Dr. L. R. Cox has examined Keeping's collection, now in the Sedgwick Museum, and has revised the determinations. His list is as follows : —

Gastropoda :
1. *Paleaoxestina occlusa* (Edwards).
2. " *Helix* " *sp. indet.* (Labelled *Helix vectensis* Edwards).
3. *Filholia elliptica* (J. Sowerby).
   (Also a number of oval bodies, similar to those found in the Bembridge Limestone, which are supposed to be the eggs of this species).
4. *Paleaoglandina costellata* (J. Sowerby).
5. *Clausilia sp. nov.*
   (Figured by Keeping as *Clausilia striatula* Edwards).
6. *Viviparus angulosus* (J. Sowerby).
7. *Viviparus sp. nov.* (Labelled " *Melanopsis*? sp.").
8. *Bembridgia cincta* (Edwards).
9. *Cochlostoma heterostoma* (Edwards).
Lamellibranchia :
10. *Unio sp. nov.*
    (No representative of this or of any other lamellibranchiate genus appears to have been found elsewhere in the Bembridge Limestone).

---

[1] The lithology of the limestone is exhaustively described by W. H. Hudleston, *op. cit.*

[2] H. Bury, ' Creech Barrow,' *Proc. Bournemouth Nat. Sci. Soc.,* vol. xxvi, 1934, p. 68.

Indeterminate specimens :

Two gastropods labelled respectively as *Limnaéa longiscata* (Brongniart) and *Callianella laevis* (Edwards). The first is too fragmentary even for generic determination. The second definitely does not belong to the species with which it has been identified.

Poor specimens of two or three other gastropod species, all indeterminate, are also present.

Dr. Cox summarizes his conclusion as follows : — " I think the fauna is undoubtedly a Bembridge Limestone one, and definitely not Miocene or Pliocene. The evidence of the *Filholia* alone, is, I think, definite on this point. The presence of *Viviparus* and *Unio* shows that it is a lacustrine deposit and not just a tufa enclosing only land snails." I had asked him to bear in mind especially the possibility of a terrestrial fauna of Oligocene date surviving into the Miocene or Pliocene.

Thus the conclusion seems inevitable that the Upper Chalk was undergoing erosion in the immediate vicinity of Creechbarrow before the deposition of the Bembridge Limestone ; namely in early Oligocene or, as some stratigraphers would maintain, in late Eocene times. Presumably this erosion can only have been caused by the beginning of upheaval of the Purbeck Fold. There is even some evidence that might be taken to mean that upheaval was already far advanced. About 1,100 ft. south-east of the summit of Creechbarrow is a chalk pit (seen in Pl. XIII, B) in vertical Mucronata Zone showing pipes filled with brown earthy loam and red clay, with quartz grains and many flints. The best preserved pipe in 1938 was 8 ft. wide and was seen to pass down vertically for 7 ft. and disappear below the floor of the pit. In the filling were many flints of the peculiar Creechbarrow type, like those described by Hudleston, and quite different from the flints in the Reading or Bagshot Beds. This suggests that although the Upper Creechbarrow Beds dip at the same angle as the Bagshot Beds, they may have overstepped rapidly a little farther south on to vertical Chalk. But it is possible that the flints in the pipes were brought southwards on to the surface of the vertical Chalk in Pliocene or Pleistocene times. If the Chalk had been vertical and planed off at the time of deposition of the Upper Creechbarrow Beds, one would expect to find in those beds traces of the erosion of Greensand or Jurassic strata ; but none has been found.

V. Sarsen stones

Big sarsens of normal Reading Beds type occur at Broad Mayne (p. 7) and others of Bagshot age like Hertfordshire Puddingstone around Portisham (p. 233). The prehistoric stone circle at Poxwell (p. 274) is composed of a recrystallized variety of sarsen which fractures like chert.[1] The original sand grains have been replaced by secondary quartz, which locally exhibits spherulitic structure.

---

[1] J. W. Judd, *Geol. Mag.* (4), vol. viii, 1901, p. 2.

CHAPTER XIII

TECTONIC STRUCTURE

INTRODUCTION

THE MAIN TERTIARY FOLDING

The promontories of Weymouth-Portland and Purbeck, and the Isle of Wight, are dominated structurally by a major east-west anticlinal fold of Tertiary date. By it the Mesozoic rocks are thrown into a broad arch. The southern limb or flank has been for the most part destroyed by the sea, but fragments still survive in the Isle of Portland, southern Purbeck (St. Alban's Head), and the south of the Isle of Wight (Ventnor district). In all these places the rocks are almost undisturbed and form a tableland tilted very gently (1-2°) to the south.

The northern limb of the anticline is much steeper, as is indicated on the geological map by the narrowness of the outcrops. The rocks composing it dip sharply northwards, giving rise to a series of parallel ridges aligned east and west. The ridges formed by the Corallian and Portland rocks are the dominant feature of the landscape in the country north of Weymouth, between Abbotsbury and Upwey. The dip here is from 20° to 30°. Farther east the Chalk plays the same rôle and, standing more or less vertical, gives rise to the long narrow hog's backs of the Purbeck Hills and the downs from the Needles to Culver.

The anticline is therefore strongly asymmetric, a character which it shares with the other chief east-west Tertiary folds in the South of England. The steep (often vertical) limb is always to the north and overlooks a basin or broad syncline filled with Lower Tertiary sediments. It suffices to mention the Hog's Back fold near Guildford, the Kingsclere and Ham Anticlines near Newbury, and the Portsdown Anticline. Such asymmetric structures can only have arisen through pressure coming from the south.

Near Lulworth the northern limb of the Purbeck Anticline passed the vertical and was inverted, so that the Chalk dips to the south, upside-down. Hereabouts the pressures have been so great that the vertical or inverted Chalk has given way along numerous gently-inclined shears and small thrust-planes. The beds have been driven northwards and upwards, obviously by pressure from the south. Similar thrusting on a small scale occurred in the Isle of Wight.

There is another feature of these anticlines which is likewise common to the many minor folds that have been traced across the Chalk Downs, Salisbury Plain, and the Weald. They are not of equal intensity throughout their length, but are divided into a number of elongated domes or inverted boat-shaped structures called periclines. Moreover, the periclines often do not replace one another exactly in line from east to west, but are commonly offset slightly to the south or north. This arrangement is known as *en échelon*. A good example is displayed in the Isle of Wight, where the Sandown Anticline dies out and is replaced by the Brixton Anticline, about six miles farther south. The northern front of the steeply-tilted Chalk is nevertheless continuous and shows little sign of the replacement of one pericline by another. For this reason, although the Chalk of Ballard Down appears to be exactly in line with that of the Needles, the Purbeck and Brixton Anticlines are unlikely to be strictly speaking one and the same structure. They are probably separate periclines within the major anticline. Closer study of the Jurassic rocks reveals similar minor periclines within the Purbeck portion of the fold.

SECONDARY STRUCTURES DUE TO THE TERTIARY FOLDING

When a thick series of heterogeneous strata such as comprise the Purbeck Anticline are sharply folded, they do not behave as one bed, but each bed folds separately, in so far as the beds surrounding it allow. Thus the strong or competent formations, such as the White Chalk and the Portland Stone, capable of transmitting the forces communicated to them, take control of the shape of the fold, and the weaker or incompetent formations in between have to accommodate themselves as best they can. The thin-bedded and soft formations from the Purbeck Beds to the Lower Chalk have been squeezed up out of the foresyncline and down from under the crest of the anticline, with the result that they have been thrown into small crumples, which are well exposed in the Lulworth district and at Peveril Point, Swanage. Such adjustment-folds and crumples are called drag folds by the Americans, but they should not be confused with the folds produced by drag along a fault. Another form of adjustment has been by sliding along a weak or brittle bed, perhaps to some extent already brecciated by the hydration of anhydrite to gypsum, producing the so-called Broken Beds.

Within the competent formations where they were involved in the steep middle limb and the foresyncline, other adjustments took place, which can be studied to advantage in the White Chalk near Lulworth. The middle limb was drawn out and attenuated by bed-over-bed sliding, with the production of deeply grooved surfaces (slickensides), and there was a great deal of shearing and the production of fracture cleavage (strain-slip cleavage) or close-set jointing. The foresyncline in this type of fold is acutely angular, with the result that the chalk about the axial plane is smashed, packed, and slickensided in all directions, as may be seen west of Lulworth. Another very puzzling structure, the Ballard Down Fault, may possibly result from parts of the Chalk seeking a special form of relief from the stresses set up during the closing of the angular foresyncline (*see* p. 311).

DATE OF THE TERTIARY FOLDING

At Studland Bay and Alum Bay the Eocene Beds can be seen to be involved in the folding, and at Headon Hill in the Isle of Wight the Oligocene Hamstead Beds also are involved; whereas in the Wealden area folding had ceased by the Lower Pliocene. Hence it is generally inferred that the principal tectonic structures of the district took shape in the Miocene period. That considerable disturbances occurred during and before the deposition of the local Eocene (Sparnacian), however, cannot be denied. The Reading Beds rest upon a deeply pot-holed surface of the Chalk, and upon different horizons of the Chalk in different places, and both the Reading and the Bagshot Beds contain abundant Upper Greensand chert, testifying to the upheaval and total removal of the Chalk somewhere to the west or south. Moreover the Bagshot Beds overlap the London Clay and Reading Beds and rest upon an uneven surface of the Chalk in the Dorchester area, and they contain abundant small fragments of silicified Purbeck Beds. Where these came from is still an unsolved problem. West of Abbotsbury the Purbeck Beds were already removed before the Upper Greensand was deposited, and this suggests that the fragments must have come from the south and must indicate an intra-Eocene date for the Ridgeway Fault and Fold. But it is possible that, south of the intra-Cretaceous Abbotsbury Fault, Purbeck Beds escaped destruction much farther west and survived until Bagshot times in the area now occupied by West Bay. If so, tilting of the periphery of the Eocene basin would have brought them within the range of erosion and their presence need have no bearing on the date of the folds in our area. Some folding in Purbeck before the Bembridge Beds (Oligocene) were deposited, however, seems indicated by the strata on Creechbarrow (p. 241).

THE EASTERLY TILT

The general arrangement of the outcrops in the south-eastern half of England, the N.E.-S.W. strike of the Mesozoic rocks from

Yorkshire to Dorset and the incoming of successively younger sediments towards the south-east, indicates that the country has been tilted down towards the south-east since the deposition of the Chalk. This is still evident in spite of the complicated pattern

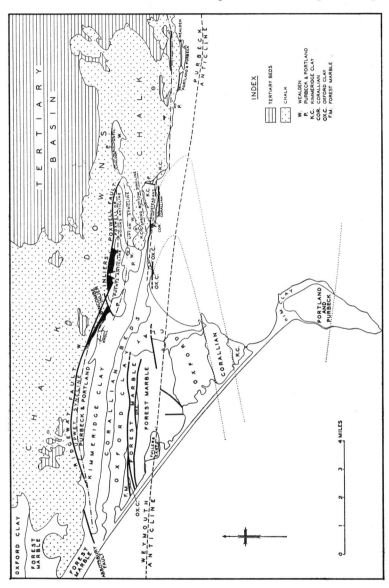

FIG. 48.—*Tectonic sketch-map of the Weymouth district.* The Bincombe and Sutton Poyntz inliers are marked in black. Thick lines represent faults.

resulting from interference by the east-west folds. The tilting was an epeirogenic movement and was spread over a long period of time. In Dorset its effects have been greatly enhanced by differential movements.

That the Purbeck Fold itself is tilted (pitches) eastwards is
obvious from the map. The extent of the tilting is well shown by
following the chief datum-bed, the Chalk, westwards. In the
south of the Isle of Wight some of the south limb of the Chalk
fold remains, as well as the crest and the down-turn into the middle
limb, enabling the amplitude to be measured.[1] In the Lulworth
district the whole south limb and crest and most of the middle
limb have been removed. Instead the bottom of the middle limb
and the foresyncline can be seen; and from Ringstead Bay westwards the coast is carved out of the Jurassic rocks which originally
lay beneath the Chalk of the foreland. On the immediate foreland, the basal Eocene Beds lie buried at least 2,000 ft. below sea-
level in the Isle of Wight and cap the highest hills in the
Weymouth district (Black Down). This eastward tilt of the base
of the Eocene is much steeper in the region of the foresyncline of
the fold than inland, along the north rim of the Tertiary basin.
It is therefore mainly differential, due either to deeper downfold-
ing in the east than in the west, or to subsequent sagging of the
fold.

The eastward tilt of the base of the Eocene in the foresyncline
is in turn far exceeded by the pitch of the Jurassic and Lower
Cretaceous rocks within the axial region of the fold. The top of
the Fuller's Earth projects above sea-level at Langton Herring but
must lie some 6,000 ft. below sea-level in the Isle of Wight.

The excess tilt of the Jurassic and Lower Cretaceous rocks
towards the east was acquired long before the Tertiary folding.
It is a survival of their pre-Chalk arrangement within a basin
whose floor sagged epeirogenically while they were being
deposited.

A similar sagging before the folding but after the consolidation of the Chalk is proved by the westward overstep of the Upper
Chalk by the basal Eocene Beds, which are largely composed of
derived Chalk flints and Greensand chert.

INTRA-CRETACEOUS STRUCTURES IN THE FORELAND

In the Isle of Wight and Purbeck, in the backland and axial
region of the Tertiary anticline, the Chalk and Albian appear to
be conformable with the great thicknesses of Aptian, Wealden,
and Jurassic sediments underneath.

At Lulworth Cove, Dungy Head, and Durdle Door, however,
the Gault (Albian) dips at a somewhat lesser angle towards the
north than the underlying beds, and overlaps the Lower Greensand (Aptian) on to the Wealden. At Durdle Door the Upper
Wealden is only a fraction of the thickness it ought to be, and
most of it seems to have been eroded away before the deposition
of the Gault.

---

[1] About 4,800 feet. H. J. O. White, ' Short Account of the Geology of the
Isle of Wight,' *Mem. Geol. Surv.*, 1921, p. 150.

These localities are on the axis of the fold, near its west end. When the foreland is entered at Ringstead Bay, violent unconformity is apparent between the Albian and the formations underneath. From here westwards, and farther north round the edge of the Upper Cretaceous escarpment by Long Bredy and Litton Cheney, the Jurassic and Wealden formations were thrown into a series of sharp east-west folds, cut by strike faults and dip faults, and finally peneplaned, before the deposition of the Albian.

The intricate pattern made by these earlier folds and faults and those of Tertiary date superimposed upon them will be described in the sections below dealing with the Abbotsbury-Ridgeway-Chaldon Fault Zone and the Ringstead Anticline. The key to the structure of this fascinating zone is the Abbotsbury Fault, an intra-Cretaceous fault which has now been proved for at least 13 miles, from Abbotsbury to Poxwell, with a downthrow of probably more than 1,500 ft., towards the south. In the Tertiary era it was revived in the opposite sense and became a reversed fault thrusting about 200 ft. up towards the north (Ridgeway Fault).

DATE OF THE INTRA-CRETACEOUS DISTURBANCES

The mapping by Strahan of the Upton intra-Cretaceous syncline (p. 279) showed that the Wealden Beds are perfectly conformable with the Purbeck Beds and are folded and peneplaned with them and over-stepped by the Albian (see Pl. XI, A). The folding is therefore post-Wealden and pre-Middle Albian.

More precise dating is only speculative, owing to the absence of the Lower Greensand from the district where the folding occurred. None can be recognized with certainty farther west than Mupe Bay. In the most westerly good section, at Worbarrow Bay, the beds assigned to the Lower Greensand seem to be perfectly conformable with both the Wealden Beds below (from which they are only with difficulty and some uncertainty distinguishable; see pp. 175-6) and with the Gault above. The date of the disturbances, therefore, can only be conjectured by analogy with those of known date in other areas. Strahan was of the opinion that the movements were post-Lower Greensand (post-Aptian), 'immediately anterior to the Gault.'[1] The Gault, it is true, is transgressive in many parts of England; but so too is the Lower Greensand. The Lower Greensand was shown by Strahan himself to rest upon a basal conglomerate with pebbles and rolled fossils at Swanage and in the Isle of Wight, and it is markedly transgressive and has been preceded by folding and locally by faulting in Wiltshire, Berkshire, and Oxfordshire. On the adjacent parts of the Continent there was an important phase of folding during the Neocomian period. This is especially marked in the Hanover district, where there are structures similar to those found in Dorset. (For further particulars see p. 163.)

---

[1] A. Strahan, *Purbeck Memoir*, 1898, pp. 212, 228.

TERTIARY MOVEMENTS OF THE FORELAND

In the Solent region of the Isle of Wight and the neighbouring parts of the Hampshire Basin, minor east-west folds have been traced in the Tertiary beds, running approximately parallel with the major anticline to the south.[1] In Dorset similar small periclines in the Chalk and Greensand are more or less superimposed on the intra-Cretaceous structures beneath. South-west of Dorchester are the Winterborne and Ridgeway anticlines or periclines, entirely in Chalk. The Chaldon pericline is still surrounded by Upper Greensand, and by Chalk on three sides, but the centre has been hollowed out mainly in Wealden Beds, in which a small dome-shaped inlier of Purbeck Beds appears and, by its relation to the Greensand, betrays an intra-Cretaceous uplift almost concentric with the Tertiary. South of Poxwell the Poxwell pericline and Upton syncline, of intra-Cretaceous date, seem to have combined to form the site of a Tertiary pericline; but the Upper Cretaceous covering has largely perished, leaving the west end open. (*See* folding map, Pl. XIX.) West of this the intra-Cretaceous folds are entirely stripped bare, and are bounded on the north by a fairly straight edge of Upper Greensand and Chalk which is always turned up steeply towards the south and often obviously down-faulted against the Jurassic rocks.

UNDERLYING CAUSES

The tectonics of South Dorset are unique in the South of England, for their variety, intensity, complexity and interest. On a visit in 1935, Professor Hans Stille was reminded of the tectonics of the region of which he is the leading authority, the neighbourhood of Hanover, where, however, the comparable structures are associated with salt domes. Dr. G. M. Lees and Mr. P. T. Cox have made the same comparison and have followed it further. " We offer, as an explanation of the Dorset type of folding, the suggestion that there is at no great depth a plastic series which has allowed the top group of rocks to move out of harmony with those below—in other words, an *Abscherung*. Under these conditions a moderate force of compression, which normally would produce only gentle anticlines, can give rise to steep local effects and complicated structures. The age of such a salt series may be Triassic or even Permain. We know that the Upper Keuper of Devon contains gypsum beds and pseudomorphs of salt crystals, and the boring in the Trias at Lyme Regis proved gypsum beds. It is possible, even probable, that there is a greater development of salt and anhydrite towards the centre of the Triassic basin." [2]

---

[1] H. J. O. White, ' A Short Account of the Geology of the Isle of Wight,' *Mem. Geol. Surv.*, 1921, p. 149, fig. 30.

[2] G. M. Lees and P. T. Cox, ' The Geological Basis of the Search for Oil in Great Britain by the D'Arcy Exploration Co., Ltd.,' *Quart. Journ. Geol. Soc.*, vol. xciii, 1937, p. 174.

The Abbotsbury-Ridgeway-Chaldon Fault Zone

ABBOTSBURY

The Abbotsbury Fault (Map, Fig. 48, p. 245) first appears about 200 yards east and east-south-east of Lawrence's Cottage, behind the Chesil Beach a quarter of a mile north-west of Castle Farm. A little stream has cut its valley along the trace. On the south-east side of the valley is a high bank made of downthrown Corallian Beds dipping seawards. Some old quarries on the 100-foot contour show traces of Osmington Oolite, above which follow ferruginous grit and iron ore, the latter capping an elevation above the 400-foot contour. On the north-west or upthrow side of the fault, Fuller's Earth and Forest Marble form comparatively low ground. There are numerous small exposures of the shelly flags and clays of the Forest Marble, with abundant *Rhynchonella*, in the right bank of the stream from the spring on the 300-foot contour down to well below the 200-foot contour.

If the Oxford Clay is here 500 ft. thick as it has been estimated to be in the Weymouth district (though with no certainty), the throw of the Abbotsbury Fault is about 600-700 feet. The course of the stream suggests that the trace curves round to the south as it traverses lower ground towards the sea, thus indicating an appreciable hade to the south.

After crossing the 300-foot contour the fault strikes steadily E. 10°-12° N. across the Bridport road, across the southern corner of Ferny Hole Plantation, and under the Upper Greensand near Lady's Well, north of the village (Fig. 49). Along this stretch there are numerous exposures of the Abbotsbury Ironstone (p. 86) on the south side and Forest Marble on the north. The best is along the deep lane called Folly Hollow, just before it reaches Ferny Hole Plantation. Here the fault can almost be straddled with the legs, one foot on Forest Marble, the other on ironstone, both exposed.

Unfortunately, the point where the fault strikes under the Upper Greensand is hidden by the beginning of a curtain of landslips, consisting of jumbled blocks of Greensand, which extends almost to Portisham. As Strahan says, if the Greensand and Chalk were displaced by the fault to anything like the same extent as the Jurassic rocks, ' they would be thrown down under the village of Abbotsbury. On the contrary, so far as can be judged in the labyrinth of landslips, they are not shifted by it at all.'[1]

PORTISHAM TO UPWEY[2]

The landslips continue tantalizingly for a mile eastwards. No new evidence has been yielded by this stretch, and there seems no reason for not accepting Strahan's mapping, according to which the Greensand at the outcrop rests on Kimmeridge Clay and a

[1] A. Strahan, *Purbeck Memoir*, 1898, p. 229.
[2] The folding map at end, Pl. XIX, should be used in conjunction with pp. 249 ff.

FIG. 49.—*Section S. to N. passing 800 feet west of Abbotsbury Church. True scale. Length of section 3,000 feet.*

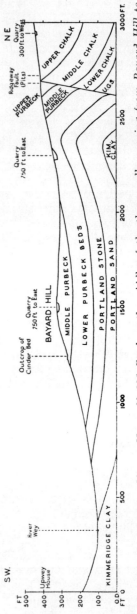

FIG. 50.—*Section from Upwey House N. 20° E. along the middle of the three walls running from Bayard Hill to the Downs. True scale. Length of section 3,000 feet.*

short distance under the hill, to the north, oversteps the Abbotsbury Fault on to Forest Marble. Then, half a mile west of Portisham, the landslips suddenly end, and the Upper Greensand is cut out by a fault down-throwing north which throws Chalk against Kimmeridge Clay.

This is the beginning of the Ridgeway Fault, which continues the line of the Abbotsbury Fault but is stepped perhaps about 500 ft. to the south and has an opposite downthrow. It is a Tertiary fault, and owing to its position and later date it masks the Abbotsbury Fault. It can be mapped for $5\frac{1}{4}$ miles eastwards, almost to Bincombe, cutting out the Upper Greensand and throwing Chalk on the north down against Kimmeridge Clay for the first half mile, and then against Portland and Purbeck Beds.

The Ridgeway Fault from Portisham to Ridgeway railway-cutting forms the northern boundary of the Upwey Syncline. The syncline is truncated obliquely by the fault at both ends, and since the Upper Cretaceous rocks show no signs of continuing the structure, it may be inferred that the syncline is of pre-Albian date.

The rocks on the south side of the Ridgeway Fault in these 5 miles dip south, in the northern limb of the syncline. The best sections are in Gould's Bottom, beside the road from Upwey to Bridport. On the east side of the valley, 300 yards south-south-east of the pumping station, a large quarry shows Lower Purbeck Beds dipping 30 to 50° S. in the northern limb of the syncline. At the north extremity of the quarry, within perhaps 20 yards of the fault, the beds suddenly flatten to 20°. The section is continued towards the fault by a smaller quarry on the opposite side of the valley. This lies within a few yards of the fault and shows the same beds dragged over to dip 60° to 85° N., a complete reversal of their original southward dip a few yards to the south. Further, at the south end of the quarry the strata are bent in a sharp elbow.[1]

The larger of the two quarries, that on the east side of the valley, shows in addition two minor faults parallel to the main fault near by. One is a simple reversed fault upthrown 2 ft. on the south side and hading 10° S. (dipping 80° S.). The other is difficult to interpret, but seems to show reversed movement in the same direction, perhaps combined with some torsion or hingeing. The end of a faulted band of limestone is bent round to form half a circle and then overthrust towards the north for about 4 feet. From this evidence it was inferred[2] that the Ridgeway Fault is a reversed pressure fault, overthrust to the north, as first interpreted by Buckland and De la Beche in 1836.[3]

[1] W. J. Arkell ' The Tectonics of the Purbeck and Ridgeway Faults in Dorset,' *Geol. Mag.*, vol. lxxiii, 1936, p. 101, and fig. 6.

[2] W. J. Arkell, *loc. cit.*

[3] W. Buckland and H. T de la Beche, ' On the geology of the neighbourhood of Weymouth . . . ,' *Trans. Geol. Soc.*, Ser. 2, vol. iv, part 1, 1836, pp. 35-6, pl. ii.

Final confirmation of this interpretation was obtained in 1938. A line of poles carrying an electric cable had been erected almost along the fault between the Dorchester and Bridport roads from Weymouth. Two of the poles, in the second field west of the Roman road up Ridgeway Hill, showed round their base red clay of Wealden appearance, where Strahan had mapped Portland Stone. Some special excavations showed beds on the boundary of Upper Purbeck and Wealden, with *Cypridea punctata,* dipping about 45° N., within 30 ft. of the solid chalk. About 150 yards farther south are Middle Purbeck Beds dipping 20° S., displayed in an old quarry in the adjoining wood (Fig. 50). Here again, therefore, the south-dipping north limb of the Upwey Syncline is dragged over northwards on approaching the fault, and higher beds are pinched in close to the fault than survive in the axis of the syncline. The line of poles proved also that the trace of the fault tongues northwards up the hill-spurs, indicating a southward hade.

Fig. 51.—*Sketch of a chalk pit at Portisham, by H. J. O. White.*   Scale about
1 inch = 10 feet.
1. Shattered chalk with irregular line of flints.
2. Chalk with conglomeratic seam at S.
3. Mass of chalk defined below by a crush-belt, CC.

The Chalk pits immediately north of the fault were examined by Mr. Osborne White in 1936. The following is a précis of his copious notes :—

Pit 1; Bishop's Limekiln quarry, 900 yds. N.E. of Abbotsbury Station. About 1,000 ft. N. of the line of the Ridgeway Fault. Middle Chalk, Labiatus Zone, is exposed, unaltered and practically horizontal.

Pit 2; 320 yds. N.W. of Portisham Church; 400 ft. from the fault.   An abandoned working in two stages, affording poor exposures.   The lower stage shows Middle Chalk, Terebratulina Zone, with suggestions of a steep northward dip (75° ?). The upper stage is probably about the junction of Middle and Upper Chalk. The bedding seems to be much disturbed, and the Chalk appears to have been crushed and reconsolidated.

Pit 3; 200 yds. N.W. of Portisham Church; within 45 ft. of the fault. This interesting section is shown in Fig. 51. At the S.W. side of the pit, the chalk (1 in the figure) is uppermost Labiatus Zone, ' rudely shattered, strongly slickensided in various directions, and shot through with narrow crush-belts of comminuted chalk. Bedding is not discernible in the chalk itself, but the few flints in sight are spaced out in an uneven line whose trend is roughly in accord with the determinable dip on the opposite side of the pit '.

The chalk on the N.E. side of the pit (2) is more normal in appearance, boldly jointed, flintless and nodular, with at the base a continuous seam of little nodules, having a conglomeratic and slightly marly aspect. This band dips about 30° N.N.E., and the chalk is believed to be in upward sequence with that on the opposite side of the pit, and therefore to be basal Terebratulina Zone; but no fossils were found in it.

In the intermediate part of the pit face (at 3) is a body of blocky chalk defined below by a downward, convex crush belt parallel to the bedding. This chalk appears out of harmony with its surroundings, as if introduced by a fault. ' I envisage this seemingly adventitious body of chalk as part of a boss or rib on the hanging wall of an undulate fault plane of high hade. Its original spatial relation to its present environment is a matter for surmise. Its stratigraphical provenance is, I believe, the Middle Chalk, and probably a higher horizon in the Middle Chalk than is represented elsewhere in the section.'

Pit 4; Corton Down, 700 yds. N.N.E. of Corton Barn; about 1,300 ft. from the fault. Old limekiln pit. Chalk referred doubtfully to the Quad-

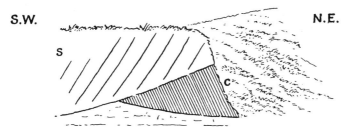

Fig. 52.—*Sketch of a chalk pit at Corton Down, by H. J. O. White.*
Scale about 1 inch = 6 feet.
S, slide-planes.   C, cleavage.

ratus Zone, showing apparently a dip decreasing from 25° to 10° towards the south in one p'ace, and (more doubtfully) of 22° to the south in another place. These dips, however, might be those of tilted fault blocks, of no great extent. ' Near the N.E. end of the section the chalk in a small area, a few feet in height and width, is traversed by a series of little slide-planes, inclined S.W. at 50°-53° (Fig. 52) . . . Between and about them the chalk is hardened, and slickensided in various directions; some at least of the striations on the slide-planes running horizontally N.W.-S.E.' The slide-planes die out downwards, and just east of, and partly below, them is ' a small triangular tract in which the chalk has a pronounced cleavage whose close-set planes, inclined about 60° E. have the darkening effect of hachure-shading '.

Pit 7; 700 yds. N.N.E. of Friar Waddon; 500 ft. from the fault. Shows a 40 ft. section in Upper Chalk, Pilula Zone, with obscure bedding dipping 13° S.[1] ' In the upper part of the section there is a conspicuous group of sub-parallel slide-planes (with associated crush-belts) of upwardly concave curvature, their N.N.W. inclination decreasing in that direction from a maximum angle of about 45°. In this part of the section the chalk is harder than elsewhere, and slickenside-striation, of diverse trend, is strongly marked.' ' Near the northern end of the section, a narrowly-spaced cross-jointing has formed a serried mass of little upright prisms of chalk, comprised in a vertical belt a yard or more in width.' In the lower part of the section are diverse slickensiding and two small normal faults downthrowing a foot or less, in opposite directions.

---

[1] This determination is in agreement with Strahan's record of 12° to 15° S (*Purbeck Memoir,* 1898, p. 188).

Pit 8; in west side of Gould's Bottom, Upwey, 130 yds. S.W. of the pumping station; probably within 180 ft. of the fault. Shows 30 ft. of Upper
Chalk, Coranguinum Zone, with numerous bands of flint which clearly show
the bedding curving up sharply towards the south as it approaches the fault.
The dip is north and decreases northwards from 45° to 15° in a distance of
15 yds., as noted by Strahan.[1] ' Though the bedding is otherwise but little
disturbed, the chalk is shattered and extensively slickensided, while the larger
flints are often minutely fractured into flakes and prisms with the longer
axes tending to parallelism with the curved bedding.'

Pit 9; in east side of Gould's Bottom, Upwey, 130 yds. S.S.E. of the pumping station; about 400 ft. from the fault. Upper Chalk, Cortestudinarium
Zone, with a well-marked band of nodular chalk seen in 1908 to be dipping
10° N. Scant signs of disturbance.

Pit 10; in east side of Gould's Bottom, 100 yds. S.E. of the pumping
station; about 550 ft. from the fault.   Upper Chalk, basal Coranguinum
Zone, dipping 4° or 5° N. A road-section about 180 yds. N.N.E. of this
pit and 180 yds. N.E. of the pumping station, now overgrown, formerly
showed 4 ft. of chalk dipping about 10° S.

With these sections are here grouped, for convenience, some chalk exposures on Ridgeway Hill, ¾ mile S.E. of Gould's Bottom.

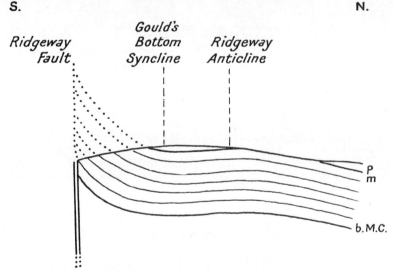

FIG. 53.—*Section of the upper part of Ridgeway Hill, along the line of the
high road.* (H.J.O.W. and W.J.A.)

p. = Pilula Zone.   b.M.C. = base of Middle Chalk.
m. = Marsupites Zone.

Pit 12; adjoining east side of main road on crest of the hill, about 30 yds.
S. of B.M. 444.2. Poor exposure of Offaster pilula Zone. ' In 1906, when
the pit was in better condition, no dip apparent.' At intervals for a distance
of some 250 yds. southward of B.M. 444.2, however, the same beds were
visible in 1906-8 in a series of small exposures in the E. bank of the high-road,
and a few definite flint bands indicated a dip of about 3° S. Nothing
unusual was noted about the structure of the chalk in these exposures. The
most southerly was about 800 ft. from the fault.

---

[1] *op. cit.,* p. 188.

Pit 13; in N.W. angle of cross-roads where the Ridgeway crosses the Weymouth-Dorchester road, 270 yds. W. of Down Farm; 1,650 ft. from the fault. Little disturbed Upper Chalk, Marsupites Zone, dipping about 4° N. Horizontal N.-S. slickenside striation noted in 1908.

Finally, at the south entrance to Bincombe Tunnel, Lower and Middle Chalk dip 85° N. adjacent to the fault.[1]

The information derived from the Chalk exposures may be summarized as follows.

All the pits nearest the Ridgeway Fault show a dip away from the fault, to the north. The steepest dip, 85° N., is actually adjacent to the fault at the tunnel mouth; but at Portisham there is a dip perhaps as steep as 75° N. 400 ft. from the fault (pit 2). The latter, however, is inconsistent with the neighbouring pit 3, which is only 45 ft. from the fault and between it and pit 2, but nevertheless shows a dip of only 30° N.[2] Apart from this anomaly at Portisham, the next steepest dip, 45° N., is in pit No. 8 at Upwey, 180 yards from the fault. In this section a very rapid reduction in dip from 45° N. to 15° N., in 15 yds. is visible. This serves to substantiate the surmise that the sharp turn-up of the chalk adjacent to the fault is due to drag and indicates once more that the downthrown side is the north side (the opposite of Strahan's conception). Another pit midway between the Dorchester and Bridport roads, less than 150 yds. from the fault, shows Upper Chalk dipping about 40° N.

Beyond this belt of upward drag with steep northward dips there follows a belt of gentle southward dips, detected at Friar Waddon (13° S., at 500 ft. from the fault) at Upwey (10° S., at 550 ft., from the fault) and at Ridgeway Hill (3° S., at 800 to 1,400 ft. from the fault).

Farther north again, the chalk flattens and turns over to resume its northward dip gently under the Tertiary basin (4° N. at 1,650 ft. from the fault).

The structure along a N.-S. line where the exposures are fullest, at Ridgeway Hill, is shown in Fig. 53.

The belt of southward dips is held by Mr. Osborne White to lie in the southern limb of a gentle Tertiary anticline, which he calls the Ridgeway Anticline. He has traced its course from Ridgeway Hill in a W.N.W. direction approximately along the Ridgeway track and nearly parallel to the fault, as far as Bronkham Hill (3½ miles), and he surmises that it continues to near Little Bredy and perhaps beyond. South-eastwards it seems to die out.

The Ridgeway Anticline is approximately parallel to the similar Winterborne Anticline, from 1 to 1½ miles farther north, ' which brings up the *Terebratulina lata* Beds of the Middle Chalk in a narrow inlier, extending along the Winterborne Valley for a

---

[1] A. Strahan, *op. cit.,* p. 188.

[2] My own impression of pit 3, which I have visited alone and in company with Mr. White, is that everything displayed in it may be more or less jumbled and incapable of giving the true dip of the Middle Chalk as a whole.

distance of about $3\frac{1}{2}$ miles, from the neighbourhood of Winterborne Abbas down to Ashton Farm, S.W. of Maiden Castle '.
It, too, dies out towards the south-east, and about a mile earlier
than the Ridgeway Anticline.

RIDGEWAY CUTTING, BINCOMBE DOWN

The Ridgeway Anticline in the Chalk (Fig. 53) was presumably flanked on the south by a parallel syncline, of which the
southern limb has been partly or wholly severed by the Ridgeway
Fault and replaced by a much steeper, shorter, false limb due to
drag against the reversed fault.   This original syncline is held
partly responsible by Mr. Osborne White for the preservation of
the outliers of Bagshot gravel, sand, and sandy clay, on the
southern slope of Bincombe Down (just east of Ridgeway Hill).

The Tertiary strata were formerly worked in extensive pits,
now nearly all overgrown.   In one pit Fisher described the beds
as vertical, and he and subsequent writers assumed that, like the
almost vertical Chalk at the tunnel mouth, the Tertiary beds
had been tilted into this attitude by the Ridgeway Fault.[1]   The
observations of Mr. Osborne White on Ridgeway Hill, however,
make this interpretation extremely unlikely.   The Chalk beneath
the Tertiary beds was not seen by Fisher, and its attitude is still
unknown.   The site lies about 900 ft. north of the Ridgeway
Fault, in a position where, by analogy with the Ridgeway road
sections, the Chalk probably dips gently southward.

Mr. Osborne White saw in 1901, in ballast-pits since overgrown, many indications of solution-settlement in these Tertiary
beds and Clement Reid described the local piping as on a scale he
had ' never seen equalled '.[2]   It is therefore Mr. White's belief
and his suggestion seems to afford the only reasonable explanation, that Fisher's ' Vertical Tertiaries ' owe their ultimate
preservation and their high dip to extensive solution-settlement in
gigantic ' pipes '.

The problem of the Ridgeway railway-cutting thus becomes
shorn of one of its major complications, though enough still
remain.

In the 250-300 yds. between the high-road up Ridgeway Hill,
which runs wholly over Purbeck Beds, and the railway line, the
axial trough of the Upwey Syncline, after shallowing temporarily,
suddenly deepens, bringing in Wealden Beds.   These are cut
through in the railway-cutting, which provides a section (now
much overgrown) through the southern limb of the syncline,
consisting of Portland and Purbeck Beds with increasing northward dip, up to the Wealden Beds, which finally, according to
the sections made at the time by Ibbetson and Weston and also
Fisher[3] stand nearly vertical, although Strahan, 50 years later,

---

[1] O. Fisher, ' Vertical Tertiaries at Bincombe, Dorset,' *Geol. Mag.*, 1896, p. 247.
[2] C. Reid, ' The Eocene Deposits of Dorset,' *Quart. Journ. Geol. Soc.*, vol. lii,
1896, p. 499.
[3] Reproduced in A. Strahan, *Purbeck Memoir,* 1898, pp. 224, 225.

mentioned no dip exceeding 55°.[1] The cutting then crosses a major fault, described and figured by Fisher as ' a curious irregular line, which appeared very well defined ', said by Strahan to be ' nearly vertical ', which throws the Wealden Beds against Oxford Clay.

The Oxford Clay occupies a stretch about 160 ft. wide and near the north end of the cutting it is brought to an end by the Ridgeway Fault, which throws it against Lower Chalk dipping 85° N., as described above. The fault plane near rail level dips 58° S. (exposed 1938-39), but higher up it undulates.

The celebrated ' dyke ' of Oxford Clay in this cutting has given rise to discussion and speculation ever since the railway was built, nearly 100 years ago. Its identity as Oxford Clay was recognized from the first by the occurrence of *Gryphaea dilatata* and other fossils, which were identified by J. de C. Sowerby. It was said by Weston to contain blocks of Cornbrash at the south end of the dyke and Fisher noted ' what appear to be nodules of Greensand engaged in it,' alined vertically near the north end.

In 1934-5 large quantities of the Oxford Clay in the west bank of the cutting began to slip down on to the railway and had to be dug into trucks and removed. In 1936-7 a passable section was again seen of the dyke from the junction with the Wealden red and green mottled clays to within 10 ft. of the Chalk. It was thus possible to determine the zones represented and the order of succession.[2] The northern half of the dyke is composed of the Red Nodule Beds of the Upper Oxford Clay, with bands of red and grey kidneystones, some of which were sufficiently undisturbed to be seen standing almost on end, with a southward dip of at least 70°. Fossils found were *Cardioceras costellatum* Buckman, *Gryphaea dilatata* J. Sowerby (fragments common, some much bored), *Lopha gregarea* (J. Sowerby), *Procerithium sp.*, and *Serpulae*.[3] In the southern half of the dyke no dip was visible and everything was much slipped, but the clays became more sandy and darker, passing up into black sandy clay with bands of sandy, soft marlstone, weathering brownish, obscurely ' fucoidal ', which can only be the lower part of the Nothe Grits. Here I collected casts of *Modiola bipartita* J. Sowerby, *Pleuromya alduini* (Brongniart), and a clavellate *Trigonia*, and from here probably came the '*Ammonites perarmatus (catena)*' identified by J. de C. Sowerby.[4] Finally, close to the southern boundary fault, there were a few large blocks (up to 2 ft. long) of yellowish-grey to rusty brown sandy limestone, obscurely shelly, which at once suggested Weston's blocks of Cornbrash. Careful inspection, however, left

---

[1] A. Strahan, *op. cit.*, p. 223.
[2] W. J. Arkell, ' Postcript Notes on the Ballard Down and Ridgeway Faults,' *Geol. Mag.*, vol. lxxiv, 1937, p. 89.
[3] A set was presented to the Geological Survey Museum.
[4] See A. Strahan, *op. cit.*, 1898, pp. 22, 225.

no doubt that they belonged to the Nothe Grits.[1] From internal evidence in Weston's papers it seems probable that his experience of Jurassic rocks was insufficient to have ensured against his misidentifying these blocks.[2] Fisher was a careful geologist, but nevertheless the grey to khaki-coloured nodules of the Oxford Clay, from their colour, shape, attitude, and position, strongly suggested that they may have been ' what appeared to be nodules of greensand ' to Fisher.

Strahan's explanation of the structure at Ridgeway is well known, and was unquestioned for nearly 40 years.[3] It involved a flat-lying southward overthrust of the Chalk for a distance of at least half a mile. The Oxford Clay ' dyke ', and the inlier of Lower Oolites and Oxford Clay at Bincombe, were explained as a slice or slices of the sub-Cretaceous floor ' caught up and carried bodily southwards with the Cretaceous rocks '.[4] Fundamental objections to this hypothesis have been pointed out and need not be repeated here.[5] It suffices to mention that Strahan's hypothesis, on his own admission, depends on the assumption that the Upper Cretaceous rocks were deposited on Oxford Clay under the Downs about ½ mile north of the railway-cutting, or ' not far north of Bincombe Tunnel ', and that this arrangement was brought about by a large intra-Cretaceous fault more or less in line with the Abbotsbury Fault.[6]

The inliers at Bincombe and Sutton Poyntz (see below) prove that the Upper Greensand and Chalk rest disconformably on Oxford Clay at those places, where the sub-Cretaceous foundation protrudes along the southern edge of the Downs. There is no need, therefore, to invoke southward thrusting, and there is nothing outside Strahan's memoir even to suggest that it has occurred. Northward thrusting at a steep angle (reversed faulting), on the other hand, has already been indicated by a considerable body of evidence at localities from Portisham to Ridgeway. Thus it can be confidently inferred that the Oxford Clay of the Ridgeway ' dyke ' belongs to the edge of the sub-Albian foundation and has been merely lifted up no great distance against the Chalk by the Ridgeway Fault which now separates the two rocks. The other fault, bounding the Oxford Clay ' dyke ' against the Wealden Beds, then becomes presumably the Abbotsbury Fault. It is in line with the Abbotsbury Fault; it has a large downthrow south (probably more than 1,500 ft.); and it must have been pre-Albian in date and have been followed by profound erosion, since to the

---

[1] No blocks were seen until April 1937, after the publication of my ' Postcript Notes on the Ballard Down and Ridgeway Faults ' in the February *Geological Magazine*. A large block appeared in 1939 only 40 feet south of the Chalk.

[2] *Inter alia*, he believed the Ridgeway Fault ran along a Jurassic shoreline against which the Jurassic Rocks thinned out completely.

[3] A. Strahan, *op. cit.*, 1898, pp. 223-7.

[4] *Ibid.*, p. 227.

[5] W. J. Arkell, *Geol. Mag.*, vol. lxxiii, 1936, pp. 107-114.

[6] A. Strahan, *op. cit.*, p. 226.

south of it all the rocks up to Wealden were preserved, whereas
north of it Albian was deposited on Oxford Clay.

The above explanation is the simplest that seems capable of
explaining the facts, and it is in harmony with the tectonics of the
region as a whole.

There remain to be explained the excessively steep dips in
opposite directions in the Wealden Beds and Oxford Clay.

The turn-over of the Wealden Beds northward to nearly vertical
is too sudden and too steep to be due to their position in the
south flank of the Upwey Syncline, in which no dip-readings
exceeding 25° have been obtained. Like the equally steep northward dip in the Lower Chalk, it is probably due to drag. Similar
steep drag dips are the rule from here eastwards wherever the
Portland and Purbeck Beds approach close to the Abbotsbury
Fault. The drag is in the opposite direction from that which
would have resulted from the original intra-Cretaceous action of
the normal fault, downthrowing south. It can only be explained
by supposing that the last movement along the fault was a reverse
movement or overthrust towards the north; and there is abundant
evidence farther east that such reverse movement took place during
the Tertiary period.

The steep southward dip in the Oxford Clay ' dyke ', or at least
the southward succession (if the actual dip seen was due to slipping), is probably explicable mainly as drag due to the original
(pre-Albian) faulting, perhaps superimposed on an original
southward dip in the north limb of the Upwey Syncline. If the
Oxford Clay, after the pre-Albian folding, dipped at, say, 20° S.,
or even was nearly horizontal, the very large downthrow of the
Abbotsbury Fault at this locality might have dragged down the
edges of the soft formation towards the south sufficiently far for
any subsequent movements along the fault in the reverse direction, under pressure, to accentuate instead of reversing the
effects.

The attitude of the Oxford Clay adjacent to the Chalk in the
Ridgeway cutting provides independent confirmation of the conclusion that the steep northward dip of the Chalk adjacent to the
fault is due to drag and not to normal folding. If folding were
the cause, the Oxford Clay now south of the nearly vertical Chalk
would likewise have been rotated through 85° from its original
position below the Chalk. But in that position it would have
been almost completely upside-down. Such an attitude in the
Jurassic rocks beneath horizontal Chalk would be inexplicable by
any likely mechanism. It is so improbable that the only alternative explanation can confidently be preferred : namely, that the
high dip of the edge of the Chalk was acquired independently of
the Oxford Clay now adjacent to it, and so must be drag along
the fault.

BINCOMBE[1]

Slight traces of green sand near rail level[2] show that the Upper Greensand is only just faulted out in Ridgeway cutting. Augering proved it in the arable field in the valley north-east of Lower Bincombe, and a special pit dug still farther east proved it again half a mile east of the railway, in the valley bottom under 5½ ft. of hillwash. Another pit 30 yds. south of this proved slickensided Oxford Clay, with broken *Gryphaea*, *Exogyra nana*, and *Lopha gregarea*, and a third pit 40 yds. farther south proved Upper Purbeck Beds dipping 48° N. in harmony with the exposed Purbeck and Portland rocks of the high ridge that joins the Knoll to Bincombe (Fig. 54).

The first exposure of Upper Greensand is in the bank north of the road, ½ mile E.S.E. of Lower Bincombe, whence the outcrop can be followed continuously past Bincombe village for ¾ mile. Numerous exposures, and some augering, prove that the outcrop is of the normal width, and the Greensand rests directly on Oxford Clay, which runs with a narrow outcrop continuously from Ridgeway cutting to Bincombe village. A quarry 270 yds. E.S.E. of the church shows practically undisturbed Upper Greensand and Lower Chalk dipping 35° N.E. (p. 212). Another, 100 yds. north of the church, displays Lower and Middle Chalk, also almost undisturbed, dipping about 40° N. (p. 213). Along this stretch there is no sign of the Ridgeway Fault, which has passed into the Chalk of Bincombe Hill. A pit near the barrows on the summit shows barren Upper Chalk with bands of flints dipping 40° N.E., at 700 ft. from the edge of the outcrop, thus giving an indication of the probable line of the fault. Its presumed continuation appears again, on the same line, at Greenhill Barton.

The intra-Cretaceous Abbotsbury Fault meanwhile can be traced from the railway-cutting eastwards to Bincombe village by its effect of separating the Oxford Clay on which the Greensand rests from the steeply-tilted Purbeck Beds of the Knoll-Bincombe strike ridge. The Purbeck and Portland Beds are well exposed along this ridge and dip at 45-50° N. Immediately to the south they turn over, in the Knoll, to dip southwards into a gentle east-west syncline. The steep northward dip is probably due at least in part to drag formed during Tertiary re-activation of the Abbotsbury Fault in the reverse direction, as will be explained below.

At Bincombe the strike-ridge of Portland and Purbeck Beds suddenly comes to an end and the village lies in a hollow of undulating pasture land, about ⅓ mile wide. Within is the Bincombe inlier, floored mainly by Oxford Clay, with Cornbrash and perhaps a thin strip of Forest Marble, in faulted contact with Kimmeridge Clay.

---

[1] See folding map at end, Pl. XIX.
[2] Found by Mr. B. H. Mottram, 1937.

The discovery of these rocks was due to the Rev. O. Fisher, and they were recorded on the original one-inch Geological Survey Map by H. W. Bristow. Augering has led to considerable modification of the outcrops as represented on the map. In

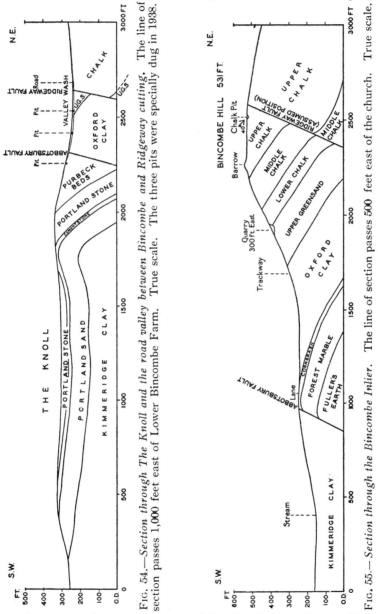

Fig. 54.—Section through The Knoll and the road valley between Bincombe and Ridgeway cutting. The line of section passes 1,000 feet east of Lower Bincombe Farm. True scale. The three pits were specially dug in 1938.

Fig. 55.— Section through the Bincombe Inlier. The line of section passes 500 feet east of the church. True scale.

particular most of the area mapped by Strahan as Forest Marble has proved to be Kimmeridge Clay, which comes up to the garden of East Farm. Dr. C. T. Barber for the D'Arcy Exploration Co.

in 1937 put down four auger holes 20 ft. deep in a N.-S. line along the hedge that runs south from East Farm, and all proved grey clay.   The belief that this was Kimmeridge Clay was confirmed by numerous   hand-auger   samples to 4 ft. in   neighbouring fields obtained by the writer in 1938.

The Cornbrash can be seen in five places, in an almost straight line from N.W. to S.E., as follows :—(1) Near the pump house at the beginning of the drive up to East Farm.   (2) In the corner of the field by the garden gate about 35 yds. S.E. of East Farm. Here Dr. Barber dug a pit 11 ft. deep in Lower Cornbrash with *Cererithyris intermedia* and other fossils, dipping 9° N.N.E. (3) In the lane 120 yds. S.E. of East Farm.   (4) Along the N.W.-S.E. hedge immediately S.E. of the lane exposure.   Cornbrash was excavated here in building the hen house in 1937 and has been left close to the building.   (5) In a ditch 200 yds. S.E. of the lane exposure, on the opposite side of the stream.

Forest Marble is proved only by the auger, but it must at one time have been quarried on a small scale, for there is plenty in the wall beside the drive up to East Farm.

The most reasonable way to explain the Bincombe inlier is to suppose that the Oxford Clay, Cornbrash and Forest Marble are the undisturbed edge of the sub-Cretaceous foundation in the footwall of the Abbotsbury Fault, and that they pass under the steeply-dipping Purbeck and Portland ridge to the north-west to join up underground with the Oxford Clay of the Ridgeway cutting.[1]   At Ridgeway the Ridgeway Fault separates the Chalk and Oxford Clay, but as already pointed out " a fault of quite trivial northward downthrow is all that is needed to bring Chalk against Oxford Clay."[2]   At Bincombe the Greensand is not cut out, and it appears that the Ridgeway Fault passes through the Chalk farther north, where its trace is temporarily lost (Fig. 55).

The dip of 35°-40° in the Greensand and the edge of the Chalk, therefore, is probably not due to drag on a fault as is the dip of 80° at Ridgeway cutting, but to monoclinal folding.   The plane of the Abbotsbury Fault must have taken part in this folding and been bent over northwards as it approached the base of the Greensand.   It therefore probably has a curved trace and gradually steepening inclination, from rather flat (perhaps 20°) under the Portland and Purbeck Beds west of the village to moderately steep along the southern margin of the inlier.

The primary cause of the inlier was beyond doubt intra-Cretaceous dip-faulting and marine erosion.   Two dip-faults raised a ridge from which most of the beds above the Kimmeridge Clay on the south side of the strike-fault were removed by pre-Gault erosion.   Since the removal of the Chalk and Upper Greensand recent denudation has attacked the Kimmeridge Clay at Bincombe more rapidly than the hard Portland and Purbeck

[1] W. J. Arkell, *Geol. Mag.*, 1936, p. 109, and fig. 7.
[2] W. J. Arkell, *op. cit.*, p. 113.

limestones on either side, and so the present hollow has been excavated into the sub-Cretaceous rocks of the foot-wall of the Abbotsbury Fault (*see* note, p. 268).

GREEN HILL

At Green Hill faulting " takes a bite as it were out of the Chalk and Greensand outcrops."[1] The salient of Portland and Purbeck Beds clearly belongs to the south side of the intra-Cretaceous Abbotsbury Fault, and an examination of its internal structure reveals that, in spite of its apparently anomalous position, it is a direct continuation of the Portland-Purbeck ridge west of Bincombe and the plateau of the Knoll.

Mapping of the Portland and Purbeck Beds on either side of Coombe Valley and round the hills of Chalbury Camp and the Tout is made easy by frequent outcrops of the basal Purbeck tufas and the Scar Cementstone at the top of the Portland Sand. The dominating structure is a syncline running from Preston W. 20° N. through the spur on which the reservoir is built, through the quarry at Boiling Rock, and across Coombe Valley and the hill west of it, to emerge, much flattened, through the old quarries E.N.E. of Bincombe Marsh Dairy. South of Chalbury Camp the dip in the south limb of the syncline is 10°, and in the north limb 13° on the average, but steeper as the axis is approached.

At the north edge of Chalbury Camp the dip is only 6° S.W., and the Portland Beds rapidly flatten northwards and then turn down suddenly to 50° N.E. in the scar on the south end of Green Hill. The point where the turn over to the N.E. occurs can be detected in the turf in the west bank of Coombe Valley near its north end, not much more than 100 ft. from the Chalk.[2] Purbeck Beds quickly come on, dipping at 70°-90°, and at Greenhill Barton the Cinder Bed has been recognized. Farther east the Purbeck Beds are cut out again and the Portland Beds are once more in contact with the Chalk. A good section in the road-cutting 150 yds. S.E. of Greenhill Barton shows the Portland Sand with the Scar Cementstones and *Exogyra* Beds suddenly turning down from 50° to 90° in a few feet.[3] The curious repetition of the Portland Beds may be due to a minor fault or to a landslide. That the Purbeck Beds are contorted or riven by minor faults is indicated by a dip of 48° S. by the sheepfold at Greenhill Barton, and more light was thrown on the structures by a pipe trench opened in 1938 (*see* Fig. 56).

The axis of this sharp anticline is in line with that in the same beds on the west side of Bincombe, although it is cut across at an

---

[1] A. Strahan, *op. cit.*, p. 222. See folding map at end of this memoir, Pl. XIX.

[2] Strahan's mapping hereabouts was far from correct, owing to his mistaking the Scar Cementstone and Exogyra Bed of the Portland Sand for Portland Freestone Series with the Tilly Whim oyster bed. In consequence he was misled into exaggerating the flatness of the rocks in the Chalbury and opposite hills (*Op. cit.*, 1898, pp. 69, 222).

[3] W. J. Arkell, *Proc. Geol. Assoc.*, vol. xlvi. 1935, p. 327.

angle of 35° by the faulted boundary of the Chalk. The Boiling Rock Syncline is the analogue, if not the direct continuation, of the Upton and Knoll Synclines.

The relations of these Jurassic rocks to the Greensand and Chalk are most remarkable. The Cretaceous rocks are cut cleanly across by two straight faults running S.W.-N.E. and S.E.-N.W., which meet at a point close to an old chalk pit 100 yds. E.N.E. of Greenhill Barton. The S.W.-N.E. fault seems to be directly in line with the intra-Cretaceous fault bounding the east side of the Bincombe inlier, which had a downthrow in the opposite direction before the Greensand was deposited and produced a big shift in the trace of the Abbotsbury Fault. The top of the Greensand is exposed from Bincombe almost continuously up to within about 40 ft. of this fault, dipping regularly 35°-40° N.E., and suffers no disturbances on approaching it. The chalk is not exposed in the vicinity, except in the small pit above mentioned, where it is metamorphosed and in an anomalous position, for instead of being Upper Chalk it is Middle Chalk. Mr. Osborne White, who gave careful attention to this pit at my suggestion, reports as follows :—

" Shows, above talus, about 8 ft. of hard semi-crystalline lime-stone . . . ., a low-grade marble, taking a polish when ground with emery. It is traversed in places by venules of clear calcite, this mineral occurring also as a lining to little cavities, which in some cases are recognizable as moulds of shell-fragments . . . . Bedding is undistinguishable. There is a bold jointing . . . . The joint-cheeks are much slickensided, and internal shear-striation is revealed on breaking the detached blocks.

" One conspicuous, and other less distinct, thin bands of crush-conglomerate, inclined S.S.E. at about 45°, are seen in the upper part of the pit-face, and a thicker band, of the same nature and nearly hidden by the talus, is discernible low down at the N. and S. extremities of the pit; this last may be Strahan's ' thrust dipping 40° S.' (Geol. Surv. field map record)."

This pit, however, is also close to and within the influence of the other, N.W.-S.E., fault, and it is rather to this that the effects should be ascribed. This fault, like the other, is con-tinuous with an intra-Cretaceous downthrow in the opposite direction, which bounds the Sutton Poyntz inlier (*see* below), and the Upper Cretaceous rocks approach to within a few yards of it, dipping normally 30° N.W. with no signs of special disturbance until within 500 ft. (measured along the fault) from the chalk pit just described. The Upper Greensand is well displayed in the road-cutting, and almost the whole Middle Chalk can be seen in the large chalk pit beside the road higher up, dipping 25-30° N.W. and quite normal.

Farther north-west, however, for the next 500 ft. the line of the fault is marked by a small strip of the top grit of the Upper Green-sand, overthrust at an angle of 45° by Purbeck Beds, and thrust in turn over a fault-breccia of very hard marmorized Chalk frag-

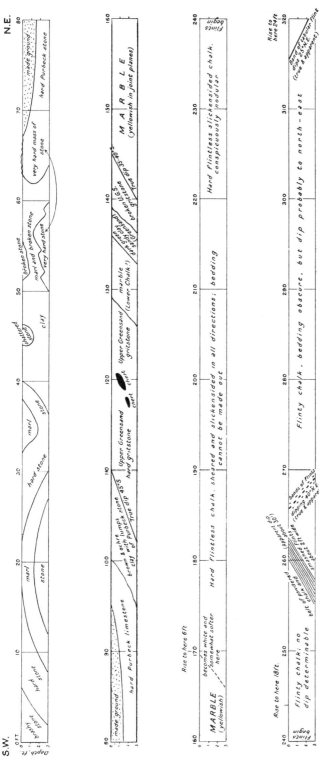

FIG. 56.—*Section exposed in trench during the laying of a water main across the Ridgeway Fault at Green Hill and West Hill, Sutton Poyntz, 1938.* The trench runs along the centre of the track up West Hill from the Sutton Poyntz—Dorchester road in a general direction N. 65° E. and crosses the Ridgeway Fault obliquely at an angle of about 55° (i.e., at 35° from the perpendicular). All dips shown are apparent and are considerably smaller than the true dips except in the section from 260 feet to the end, where apparent dips are true dips. In the part of the trench shown the rocks are Purbeck Beds (upper part of Lower Purbeck) in the section 0—110 ft., Upper Greensand (topmost gritstone and chert beds) from 110 ft. to 129 ft., marmorized Lower (?) Chalk 129—136 ft., Upper Greensand (basal dark clay) 136—139 ft., broken Upper Greensand (gritstone) 139-145 ft., marmorized Middle (?) Chalk (the " Marble Dyke ") 145 ft. to about 170 ft., Middle Chalk, 170—240 ft., Upper Chalk 240—320 ft. After the fault at 260 ft. the strike changes to about perpendicular to the line of section.

ments (Mr. White thinks probably Middle Chalk, Labiatus Zone, for the most part at least), veined by calcite. The breccia in places forms a distinct feature in the ground, and where crossed by a trackway stands up like a dyke. It passes indefinitely north-wards into hard flintless chalk, sheared and slickensided and devoid of recognizable bedding (Fig. 56). In one place slivers of Upper Greensand grit appear on both sides of the breccia, and it always seems to be separated by Greensand from the Purbeck Beds.

This N.W.-S.E. fault is directly in line with the Ridgeway Fault where it passes into the Chalk near Lower Bincombe, and almost on the line connecting them is the chalk pit on Bincombe Hill showing an anomalous dip of 40°. It is therefore probable that it is the Ridgeway Fault which has emerged again at the point where it once more coincides with the intra-Cretaceous Abbotsbury Fault, thrown north-eastwards from Bincombe. The greater disturbance along the first 500 ft. after emergence from the Chalk coincides with the stretch where hard Purbeck and Portland Beds were thrust against the Chalk and Greensand; farther south-east these rocks were removed before the deposition of the Greensand and the active or piston rock was only the relatively soft Kimmeridge Clay.

SUTTON POYNTZ PERICLINE

The Green Hill-Chalbury salient bounds the first of the three more or less closed periclines of Sutton Poyntz, Poxwell, and Chaldon, by which the fault zone is bordered on its south side for the next 6½ miles. The Sutton Poyntz Pericline is the largest and flattest of the three. If it be considered as enclosed by the Chalk on the north and the Portland Beds on the other sides, all outwardly-dipping rim-rocks, its length is 2¼ miles and its greatest breadth just over half a mile; and the rim is broken at only one point, on the south-west side, by the Jordan stream.

The 1904 edition of the Geological Survey Map (Sheet 342) showed the Portland and Purbeck Beds as almost completely encircling the pericline, except along the line of the Jordan, which rises in the Chalk north-west of Sutton Poyntz and crosses both rims, through two gaps on a N.-S. line. The whole interior was shown on the map as Kimmeridge Clay. The internal com-plications of the Sutton Poyntz Pericline, therefore, remained unsuspected until 1937, when the D'Arcy Exploration Co. began detailed work with the object of finding the true crest for drilling to reach the Corallian Beds for oil.

Five shallow test holes were dug to depths of 5 to 13 ft. at the points indicated on Pl. XIX, with results as follows :—

1. Aulacostephanus Zone ⎫
2. Mutabilis Zone   ⎬ Kimmeridge Clay.
3. Cymodoce Zone   ⎭
4. Junction of Cornbrash and Kellaways Beds, numerous fossils.
5. Mariae Zone, Upper Oxford Clay.

Mr. P. E. Kent, who was in charge of this exploration, also found Cornbrash turned up by the plough in a field 1,000 ft. S.E. of the White Horse. Here the rock is unmistakable, and *Cererithyris intermedia, Ornithella obovata, Meleagrinella echinata, Pholadomya deltoidea, Chlamys vagans, Chl. hemicostata, Entolium demissum, Kallirhynchia sp.*, were collected by the writer in a few minutes. The surface indications, moreover, give a northward sequence of Forest Marble, Lower and Upper Cornbrash, and Oxford Clay with *Gryphaea*. The large arable field west of pit 5, on the other hand, was found by Mr. A. H. Taitt and the writer to be covered with Purbeck and Portland debris. Accordingly another pit was sunk at point 6, which, although still in disturbed ground at 4 ft. 9 ins. when digging was stopped by water, showed such heavy khaki-coloured clay, with *Gryphaea,* that there could be no doubt the sub-soil was Oxford Clay.

Soon after Mr. Kent's discoveries a pipe trench was dug from Sutton Poyntz waterworks north-westward to a new reservoir at the top of West Hill, and the excavated material was found by Mr. Taitt and the writer to consist of Forest Marble, Cornbrash, Oxford Clay and Upper Greensand, in ascending sequence.

After this, a more careful examination of the ground by the writer disclosed a good exposure of Forest Marble in the bank of the Jordan stream close to where the rock had first been detected in the pipe-trench. The flaggy limestones increase in dip southwards from 70° N. to 90° N. and finally are bent over in a drag inversion close below the fault plane. Through them the stream has cut a little gorge, which suddenly terminates near the E.W. hedge 83 yds. north of the waterworks wall. At this point fresh black Kimmeridge Shale has been dug out by private prospectors for oil-shale. Alongside the road 300 yds. west of this several exposures of Kimmeridge shales (Aulacostephanus Zone) have been seen during 1937 and 1938 in foundations and cesspools for new houses. One of these excavations was in Oxford Clay, devoid of fossils but of characteristic appearance.

With practice it is easy to distinguish between Kimmeridge Clay, blue-grey in colour, and Oxford Clay, khaki-coloured to yellowish brown, by means of auger samples from depths of 3-4 feet. By this method, controlled by the known exposures, the inliers have been mapped on the 25-inch scale during 1938, and the resulting maps are reduced in Pl. XIX. On the east side of the Jordan Stream the Cornbrash cannot be found and is apparently faulted back under the Kimmeridge Clay by a dip fault earlier in date than the Abbotsbury Fault. Oxford Clay and Kimmeridge Clay are shown by the auger to be in contact. The same arrangement obtains on the east side of the East Hill spur, before the Cornbrash begins again about 1,000 yds. E.N.E. of the waterworks.

In the more easterly outcrop of Lower Oolites, north-west of

Osmington, Cornbrash with *Pholadomya deltoidea* crops out across the steep part of the lane, 500 yds. N.W. of Hall's Farm, and the wall beside the lane higher up is made of fossiliferous Forest Marble and Cornbrash. Upper Cornbrash has been quarried from a small pit marked by a depression in the field about 250 yds. south of the head of the White Horse, and presumably from this pit neighbouring walls were built. With the help of the auger the Cornbrash outcrop has now been traced continuously from about 250 ft. west of this pit for about ½ mile, to a point 450 ft. S.E. of the exposure in the lane. North of the Cornbrash is a belt of orange sand (Kellaways?), followed by khaki-coloured clay; south of it are tough marls and stone of the Forest Marble, difficult to penetrate and readily distinguishable from the Kimmeridge Clay abutting against them on the south.

At the east end of the inlier the Cornbrash and Forest Marble outcrops end abruptly against Kimmeridge Clay on the same level. The straight boundary appears to be an intra-Cretaceous dip fault, but the same effect could be produced by a sharp undulation of the nearly flat-lying Abbotsbury Strike Fault, formerly steep but turned over by the Tertiary folding.[1] Eastwards the rest of the Sutton Poyntz pericline is excavated entirely in the hanging wall of the Abbotsbury Fault. The discrepancy in strike of the rocks in the hanging and footwalls is noteworthy, as also the disappearance of the Abbotsbury Fault under the Upper Greensand and the unconformity between the Upper Greensand and the Portland and Purbeck Beds. There must have been intra-Cretaceous folding, although the sudden steep northward plunge of the Portland and Purbeck Beds (70° ±) close to the margin of the Cretaceous probably is mainly a Tertiary effect.

Another extremely interesting locality is the nameless hill spur of Portland Beds below East Hill, ¼ mile N.E. of Sutton Poyntz. About 1,100 ft. N.E. of the Springhead Hotel the lane crosses a band of white limestone believed to be a cementstone in the Kimmeridge Clay (not The White Band, however). Higher up the Scar Cementstone and oyster bed at the top of the Portland Sand are crossed, well exposed through the turf, and dipping 70°-80° N. The lane passes from this almost directly on to Upper Greensand, which is well exposed in a long section; although a little distance east, up a parallel traverse, cherty Portland Stone crops out and has been quarried. There follows on the stone a small thickness of clay (Gault or basal Upper Greensand?) and then the Upper Greensand to its normal thickness but most abnormally placed (as Pl. XIX shows).

---

[1] This interpretation was once favoured by me and has been championed by Dr. E. B. Bailey in discussions on the spot, and he asks me to refer to it. It appears to me, however, that the lines forming the east and west boundaries of the inliers pass under the Gault and that the inliers were determined by pre-Gault erosion acting on pre-existing irregularities. If so the boundaries must have existed before the Tertiary movements turned the thrust plane over into its nearly flat position. (*See* p. 271.)

The wedge of Upper Greensand which is here thrust up over
the Lower Chalk was apparently deposited upon Purbeck or
Portland Stone and so belongs to the south side (hanging wall)
of the Abbotsbury Fault. Its displacement (maximum about
200 ft.) is a measure of the shift at this point due to the Tertiary
reactivation of the fault in the reverse direction.

The smaller wedge adjacent on the west, which is exposed in
the lane, was shifted only about 80 feet. The lane section shows
it to be composed of several successive thin sheets of Greensand,
Chloritic Marl and Chalk Marl, repeated by gently-undulating
but on the whole flat-lying thrust-faults. The structure here
(Figs. 57, 58) was proved in February, 1938, by clearing the section

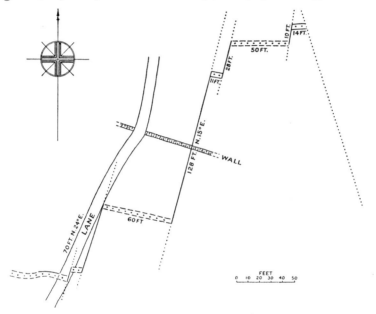

⌄⌄⌄ *Outcrops of Calc-Grit in Upper Greensand*

Fig. 57.—*Faults in East Hill near Sutton Poyntz* (H.J.O.W. and W.J.A.)

at the instigation and with the help of Dr. E. B. Bailey. The chalk
in front of the thrust Greensand is indurated, as may be seen in
the lane higher up, and in a small pit beside it, 300 yds. E.S.E. of
the springs of Spring Bottom. This last pit shows a few feet of
hard greyish to nodular chalk, without flints and without distinguishable bedding, which Mr. Osborne White is uncertain
whether to place in the Lower or Middle Chalk. The flat-lying
thrusts presumably continue into and lose themselves in the chalk
of East Hill, after the manner of those at Durdle Cove and
Scratchy Bottom, near Lulworth (*see* p. 289). This may partly
account for a dip of 53° N. recorded by Strahan in the chalk
escarpment higher up the same lane cutting, just above the 400

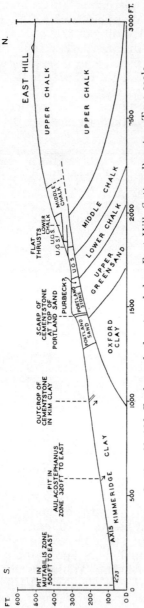

FIG. 58.—*Section N. 12° E. through the spur below East Hill, Sutton Poyntz. True scale.*

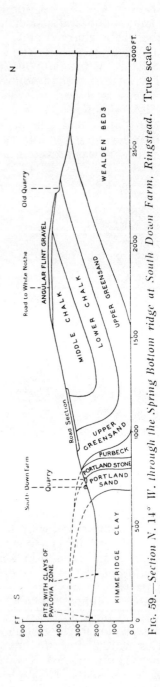

FIG. 59.—*Section N. 14° W. through the Spring Bottom ridge at South Down Farm, Ringstead. True scale.*

foot contour. Dips of 42° and 45° were recorded by Strahan in Chalk Marl and flinty chalk respectively in two old pits 450 ft. and 360 ft. east of the White Horse.

The spur of Portland Beds below East Hill, Sutton Poyntz, standing out like a flying buttress from the escarpment wall, is a relic of a once continuous sheet of Portland and Purbeck rocks which formerly overspread the inliers on either side and joined up with the other spur north of Hall's Farm, Osmington. The debris of Portland and Purbeck Beds scattered thickly on the Oxford Clay below White Horse Hill may represent the last vestiges of the lost parts of the sheet, though much was probably removed by the Gault erosion. On the other hand, the fact that this spur was left where it is, just as the fact that the corresponding spur begins were it does north of Hall's Farm, is probably due to erosion having been guided and its effects predetermined by pre-Greensand dip faults.[1] At these places blocks of the hanging wall rocks were thrown northward and lowered after the formation of the Abbotsbury Strike Fault but before the deposition of the Greensand. In this position they escaped attack and perhaps partial removal by pre-Greensand erosion as well as by much later subaerial denudation. How nearly pre-Greensand erosion achieved total removal of the Portland Beds in some places on the south side of the Abbotsbury Fault is shown at the east end of the pericline, $\frac{1}{4}$ mile N.E. of Hall's Farm, Osmington.

The Tertiary movements involved the area in a certain amount of monoclinal folding, which gave the Upper Greensand and basal Chalk their present average dip of 40°-50° along the present escarpment edge, and bent over the fault plane through a corresponding number of degrees to the north. Hence the flat-lying thrusts at the East Hill spur can be the direct projections in the Greensand and Chalk of reversed movements on the Abbotsbury Fault plane, which originally dipped at least 45° S. at this point, probably more; and there is no difficulty in picturing the flat thrust here as continuous with the rather steeply southward hading Abbotsbury Fault mapped across the low ground on either side, although the continuity is broken by the dip faults or undulations already mentioned (Fig. 58).

POXWELL PERICLINE

The Poxwell Pericline is a sharply-folded pre-Albian structure, running due E.-W., about 1 mile in length and about $\frac{1}{4}$ mile wide. It is almost continuous with the narrow east end of the Sutton Poyntz Pericline, but the two are separated by a saddle of Portland Stone (wrongly mapped as Lower Purbeck Beds on the 1904 edition of Sheet 342). The centre is hollowed out to form two narrow elliptical inliers of Kimmeridge Clay, surrounded by an almost continuously

---

[1] See footnote on p. 268 above. Professor O. T. Jones suggested to the writer during an excursion on the ground in March, 1939 that he believed the dip faults to be tear faults.

traceable outcrop of the hard cementstone at the top of the Portland Sand, which here as around Chalbury and Upwey forms a
scar showing through the turf. On the outer slopes to the south
the Lower Purbeck limestones have been extensively quarried and
afford numerous dip-measurements of 25° to 45° S. The best
section is in the road-cutting described on p. 143. Along the north
outcrop of the Purbeck Beds, as usual, the dip is steeper, presumably owing to drag. A quarry south of Moigns Down Barn
shows a dip of 64° N.; in the old quarries south-west of Poxwell,
near Pixon Barn, the dip is about 45° N.; and ⅔ mile west-south-
west of Poxwell, the Cypris Freestone dips 70° N.

Owing to its apparently simple structure and perfect closure,
the Poxwell Pericline was selected by the D'Arcy Exploration Co.
for their first deep boring in Dorset to possible oil-bearing
horizons in the Corallian Beds. As a preliminary, three shallow
test-wells were sunk on a N.-S. line on the east side of the road
south of Poxwell. The most northerly hole was located about
400 ft. S.E. of Poxwell House and was sunk to a depth of 62 ft.
in Chalk, of which the lowest 22 ft. were identified by the micro-
fauna as Upper Chalk, Cortestudinarium Zone. The next hole,
120 ft. farther south, passed through 20 ft. of detritus, consisting of Purbeck limestone mixed with Chalk, and then
through Middle Chalk, Labiatus Zone, for a further 20 feet.
The third hole, about 160-170 ft. farther south again, penetrated Purbeck beds to a depth of about 120 ft. (exact base
uncertain as no cores were taken until lower down), then
Portland Stone to 171 ft., and Portland Sand to 230 feet. At
this level the sands suddenly began to contain abundant
glauconite. Cores were taken in this lower part of the boring and
showed Portland Sand resting on unmistakable Upper Greensand, the latter of an intense green colour. Upper Greensand,
sand and silts with one 2-foot hard band, were passed through
from 230 ft. to 432 ft., at which depth the boring was discontinued.[1]

Since no cherty beds were met with, the Upper Greensand
must have been entered well below its top, and yet almost uniform
sandy beds were penetrated for 200 ft., which is probably 50 ft.
more than the total normal thickness of the Upper Greensand and
Gault. Hence the beds must be dipping very steeply, presumably
as the result of drag below the fault.

It was thought at first that the fault passed in the third boring
at a depth of 230 ft. was probably the same as that which seemed
to be indicated at or above a depth of 20 ft. in the middle boring,
but in reality the fault, as appeared later, probably passes out at
the surface a little way south of the middle boring, where the
ground is deeply covered in hillwash. It must be a reversed fault
or overthrust to the north, hade about 30° S., and the effects are
in harmony with what has been described above of the Tertiary

[1] A. H. Taitt and P. E. Kent, 'Notes on an Examination of the Poxwell Anticline,
Dorset,' Geol. Mag., vol. lxxvi, 1939, pp. 173-181.

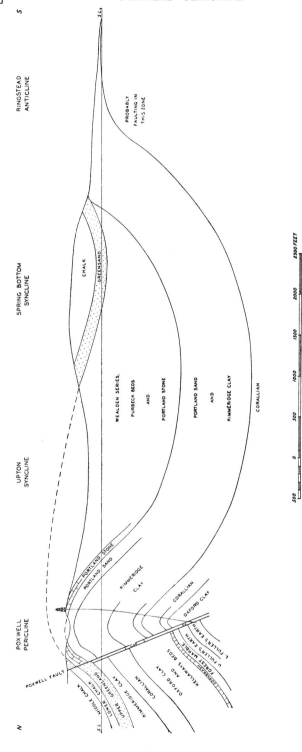

Fig. 60.—*Geological section through the deep boring for oil at Poxwell and southward to the sea.*
By A. H. Tait and P. E. Kent.

movements along the Abbotsbury Fault at, for instance, East Hill, Sutton Poyntz. There too, it will be remembered, it is probable that the Upper Greensand of the ' foreland ' passes beneath the Portland Beds, separated by the fault-plane. It is probable, in view of facts to be mentioned presently, that if No. 3 boring at Poxwell had been continued deeper, the Upper Greensand would have been found to rest on Lower Kimmeridge Clay or Corallian Beds.

In the light of this information a site was chosen for the Poxwell deep boring on the crest of the southern rim of the pericline, at a point about 1,000 ft. east of the ancient stone circle north of Upton. The derrick is shown in Pl. XVIII. The boring proved Portland Stone to 28 ft., Portland Sand to 160 ft., Kimmeridge Clay to 1,002 ft., Corallian Beds to about 1,300 ft., Oxford Clay to 1,530 feet. At 1,530 ft., having passed through the highest 185 ft. of Oxford Clay, the boring crossed a fault into Forest Marble, with the *Goniorhynchia boueti* bed at 1,603 ft., and then passed into Lower Fuller's Earth with *Oppelia fusca* at 1,646 ft. Finally the boring was stopped at 1,666 ft. in Fuller's Earth.[1]

If estimates of the thickness of the Oxford Clay in the Weymouth district are right, the fault must have cut out about 300 ft. of Oxford Clay, all the Cornbrash (20 ft.), and at least 30 ft. of Forest Marble; total 350 feet. Since in West Dorset *Oppelia fusca* is found only near the base of the Fuller's Earth, whereas it occurred here only 40 ft. below the Boueti Bed, there must at some level below 1,604 ft. be a second fault cutting out at least 200 ft., perhaps 300 ft., of Fuller's Earth. Hence the two faults, at least 75 ft. apart, have a combined throw of 500-600 ft.; and to produce the observed effects, they must both be normal downthrows to the south. The beds below the faults have a dip of about 10°, those above have dips increasing downwards from about 20° to 30° or more.

The cross-section of the Poxwell Pericline through the pits and deep boring (Fig. 60) shows that the structure is only explicable by invoking movements in opposite directions at two different periods. The reversed movement affected the Greensand and Chalk; the normal movement, although so much greater, did not, hence was pre-Albian. Here again, then, is the picture that has already become familiar in tracing the Abbotsbury Fault eastwards.

Some information regarding the structure of the Chalk immediately to the north of the Poxwell Pericline is provided by Mr. Osborne White's careful notes on all the existing chalk-pits, on which the following remarks are based.

An exposure perhaps 300 ft. from the fault on the E. side of Poxwell Drove, 760 yds. W. by S. of Poxwell Church, is in

---

[1] For details see Taitt and Kent, 1939, *loc. cit.*

Middle Chalk, Labiatus Zone, hardened and flaggy, with a high dip, apparently about 70° N. The rock is hard enough to protrude through the turf in the drove close by. Northward there seems to be a sharp flattening of dip, for a pit about 450 yds. E. of Poxwell Church shows less hardened but firm blocky Upper Chalk, Coranguinum Zone, dipping 30° N. This is probably about 400 ft. from the fault.

At Moigns Down Barn, 5 furlongs E. of Poxwell Church, is a somewhat problematic pit, again in the Labiatus Zone. It is less than 200 ft. from the fault, and Strahan noted a dip of 40° N. This may have been in the southern part of the pit, now obscured by talus, for in the recently-worked northern part the dip appears to be about 20° N.E. ' An ill-defined belt of shattering and crushing runs nearly vertically (with slight S. inclination) through the section.'

Finally, 800 yds. N. of Holworth, an old pit in Lower Chalk yielded Strahan a dip-reading of 35° N.N.E. This cannot be much more than 100 ft. from the fault, which here appears to die out.

CHALDON PERICLINE

The Chaldon Pericline, with a length of 2 miles and maximum breadth of ¾ mile, is completely surrounded by Upper Cretaceous rocks with quaquaversal dip, and so is Tertiary. Within it, however, there is a sharper pericline of pre-Albian date, whose crest appears as an elliptical inlier of Purbeck Beds, surrounded by Wealden, and situated close to the middle of the north rim. On the north margin of the Purbeck inlier the Upper Greensand oversteps from Wealden Beds on to Middle Purbeck Beds, thus proving the pre-Albian date of the inner structure. The crest-maxima coincide.

As the Survey's mapping of the Purbeck inlier seemed doubtful, the D'Arcy Exploration Co. in March-April, 1937, undertook a re-investigation of the structure. Ten pits and numerous auger holes were sunk under the direction of Mr. A. H. Taitt, whose resulting map and section are reproduced as Fig. 61.

Some old quarries south-east and south of the crest still show 4 ft. of porcellanous limestone, *Cyrena* limestone, and marls, with fish teeth and *Cypridea,* belonging probably to the Middle Purbeck, and dipping 11° S.E. and 10° S. On the north side of the crest Mr. Taitt proved Cinder Bed 1 ft. below the surface, dipping 10-12° N. Towards the north-west he proved that, as surmised, the Middle Purbeck is followed by north-westward dipping Upper Purbeck clays, which swing round the Middle Purbeck in an elliptical outcrop instead of striking straight to the north-west under the Cretaceous as shown on the 1904 edition of the map. On the north flank, by means of augering, he was able to prove the basal pebble bed of the Albian, a ferruginous, sandy, glauconitic clay with pebbles up to 1 in. in diameter, of quartz,

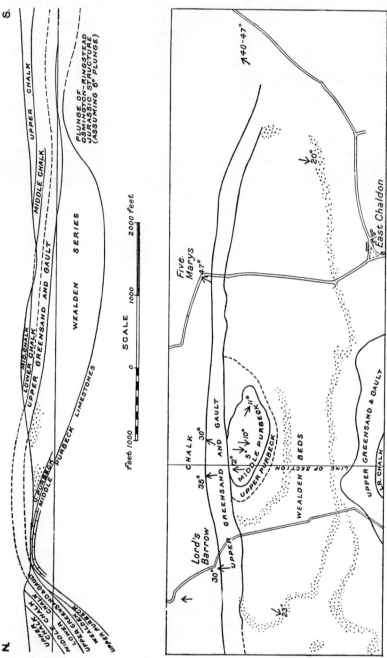

Fig. 61.—*Geological map and section of the Chaldon structure.* By A. H. Taitt, 1937.

black chert, and dark crystalline limestone, underlying from 10 ft. to 13½ ft. of sandy glauconitic clays with streaks of ferruginous sand, and resting on hard limestone, presumed Middle Purbeck. The depths at which the pebble-bed and limestone were reached in two holes 18 ft. apart on a N.-S. line indicated a dip of 24° N. for the Purbeck-Greensand junction.

Two sandy bands in the Wealden Beds were also mapped by Mr. Taitt from surface indications. They have a roughly concentric outcrop, as shown in Fig. 61. Of one of these bands Strahan saw two exposures, which gave him dip-readings of 23° S.S.E. about 280 yds. N.W. of Northground Dairy and 20° S. about 380 yds. N.E. of Gostelowes Farm.

The previously uncertain question is now settled, therefore, that there is no fault along the inside of the north rim of the pericline, between the Purbeck-Wealden rocks and the Albian. The discordance is due entirely to pre-Albian folding and erosion.[1]

Nevertheless, the idea cannot be so readily dismissed that there is a probability of the Abbotsbury Fault continuing its course as far east as Chaldon, for it has now been traced for 12 miles from Abbotsbury to Poxwell, and the Poxwell borings proved that there, only 2 miles away, it was still very active, with its usual pre-Albian and Tertiary double throws. Since this was written a boring by the D'Arcy Exploration Co. at Chaldon Down has proved that the Gault there rests on Lower Purbeck Beds.

The Jurassic-Albian succession of the Chaldon inlier is that proper to the south side of the Abbotsbury Fault. Hence, if the fault is present near Chaldon it should be sought north of the inlier. There does, in fact, run east and west along the north side of the high Chalk ridge of the Five Marys and Lords Barrow a zone of complication which Strahan marked on the Survey Map (Sheet 342) as ' Probable Fault ', shown by a dotted line 1 mile in length, accompanied by the words ' Much shattered flinty chalk '. Examination of the ground and of the chalk pits leads me to believe that this line may represent a continuation, or more likely a separate branch, *en échelon,* of the Abbotsbury Fault, expressed here at the surface entirely within the chalk. The dips and shattering along this line are consonant with the idea that there has been a reversed fault, upthrown on the south side, with the formation of the usual drag, or monocline passing into drag.

The most important fact is that the dip of the Chalk steepens suddenly a short distance north of the escarpment and then flattens rapidly in the country below. This is first noticeable north of the saddle or ' greensand bridge ' which separates the Poxwell and Chaldon periclines. In the Upper Greensand about 200 yds. north of Holworth, Strahan observed a dip of 50° N. In a Chalk Marl pit about 500 yds. N.W. of Holworth, at the edge of the

---

[1] Bristow mapped a fault in the original Survey Map, Sheet 17, Old Series (1855); Strahan took it out in the New Series map; I tentatively replaced it. (*Geol. Mag.* 1936, fig. 5.)

Chalk outcrop, he marked a dip of 15° N. (confirmed by
Mr. White). From 400 to 600 yds. farther north, in two old pits
(now overgrown) south-west of Owermoigne Down Barn, he
observed dips of 45° N. and 44° N. This is close to the line of
Strahan's ' probable fault ' if projected a mile westward. After
crossing the line, some 300 yds. farther north, the dip decreases to
13° N.W. in a pit 260 yds. N.N.E. of Owermoigne Down Barn,
which Mr. White assigns tentatively to the Quadratus Zone.
Another 600 yds. farther north the dip is 3° N. in the Mucronata
Zone in a pit beside the main road 400 yds. S.W. of Owermoigne
Church.

This south-north traverse is probably typical of any that could
be taken north of the Chaldon inlier if exposures permitted. The
north-eastward curve of the rim of the inlier, however, deprives us
of the region of initial low dips found north of Holworth. In
fact, towards its north-east corner, the inlier has cut forward into
the region of high dips close to the presumed fault.

Near Lord's Barrow there are two highly instructive sections.[1]
On the south face of the Chalk escarpment a pit, by the roadside
60 yds. S.E. of the barrow, shows Lower Chalk dipping 30° N.,
with two conspicuous side-planes inclined 30°-40° S. On the
opposite face of the hill, 200 yds. farther north in the direction of
dip, but actually rather north-west, is another pit (130 yds. N.W.
of Lord's Barrow), in Upper Chalk, Coranguinum Zone, dipping
50°-55° N. Strahan marked the dip here as 62° N., perhaps in
the older northern part of the pit. Mr. White observed ' slight
crushing in thin belts, of which the most distinct, 2 ins. thick,
slopes N.E. at 35°. Striation frequent on joint-cheeks '.

The ' probable fault ' presumably runs not far north of this pit,
along the foot of the hill.

A large pit, 500 yds. N.W. of Five Mary's, ⅓ mile farther east
in the direction of strike, but probably less than 200 yds. north of
the fault, seems to be on the edge of the region of southward turn-
up and associated packing. It is in the Mucronata Zone and
shows a great deal of disturbance, but Mr. White believes the
general dip to be about 25° N.[2] The north face shows ' a belt of
close cleavage, inclined 70° W.', and ' narrow crush-belts, with
associated slickenside-striation, running nearly parallel with the
bedding.' The west face, towards the south end, has ' two parallel
belts of flaggy cleavage, respectively about 2 ft. and 10 ft. wide,
about vertical (with a slight north-easterly convexity), and striking
5° west of north. North of them their appears a series of ironstained crush-belts, inclined about 20° N., and in a few cases
visibly continuous with similar belts in the north face. The

---

[1] Mr. Osborne White has provided detailed notes on all the chalk-pits north and
north-east of the inlier, and his notes supply most of the facts on which the following remarks are based.

[2] On a previous visit I obtained a reading of 32° in the western part of the
north face of the pit. Strahan (Sheet 342) published a dip reading of ' Abt. 2° '
north, which may be a misprint.

accompanying striations are deeply engraved. Intersecting these dipward crush-belts are two others; one straight and inclined 60° S.; the other similarly inclined near the top of the section, but curving south as it approaches the quarry floor '.

The remaining chalk pits round the pericline can only be referred to briefly. Farther east, as the rim of the pericline converges towards the presumed line of the ' probable fault ' (which may run rather south of east instead of rather north of east as drawn by Strahan), the dips along the escarpment edge increase. Two old Lower Chalk pits between Lord's Barrow and Five Marys were reopened by Mr. Taitt to expose the top of the Upper Greensand, which was found to dip at 30°-35° N. By the roadside 60 yds. S. of Five Marys a pit shows Middle Chalk, Labiatus Zone, dipping 45°-50° N.N.E., with some slickensiding. Another pit in the same zone, 320 yds. S.W. of Winfrith Rectory Farm, in the north-east corner of the inlier, shows dips varying from 40° to 47° N.N.E., again with some slickensiding. Since the dip is here in the same direction as at Five Marys, although the rim of the pericline has turned southward through 30°, the inference is that this dip is controlled by the ' probable fault ' and not by the Chaldon Pericline. A much gentler dip which is more likely to be controlled by the pericline was formerly visible 350 yds. farther southeast, in two small openings in a hedgebank on Lower Chalk, where Strahan marked it as 7° N.E. At the south east corner of the rim of the pericline a lime-kiln pit, 450 yds. east of Chaldon Vicarage Farm, shows that the Lower Chalk has swung round to dip 12° S.E.

The ' probable fault ' may break up into several branches or flexures towards Winfrith before it dies out eastwards.

The question of a possible further dome or pericline still completely rooted by Chalk, in the Vines Down-Belhuish Farm area, was exhaustively investigated in 1937 by the D'Arcy Exploration Co. Samples were taken from numerous trial pits and auger holes. From study of these samples Mr. E. W. Mitchell found it possible to identify enough foraminifera of zonal value to enable a structural contour map on the top of the Middle Chalk to be constructed (Fig. 62). This map shows no indication of a saddle south of Winfrith, between the Chaldon Pericline and Vines Down. It indicates that, so far as expression in the Chalk is concerned, the two anticlinal folds of Chaldon and Ringstead gradually coalesce eastwards and fade away as one broad roll, plunging gently eastward under the Lulworth Tertiary beds.

THE OSMINGTON-RINGSTEAD FOLDS AND FAULTS[1]

UPTON SYNCLINE

This structure is of pre-Albian date. The southern limb is overstepped by the Greensand to a diminishing extent westwards,

---

[1] The folding map at end, Pl. XIX, should be used in conjunction with pp. 279 ff.

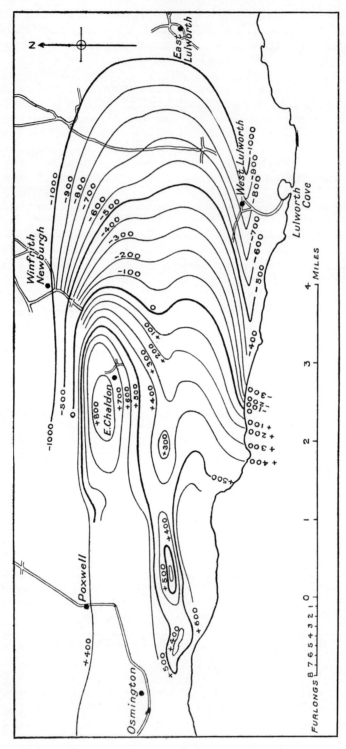

FIG. 62.—*Contours on top of the Middle Chalk in feet above and below sea-level in the Lulworth area. By A. H. Taitt, based on foraminiferal zones determined by E. W. Mitchell.*

in which direction the syncline narrows and approaches closer to the south side of the Poxwell-Sutton Poyntz Anticline. The axis passes through Upton and 100 yds. north of Osmington Church, whence it strikes down the valley between the high road and the dairy, bringing basal Purbeck tufa down almost to the 200-foot contour. On the east side of Winslow Hill no synclinal structure is apparent, but on the west side of the hill it is again strongly developed and continues across the Preston valley, along the reservoir ridge, and passes into the Boiling Rock Syncline (*see* p. 263).

The Upton Syncline and the Poxwell Pericline seem to have combined to form a single positive unit during the Tertiary folding. It appears that a gentle anticline in the Cretaceous rocks was formed over them.[1]

SPRING BOTTOM SYNCLINE

This syncline is a much shallower trough of Tertiary date, developed in the Albian and Lower and Middle Chalk which were deposited unconformably upon the southern limb of the Upton syncline. It has resulted in the survival of a tongue of these rocks $\frac{1}{2}$ mile wide extending for $2\frac{1}{2}$ miles westward from north of Holworth House to south of Osmington village. It is characterized by sharp upturns along part of the south side, which will be described below, but the rest of the structure is gently synclinal. At the point where the tongue crosses the stream north of Osmington Mills the synclinal appearance is exaggerated by extensive slips of Chalk and Greensand, which are exposed in a quarry on the 150-foot contour on the west slope of Spring Bottom Hill, and in the stream banks.

RINGSTEAD ANTICLINE

This anticline extends for a visible distance of $3\frac{1}{2}$ miles in the Jurassic rocks from Ham Cliff to Holworth House and is prolonged for a further 2 miles or more in the Chalk of Chaldon Down, east of which it gradually fades away.

At Ham Cliff it begins as an arch in the Oxford Clay and Lower Calcareous Grit, and the south limb is cut by a normal strike fault downthrowing north, which throws up Oxford Clay at the tip of Redcliff Point. From Shortlake eastward to Osmington Mills the sea has cut back to the hard Corallian rocks of the north limb, which becomes very steep, with dips of 50°–60° N. under Black Head and the mud slides. The various hard limestone bands in the Corallian Beds hereabouts run as a series of parallel ledges along shore, exposed at low tide. The Kimmeridge Clay likewise dips steeply inland under the Upper Greensand and

---

[1] According to Strahan (*Purbeck Memoir*, p. 131) ' the axis of the later anticline is not far from coinciding with the axis of the earlier syncline in the Chaldon Inlier ', but there seems no evidence for the direction of dip of the Wealden Beds at the southern margin of the Chaldon Inlier where it is widest.

Chalk; but although Strahan's mapping proves that there is sub-
stantial unconformity below the Gault, the contact is now so much
slipped that it is impossible to disentangle the pre-Albian tilting
from the Tertiary tilting in the same direction which gave the sharp
upturn to the southern edge of the Spring Bottom Syncline. This
southern edge and its complicated faulting is crossed at Osmington
Mills.

Approaching the Mills from the west along the shore, we cross
the first and largest fault about 700 ft. due west of the coastguards'
cottages. This is a downthrow south, bringing Lower Kimmeridge Clay against Nothe Clay (Fig. 63). It runs nearly due
east and crosses the stream, in the bed of which Osmington Oolite
and Trigonia Beds can be seen opposite the coastguards' cottages
and Kimmeridge shales opposite the Picnic Inn. Farther east
this fault cannot be traced, but it probably runs past Ringstead
and under the Gault between Holworth House and Holworth
Cottages, causing the repetition of the Portland-Purbeck outcrop
at Holworth House.

The broad effect of this strike fault is to step back the outcrop
of the Corallian Beds southwards. The outcrop of steeply tilted
Corallian Beds at Black Head and the mud slides is on its
upthrow side; the relatively horizontal outcrop east of the Mills
belongs to its downthrow side. Two structural parts of the intra-
Cretaceous Ringstead Anticline are thus brought on to the same
level : the steep north limb and the flat axial region. There can
be little doubt that east of the Mills, near Upton House, the Corallian Beds roll over northwards a short distance inland from the
cliffs and at sea-level (underground) they probably dip at 40-50° N.
like their former continuation in the north limb seen in the stream,
and like the Portland and Purbeck Beds at Holworth House.

This broad effect of the Osmington-Ringstead Strike Fault is,
however, masked by a belt of intense complication at Osmington
Mills, due presumably to the superimposition of Tertiary faulting
and folding upon the intra-Cretaceous, as along the Ridgeway
line. The visible outcrops of solid rock are marked on the sketch-
map (Fig. 63), together with dips where they have been measured.
Much of the area is a mosaic which cannot be restored to its
original condition on the fragmentary evidence available. One
feature stands out, however : a tightly-folded asymmetric and
much faulted anticlinal nose closing eastwards and admirably
dissected on the foreshore at low tide west of the Mills. The north
limb, in which the Corallian sequence is complete, represents the
north limb of the Ringstead Anticline, shifted south by the big
strike fault discussed above, but with its dips over-steepened from
45-50° to 75-90°. The south limb is incomplete, the whole
Osmington Oolite Series faulted out by a strike fault. It is a
' spurious limb ', for its dips decrease from 90° to 10° in 100 yards.
This little structure, in fact, is far too small to be identified with
the main anticline which causes the northward dips from Ham

Cliff eastwards.[1]　It is only an incidental detail or crumple in the major anticline, probably due to Tertiary compressive forces.

The most remarkable feature at the Mills is a cake of north-east dipping Osmington Oolite (Littlemore Clay facies, with the

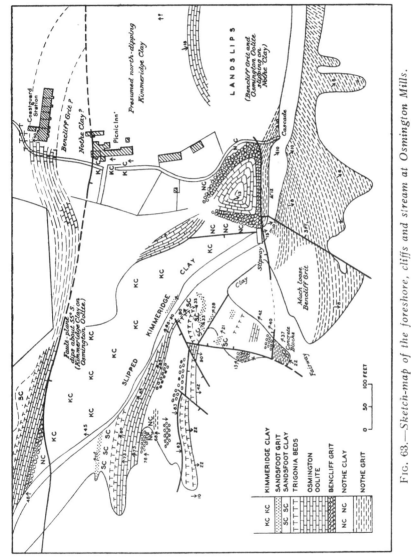

FIG. 63.—Sketch-map of the foreshore, cliffs and stream at Osmington Mills.

Pisolite at the base) crossed by the footpath from the bus terminus to the boat slipway.　It forms the crest of the col between the sea and the stream, and on the seaward side it can be seen to rest upon Kimmeridge Clay (Aulacostephanus Zone) which extends to the foot of the cliff.　The plane of contact slopes south-eastward, and

[1] *Cf.* Strahan, *Purbeck Memoir,* 1898, p. 32.

at first sight an overthrust is suggested. It is more likely, however, that this is a landslip from higher ground formerly standing on the site of the present shore; the structure there revealed is so complicated that it cannot be said with confidence that Osmington Oolite could not at one time have existed at a higher level than the supposed slip. (*Cf.* the exposure of vertical Oolite only 200 ft. distant).

Underneath this anomalous cake of Oolite runs an important fault, apparently due north-and-south, separating Kimmeridge Clay and Nothe Clay, which latter forms the base of the triangular headland west of the cascade. There must be another fault somewhere between this headland and the Kimmeridge Clay at the Picnic Inn, but its direction can only be conjectured. There is at present no evidence for either of the two step faults introduced by Strahan to explain these difficulties.[1]

On the corner by the slipway is seen another fault of rather flat hade downthrowing north, which brings Bencliff Grit into contact with Nothe Grit and can be traced round the cliff until it passes inland just before reaching the cascade. Beyond the cascade a bay in the cliffs is filled with landslips of Corallian limestones foundering on the Nothe Clay. The slips seem to extend to the stream bank, and as some very large masses are involved, it seems hopeless to disentangle slipping from faulting. It is quite possible that the whole of the triangular headland west of the cascade is a slipped block, and therefore that the flat-lying and irregular fault-plane beneath it, cutting out the Nothe Clay, is not of tectonic origin at all. The same contact of Bencliff Grit on Nothe Grit, however, is continued between tide marks on the rocky promontory at the west side of the boat fairway.

East of Osmington Mills the coast more nearly coincides with the axial region of the Ringstead Anticline, where dips are low. The minor rolls within this region are well seen from the top of the cliff east of the Mills when the tide is low and displays the curving Pool, Frenchman's and Hannah's Ledges. Seaward of these but skirting the coast at Bran Point and continuing off shore for about 1 mile eastward is another minor roll. This is a drag-anticline adjacent to the Bran Point Fault, which throws down to the north and gives rise to the Ringstead Ledges, made of Osmington Oolite and Trigonia Beds (Fig. 10, p. 43). Probably the axial line of the Ringstead Fold, if there are not several, passes through the low ground just behind the shore at Ringstead, then crosses the head of Ringstead Bay, to disappear under the cliff of White Nothe.

The north limb with its steep dips and interesting Jurassic-Albian junction passes inland from Osmington Mills along the foot of the down. The Portland Beds cross under the down from

---

[1] *Op. cit.*, 1898, p. 31. The promontory on which the two faults are shown to meet on Strahan's map does not exist; there is only one such promontory where Strahan, following the old edition of the ordnance map, showed two (*vide* the new 6-inch ordnance map, Sheet LIV, N.W.).

north of the Mills to crop out for ½ mile at Ringstead Dairy and South Down Farm, and a small patch of Purbeck Beds also appears. Old quarries and a steep road leading up from South Down Farm give a succession of small exposures (Fig. 59, p. 270). Just north-east of the farm a pit shows the Basal Shell Bed and top of the Portland Sand dipping 50° N.N.W., and 200 yds. to the west Strahan observed Portland Stone dipping 82° in the same direction. The dip in the lower part of the Upper Greensand is much flatter. In the road about 250 ft. north-west of the farm hard bands above the middle of the Greensand dip only about 20° N.N.W. Above this the dip increases rapidly, and a little higher up the road the Lower and Middle Chalk are well displayed dipping at 80° to 90° and much sheared. The Lower Chalk and top of the Greensand also seem nearly vertical in an old pit in the side of the coombe immediately west of these exposures. Verticality in the southern limb of the Tertiary Spring Bottom Syncline seems to be quite local, and may be due to the coincidence at this point of the Tertiary southern limb and the Portland Stone in the northern limb of the intra-Cretaceous Ringstead Anticline.[1] In ½ mile both to the west and to the east dips in the Chalk are much flatter. Beside the road to Ringstead a quarry and old road-cutting above show good exposures of Lower and Middle Chalk, dipping 12° N.W.

At the east end of the Ringstead amphitheatre the northward dipping Purbeck and Portland Beds are shifted a distance of 2,300 ft. southward, to outcrop at Burning Cliff and Holworth House (Pl. XI, A). At first sight this appears to be due to a N.-S. dip fault which can be seen to throw the base of the Purbeck Beds nearly against the White Band near the middle of the Kimmeridge Clay. But the dip is 30° and since the throw of the dip fault is under 500 ft., this fault could not by itself produce a shift of more than 350 ft. in the outcrop. To overcome this difficulty Strahan postulated a second dip fault about 200 yds. farther west which should bring in an intermediate outcrop of Portland Beds at South Holworth Cottages; but as stated elsewhere there is no evidence for either fault or outcrop: the bluff at the cottages is slipped Upper Greensand. The true explanation is most likely that the greater part of the shift in the Portland Beds is due to an intra-Cretaceous strike fault, probably a continuation of the northernmost of the faults at Osmington Mills, which produces there a similar repetition of the Corallian outcrop, though at a lesser distance.

THE PURBECK FOLD

WHITE NOTHE TO BAT'S HEAD

On rounding White Nothe we enter the region which is entirely subordinated to the Purbeck Fold. The first section of

---

[1] *Cf.* the marked local effect of the Portland and Purbeck Beds during Tertiary reactivation at Green Hill, p. 266.

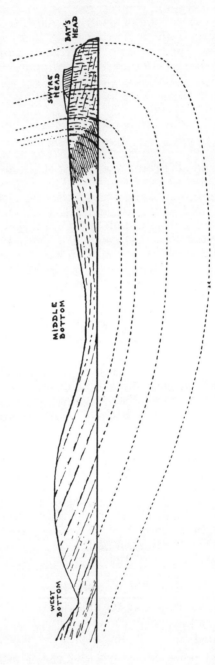

FIG. 64.—*Section of the chalk cliffs west of Bat's Head, with Swyre Head behind.* The shaded area represents the zone of packing in the axial plane of the foresyncline of the Purbeck fold. The lowest dotted line represents approximately the top of the Planus Zone. The highest chalk exposed belongs to the Quadratus Zone. Length of section 1 mile. True scale. (Reproduced from *Geol. Mag.*, 1936, p. 67.)

cliff, from White Nothe to Bat's Head, gives a very oblique cross-section of the foresyncline, an asymmetric syncline similar to that passing through Gould's Bottom, Upwey (p. 254), with gently but increasingly dipping north limb, extremely sharp upturn, and vertical south limb (Pl. XIV, A).

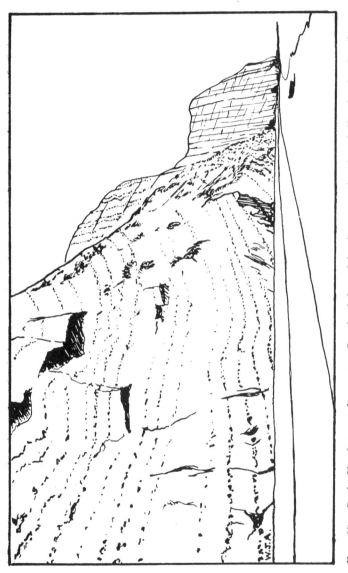

Fig. 65.—*Bat's Head from the west.* On the left and in the centre bands of flint in the Quadratus Zone chalk can be seen curving up towards the south. The zone of packed chalk rises up the cliff in the confused region opposite the boat and passes under the vertical portion forming the top of the cliff. Vertical to slightly inverted chalk down to Planus Zone forms the head on the right and is cut by numerous shears of group 3. (Reproduced from *Geol. Mag.*, 1936, p. 65.)

From White Nothe eastwards (Fig. 64) the Chalk falls steadily until Middle Bottom is reached, where for a short distance it becomes horizontal. This is the trough of the foresyncline, which passes inland through West Lulworth and eventually pitches under the Tertiary beds, where it is lost. [1]

A short distance east of Middle Bottom the bedding in the Chalk, clearly marked by bands of flints, begins to turn up towards the south at an increasing rate (Fig. 65). Where the upturn (northward dip) begins to steepen at the foot of the cliff, a belt of disturbance about 50 yds. wide interrupts the bedding. Here the chalk is apparently packed together, and slickensided in all directions. Beyond the belt of packing the bedding stands vertical and so continues to the tip of Bat's Head, where the lowest beds exposed belong to the Planus Zone. This is the middle limb of the fold.

The belt of packed and slickensided chalk rises upwards and northwards. Towards the top of the cliff vertical chalk can be seen to overlie it, the vertical bands of flints crumpling and losing themselves downwards in it, without, however, showing any appreciable drag in either direction. The packed rock is not a fault breccia, but it corresponds with the rock which on theoretical grounds ought to be found in the axial plane of the angular fore-syncline of a fold of this kind. For many years it was supposed to represent the ' Isle of Purbeck Thrust Fault ' (supposedly a thrust towards the south), and was so marked for $5\frac{1}{2}$ miles east-ward on the 1904 edition of the Survey Map (Sheet 342). But the ' hade ' is to the south, whereas such a fault would hade to the north; there is no displacement and no drag, and nothing is missing; and the packed rock does not resemble a fault-breccia. The structure was correctly interpreted by Thomas Webster in 1812,[2] and also correctly figured by W. D. Conybeare in 1822.[3]

BAT'S HEAD TO DURDLE DOOR AND DUNGY HEAD.

The mile of magnificent chalk cliffs in this stretch of coast present an unrivalled section of the vertical and overturned middle limb of the fold; and the promontory of Durdle Door provides an insight into the tectonic condition of the older rocks immediately behind.

At first sight the chalk seems to be riven in all directions by joints, shears, thrusts and slide-planes, but when the eye becomes familiarized these fall into a series of groups, characterized each by a particular effect and more or less constant inclination (dip). Some sequence-dating, moreover, becomes possible.[4]

Structures of the oldest group (1) are mainly developed in the overturned Upper Chalk and are best seen below Hambury Tout,

[1] W. J. Arkell, ' The Tectonics of the Purbeck and Ridgeway Faults,' *Geol. Mag.,* vol. lxxiii, 1936, pp. 64-8.

[2] T. Webster *in* Sir H. C. Englefield's *Picturesque Beauties of the Isle of Wight,* 1816, p. 195, and pl. xlvi. London.

[3] W. D. Conybeare, *in* W. D. Conybeare and W. Phillips. *Outlines of the Geology of England and Wales,* 1822, p. 113. London.

[4] For more detailed description of the sections see W. J. Arkell, ' Three Tectonic Problems of the Lulworth District,' *Quart. Journ. Geol. Soc.,* vol. xciv, 1938, pp. 1-45.

in the vicinity of Red Hole,[1] but also in Man-o'-War Cove and Durdle Cove (high up). They dip 60°-70° S. and coincide with the overturned bedding, but are deeply grooved up and down. They are believed to have been formed by the drawing out of the middle limb of the fold and the movement of the older beds individually upwards and northwards relative to the younger. Always associated with these are minor grooved shears (group 2), dipping 60°-70° N., neither cutting nor cut by group 1, and so apparently formed at the same time and by the same force. Groups 1 and 2 together give a conspicuous ' stepped ' appearance to the cliffs of Cortestudinarium Zone chalk below Hambury Tout.

Fig. 66.—*View of the west side of Bat's Head (looking east); Upper Chalk vertical, with numerous shears of group 3.* From a photograph.

A third group of shears is especially conspicuous at Bat's Head (Fig. 66) and Swyre Head, and again in the Middle Chalk of Durdle and Man-o'-War Head. They are flatter, dipping usually 25°-40° S. Here and there, as may be seen in Swyre Head and Durdle Cove, shears of this group become larger and acquire a still flatter inclination, until they develop into true thrusts dipping 0° to 20° S. To this group (3a) belong the well-known slide-planes in Durdle Cove, along which the sea has hollowed out a line of caves. They are best developed about the

_____
[1] A huge solution pipe containing Tertiary beds, sectioned by the cliff.

junction of Middle and Upper Chalk, mainly in Planus Zone, but others twice shift the Plenus Marl of the Lower Chalk. Always the hanging wall has moved northwards relative to the foot wall. The larger slides have a crush-breccia, varying in thickness from a few inches to a foot or more. The extent of the displacement in the largest example may be 12 feet.

The thrusts of group 3a cut the shears of groups 1 and 2, and their inclination and effects indicate that groups 3 and 3a resulted from horizontal earth-pressure applied after the middle limb had

FIG. 67.—*View of Man-o'-War Head* (*looking west*) *from below Red Hole.* F4-F4, group 4 fault, running through a crush-breccia and bringing vertical Planus Zone and Middle Chalk, cut into rhombs by shears of group 3, against overturned Micraster chalk with bands of flints dipping 115° N. and numerous shears of groups 1 and 2 and a few of group 3. (Reproduced from *Quart. Journ. Geol. Soc.,* vol. xciv, 1938, p. 35.)

reached its vertical and overturned position and could yield no more by folding.

The relatively soft Lower Chalk of Durdle Cove has been much jumbled and reduced by about 30% in thickness, as if by a grinding down into it of the hard gritstone bands at the top of the Upper Greensand. It will be noticed that there is a tendency for small discordances to develop within the Lower Chalk, the beds below dipping at 80°-90° N., those above them in the cliff resting across their edges with a smaller dip in the same direction.

This tendency finds greater expression farther east, where a peculiar type of fault (group 5) develops at or near the junction of the Lower and Middle Chalk. The best section is at St. Oswald's Bay (Fig 68). Here the lower part of the Lower Chalk is ground and reduced in thickness as at Durdle Cove, but the upper part retains its bedding fairly undisturbed, dipping 88°-98° N., in conformity with the Upper Greensand, up to the Plenus Marl. There then follows a fault dipping 55° N., which cuts out the Plenus Marl higher up and is succeeded by Middle Chalk. The latter is much sheared and indurated, but its bedding can be determined on careful inspection to dip 55° N., parallel to the fault plane. Drag joints in the Plenus Marl of the footwall indicate that the hanging wall moved upwards and southwards (relatively).

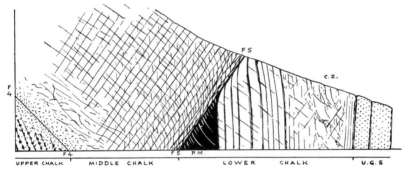

Fig. 68.—*Section at the east end of St. Oswald's Bay (looking east).* On the left, inverted Upper Chalk with flints, bounded by a fault of group 4 with thick crush-breccia. Above the fault, Middle Chalk dipping 55° N. (outcrop shortened to fit into diagram) with shears of group 3 (about 40-45° S.), which run into and are augmented by vertical fracture cleavage towards the base, which is a fault of group 5. Beneath this the Lower Chalk displays drag joints in the Plenus Marl (P.M.) and a thick crush-zone (C.Z.) and shears of group 3. (Reproduced from *Quart. Journ. Geol. Soc.,* vol. xciv, 1938, p. 37).

A similar fault (group 5) occurs at or near the junction of Lower and Middle Chalk at Lulworth Cove, Mupe Bay and Worbarrow, and it is best explained as an adjustment fault formed between the competent White Chalk and the less competent strata below during the folding. Below sea-level, and upside-down, there is probably a drag-fold in the incompetent beds adjacent to the White Chalk, analogous with the Lulworth Crumple in the Purbeck Beds adjacent to the Portland Stone, described on pp. 294-6. Both foot-wall and hanging-wall of the group 5 fault or faults are affected by shears of group 3, and since these shears have not been rotated by the faulting which rotated the bedding, the group 5 movements must have come to an end before the formation of the group 3 shears.

North of the group 5 fault at both ends of St. Oswald's Bay the Middle Chalk increases in dip until it is vertical, and it is

then cut off at or about the junction with the Upper Chalk by
another major strike-fault, which likewise causes a change of dip,
this time an increase northwards, and has the effect of cutting out
variable amounts of the Planus Zone. The best section is that
on the east side of Man-o'-War Head, the small promontory of
Chalk separating Man-o'-War and St. Oswald's Bays. Here a
remarkable curved line, a plane of final movement cutting a thick
crush-breccia which grades off into both hanging and foot walls,
rises from the beach and when some 8 ft. above it turns north-

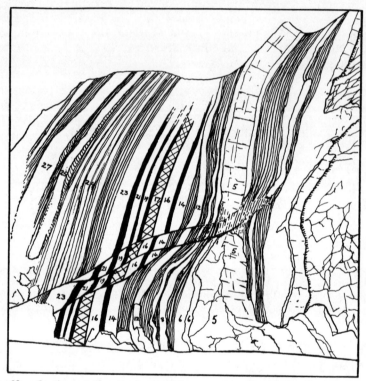

Fig. 69.—*Section of the Purbeck Beds on west side of Durdle promontory,
showing a composite southward overthrust below the Lulworth Crumple.* The
top bed (5) of the Cypris Freestones is pulled apart.   The appearance of
unconformity between beds 12 and 14 near top of cliff is due to perspective.
Scale of 3 feet shown by walking-stick leaning against base of bed 16.
(Reproduced from *Quart. Journ. Geol. Soc.*, vol. xciv, 1938, p. 8.)

wards and follows a shear-plane of group 1, dipping 62° S.
Rowe's investigations showed that the inverted chalk of the foot-
wall (to north) belongs to the Cortestudinarium Zone, while that
of the hanging wall (to south) belongs to the Planus Zone, which
is almost completely faulted out near the base of the cliff, being
reduced to 6 ft., almost all brecciated, from its original thickness
of 50 feet.   Upwards the Planus Zone thickens by the addition of
progressively higher beds.   (*See* Fig. 67).

The same fault also appears along the line of strike on the west side of Man-o'-War Head, where there is some dragging of the nearly vertical bedding of the hanging wall of such a kind as to indicate that this is a normal fault, downthrown to the south. The unusual attitudes of the bedding both above and below the fault-plane, however, are not conducive to the formation of drag, and most of the sections show none. Other conclusions also point to this and similar strike faults in the older formations on the south being normal faults with downthrow to the south, which have cut out considerable thicknesses of strata and have lowered the crestal region or brow of the fold on to a level with the middle limb.[1]

At St. Oswald's Bay (east side) the group 4 fault has utilized, for part at least of its course, a shear-plane of group 3, and so has a flatter southward inclination than usual. The group 4 faults are considered to represent the latest of all the movements of the Lulworth Chalk.

The Albian, Wealden and Purbeck rocks of the Durdle Promontory (Pl. VIII, B) have been attenuated in two different ways. Near the neck of the promontory it can be seen that the Gault and Wealden Beds dip at different angles, and the basement bed of the Gault can be traced, overstepping southwards across the Wealden. It is estimated that about 130 ft. of Upper Wealden Beds were removed by denudation before the deposition of the Gault. The Gault itself has about its full thickness on the west side of the promontory, but at beach-level on the east side it and the lower part of the Upper Greensand are largely cut out by a strike fault, the total thickness of the Albian of Man-o'-War Cove being only 60 ft., about half its thickness in Durdle Cove.

Another strike fault cuts out about half the Lower Wealden Beds, the whole Upper Purbeck, and part of the Middle Purbeck Beds, leaving a jumble of blocks of limestone, beef beds, etc. The total thickness of the Purbeck to Albian strata inclusive on the east side of the promontory is about 342 ft., as compared with an estimated original thickness of 586 feet.

Between Man-o'-War Rock and Head the strike-faulting has been even more intense, for the total thickness of these formations is reduced to less than 250 feet. Most of the outcrops being under water, however, the details of what is missing are unknown.

In the east end of St. Oswald's Bay, near Dungy Head, there is a similar strike-fault between the Wealden and Middle Purbeck Beds, and another cuts out much of the Lower Purbeck Beds. Here, too, the unconformity between the Wealden Beds and Gault can be detected. Another strike fault begins here and crosses the neck of the promontory to Lulworth Cove, bringing Wealden Beds against Chalk between the two places, as may be seen in some exposures above the path from Lulworth Cove to St. Oswald's Bay.

[1] For details see W. J. Arkell, *op. cit.*

Both at Dungy Head and at Durdle there are good exposures of Broken Beds near the base of the Purbeck. At Durdle Door they are 9 ft. thick and contain numerous splinters of black chert. At Durdle the Lower Purbeck Beds also show some deformation due to a drag fold such as that seen best near Lulworth; but the fold itself, which was doubtless developed at a higher level, has

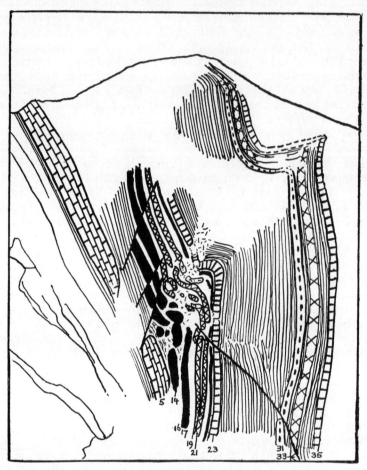

Fig. 70.—*Section of the Lulworth Crumple in the west side of Stair Hole (looking west).* The two conspicuous black bands are beds of hard, grey, calcareous mudstone. (Reproduced from *Quart. Journ. Geol. Soc.,* vol. xciv, 1938, p. 6.)

been eroded away. A southward thrust connected with the drag-folding crosses the Purbeck Beds on the west side of the promontory and exhausts itself by turning upward and pulling the Cypris Freestones apart for several yards (Fig. 69).[1]

---

[1] The gap is inaccessible to direct measurement.

LULWORTH COVE AND STAIR HOLE

Lulworth Cove offers a great variety of interest to the student of tectonics.

At the horns of the cove, and on the east side in particular, there are excellent sections of the Broken Beds (Fig. 32, p. 140),

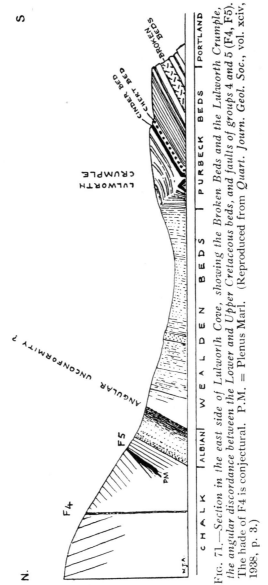

Fig. 71.—Section in the east side of Lulworth Cove, showing the Broken Beds and the Lulworth Crumple, the angular discordance between the Lower and Upper Cretaceous beds, and faults of groups 4 and 5 (F4, F5). The hade of F4 is conjectural. P.M. = Plenus Marl. (Reproduced from Quart. Journ. Geol. Soc., vol. xciv, 1938, p. 3.)

but these are still better developed a short distance farther east, where they will be more fully treated. In addition there are in the east side of the cove some small structures of interest con-

nected with a small southward overthrust which cuts the Cypris
Freestones, as at Durdle Door.   Some soft shaly beds within the
Freestones have had to accommodate themselves to the folding
of the stone bands with remarkable results.   A triangle of
laminated shaly beds has been pinched downwards and the
underlying softer material has cushioned off the movement; and
some small-scale backfolding has developed in an elbow of a more
competent bed.[1]

The Lulworth Crumple, a superbly-exposed drag-fold in the
Purbeck Beds, is best seen at Stair Hole (Pl. XIVB, and Fig. 70).
The vertical limb of the Crumple where it plunges below the
beach is directed to meet the Cypris Freestones of the basal
Purbeck Beds at an angle of 50°; hence the line where they meet
must resemble the group 5 faults in the Chalk (p. 291), only upside-
down.   There are within the Crumple numerous signs of
upward and southward overthrusting, which, taken in conjunction with the shape of the structure as a whole, point to the movement that formed it having been upwards, against the dip,
towards the crest of the major (here Purbeck) anticline, as is the
rule in drag-folds.   Near the top of the cliff on the east side a
second but smaller sharp anticline is developed above the horizontal limb of the main crumple, and there are signs of a third
just below the turf.   These are more overturned northwards and
do not affect strata below the Cinder Bed.   The intervening
synclines are closed and approaching recumbent.   These smaller
crumples are seen only at Stair Hole.[2]

The Lulworth Crumple sinks eastwards, in harmony with the
pitch of the Purbeck Fold.   The disturbances at Durdle Door
suggest that this or another crumple was originally not far above
the present cliffs, whereas on the east side of Lulworth Cove all
but the apex has sunk below sea-level (Fig. 71).   A good section
of the apex is displayed close above the beach, but higher up
original structures have been modified by landslips.   At Bacon
Hole there is only a gentle roll in the strata, suggesting that the
Lulworth Crumple is continued underground.

In the cliffs of Lulworth Cove the Upper Purbeck and Wealden
Beds north of the Crumple are quite or nearly vertical (Fig. 71).
Dips of 90°-70° N. continue until the base of the Gault, at which
the angular unconformity reduces the dip 10 or 15°.   The upper
Greensand and Lower Chalk, well displayed on both sides of the
cove, dip 55°-60° N., up to the Plenus Marl inclusive.   At the
top of the Plenus Marl a fault of group 5 reduces the dip again by
20°.   Above the fault the Middle Chalk, dipping 35°-40° N., is
much jointed by fracture cleavage inclined nearly 90° S.

The dip in the Middle Chalk gradually increases until in the
highest chalk seen at beach-level (Terebratulina Zone) it is 60°-65°
N.   The lower half of the cliff (approximately) consists of this

---

[1] Figured in W. J. Arkell, *op. cit.*, 1938, plate iv.
[2] For fuller discussion of the Lulworth Crumple see W. J. Arkell, *op. cit.*

Middle Chalk dipping about 60°-65° N. It is succeeded abruptly (Fig. 72) by Upper Chalk which forms the upper half of the cliff and dips at 108° N. (inverted). The two rocks therefore dip into one another along a sharp line at an angle of 45°. The sharp

Fig. 72.—*View of the west cliff, Lulworth Cove (looking west).* **On the** left, the Upper Greensand (dotted) ends just beyond the old lime-kiln (LK). The Plenus Marl (outcrop black) descends to the beach behind the Black Rocks and is cut out upwards by a fault of group 5 (F5), which reduces the dip of the bedding by 20°. Beyond it (to right) the main bulk of the cliff is formed by Middle Chalk dipping about 40°-60° N. At F4 is the inferred undulating trace of a group 4 fault, above which is Upper Chalk with flints, overturned, dipping 108° N. In top right corner are bedding-plane surfaces. (Reproduced from *Quart. Journ. Geol. Soc.,* vol. xciv, 1938, p. 39).

dividing line undulates in such a way as to indicate that it marks the trace of a strike fault inclined steeply southwards, and the inclination and the effects agree with the powerful normal faults of group 4.

FOSSIL FOREST AND BACON HOLE

The mile of cliffs from Lulworth Cove to Bacon Hole (Mupe Rocks) display the best sections of the Broken Beds. These remarkable limestone-breccias are near the base of the Purbeck Beds, between the tufaceous Caps, with their Dirt Beds and fossil trees (*see* p. 139), and the overlying Cypris Freestones. They attain their greatest thickness (20 ft. or more) in the present stretch of coast, but continue in diminishing thickness to Durlston Head, Swanage; and westwards, as mentioned above, they are still 9 ft. thick at Durdle Door. The next sections westward, at Ringstead and Poxwell, contain hardly a suggestion of Broken Beds, although the suitable strata are well developed and the usual tufas and forest bed occur below. Nor do they reappear

thence to the west end of the outcrop at Portisham. In the Isle
of Portland there are no Broken Beds in the principal quarries
and cliffs of the north part of the island, but they reappear at
Portland Bill. These last, however, may be of different origin.[1]

The limestone composing the Broken Beds is grey to cream-
coloured, fissile, of peculiar brittle fracture. It is broken into
small fragments and blocks of all sizes up to a yard thick and 5 ft.
or more long. In some sections the blocks appear to lie in a
complete jumble, but in others, especially at Bacon Hole and
Pondfield, there are structures indistinguishable from small overthrusts and overfolds with lateral packing. Higher horizons are
involved in some places than in others, but everywhere a short
distance above and below the Broken Beds the strata are undisturbed. Slickensides are as a rule absent, though a single
instance has been recorded.[2] The. rocks are probably too soft to
scratch each other deeply, and any superficial scratching that may
have existed is likely to have been obliterated by solution.

Black chert is distributed as splinters in variable quantities
through the Broken Beds. It is best seen in the sea-washed
exposure at Durdle Door, where it resembles the crushed and
splintered black flints in the neighbouring Chalk.

There is a marked contrast between the strike-sections and
dip-sections of the Broken Beds. The best accessible strike-
section is the long and very fine one on the shelf half-way down
the cliff at the Fossil Forest, from $\frac{1}{4}$ to $\frac{1}{2}$ mile east of Lulworth
Cove entrance. In this section no appreciable folding occurs,
but there is a tendency for the large and small blocks in the Broken
Beds to have their longer axes parallel to the direction of strike.
So soon as the corner is rounded into Bacon Hole, and the strike-
section gives place to a dip-section, the aspect of the Broken Beds
changes. A series of curious asymmetric folds immediately
appears. They have their short limbs to the north, which at first
sight suggests northward movement of the overlying beds. But
closer inspection shows that these are not normal overfolds, for
each short limb is rammed against the fractured end of a plate of
the underlying limestone, which appears to have been raised and
broken at its north end. Thus each short limb seems to have
acted as a piston, ramming southward against the edges of plates
of the underlying limestone, against which the overtravelling bed
seems to have jammed. The movement, in fact, on closer inspection seems to have been southward, against the dip. This would
be in harmony with the movement of the Lulworth Crumple, and
the causes were probably the same.

The Broken Beds were for many years explained as due to
collapse in Lower Purbeck times of limestones laid down over
masses of vegetation, which subsequently rotted away. ·The

---

[1] W. J. Arkell, *op. cit.*, p. 13.
[2] H. B. Woodward, ' Jurassic Rocks of Britain,' vol. v, *Mem. Geol. Surv.*
1895, p. 249.

overlying undisturbed strata were then deposited upon the breccias.[1]

That they are in reality small-scale accommodation effects due to adjustment between the competent Portland Stone and the incompetent Purbeck Beds during the Tertiary folding is believed to be indicated by the following :—

1. The difference between dip and strike-sections, showing definite lateral movement and direct relationship of the movement to the Purbeck fold.

2. The distribution. Maximum brecciation is in the steep north limb of the Purbeck fold, minimum in the flatter south limb.[2] Broken Beds are almost entirely absent from Ringstead westwards in the foreland where the outcrop of the Purbeck Beds was disconnected from that in the middle limb by the intra-Cretaceous unconformity, bringing Gault on to Kimmeridge Clay (*see* Pl. XIX, horizontal section). No other explanation adequately accounts for this distribution.

3. The presence of splintered chert in the Broken Beds. According to the collapse theory the limestones were brecciated when support was removed from below; but it is improbable if not impossible that chert should have been so broken and splintered by collapse under its own weight, *ex hypothesi* before the overlaying strata were deposited.[3]

4. Absence of all signs of decayed vegetation below the Broken Beds. There is not so much as a carbonaceous streak below many feet of breccia, and this although the presence of the Dirt Beds at slightly lower horizons proves that carbonaceous and earthy matter was capable of preservation where it existed. The Dirt Beds are insulated from the Broken Beds by the unbrecciated tufaceous Top Cap.

5. Sudden vertical augmentations of the Broken Beds, involving higher beds of limestone, unaccompanied by any sagging of the overlying beds, whether by collapse or original deposition. The fragments have been packed laterally and occupy as much space where the breccia is thick as the breccia and unbroken beds do where the breccia is thin.

It has been suggested that the horizon on which the Broken Beds formed was in the first place weakened, and the brecciation may even have been begun, by hydration of anhydrite and solution of the resulting gypsum.[4] Collapse due to removal of gypsum or salt may have contributed to the striking ' foundered ' appearance of the Broken Beds in the Lulworth district.[5]

---

[1] Fisher's hypothesis, accepted by Strahan, *Purbeck Memoir*, 1898, pp. 80-82.

[2] This was pointed out by H. B. Woodward (*op. cit.*, 1895, pp. 247-9) who believed the Broken Beds to be of tectonic origin but adduced insufficient reasons.

[3] Some authorities on chert and flint would not concede that the chert could have been formed and consolidated so soon after deposition.

[4] S. E. Hollingworth, *Geol. Mag.*, vol. lxxv, 1938, p. 331.

[5] Professor O. T. Jones on an excursion in March, 1939, emphasized the resemblance to Gash Breccias in South Wales and favoured a penecontemporaneous origin for the Broken Beds.

MUPE BAY

At Mupe Bay the Upper Greensand and basal Chalk dip 45°
N.; the dip then increases gradually to 53° N., until in the upper-
part of the Lower Chalk a group 5 fault inclined 35° N. reduces
the dip by about 20° as at Lulworth Cove.   The fault-plane breaks
up   near the beach into several branches.   There is the same
formation of lenses along the fault-plane and fracture-cleavage in
the hanging wall, as at St. Oswald's Bay and elsewhere, and
some shears of group 3 are developed both above and below the
fault.   At this locality the group 5 fault is at a rather lower
horizon in the Chalk than elsewhere.   Nowhere else is it known
to be below the Plenus Marl, unless the disturbances in the lower
part of the Lower Chalk at Durdle, mentioned above, are its
equivalents.

Some minor normal faulting is seen in the Plenus Marl, after
which the section is interrupted by a landslide, which at present
hides everything.   Under the landslide there is presumably a
fault of group 4, for beyond it nodular Middle Chalk emerges,
dipping 70-75° N.—a difference of 40° of dip in a few yards.   In
the Planus Zone the dip increases to vertical, accelerated by at
least one minor fault of group 4.   The cave and arch at the
farthest point accessible on foot at normal tides provide a good
exhibition, in dip and strike section, of shears of group 1 (dipping
55°-60° S.) and group 3 (dipping 35° S.), with in addition some
vertical slickensiding along bedding-planes.   Shears of group 1
occasionally turn up through 25° and run into the bedding-planes.

ARISH MELL[1]

The west cliff of Arish Mell (Bindon Hill) consists of
Quadratus and Mucronata chalk dipping 75°-80° N.N.W., sliced
through and through by shear-planes, the majority of which are
inclined about 35° N. or N.N.W.   It is difficult to make out any
prevalent direction of movement, for the bands of flint that are
shifted south along some of the slide-planes are shifted north
again on others.   Similarly the cliff in Quadratus and Marsupites
Zones farther east shows a meshwork of shears and slides in all
directions; the section here is too oblique for a clear elucidation
of the movements.

The Chalk of Arish Mell is higher stratigraphically than that
exposed in any other sea cliffs east of Bat's Head, and the corresponding difference in its tectonics leads to the surmise that it is
near the zone of packing which is known from the Middle Bottom
section (p. 286) to lie in the axial plane of the foresyncline. Further
complications may have been introduced by the change of strike
from E. to E. 18° N. which takes place at this point.

In the east cliff (Cover Hole) the Planus and Micraster Zones
forming the arch and headland are normal, dipping 65° N., with

---

[1]   Shown in the Frontispiece.

shears of group 1 dipping 65° S., showing distinct upward displacement. The group 1 shears are cut and shifted by conspicuous shears of group 3a, dipping 10°-12° S.

The change of strike in the Chalk at Arish Mell is associated with a sudden eastward thickening of the Wealden and Purbeck Beds, which takes place somewhere between Mupe and Worbarrow Bays.[1]

WORBARROW BAY

Worbarrow Bay is the only section showing any of the Chalk bending down into the middle limb of the Purbeck Fold. The Lower Chalk dips 35° N. at the top of the cliff and bends down to 50° N. where it passes under the beach. At the top of the Plenus Marl there is a mild group 5 fault, above which the basal beds of the Middle Chalk show the most remarkable development of fracture cleavage to be seen on this coast. The close-set cleavage-planes, about vertical, have been etched out to perfection on the sea- and spray-washed cliff at the farthest accessible point of the bay.[2]

WORBARROW TOUT AND PONDFIELD

The view eastward from Worbarrow Tout gives a good impression of the structure of Purbeck. From here can be seen the lowland core of Kimmeridge Clay with its black cliffs, and the escarpment of the Portland Stone, which forms a nearly level plateau at St. Alban's Head and Swyre Head and then turns over to plunge down northward at 30°-40° all along the ridge of hills which ends in the splendid precipice of Gad Cliff (Frontispiece, and Pl. VIII, A).

The sides of Pondfield Cove and Worbarrow Tout provide three sections of the Broken Beds which show features nowhere else seen to such advantage. The best section is that on the east side of the Tout, where the basal Purbeck Beds, dipping 35° N., are as follows[3] :—

	BASAL PURBECK BEDS, WORBARROW TOUT	Ft.	Ins.
13.	Cypris Freestones		
12.	Broken Beds : the main mass ; encroaching irregularly on Bed 13 ... ... (Average about)	12	0
11.	Tufaceous limestone with much saccharoidal calcite ; in 2 layers ... ... 9 ins. to	1	0
10.	Laminated marl ... ... 3 ins. to		4
9.	Brecciated tufa ... ... 5 ins. to		6
8.	Laminated marl ... ... 1 in. to		4
7.	Breccia (Broken Beds), tightly packed and cemented in a laminated matrix, with some black chert near the base ... ... 1 ft. 7 ins. to	1	9

---

[1] For a quantitative examination see W. J. Arkell, *op. cit.*, 1938, p. 49.
[2] See Arkell, *op. cit.*, 1938, pl. v, fig. 2.
[3] Figured Arkell, *Proc. Dorset Nat. Hist. Arch. Soc.*, vol. lxi, 1940, pl. iv.

		Ft.	Ins.
6.	Black-speckled limestone		6
5.	Lenticular pebbly black-speckled limestone 0 to	1	5
4.	Tufa ... ... 3 ins. to		6
3.	Laminated white limestone with a 2 inch black paper shale near the base and lines and nests of little tufa nodules which at Pondfield swell into burrs	4	0
2.	Dirt Bed ... ... ½ in. to		1
1.	Hard limestone ... ... average	1	0

(Portland Stone—Shrimp Bed, calcite mudstone—below)

While the main mass of the Broken Beds (bed 12) is the usual loose breccia and encroaches irregularly on the beds above, being thus best explicable by tectonic movements, bed 7 is different. The fragments of laminated limestone are cemented together, and the mass is veined by hardened laminated marl, and the upper and lower contacts look like bedding.

It could be argued that bed 7 is a contemporaneous slumped bed. On the other hand at the contact between beds 7 and 9 a hardened, clean, sea-worn section shows foliated structure with calcareous white pellets drawn out as in a schist, and it suggests that bed 8 is a kind of mylonite. Identical relations recur at the bottom of bed 7. The laminated interstitial matter in bed 7 could have been deposited by infiltration or percolation or by injection during the Tertiary folding. In either case it gives the impression that it was kneaded by movements of the broken blocks it surrounds. In the Pondfield sections a cavernous tufa band in bed 7 can be followed for long distances and its behaviour is better explicable by Tertiary disturbance than by contemporaneous slumping. But the fact that such thin beds are all recognizable and essentially unaltered in thickness in the three sections covering a total distance of 300 yds. suggests that the Tertiary tectonic movement which brecciated the main mass of the Broken Beds was superimposed on the products of some earlier process not yet understood.

KIMMERIDGE TO DURLSTON HEAD

The lowest beds exposed in Purbeck come to the surface on the upthrow side of a normal N.N.E. fault in Hobarrow Bay. The beds here still dip about N.W., towards Gad Cliff and Tyneham Cap, but a little farther south, on Broad Bench Promontory, they become horizontal and at the tip of the promontory at low tide they can be seen to be turning gently seaward. Here, then, is the axis of the anticline. It is not, however, parallel to the strike of the Purbeck Anticline as a whole, as reflected in, for instance, the outcrop of the Purbeck-Wealden junction from Swanage to Worbarrow. The Broad Bench axis strikes E. 30° N., towards Kimmeridge village, if not still farther north. The coast south-east of Hen Cliff lies in a kind of no man's land between this axis and another which controls Mid Purbeck and seems to run rather south of east about ½ mile off-shore, passing under Emmit Hill on the St. Alban's Head promontory. This St. Alban's Head axis is a broader structure than the Broad Bench axis, with flatter dips. To the influence of the former are due the gentler dips in the Purbeck outcrop east of Kimmeridge, to the latter the steeper dips in the same beds from Kimmeridge to Worbarrow Tout. To this change of dip is in turn due the great bay in the Portland scarp behind Kimmeridge. The lack of continuity in the two axes is doubtless reflected even so far away as the Chalk outcrop by the gentle northward convexity of the Purbeck Hills which culminates at Corfe Castle.

It may be surmised that the more abrupt change of strike in the Chalk at Arish Mell, mentioned above, indicates that west of that place the strata come under the control of a third axis, which may be called the Lulworth axis, with a true E.-W. strike. The progressive westward diminution in the width of the axes, with proportionate increase in the dips, is probably connected with the marked and uneven westward decrease in thickness of the Jurassic and Wealden rocks.

The other change of strike in the Chalk at Nine Barrow Down, associated with a further diminution in dip and rather abrupt widening of the Purbeck outcrop from Downshay to St. Alban's Head, seems to denote that East Purbeck is controlled by a fourth small axis running almost along the coast through Anvil Point, somewhat north of east. The St. Alban's Head axis seems to close on the east side of the promontory, and the region round Seacombe has the appearance of another no man's land, with gentle dips in no definite direction.

The Purbeck Anticline is not so simple and homogeneous as it appears at first sight, but these axes are entirely subordinate and do not affect the essential truth of the generalization implied by a single line drawn from Anvil Point westwards through Purbeck and onwards through the centre of the Weymouth Anticline to Langton Herring.

The cliffs of Kimmeridge and Portland strata from Brandy Bay to Durlston Head provide cross-sections through 40 minor faults, shown on the Survey Map (Sheets 342, 343). The largest is near Dancing Ledge and has a downthrow west of 80 feet. The next largest is the fault in Hobarrow Bay, with a downthrow east of 50 feet. The majority range from 6 to 20 feet. All except a few are normal, but one or two are reversed, notably one at Clavell's Hard.

The broad ledges or benches of cementstone bared by the falling tide along the Kimmeridge coast display an interesting pattern of joints, which might repay closer study. At intervals also they are crossed by meandering ridges or ruckles, less than 1 ft. high, which when cross-sectioned seem to be the traces of small compression faults.

DURLSTON BAY AND PEVERIL POINT (PL. X, A)

The Portland-Purbeck junction at Durlston Head is obscured by some complex minor strike-faults, which Strahan interpreted as a combination of step faulting and trough faulting.

In the middle of Durlston Bay the section is repeated by a double strike-fault with a downthrow of 100 ft. to the south. Near the Zig-Zag path there is a small reversed fault in the Broken Shell Limestone.

At Peveril Point the Upper Purbeck Beds are intensely crumpled in a fashion reminiscent of Lulworth. The sections to be seen at the east end of the Point and on the north side are shown in Fig 73. The structure is a sharp syncline with minor and still sharper folds within it. The general dip here is only about 15° N. The axis of the crumple meanders, not keeping

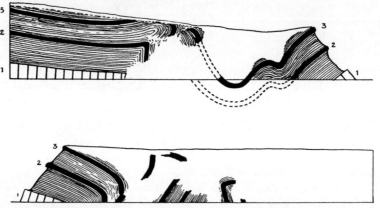

Fig. 73.—*Crumpled Upper Purbeck Beds at Peveril Point, seen at east end of point (above) and on north side (below).* 1, Broken Shell Limestone; 2 and 3, Viviparus Marble beds; hatched, clays and shales (including Unio Beds). (Reproduced from *Quart. Journ. Geol. Soc.,* vol. xciv, 1938, p. 4.)

strictly parallel to the general strike of the rocks. The structure is presumably an accommodation fold (American ' drag fold '). Another is exposed in quarries and a stream bed near Blashenwell and Lynch Farms, south of Corfe Castle, and is shown by the mapping to be a mile in length.

BALLARD DOWN

At Ballard Down, the Chalk headland north of Swanage Bay, is exposed the most puzzling feature of Dorset tectonics, the Ballard Down Fault (Pl. XV). Approached again after a study of its milieu, of the tectonics of all the rest of the Purbeck Fold and the Fault Zone farther west, it still stands unique. It is, in fact, one of the most extraordinary faults in the British Isles, and some unusual explanation is therefore probably necessary to explain it.

The uniqueness of the Ballard Down Fault needs stressing. Strahan, in writing his Memoir on the Isle of Purbeck and Weymouth, unhappily began his account of the tectonics at Ballard Down and worked westwards, attempting to interpret everything else by what he believed Ballard Down had shown him. As the result he misinterpreted the whole of the tectonics of the area, from Swanage to Portisham. For this reason, the order of description in the present account has been reversed, so that the reader may proceed from west to east unprejudiced by the one major feature about the interpretation of which there will probably always be differences of opinion.

Strahan called the fault which runs out in the cliffs north of Ballard Point the Isle of Purbeck Fault, and he assumed it to follow the north side of the vertical limb of the Chalk fold throughout Purbeck and past Lulworth, to run out to sea again between Bat's Head and Middle Bottom. All his horizontal sections in the Lulworth district show the ' Purbeck Fault ' as the controlling factor in the structure, and all the various dips and faults which really exist there in the Chalk were ignored. He even drew a slightly modified replica of the Ballard Down section to represent the cliff between Bat's Head and Middle Bottom, where nothing of the sort can be seen.[1] To be rid of these pre-conceptions it is better to discard the term Purbeck Fault (which for perhaps most of its length is a misnomer for the Purbeck Fold), and to use the term Ballard Down Fault for the original structure seen at Ballard Down.[2]

The section there visible is shown in Pl. XV and Fig. 74. The principal features to be seen can be tabulated as follows[3] :—

1. The cross-section of the fault-plane is an even curve, concave northwards and upwards, which runs from sea-level to the cliff-top so as to form nearly a quarter of a circle.[4]

2. The strata below and south of the fault-plane stand vertical and are truncated by it, those above it are curved exactly parallel to the fault-plane.

3. Southwards the strata gradually assume a decreasing northward dip, which becomes 60° at the base of the Chalk. Northward they flatten suddenly a short distance from where the fault disappears under the sea, and thence continue northwards to Studland with a dip of only two or three degrees to the north.

4. The Chalk south of the fault is intensely hard. It ' breaks with a conchoidal fracture and, so far from soiling the fingers as is usual, is hardened into a limestone and can only be scratched by a knife, while the whole cliff is traversed by veins of calcite and innumerable planes of slickenside . . . . The flints are not only broken to fragments, but the fragments are more or less

[1] A. Strahan, *Purbeck Memoir*, 1898, pls. vii. ix.

[2] W. J. Arkell, *Geol. Mag.*, vol. lxxiv, 1937, p. 86.

[3] The section can only be approached by boat.

[4] A small cave with roof formed by the hanging wall shows that the cliff gives a true cross-section, not appreciably oblique.

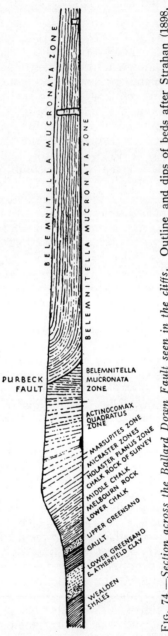

BELEMNITELLA MUCRONATA ZONE

BELEMNITELLA MUCRONATA ZONE

PURBECK
FAULT

BELEMNITELLA
MUCRONATA
ZONE

ACTINOCOMAX
QUADRATUS
ZONE

MARSUPITES ZONE
MICRASTER ZONES
HOLASTER PLANUS ZONE
CHALK ROCK OF SURVEY
MIDDLE CHALK
MELBOURN ROCK
LOWER CHALK

UPPER GREENSAND

GAULT

LOWER GREENSAND
& ATHERFIELD CLAY

WEALDEN
SHALES

Fig. 74.—*Section across the Ballard Down Fault seen in the cliffs.* Outline and dips of beds after Strahan (1898, pl. xi), the Chalk zones added after Rowe (1901, p. 32). Length of section about ¾ mile. True scale. (Reproduced from *Geol. Mag.*, 1936, p. 58.)

separated from one another '.[1]　The Chalk north of the fault is much less altered and much softer, but nevertheless ' it has been compacted considerably . . . . All large fossils are broken, and a perfect Echinid is a great rarity '.[2]　It was said by Rowe to be intermediate in condition between the Chalk south of the fault and that in the undisturbed basin about Wool.

5.　In spite of the difference in condition, the Chalk on both sides of the fault belongs to the Mucronata Zone, according to Rowe.[3]　It is not established whether the fault causes any repetition within the zone, but Rowe's reading of the section does not suggest that there is any need to suppose there is repetition.[4]

6.　The Chalk south of the fault is much sheared, as in the vertical and overturned middle limb in the Lulworth district, and the predominant shear-planes are those of group 1, inclined 60°-70° S.　The Chalk north of the fault does not exhibit this shearing.

7.　The fault-plane is a clean and even plane, devoid of fault-breccia.

8.　In the foot-wall the inclined shears and vertical bedding-planes are bent back a little southwards as they approach within a few feet of the fault.

The explanations hitherto suggested of the origin of this structure may be classified as follows : —

A.　Unconformity (T. Webster, 1816).
B.　Southward overthrust (W. D. Conybeare, 1822, A. Strahan, 1895, 1898).
C.　Northward underthrust (W. B. Clarke, 1837).
D.　Normal fault downthrown north (W. J. Arkell, 1936).
E.　Onion-scale adjustment-faulting (O. T. Jones, 1937, and A. H. Taitt, 1937, independently, unpublished).

A.　Such a sharp angular unconformity within the Upper Chalk[5] is so unlikely that the possibility may be passed over. Unconformity would not explain the differences of tectonic condition of the Chalk above and below the fault-plane unless the movements which produced them occurred during the deposition of the Mucronata Zone, whereas they are proved to be Tertiary.

B.　Southward overthrusting was suggested in every detail, save the actual use of the word overthrust, by Conybeare.[6]　It was elaborated and adopted as the official Survey explanation by Strahan,[7] and remained unquestioned for 40 years.

[1] A. Strahan, op. cit., 1898., pp. 167, 215.

[2] A. W. Rowe, ' The Zones of the White Chalk of the English Coast, Part 2, Dorset,' Proc. Geol. Assoc., vol. xvii, 1901, p. 37.

[3] Rowe, op. cit. pp. 32, 36.

[4] The statement that there is (Strahan, op.cit., 1898, p. 217) was based on an erroneous identification of the zonal sequence by Ch. Barrois (Recherches sur le terrain Crétacé supérieur de l'Angleterre et de l'Irlande,' Mém Soc. géol. du Nord, 1876, plate iii, fig. 7).

[5] T. Webster, in Sir H. C. Englefield's Picturesque Beauties of the Isle of Wight, 1816, p. 218 (written 1812). London.

[6] W. D. Conybeare, in Conybeare and W. Phillips, Outlines of the Geology of England and Wales, 1822, p. 111. London.

[7] A. Strahan, ' On Overthrusts of Tertiary Date in Dorset,' Quart. Journ. Geol. Soc., vol. li, 1895, p. 549 ; and Purbeck Memoir, 1898, p. 214.

The essence of the hypothesis is that the curved Chalk above the fault is the lower bend (foresyncline) of the S-shaped Purbeck fold which has been thrust southward on to the middle limb. As enunciated by Strahan, on the assumption that the beds under the fault are younger than those above it, ' that this newest Chalk is actually surrounded on every side by older rock ',[1] this is impossible, for the lower bend is still in position below the fault, as shown on Strahan's own horizontal section.[2] If the Chalk above the fault is younger than any below, as seems more probably from Rowe's researches, this objection is removed. There still remain, however, the following objections to the southward overthrust hypothesis.[3]

1. If the curved strata above the fault belonged to the middle of the foresyncline they should be in as advanced a state of alteration as the strata below the fault. If anything they should be still more crushed, packed, and slickensided, as are the beds in the axial plane of the foresyncline west of Bat's Head.

2. If the curved strata above the fault obtained their curvature during the primary folding and have been thrust up with their curve intact, then since the bedding is exactly parallel to the fault-plane, the latter must have been made in the hard chalk below so as exactly to accommodate the softer curved strata to be thrust up. This is inconceivable.

3. On general grounds, it is improbable that a major overthrust such as visualized by Strahan would develop southward, against the brow of an asymmetric anticline overdriven northwards.

C. Northward underthrusting was postulated by W. B. Clarke in 1837.[4] According to him, as the anticline rose a crack developed along the present line of fault. As the anticline south of the crack continued to rise, it pushed up the fault-plane and the broken ends of the chalk to the north of it until they were bent into a quarter circle. At the same time the chalk below the fault gradually turned over to the north until it became vertical and underthrust slightly the broken and upturned ends of the chalk north of the fault. Fig. 75 is a reproduction of Clarke's sketches.

This hypothesis is more acceptable than Strahan's for it is not open to objections 1, 2, or 3 above. Against it, however, are the following.

4. It postulates that the vertical chalk below the fault received its intense shearing and induration whilst actually in contact with the almost unaltered chalk, which was escaping alteration by overthrusting (relatively) southwards. It is difficult to believe that such alteration could be imposed on the rock on one side of a

---

[1] A. Strahan, *Purbeck Memoir*, 1898, p. 217.

[2] *op. cit.*, pl. vii.

[3] See W. J. Arkell, ' The Tectonics of the Purbeck and Ridgeway Faults in Dorset,' *Geol. Mag.*, vol. lxxiii, 1936, pp. 59-60.

[4] W. B. Clarke, ' Illustrations of the Geology of the South-East of Dorsetshire,' *Mag. Nat. Hist.*, n.s., vol. i, 1837, pp. 414-421, 461-9.

sharp line of fracture and not on that on the other. The difference of condition in the chalk above and below the fault-plane seems to demand that the fault came into existence after the shearing and alteration. The dragging of the shear-planes in the foot-wall points to the same conclusion.

5. On general grounds an underthrust on the brow of a rising anticline is improbable. Any ' cracks ' that might form at

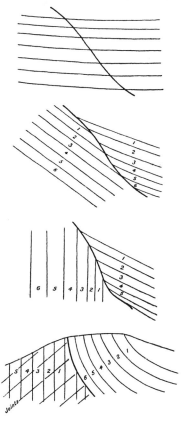

FIG. 75.—*Diagrams from Clarke's paper illustrating his underthrust hypothesis.* (Redrawn from *Mag. Nat. Hist.*, N.S., vol. i, 1837, p. 464-8.)

the beginning of or during the rise of such an anticline would tend to develop into overthrusts not underthrusts.

D. A normal fault downthrown north with unusually flat hade and an undulation in the fault-plane where it crosses the hard vertical chalk (as seen in the cliff), explains the structure without any thrusting[1] (Fig. 76). Nor is it open to any of the objections 1 to 5 above. Its main advantages are : that normal faulting would have occurred at a later period than the folding

---

[1] W. J. Arkell, ' The Tectonics of the Purbeck and Ridgeway Faults in Dorset,' *Geol. Mag.*, vol. lxxiii, 1936, pp. 61-3.

which caused the alteration of the chalk in the middle limb; that the two kinds of chalk in different states of alteration were therefore brought together afterwards, by a separate tectonic act; that a source for the relatively unaltered chalk is provided in the upper or crestal limb of the fold; that the parallelism of the strata of the hanging wall to the fault-plane is explained in the most natural way as adaptation of the down-travelling strata to an undulation in the fault-plane; that a second but gentler northward plunge of the strata in the Lower Eocene rocks at Studland is explained (Fig. 76).

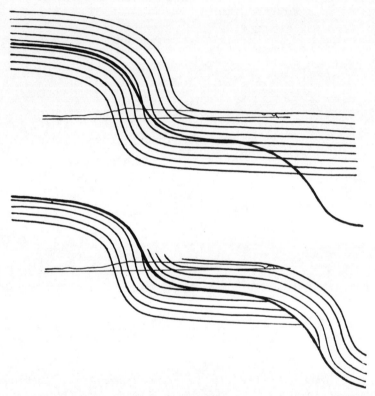

Fig. 76.—*Diagrams illustrating the explanation of the Ballard Down Fault by normal faulting.* Above, the monocline before faulting, but with the fault-plane drawn in. Below, the same after faulting, but without the straightening of the fault-plane and curved chalk below sea-level by plastic adjustment, which would probably have taken place. (Reproduced from *Geol. Mag.*, 1936, p. 62.)

Two objections can be brought against this hypothesis:

6. The inclined shears and vertical bedding in the footwall are dragged up and south as they approached the fault-plane, suggesting reverse movement (Pl. XV). This may be deceptive, however. The drag is slight and superficial, not of the extent

that might have been expected to result from an overthrust at such an angle and on such a curve. It seems more of the order that might be produced by the southward component of the force exerted by a down-travelling block above the fault-plane.

7. The hade of the postulated normal fault, to satisfy the observed facts, has to be drawn unusually flat, and the lateral shift must be as great as nearly ¾ mile.

E. The onion-scale adjustment-faulting hypothesis was first suggested to me in February, 1937, by Mr. F. W. Shotton, as the explanation put forward by Professor O. T. Jones, who had seen similar structures on a smaller scale in South Wales. In September, 1937, Mr. A. H. Taitt suggested to me the same process, independently, as the result of seeing some folds of this kind in Persia.

According to this hypothesis the uppermost zone of the Chalk caught in the closing foresyncline of the Purbeck fold and forced, if it remained there, to shorten itself by about 1,500 ft. on its upper surface,[1] has escaped by ' popping out like the layers of an onion when squeezed ' (Fig. 77). The lower zones of the Chalk,

☷ Crushed chalk

Fig. 77.—*Diagrams illustrating ' onion-scale faulting.'*

faced with less shortening, would have yielded by crushing, as in the zone of packing seen in the axial plane west of Bat's Head (p. 287). There may, therefore, have been a structure resembling that at Ballard Point all the way along the vertical limb, but at the cliff-section west of Bat's Head it would have been removed by erosion.

It will be seen that this hypothesis bears a strong resemblance to Clarke's underthrust of exactly a century earlier (C), but that the postulated cause and mode of initiation of the fault are different. It shares the advantages of Clarke's underthrust in not being open to objections 1, 2, or 3, and it is an improvement on it in not being open to objection 5. The only objection that still seems to apply to this hypothesis is No 4.

THE PURBECK HILLS, INLAND

How far inland the Ballard Down Fault extends it is impossible to say, but on any hypothesis it must be too big a feature to die out within a mile or two. No inland sections of the junction of Chalk and Eocene are known along the 12-mile ridge of the

---

[1] See H. G. Busk, *Earth Flexures*, 1929, p. 10. Cambridge.

Purbeck Hills, but the clay workings approach close enough to the Chalk to show that this junction lies along a complicated and variable tectonic belt. An axial zone of packing as in the Chalk of Middle Bottom is suggested by the chalk pit 500 ft. north of the castle, and also by the clay pit at Norden (p. 225). Both there and north-east of Corfe Castle (p. 224) horizontal Bagshot Beds approach abnormally close to the vertical Chalk, and remain at a low altitude.[1] At other places the Bagshot Beds mount up to much greater altitudes with a dip of about 10° N. (as at Creechbarrow, to over 500 ft., and Swanage golf links, over 400 ft.), suggesting a structure of the Studland type. It is possible that Strahan was right when he wrote of the ' Purbeck ' [Ballard Down] Fault ' running out of the Chalk into the Tertiaries ' in places. It is not inconceivable that the same fault does continue westward and run into the Tertiary base somewhere near Rempstone Hall and back into the Chalk again up the cleft Stonehill Down opposite Creechbarrow. It is easier to draw a horizontal section through Creechbarrow and the adjoining Chalk ridge if one assumes a structure like that at Ballard Point. Moreover, the vertical Mucronata Zone south of Creechbarrow is much less hardened and sheared than the lower zones of the Upper Chalk south and south-east of East Creech. The same difference is noticeable in chalk pits on the west side of the road north of Ulwell.

Contortions in the Bagshot Beds in the heaths 1 mile north of Rempstone Hall are referred to on p. 225.

---

[1] H. W. Bristow accounted for this by a strike fault in 1859 (Horizontal Sections, sheet 56, *Geol. Survey.*). See also W. H. Hudleston, *Proc. Geol. Assoc.*, vol. vii, 1883, p. 378 and horizontal section. Cf. a fault in analogous position at Ashey, south of Ryde, Isle of Wight, which cuts out 700 ft. of strata (*Proc. Geol. Assoc.*, vol. xlviii, 1937, pp. 214-5).

CHAPTER XIV

DEVELOPMENT OF THE TOPOGRAPHY AND DRAINAGE : PLEISTOCENE AND RECENT DEPOSITS

I. Development of the Topography and Drainage

After the Tertiary earth-movements described in the last chapter had at length come to rest there began a long period of destruction. Forces of erosion attacked the great arches thrown up in the preceding age and removed stupendous thicknesses of rock to be deposited as new sediments outside our area. Probably the greatest amount of this erosion was accomplished in the Miocene period, almost entirely unrepresented by strata in the British Isles. We can only judge of the extent of the geological processes enacted in our area, and of the time that must have elapsed for their completion, by contemplating the results. A relief model constructed to scale shows the present topography as mere roughnesses : the tectonic structures have been levelled off almost to a plain.

By the time the next strata were formed—the plateau gravels and the angular flint gravels on the downs—at least nine-tenths of this great task of erosion had been accomplished. The Miocene and the whole of the Pliocene and Plio-Pleistocene periods had passed by, the principal rivers were flowing along their present valleys, though at higher levels, and the high chalk hills already stood where now they stand. The Pleistocene ice ages were unfolding, and Palæolithic man was already hunting over Devon, Dorset and Hampshire, dropping his flint hand-axes which became embedded where we find them in the gravels.

Just what was the sequence of events through the long ages represented by this hiatus in the stratigraphical record of Dorset will probably remain always a subject for conjecture. We can, however, extrapolate from neighbouring areas where the record is less imperfect, and by that means gain some idea of the major events that must probably be allowed for. Such evidence as there is suggests that there was not a continuous, uninterrupted history of subaerial erosion.

The nearest fossiliferous deposits of the Pliocene are at Lenham near Folkestone, where patches of Lower Pliocene (Diestian) marine sands and gravels cap the downs and fill solution pockets in the Chalk at 580 ft. above the sea. Similar patches in similar situations extend over parts of Sussex, Kent and Surrey, and have been correlated in a general way with unfossiliferous cobble gravels and sands in north-east Hampshire and the Chilterns. At Netley Heath on the North Downs in Surrey, and at Rothamsted, Hertfordshire, Red Crag fossils have been found.[1] These deposits were laid down on a peneplain, probably of marine origin, though doubtless that in turn was superimposed upon a topography already much lowered by subaerial erosion. However that may be, it is inferred that the higher parts of the Wealden arch had already been planed down to the core of Wealden Beds before the Lower Pliocene transgression.

The peneplain upon which the Pliocene sea transgressed became more or less covered with gravels and sands and was eventually uplifted epeirogenically. The motion was not absolutely even, but was accompanied by slight warping more or less along the principal axes of the previous folding; thus broad flat upwarps arose along the Vale of Pewsey and Weald regions. There is evidence, much of it more or less indirect, that upon the uplifted and upwarped Pliocene peneplain a new drainage system was initiated, which had no connexion, unless accidentally here and there, with any that had gone before, but which was the direct ancestor of the present river system.[2]

Recently Linton[3] has analysed the rivers of Wessex in the light of the results of previous workers on the Weald, and has arrived at some interesting conclusions. He points out that whereas a river system owing its origin directly to the Miocene folding would be essentially longitudinal, the rivers running east and west along the synclines, the modern drainage of Wessex is predominantly transverse, " large trunk streams running inconsequently across fold and outcrop." For instance, four streams have trenched their way across the Portsdown anticline, the Itchen, Hamble, Meon, and Wallington River, and the Meon, while still a small stream within 15 miles of its source, cuts successively across the Winchester and Portsdown anticlines where their amplitudes exceed 700 and 350 ft. respectively. Since it seems improbable that such a small stream can be antecedent—have flowed in the same course since before the folds were formed and trenched through them as they rose—it is to be inferred that it is superimposed—took its origin on a gently-inclined plain and

---

[1] H. G. Dines and C. P. Chatwin, *Sum. Prog. Geol. Surv. for* 1929, part 3, 1930, p.1.

[2] C. le N. Foster, and W. Topley, ' On the Superficial Deposits of the Valley of the Medway, with Remarks on the Denudation of the Weald,' *Quart. Journ. Geol. Soc.,* vol. xxi, 1865, p. 443; H. Bury, ' The Denudation of the Western end of the Weald,' *ibid.,* vol. lxvi, 1910, p. 640.

[3] D. L. Linton, ' The Origin of the Wessex Rivers,' *Scot. Geog. Mag.,* vol. xlviii, 1932, p. 149.

then intrenched its bed into the bevelled structures beneath. Linton cites many other instances in Wessex, for the most part already noticed by Clement Reid, Osborne White, and others, and concludes with Clement Reid[1] that the river system must have originated upon a warped Pliocene peneplain, probably of marine origin.

In the Isle of Wight, on Brading and Mersley Downs, at heights of 400 and 415 ft. above O.D., White has described deposits of coarse incompletely-rounded cobble gravel which " probably contain, along with much other material, the relics of a Pliocene beach."[2] And in the north of the New Forest the highest Plateau Gravels, up to 420 feet above O.D., have been supposed to be of Pliocene age.[3]

In our area direct evidence for a peneplain is wanting. There is certainly a striking uniformity in the principal heights in the district, especially in Purbeck, where the two highest points on the Chalk range, Ridgeway Hill and Nine Barrow Down, are both 655 ft. above O.D., the Tertiary hill of Creechbarrow rises to 637 ft. and the highest point on the Jurassic beds to the south, Swyre Head, to 679 ft. above O.D. Burton[4] has emphasized this agreement and infers a peneplain; but the elevated plateau on Purbeck and Portland Beds round St. Alban's Head and Worth seems to result merely from the horizontal attitude of the hard rocks which there form the surface. Farther west the following are the chief high points:—Bindon Hill 551 ft., Chaldon Downs 544 ft., White Nothe just over 550 ft., White Horse Hill 551 ft., Bincombe Down just over 550 ft., Bronkham Hill 654 ft., Black Down 777 ft., White Hill 674 and 685 ft. (two spurs), Wears Hill 691 ft.

The drainage of our area cannot be said to afford unequivocal evidence of the period and manner of its origin. If it originated upon an upwarped Pliocene peneplain the new watershed must have corresponded with the axis of the main Tertiary anticline in Purbeck, and with the Ridgeway fault-zone in the Weymouth district. In the opinion of the present writer it seems improbable, in view of the relative softness of the rocks, that the drainage of the area is of such an extreme antiquity as must follow if it be regarded as resulting directly from the Miocene folding, and in view of the evidence from neighbouring areas the more recent origin upon an upwarped Pliocene peneplain seems more probable. However, the development of the drainage may be discussed without prejudice to the question of the date of its origin.

[1] Clement Reid, ' Geology of the Country Around Ringwood,' Mem. Geol. Surv., 1902, p. 29.

[2] H. J. O. White, ' Short Account of the Geology of the Isle of Wight,' Mem. Geol. Survey, 1921, pp. 167-8.

[3] H. Bury, ' Some Aspects of the Hampshire Plateau Gravels,' Proc. Prehist. Soc. E. Anglia, vol. iv, 1923, p. 28.

[4] H. St. J. Burton, ' A Peneplain and Re-excavated Valley Floors in Dorset,' Geol. Mag., vol. lxix, 1932, p. 474.

From the earliest times of which we have any evidence, the syncline of the Dorset-Hampshire Basin was drained by a longitudinal consequent river, the ancestor of the modern Frome. In the Pleistocene period, as shown by the vast spreads of gravel left by it on the surrounding heaths (the so-called Plateau Gravels), it was an important river, spreading over a wide tract of country and perhaps broadening into an estuary which extended through the Solent and Spithead to join the open sea somewhere to the east of the present Isle of Wight. This ancient river, analogue of the Kennet-Thames, has been called the Solent River. It received tributaries not only from the south, from Purbeck and the Isle of Wight and a lost tract of country between and south of those islands, but also from the larger dip-slope on the north, by transverse south-flowing streams of which the Stour and Avon and Test are the principal relics.

By Lower Palæolithic times the Frome, Stour and Avon had already settled into approximately their present courses and were laying down the great lateral spreads of coarse gravel called the Newer Plateau Gravel. These gravels cap terraces alongside all three rivers, and those on the south side of the Frome form the chief Plateau Gravels of our area. They are graded approximately with the present flood-plain of the rivers, but at an elevation about 100 ft. higher, and have yielded numerous Lower Palæolithic flint implements at Moreton and Bournemouth. In the Bournemouth district the Lower Palæolithic terraces of the three rivers, Frome, Stour and Avon, mingle and the rivers which laid them down probably joined a tidal estuary not far away, now destroyed by the sea in Bournemouth Bay.[1] At what period the sea finally destroyed the land to the south of this estuary, thus dismembering the old Solent River system and separating Purbeck from the Isle of Wight, is not exactly known, but Clement Reid, H. Bury and Osborne White agree in placing it " probably towards the close of the Pleistocene period ",[2] while J. F. N. Green favours a slightly earlier time, that of the 60-foot Bransgore Terrace (see p. 329).[3] It may be supposed that the sea first gained access through a valley in the Chalk downs cut by a southern tributary of the Solent River, analogous to the Medina and the two Yars in the Isle of Wight. Judging by the frequency of gaps in the Isle of Wight there may have been several such tributaries between Handfast Point and the Needles.

Throughout Pleistocene times the land rose spasmodically in relation to sea level, and with each rise (probably separated by

---

[1] See H. Bury, ' The River Solent and its Tributaries,' *Proc. Bournemouth Nat. Sci. Soc.,* vol. xx, 1927-8, p. 88 ; ' The Bournemouth Plateau Gravels,' *ibid,* vol. xvi, 1925, p. 72 ; ' Some Aspects of the Hampshire Plateau Gravels,' *Proc. Prehist. Soc. E. Anglia,* vol. iv, 1923, p. 15 ; ' The Plateau Gravels of the Bournemouth Area,' *Proc. Geol. Assoc.,* vol. xliv, 1933, p. 314.

[2] H. J. O. White, ' Geology of the Country around Bournemouth,' 2nd ed., *Mem. Geol. Survey,* 1917, p. 48.

[3] J. F. N. Green, ' The Terraces of Southernmost England,' (Pres. Address Geol. Soc.), *Quart. Journ. Geol. Soc.,* vol. xcii, 1936, p. lxxiv.

large oscillations in the opposite direction as demonstrated by Bury) the rivers cut their beds deeper. At the end of the Palæolithic period, however, the general upward movement was finally reversed. The land subsided, carrying the latest Pleistocene river gravels down to about 100 ft. below sea-level, and burying with them also the succeeding deposits with traces of Mesolithic and Neolithic man and the faunas contemporary with them. This final subsidence has continued down to the beginning of the Christian era. It is proved by three classes of evidence :

First, the occurrence of submerged land surfaces with tree stumps and peat under the sea. Such "submerged forests" occur opposite the mouth of the Char at Charmouth, opposite the mouth of the Bourne at Bournemouth, and under the docks at Southampton, where they have yielded Neolithic implements to a depth of 40 ft., associated with bones of red deer, *Bos primigenius* Blumenbach, and an assemblage of animals and plants denoting a climate much like that of the present day, resting upon gravel with reindeer and mammoth down to a depth of 50 ft. below sea-level.[1] The gravel at the bottom is river gravel, and when it was deposited the land must have stood at least 50 ft. higher than at present. The fauna shows that this was at the end of the Pleistocene Period, when the climate was still under the influence of the last ice age. Some river estuaries are underlain by these gravels down to 100 ft. below sea-level.

The second class of evidence is the occurrence of "drowned valleys," which are well represented in our area by Poole Harbour, Radipole Backwater and Lodmoor. These harbours and marshes can only have been excavated by river or stream action, and the sea can only have entered them as the result of subsidence of the land. Their outlines present the pattern that results when a dam is built across an inland shallow valley and the water behind is ponded back to form creeks and inlets.

The third class of evidence comes from inland and may be observed wherever there are rivers or considerable streams. The English rivers such as the Frome do not flow on rock bottoms but meander across alluvial flood-plains, wide out of all proportion to the sluggish streams that now water them. When borings are made through the alluvium it is found to descend to great depths and generally passes into gravel towards the bottom. Obviously the valleys can only have been cut when the land stood higher relative to the sea than at present. Owing to the sinking of the land the rivers have been ponded back and, their currents checked, they have aggraded their beds by depositing silt and mud.

---

[1] Clement Reid, ' Geology of the Country around Southampton,' *Mem. Geol. Surv.*, 1902, pp. 47-8 ; H. J. O. White, ' Geol. Country around Bournemouth,' 2nd ed., *Mem. Geol. Surv.*, 1917, pp. 65-6 ; W. D. Lang, ' Submerged Forest at the Mouth of the River Char,' *Proc. Geol. Assoc.*, vol. xxxvii, 1925, p. 197 ; C. Reid, *Submerged Forests*, 1913, Cambridge ; K. P. Oakley, ' Late Glacial Submergence of the Solent Margins,' *Proc. Prehistoric Soc.*, N.S., vol. ix, 1943, p. 56.

Thus two of the outstanding physical features of our area, the rich alluvial valley of the Frome with its famous dairy lands, and the coastal marshes and lagoons of Poole, Radipole and Lodmoor, owe their existence to the final subsidence of the land during and since Neolithic times.

A marked contrast is provided by other parts of the coast, where high ground approaches close to the sea, as along the south of Purbeck and in the Lulworth district. Here at first sight the last movement might be taken to have been elevation. At Chapman's Pool, Winspit, Seacombe, Lulworth Cove, and at many small ' gwyles ' elsewhere, broad valleys end off abruptly half way up the cliff, as if cut across with a knife, and in the floors small rejuvenated streams tumble rapidly to the sea through narrow gorges like the chines of Bournemouth, or end at the cliff edge in a waterfall, as at Freshwater Steps and Osmington Cascade. But these valleys are all very short and have a rapid fall seawards. They are, in fact, only the heads of much longer valleys which formerly extended southward to join some lost trunk stream flowing down the Channel. The surviving heads are too high to have been affected by the submergence of the mouths of the streams. Instead they furnish a measure of the coast erosion that has taken place, for they are the last remnants of a valley system almost entirely consumed by the sea, which is advancing faster than the dwindled streams can cut down to reach it.

Problems of great interest, with important bearing on some of the broader geological questions, are presented by the development of the individual streams and brooks of the district.

The drainage of Purbeck is comparatively simple. It results directly from uplift along the axis of the Purbeck Anticline, whether the original uplift as Strahan believed, or a re-elevation at some later time after peneplanation. As the axial region rose, it shed its water northward into the syncline of the Dorset-Hampshire Basin and southward into the vanished syncline in the Channel. As in the Weald, the north-flowing consequent streams deepened their beds and scoured out the softer Wealden strata below, carrying the debris through ever-deepening gaps or gorges across the Chalk outcrops on to the Tertiary plain. Just as the Wey, Mole and Medway cut through the North Downs, apparently regardless of the obstruction, on their way to join the Thames or its estuary, so in Purbeck the little Corfe River collects its water from the low-lying Wealden outcrop, where two streams, the Steeple and Byle Brooks, lead it through gaps on to the Tertiary plain to the north. The course of these brooks is especially remarkable because the Wealden outcrop is now open to the sea at both ends; yet the brooks drain towards the middle and out through the high ridge of vertical Chalk, which has been so hardened by earth-pressures that it is used for road-metal. Moreover, each brook has cut its own gap, one on either side of the conical hill on which Corfe Castle was built, although their courses approach each other so closely that they unite before they reach the Tertiary outcrop, thenceforth to flow together as the Corfe River into Poole Harbour.　Such a drainage can only have arisen through the gradual lowering of the gorges as the general level of the catchment behind was lowered.

An outstanding problem is provided by the anomalous behaviour of the streams in the Weymouth district, which do not run outwards from the axis of the Weymouth Anticline but across it.　West of Poxwell no water falling on the Jurassic coastal region flows northward through the Chalk into the basins of the Frome and the Bride, for the water-parting follows the crest of the Ridgeway downs.　The streams, of which the principal are the Wey and the Jordan, with the brooks at Osmington, Rodden and Abbotsbury, flow from the Chalk hills southward across the ridges of contrary-dipping Portland Stone and Corallian Beds, over the centre of the Weymouth Anticline, to the sea.

There are three possible explanations of this.　The first, which appears to have been favoured by Clement Reid,[1] is that the streams are of the type known as ' successful obsequents.'　On this view they were originally north-flowing consequents, but their headwaters have been ' captured ' by active south-flowing streams accelerated by the encroach of the sea, so that eventually the drainage has been reversed.　There are ' wind gaps ' in the Chalk range at Poxwell and Lords Barrow by which a north flowing Osmington stream might conceivably have passed, and even the upper Jordan (via the gap at Osmington village), but the largest stream, the Wey, has no satisfactory wind gap.　The second and third explanations agree in regarding the drainage as of the type known as superimposed.　On this hypothesis the streams arose as consequents flowing southward down an inclined plain from an axis on the present water-parting.　They cut their beds into the plain and then gradually deepened them into the contrary-dipping Jurassic rocks beneath.　The point at issue between the second and third views is the age of the planation that bevelled off the Jurassic rocks.　Strahan considered the bevelling occurred before the deposition of the Gault and visualized the plain as consisting of a southward-tilted plateau of Chalk and Tertiary beds.　Alternatively, in accordance with the ideas outlined above, it may have been the Pliocene peneplain, cut across folded Chalk and Tertiary beds.　The point is of the utmost importance for the problem of the age of the Weymouth Anticline (*see* p. 244).

Bury sees support for the Pliocene peneplain hypothesis in certain anomalous Purbeck stream features.[2]　He believes that two streams ran southward through the Jurassic escarpment at Worbarrow in opposition to the dip : one through Arish Mell gap

---

[1] Clement Reid, ' Geology of the Country around Ringwood,' *Mem. Geol. Surv.,* 1902, p. 33.

[2] H. Bury, ' Some Anomalous River Features in the Isle of Purbeck,' *Proc. Geol. Assoc.,* vol. xlvii, 1936, p.1.

and another gap between Worbarrow Tout and the Mupe Rocks, where the sea first broke through to form Worbarrow Bay; the other along the course of Tyneham Brook and southwards through the gap at Pondfield.   But the very considerable deposit of current-bedded gravel at Bucknowle (p. 330) indicates that at the 100-foot stage a volume of water was passing eastwards in the direction of the Corfe gaps too great to have been supplied by the catchments of Steeple Brook and Tyneham Brook combined, and probably derived from a much larger area of Kimmeridge terrain via the Worbarrow-Mupe gap in the Portland escarpment.

Linton[1] refers to the dry valley (there is now no stream) which cuts northward through the Chalk upland from Daggers Gate, one mile north-west of West Lulworth, to Winfrith Newburgh,

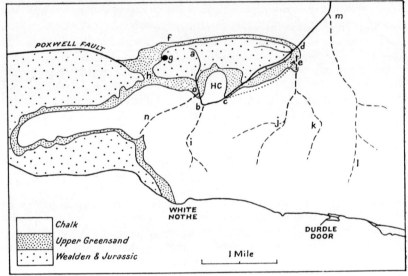

FIG. 78.—*Sketch map of the Chaldon Inlier to illustrate the drainage area of the Winfrith Brook.*

" trenched indifferently across the fold axes . . . . a minor anticline of Ringstead . . . . and . . . . the major anticline of Chaldon." But, as shown in the last chapter (p. 280) the Ringstead and Chaldon Anticlines have both nearly died out so far east, leaving only a gentle dome.

The Winfrith Brook, which drains the Chaldon Pericline, and into which this dry valley leads at Winfrith village, shows particularly interesting features.   Mr. Osborne White supplies the following notes :—

" While conforming on the whole to the imperfectly-evolved subsequential type usually met with in soft-cored anticlines in an advanced state of dissection, the drainage of the Chaldon Pericline is anomalous in one respect.   Its trunk-stream (a, b, c, d, Fig. 78),

---

[1] D. L. Linton, *op. cit.*, 1932, p. 156.

having escaped southward from the interior lowland on the Wealden clays by the gap at West Chaldon (b), returns thereto (at c) after a short excursion through a gorge (b-c) in the Chalk and Upper Greensand country, and finally quits the ' Wealden ' vale in a north-eastward direction through the gap (d) near Winfrith Rectory Farm.

Of the three distinct reaches of this stream indicated in Fig. 78 : —

> a-b apparently belongs to the transverse consequent class, and carries off the drainage of that western sector of the interior lowland which has been opened in the structurally higher, apical half of the dome;
>
> b-c is of the longitudinal consequent type, and looks like a relic of a ' synclinal ' stream, formerly skirting the southern side of the dome; and
>
> c-d seems to be an aberrant example of the last-named type, and to owe its present situation to lateral displacement from an earlier course (c-e) on the Chalk, either by deliberate migration from a harder to a softer terrain, or by fortuitous digression on a flood-plain formed during a lengthy pause in the elevation of the region.''

Mr. White's interpretation, however, does not entirely explain the anomalies in the drainage of this interesting area, which has probably had a rather more complicated history. About 400 yds. north-east of Holworth Dairy is a patch of flint and chert gravel over 150 yds. in diameter and about 1 ft. thick (g), covered with rainwash from the Greensand. It lies on about the same level as the col between the two periclines at Holworth (h) and also a wind-gap in the chalk downs immediately to the north (f) ($\frac{1}{4}$ mile west of Lord's Barrow). This suggests that at an early stage the Chaldon Pericline was divided into two halves like the Poxwell Pericline, each half draining northwards through its own gap in the Chalk rim, the two gaps being the wind-gap just mentioned (f) and the existing gap at Winfrith Rectory Farm (d). The projecting bluff of High Chaldon (HC) would represent the remains of the dividing col. For some time the drainage of the eastern part of the Upton Syncline probably passed over Holworth and out of the western gap of the Chaldon Pericline, but it was captured by the successful Osmington Stream with its direct access to the sea. The eastern effluent of the Chaldon Pericline, the ancestor of the Winfrith Brook, soon became the stronger stream, for it was early reinforced by the longitudinal consequent in the syncline between the Chaldon and Chaldon Down (= Ringstead) Periclines, which had no other outlet. This brought into the Winfrith Brook the drainage from a wide Chalk area to the south, whence several important dry valleys (n, i, j, k) lead northwards to the present brook. Another but much smaller tributary from the north joined at West Chaldon (b), and this eventually captured the drainage of the western half of the pericline.

Both these interpretations assume the drainage to have originated with the formation of the folds, which may not be justified. On the assumption that it originated on a Pliocene

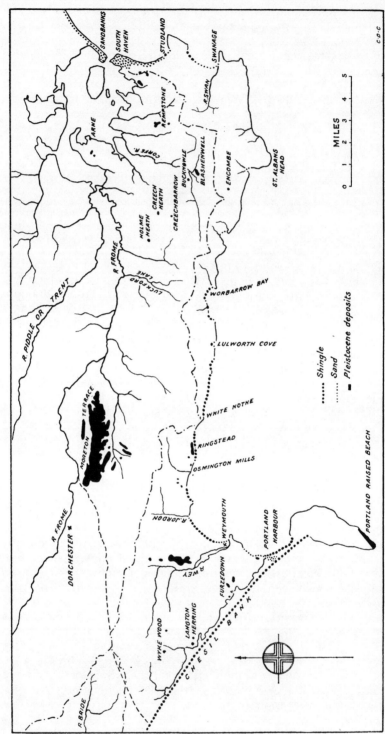

Fig. 79.—Sketch-map showing the Pleistocene deposits of the area and the nature of the beaches. Water-partings between the River Frome and the sea and around the River Bride catchment shown in dots and dashes. The broken line shows the north-west boundary of the area dealt with in this memoir.

peneplain the history would be somewhat different. The water-shed would have lain near the coast between White Nothe and West Lulworth, and consequent streams would have flowed north-ward across the almost levelled Chaldon Pericline to the Frome. At High Chaldon, however, there was still a ridge, which the streams avoided. The ancestor of the Brimstone Bottom stream (now dry valley) (n) would have flowed west of High Chaldon and out by the wind-gap (f), gathering a subsequent from the west near Holworth (h). All the other dry-valley streams turned obliquely east of the High Chaldon ridge and joined to form a much larger trunk stream which was the ancestor of the Winfrith Brook. A small subsequent of this stream cut back to West Chaldon (b-o) and captured the Brimstone Bottom stream and eventually also the drainage of the western part of the pericline. On both views the uppermost reach of the present Winfrith Brook (a-b) is an obsequent stream, its original direction of flow having been reversed.

The Chaldon Pericline evidently is highly important as a test area for the two rival theories of drainage. The explanation based on the assumption of Pliocene peneplanation seems the simplest and most satisfactory. Neither of the other two explanations, based on the assumption of direct continuity from the Miocene folding, accounts satisfactorily for the longitudinal consequent in the syncline between the Chaldon and Chaldon Down Periclines finding an outlet by crossing the eastern end of the Chaldon Pericline.

II. PLEISTOCENE AND RECENT DEPOSITS

(a) ANGULAR FLINT GRAVEL OF THE DOWNS

The tops of the high Chalk Downs inland of Lulworth and westward to White Nothe and along the ridge of Spring Bottom Hill, Ringstead, are capped with irregular accumulations of smashed angular flints with a little matrix of sand or gritty clay. Similar gravel occupies the highest ground along much of the Chalk ridge of the Purbeck Hills. There is a good section in the western face of White Nothe, where the warm yellow colour of the gravel at the top of the cliff can be seen from afar and stains the landslips beneath. Another cliff section can be seen at Rings Hill, Worbarrow, and pits are or have been recently worked on West Creech Hill, beside the road leading down to Ringstead Bay, on the hillside above Osmington Mills, and at other places on the Spring Bottom ridge. There is no definite stratification, and the thickness varies greatly, owing to the extremely uneven surface on which the accumulation rests. It often mantles the hills in a dense mass of flints from the summit for 100 ft. or more down the slopes in all directions, thus giving the impression of a great thickness; but it is impossible to tell how convex the surface of the Chalk may be underneath. At least 30 ft. is certainly not an excessive estimate for the thickness in places, not counting pot-holes.

Above the 400-foot contour on the plateau[1] between Brimstone Bottom and the head of the Upton Wealden Valley, between North and South Holworth, the Angular Flint Gravel is replaced by a buff-coloured loam with a variable quantity of scattered large flints.   The loam gives rise to a totally different soil from the flint gravel, but the two are mapped together owing to their similar position in the topography.   A hole dug 2,000 ft. S.S.W. of Holworth Farm showed red and white mottled clay at a depth of 4 to 5 ft., and it appears that an outlier of Reading Beds lies beneath the loamy gravel.

In other parts of the country, and on the Continent, the matrix of the flints is usually more clayey and the deposit is called Clay-with-Flints.   It consists of the flints and insoluble residue of the Chalk, mixed with a variable proportion of Eocene material.[2]   In Devon the Upper Greensand country carries a similar Clay-with-Cherts, in which, between Beer and Seaton, Middle Acheulian (Clacton III) implements have been found.[3]   Reid Moir considers the deposits a product of the Pleistocene glacial periods, a view which best accounts for the smashed state of the flints and cherts. Either great and rapid changes of temperature seem required, or else grinding under ice.   The only regions where there is a sufficiently great diurnal range of temperature at the present day are in the neighbourhood of the Arctic Circle.

In this connexion a pit and road-cutting up the hill from Steeple to Lulworth are of interest, for in a section about 8 ft. deep are shown Angular Flint Gravel mixed with large masses of broken chalk, in a manner suggestive of ice action.   It would be difficult to account for the phenomena by slipping or solution. The base of one large wedge-shaped mass of chalk resting on Flint Gravel dips into the hill at 10°.   Although no ice-sheet covered the district, it is probable that during the glacial periods considerable accumulations of frozen snow and ice formed on the hills and were set in motion by the spring thaws.

At Poxwell, 300 yds. east of the Manor House, a patch of Flint Gravel on the Chalk hill whose highest point is 446 ft. above O.D. sends a tongue southwards across the Poxwell Fault on to the Purbeck and Portland Beds.

(b)   TERRACE GRAVELS (" PLATEAU GRAVEL ") OF THE SOLENT RIVER BASIN.

The flat gravel sheets which cover nearly all the tablelands on the Eocene heaths and are mapped as Plateau Gravel are the ancient terraces of the Frome or Solent River.   In the area north of the present River Frome, not included in the scope of this

---

[1] Maximum height 465 ft. O.D.

[2] For an exhaustive treatment of the Clay-with-Flints, see B. Brajnikov, ' Recherches sur la formation appelée " argile à silex " dans le Bassin de Paris,' Revue de Géographie Physique, vol. x, fasc. 1, 2, 1937.

[3] J. Reid Moir, ' Ancient Man in Devon,' Proc. Devon Arch. Expl. Soc., vol. ii, 1936, p. 264.

memoir, successive terraces have been mapped up to 250 ft. or more above the river flood-plain, but the higher ones, as in other regions, contain no flint implements or fossils.

The terrace of greatest importance south of the present river is the 100-foot or Lower Palæolithic terrace, which has its counterpart on the Thames, the Somme, the Nile, and many other rivers. In the Chalk country near Dorchester it forms a belt about ½ mile wide adjoining the river valley on its north side past Stratton, Charminster, Dorchester and Stinsford. On entering the Tertiary tract it broadens out and spreads over the heathland south of the river from West Stafford to Moreton, capping all the high land of Ower Heath, and extending as outliers on to Warmwell and Winfrith Heaths. It is graded approximately with the present river, and the outliers north-west of Warmwell show that it also slopes upward towards the southern edge of the basin. Farther east this terrace is continued by a series of outliers in the heaths west, north-west and north of Wareham, which link up with further large spreads in the Bournemouth district, at rather over 100 ft. above the sea, laid down by the ancestral Stour and Avon.

South of the River Frome the Lower Palæolithic terrace is very well exposed in extensive gravel and sand pits at Moreton Station and between there and Warmwell. The gravel is generally about 8 ft. thick (varying from 6 ft. to 10 ft.), but sometimes thickens to fill channels 15 ft. deep, cut in the underlying Bagshot sands. A striking example was exposed in Warmwell Pits, south-west of the aerodrome, in 1938 (Pl. XVI, B). The gravel consists mainly of coarse subangular flints, with an admixture of Greensand cherts, quartz and " Cornish " rocks derived from the Tertiary beds. There is no sign of loamy or alluvial deposits in any of the sections. It is a gravel that can only have been carried by a river much greater and swifter than any in this part of the world at the present day.

In the Dorchester Museum there are more than 50 'Chellian' and early Acheulian flint hand-axes and a few coarse Lower Palæolithic flake implements from the 100-foot terrace near Moreton Station. A few are illustrated (half natural size) in Figs. 80, 81. All are more or less rolled, their edges and arrêtes abraded by contact with other pebbles in the gravels as they were swept along by the river. The implements are very rare and were collected by a former vicar of Moreton (Rev. M. H. Marsden) from the workmen over a period of many years, when the gravel was excavated and screened by hand. Since the introduction of mechanical methods of working scarcely any have been found.

Below Wool the heaths on the south side of the river have been eroded almost clear of gravels, though a thin sprinkling is widespread. The principal vestiges of true terraces that remain are some outlying patches of gravel belonging to one or more stages at about 150 ft. to something over 200 ft. above the Frome. One patch caps the conspicuous flat-topped hill which is the

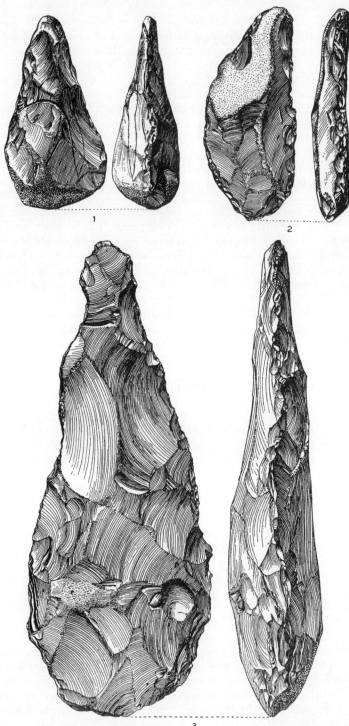

FIG. 80.—*Two Lower Palaeolithic core implements (hand axes) of Early Acheulian types (formerly called Chelléan), and a flake implement, from the* '100 foot' *terrace at Moreton Station gravel pits.* Marsden Collection, Dorset County Museum, Dorchester. ($\times \frac{1}{2}$).

highest point on Holme Heath (210 ft. O.D.) 2 miles south-west of Wareham. A marginal fragment of the same terrace at a some-what greater height (about 220 ft.) is well exposed in Pike Bros.' gravel pit on Creech Heath (300 yards east of the office). The pit shows 12-15 ft. of well-bedded coarse Plateau Gravel of Moreton type with many ' Creechbarrow flints ' (see p. 238) and fragments of quartz-grit ironstone from the Bagshot Beds, resting on yellow Bagshot sand (5 ft. seen). The base of the gravel slopes to the north.

Farther east there are two larger patches of the same terrace on a spur of high ground between Rempstone Hall and Bushey. A patch near the margin, close to the road, is crossed by the 200-foot contour. It has been separated by erosion from a larger patch ½ mile farther north, which forms a considerable plateau at the end of the ridge, well above the 150-foot contour. There are several exposures, showing up to 5 ft. of gravel, with a higher proportion of Eocene materials, especially battered beach pebbles and quartz, resting on Bagshot sand. From this plateau Arne Hill is seen to be a flat-topped ridge and its capping of gravel (highest point 168 ft. above O.D.) evidently belongs to the same terrace.

Small relics of terraces and channels at lower levels occur on Studland Heath (partly above and partly below the 50-foot con-tour) and elsewhere. The best exposed is at Shipstal Point, Arne. The cliff shows a partial cross-section of an ancient channel. About 10 ft. of typical Plateau Gravel is well exposed above the beach and can be traced north-eastwards into quartz sand at a higher level and barely distinguishable from the Bagshot sand on which it rests. Inland, towards the north, the gravel remains coarse and rises steadily to the summit of a little hill. No imple-ments were found here, but some of the flaking suggests human workmanship and prolonged search would probably be rewarded.

(c) GRAVELS MAPPED AS PLATEAU GRAVEL SOUTH OF THE CHALK DOWNS

On the Jurassic and Wealden rocks south of the Chalk downs are several isolated patches of gravel which cannot all be brought into relation with the sheets within the basin of the Frome.

The largest patch forms a terrace nearly 1 mile long and ¼ mile broad, running north and south parallel to the River Wey between Broadwey and Radipole. It rests on Oxford Clay and occupies the flat ridge which separates the Wey from Lodmoor, but at its north-east corner it is banked against higher ground. The surface of this terrace slopes steadily upwards from 70 ft. above O.D. at the south end to 110 ft. at the north end. It is continued by two smaller outliers on the Corallian Beds and Kimmeridge Clay at half-mile intervals northwards. The patch at Broadwey cemetery is at 120 ft. above O.D., that at the Congregational church

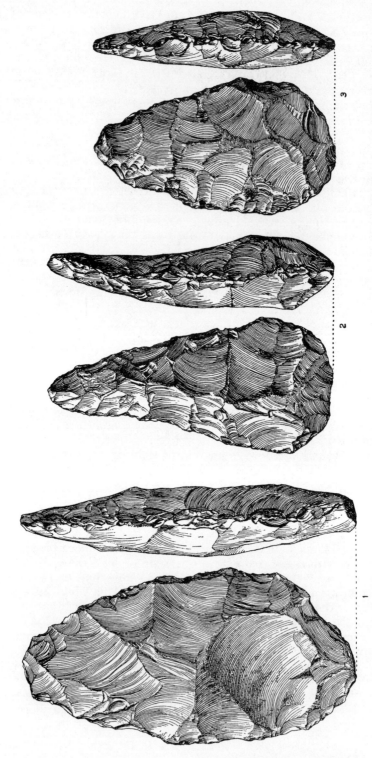

Fig. 81.—*Lower Palaeolithic flint implements of Early Acheulian types, from the ' 100 foot ' terrace at Moreton Station gravel pits.* 1, a ' limande ' or ovate ; 2, 3, ' Coups de poing ' or hand-axes. Marsden Coll., Dorset County Museum, Dorchester. (× ½).

at 140 feet. The main patch was formerly exposed in the railway-cutting near Lorton House, where it was said to be 6 ft. thick. The section is now grassed, but many pebbles can still be seen, and among them I picked up one $3\frac{1}{2}$-inch Bunter quartzite pebble. Numerous temporary excavations for sewers and foundations have recently been made along the main road at Redlands, and material from the other patches can always be seen at the cemetery and the graveyard at the Congregational church. The gravel consists of subangular flints, with smaller vein quartz pebbles and quartz sand, and occasional round battered Eocene flint pebbles. In the cemetery flints 6 to 10 ins. long are numerous. These three patches seem to be the remains of a terrace of the River Wey, laid down when it flowed about 60 ft. above the level of its present flood-plain. The height above flood plain is the same as that of the Bransgore Terrace of the Avon and Stour,[1] which is not dated by implements but is presumably Middle Palæolithic.

Farther west are some eight other patches of problematic origin. One caps a hill of Oxford Clay north of Wyke Wood at a height of 135 ft. above O.D. There are no exposures, but material in ditches shows a composition similar to the Wey terrace. The position of this patch behind the higher ridges of Forest Marble and Cornbrash (Chester's Hill, Walls Down, Rodden Ridge, South Sleight Knap) which entirely shut it off from the Fleet valley precludes its having been deposited by a river flowing along the site of the Fleet. On the other hand it occupies a position in relation to the gaps in the Corallian and Portland escarpments at Rodden and Portisham analogous to the relation of the Wey terrace to the gaps at Broadwey and Upwey, and it seems likely to have been laid down by a south-flowing stream which cut those gaps, the ancestor of the present Rodden brook. The Wyke Wood gravel is at a height of approximately 100 ft. above the flood plain of the present brook. A smaller patch 1 mile farther east, on Oxford Clay west of the high road, also caps a watershed, and may belong to a subsequent strike stream flowing into either the Rodden brook or the Wey. Its height is 198 ft. above O.D.[2]

The patch on the summit of Fleet Common, resting on a thin layer of Kellaways Clay over Cornbrash, covers a considerable area. Its highest point is 223 ft. above O.D., but it slopes south-westward almost to the 200-foot contour. The gravel is thin and consists of the usual subangular flints, greensand chert, and rarer battered Eocene beach flints, to which are added pieces of Forest Marble and Cornbrash. Strahan[3] recorded " an occasional Budleigh pebble " here, and in half an hour's search of the

---

[1] H. J. O. White, ' Geology of the country around Bournemouth,' 2nd edition, *Mem. Geol. Survey*, 1917, p. 51.

[2] The second patch mapped $\frac{1}{3}$ mile east of this on much lower ground, north of Drift Plantation, seems to consist of scattered flints only and not to form a true gravel deposit.

[3] A. Strahan, *Purbeck Memoir*, 1898, p. 198.

ploughed field on the summit I found one specimen $3\frac{1}{4}$ ins. in diameter. Since this patch of gravel stands alone on the highest point for miles in any direction except the north, its origin can be only conjectured. A stream at such a height could have flowed in almost any direction. The problem of the occasional Bunter quartzite pebbles is still unsolved, for none has been found in the Eocene rocks. Their occurrence in the 60-foot terrace of the Wey indicates that they were brought from the west at a period earlier than these gravel terraces, although later than the Eocene; perhaps, therefore, during the Pliocene submergence.

Strahan[1] also found " a very few " Bunter pebbles in the patches of flint and chert gravel on the Oxford Clay at Furzedown, which lie at about 60 ft. (the south-easterly patch) and 70-75 ft. (the north-westerly patch) above O.D. and may mark a former course of the Wey, or of a strike tributary that flowed eastward to it. No sections are to be seen. There are two other patches at about the same height on Fuller's Earth south of Langton Herring. Baden-Powell[2] associated all these with the Fleet River, but an examination of the ground seems to make it more probable that they belong to separate streams or to separate tributaries of the same stream. The Langton Herring patches seem to be associated with the Rodden brook, whereas those at Furzedown are connected with the Wey by the gravel-sprinkled plateau on which the isolation hospital stands. There is another patch at approximately the same height above sea on the water-parting north of the station at Small Mouth (obscurely exposed at the back of the bowling green club house). Each clay strike vale thus preserves relics of its earlier drainage.

In the neighbourhood of Osmington are several small patches of high-level gravel without any obvious relation to the topography or the drainage lines. The largest, on Shortlake Drive, seems to slope down from a little below the 300-foot contour to the 200-foot contour in a distance of 200 yds., but the lower part is probably washed down the hillside. Other patches near Sandy Barrow are difficult to distinguish from Angular Flint Gravel, of which sections are seen on Lower Chalk in the mud slides. The most easterly patch, 250 yds. east of the cascade at the Mills, is 8 ft. thick and rests on basal Kimmeridge Clay at the cliff top, 163 ft. above sea-level. This may possibly be connected with an early stage of the Osmington stream.

In Purbeck only two small patches of Plateau Gravel are known. The more important, a couple of acres in extent, caps a small hill on the Wealden Beds between Bucknowle House and West Bucknowle, one mile south-west of Corfe Castle. The level top of the hill is 100 ft. above the flood plain of the adjoining Steeple Brook or Corfe River. A gravel pit shows 14 ft. of well

---

[1] loc. cit., 1898.

[2] D. F. W. Baden-Powell, Geol. Mag., vol. lxvii, 1930, p. 502.

bedded, medium-grained, subangular flint gravel with seams of rusty-coloured coarse sand and loam. The finer gravel and loam are false-bedded towards the east, in the direction of flow of the present stream. There are occasional larger flints, and rare pebbles of quartz, Wealden grit, Upper Greensand, Purbeck Beds, and quartzite (one found, 1½ ins. in diameter). Coarse flint flakes believed to be of human making are not uncommon. The base of the gravel is not seen. It was the river of this stage that cut the platform in the Chalk north-west of Corfe Castle. The gravel suggests a river much larger than could be supplied by the present catchment of Steeple Brook.

The other patch of gravel, made up of chert and limestone, caps a knoll of Kimmeridge Clay just above the 300-foot contour south-west of Encombe House.

A Palæolithic hand-axe presented to the British Museum was said to have been picked up below the Grand Hotel at Swanage, but no gravel is visible there in the cliff.

(d) PORTLAND RAISED BEACH

At Portland Bill, where the building stones dip gently south-eastwards and are quarried only 20 ft. above sea-level, a bank of raised beach shingle, with marine shells, overlain by loam and angular limestone gravel, stretches along the coastal flat for a mile. The cliffs provide two cross-sections, the best on the west coast north of the Bill Quarries, about 400 yds. north-west of the lighthouse, and another at Sand Holes, 1 mile from the lighthouse up the east coast. The upper limit of the deposits reaches a height of 65 ft. above sea-level. The old beach ran in a direction N.E.-S.W., at right angles to Chesil Beach, although the materials are similar.

The section in the cliff 400 yds. north-west of the lighthouse at present shows the following[1] (Pl. XVII, B) :—

	Ft.
Head : angular rubble of Purbeck and Portland beds, roughly stratified, especially in the lower part, where it is inter-stratified with the loam	4 to 5
Loam, yellowish brown, with many calcareous pellets and layers of rubble, especially towards the top. Non-marine shells	4
Shingle, well-rounded, clean washed, obliquely bedded, becoming sandier towards the lighthouse, where marine shells are common ; gastropods predominate. Locally cemented	9

The shingle is gently false-bedded towards the south-east. Towards the north-west all the deposits except the Head can be seen to be banked up against a small cliff of Lower Purbeck tufas,

---

[1] Previously described by Whitaker (1869), Prestwich (1875), Strahan (1898), Baden-Powell (1930) and others. For history of research prior to 1898 see A. Strahan, *Purbeck Memoir*, p. 201.

from which they are separated by a consolidated scree of large angular blocks. Southward the platform on which they rest slopes down from 50 ft. to about 20 ft. above O.D.

The eastern section at Sand Holes is now much modified by quarrying and has deteriorated. Prestwich[1] described it as follows:—

						Ft.	Ins.
[Head] Angular debris	...	...	...	...	...	5	0
Loam with land-shells and layers of angular debris		...	...	...	...	6	0
Sand ...	...	...	...	...	...	1	6
Raised beach...	...	...	...	...	...	3	6

The wave-washed platform is still well shown here, with parts of the raised beach adhering to it. Quarries afford numerous less complete sections.

The petrology of the raised beach presents interesting problems. The pebbles are composed of the following rocks, listed in order of abundance[2]:—

1. Flints and cherts, forming about 90 per cent in the west, but only 40-50 per cent farther east.
2. Limestones, local Portland and Purbeck, rising from about 9 to over 50 per cent at the east end.
3. Black hornstones, quartz, tourmalinized slate, etc., all well rounded.
4. Black and brown cherts.
5. Purbeck ' beef,' small fragments.
6. Ferruginous grit, in large partly-rounded lumps; either Tertiary or Wealden.
7. Bunter quartzites, well-rolled, oval, 3 to 4 ins. long; like those in the Trias at Budleigh Salterton.
8. Granite, coarse, pegmatitic, pink.
9. Porphyry as in the Permian breccias of Dawlish, Devon.

Granite boulders (size not stated) were recorded by Prestwich.

Baden-Powell[3] points out that most of the shells of the raised beach are found on the lower slopes of the platform, where the deposits are more sandy and accumulated near the low watermark of the time; higher up, in the shingle, they become rare. He finds that the conditions of gradient, coarseness of material and mode of occurrence of the shells closely resemble those on modern beaches of similar type. The list now includes over 50 species, of which a large majority are rare. The commonest are various periwinkles, *Neritoides littoralis* (Linné), *Littorina littorea* (Linné), *Rissoa spp.*, and the tiny bivalve *Turtonia minuta* (Fabricius). The facies is rocky rather than sandy. Several authors (Damon, Sykes, Gwyn Jeffreys, Baden-Powell) have pointed out that the

---

[1] J. Prestwich, ' Notes on the Phenomena of the Quaternary Period in the Isle of Portland and around Weymouth,' *Quart. Journ. Geol. Soc.,* vol. xxxi, 1875, p. 35.

[2] A. Strahan, *Purbeck Memoir,* 1898, p. 202; D. F. W. Baden-Powell, ' The Geological Evolution of the Chesil Bank,' *Geol. Mag.,* vol. lxvii, 1930, p. 504; all the rocks mentioned have been found also by me.

[3] D. F. W. Baden-Powell, ' Notes on Raised Beach Mollusca from the Isle of Portland,' *Proc. Malacological Soc.,* vol. xix, 1930, p. 67.

assemblage as a whole now lives on the shores of northern England and Scotland, from which it is to be inferred that at the time the raised beach was being formed the sea was somewhat (perhaps 3 or 4°) colder at Portland than it is now. Prestwich suggested that the Cornish pebbles were brought by floating ice, and this seems the only likely agent to have transported the rare boulders of granite (*see* p. 332); but their arrival must have antedated the fauna, which is of temperate type. No arctic or sub-arctic species have been recognized and, with the possible exception of one *Rissoa,* none of the species or varieties is extinct.

The age of the Portland raised beach cannot be fixed with certainty, but it is older than the Head and loam which overlie it (*see* p. 331) and yet cannot be of any great antiquity since all its species and varieties of shells are still living in the British seas. Its height above sea-level suggests correlation with the 60-foot terrace of the Wey, which represents the Bransgore stage of the Avon and Stour (post-Middle Acheulian and presumably Middle Palæolithic). Baden-Powell considers the sea level of Portland raised beach times to have been about 40 ft. higher than at present, in which case the beach is probably somewhat younger than this; but deductions of sea level from raised beaches are admittedly inexact, and the tidal fall of the time is unknown.

It is highly probable that the westward continuation of Portland Raised Beach is to be found at Hope's Nose, Torquay. The ancient shingle and sand there rests upon a platform about 25-30 ft. above high water mark of ordinary tides and likewise contains an assemblage of marine shells indicating a somewhat colder climate than the present.[1] In the Start district a raised beach platform is met with only from high water mark up to about 10 ft. O.D., and it is overlain by a great accumulation of Head, which in places reaches a thickness of 40-50 ft.[2] It is possible that the platform slopes up to a somewhat greater elevation beneath this mantle, but it abuts against high ground in a short distance. At Hallsands near the Start a cemented Raised Beach is banked against the old cliff to a height of at least 20 ft. above high water mark.

(e) HEAD AND ASSOCIATED FORMATIONS

During the Pleistocene period alternate freezing and thawing of the soil and probably torrential rains on frozen subsoil, and melting snow, caused movements of mud and rock-debris far greater than any possible at the present day, when the surface is also protected by a coating of humus and vegetation. These movements resulted in the accumulation in favourable places of considerable thicknesses of angular local rock-waste. Near the

[1] W. A. E. Ussher, ' Geology of the Country around Torquay,' *Mem. Geol. Surv.,* 1st. ed., 1903, pp. 118-121 ; and 2nd. ed., 1933.

[2] W. A. E. Ussher, ' Geology of the Country around Kingsbridge and Salcombe,' *Mem. Geol. Surv.,* 1904, pp. 66-71.

foot of cliffs and steep hills such accumulations cannot be distinguished from scree, downwash and landslip, but their special feature is that they spread out over slopes too gentle to admit of their movement and accumulation under present day conditions of climate. They have been called Coombe Rock, Angular Debris, and Head in various places in accordance with local variations dependent on slope and materials. Head is the generic term now most in use.

One of the classic examples of Head overlies the Raised Beach at Portland Bill (described on pp. 331-2) and was studied exhaustively by Prestwich.[1] It consists of up to 5 ft. of angular rock fragments which spread over the raised beach and loam and on up the slope over the old buried cliff. Local Portland and Purbeck limestones and cherts form the bulk of the fragments, but there are also pieces of Cinder Bed, Beef Beds and Tertiary sandstone, rocks no longer found *in situ* in the island. Downwards the Head merges imperceptibly into the light brown loam over the raised beach (*see* pp. 331-2) and seams of Head are interstratified with the upper part of the loam, so that it is impossible to separate the two. In view of this, special interest attaches to the land and freshwater shells found in the loam. Bullen[2] estimates that nearly 50 per cent consist of *Pupilla muscorum* (Linné), 25 per cent of *Succinea oblonga* (Draparnaud), with *Limnaea pereger* (Müller) (11 per cent), *L. truncatula* (Müller) (8 per cent), *Hygromia rufescens* (Pennant)(= *Trochulus striolatus* C. Pfeiffer) (5 per cent), and much smaller quantities of *Vallonia*, *Helicella*, *Cyclostoma*, *Pisidium and Helix*. The abundance of *Succinea oblonga* points to a late Pleistocene age. The assemblage could only have lived in a temperate climate, certainly not subarctic. The mixture of land and freshwater or marsh forms can be explained by supposing that the terrestial forms were washed by rain into a marsh, or, as Baden-Powell suggests, there may have been disturbance and mixing during the formation of the Head. Since the Head overlies the fossiliferous loam although the two grade into one another, it seems that the formation of the Head was beginning intermittently during the marsh era, but that eventually the marsh and the snails living there and on the neighbouring land were overwhelmed by cold and buried under rock debris.

Thus the Pleistocene deposits of Portland Bill, as Baden-Powell has pointed out,[3] give evidence of two glacial periods and an interglacial. The Head indicates a late Pleistocene glaciation; the loam and raised beach indicate an interglacial period; and the ice-carried granite boulders in the raised beach must have been brought during an earlier glacial period.

---

[1] J. Prestwich, *op. cit.*, 1875, pp. 35 ff.

[2] R. A. Bullen, ' Shells from Portland Rubble Drift,' *Geol. Mag.*, N.S., Dec. iv, vol. vii, 1900, p. 286.

[3] D. F. W. Baden-Powell, ' The Evolution of the Chesil Bank,' *Geol. Mag.*, 1930, p. 508.

Prestwich[1] believed that " the broken and disturbed state of the upper 2 to 3 ft. of the fissile Purbecks in all the higher parts of the Island is part of the same phenomenon " as the Head ; but it is difficult to decide where Head becomes soil-creep or hillwash.

At the north end of the Island, in the cliff near the end of the Chesil Beach at Chesilton, there is a spectacular section of angular rock debris consisting entirely of Portland and Purbeck Beds, exposed to a thickness of about 50 ft. (Fig. 82). The blocks are of all sizes. Here and there they show rough stratification in various directions, and here and there enormous angular rocks are supported in a gravel, or the gravel passes into seams of loam resembling that at the Bill. From a thin loamy seam near the base Prestwich recorded *Bythinia*, *Planorbis*, *Limnaea* and *Pupa*, and he classed the whole as Head. It may be as old as the Head, but in origin it is clearly landslip debris from the high cliffs of Portland Stone above. It can be seen to pass up continuously

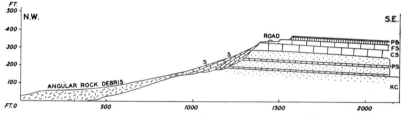

Fig. 82.—*Horizontal section (true scale) north-west to south-east, from near the end of the Chesil Beach at Chesilton to the top of the escarpment at the hairpin bend on the main road, Portland Island.* S, S, slips of Portland Stone. KC = Kimmeridge Clay. PS = Portland Sand. CS, FS, Cherty Series and Freestone Series of the Portland Stone. PB = Purbeck Beds, caps and slatt.

from the beach to the parent cliff, climbing to a height of 352 ft. in a horizontal distance of 1,250 ft., and at the top it merges into a huge landslide, a foundering cake of Portland stone tilted seaward. Marsh shells are often to be found in recent landslips, as at Holworth House and Osmington mud-slides, for as the rocks tilt and founder they give rise to enclosed hollows in which ponds form and may survive for many years (*see* p. 352). All that can be said as to the age of this particular debris is that it has formed since the formation of the cliff that now bounds the north side of the island, but that it long ago reached a state of repose and is only now being attacked and redisturbed by the encroach of the sea.

At Ringstead Bay the cliffs are capped for a distance of about ½ mile by a deposit mapped as Valley Gravel, which Dr. Baden-Powell and I agree is Coombe Rock. It rests on Kimmeridge Clay, to which it gives a flat top, sloping eastwards from 43 ft. above high-watermark of ordinary tides to about 24 ft. near the smuggler's cottage, and thence rising a little eastwards once more.

---

[1] J. Prestwich, *op. cit.*, 1875, p. 39.

Inland it extends at least to the 50-foot contour. At its thickest where exposed, at the west end, it reaches 6 feet. It consists mainly of angular chalk and white-coated brown flint, with a large quantity of Upper Greensand gritstone and glauconitic sandstone, in an abundant clay matrix. The harder blocks of greensand are up to 5 ins. long. Black slate and quartz pebbles are rare. There is no appreciable bedding, but a layer of gravelly clay comes in near the top (1 ft. at thickest). No trace of Corallian limestones has been found, though broken *Ostrea delta* from the subjacent Kimmeridge Clay are abundant. On the other hand, fragments of Portland and Purbeck limestone are not uncommon in the eastern half only of the deposit, where the outcrops of those formations project half way up the hillside behind. It is therefore certain that the deposit is derived directly from the hills ½ mile to the north. There is so much clay that a kind of sludge-creep and melting snow are suggested as the distributing agents (solifluxion).

Many of the dry valleys in the chalk country are partly choked with an ancient debris or ' slurry ', older than the modern hill-wash, as may be seen at Middle and Scratchy Bottoms, near Lulworth. Excavations in a similar deposit, 12 ft. deep, in the bottom of a dry valley at Beer in Devon yielded about 4,000 humanly-flaked flints and 300 burnt flints or cooking stones, irregularly mixed throughout the deposit. The flints are patinated and so are probably older than the deposit, which itself suggests glacial conditions; but their cultural age is problematic, and they are associated with primitive pottery.[1]

At West Stafford, by the road-railway bridge 4/5 mile west of the church, a pit shows 15 ft. of broken chalk rubble (Coombe Rock), now remote from any adequate source.

(f) " MAMMALIFEROUS DRIFT " AND BONE FISSURES OF PORTLAND

In the old Admiralty Quarries near the prison a few hundred yards south of the Verne Fort, on the top of Portland Island, a remarkable deposit was encountered during quarrying operations some 80 years ago. A description of it was published by Prestwich, who saw the last remnants before they were quarried away.[2] Its origin remains problematic.

At a spot where the surface was level and gave no indication of what lay beneath, a trough had been cut down through the Purbeck Beds and the upper part of the Portland Stone to a depth of from 10 to 20 feet. The trough extended for a distance of from 200 to 300 yds. in a N.E.-S.W. direction and had a width of from 50 to 60 yards. It was filled with "red clay or loam . . . in places full of angular local debris of the Portland and Purbeck Beds together with a considerable number of small blocks (some ¼ ton in weight) of hard sandstone or sarsen-stone of the Lower Tertiaries,

[1] G. Woods, and R. M. Woods, *Proc. Prehist. Soc. East Anglia*, vol. vij, 1934, p. 355.
[2] J. Prestwich, *Quart. Journ. Geol. Soc.*, vol. xxxi, 1875, p. 31.

much worn and stained reddish brown, and sometimes blackened by manganese oxide. At a few places this was underlain by a layer of pebbles, waterworn and perfectly rounded, in a matrix of sand and red loam . . . and occasionally cemented together in a thin layer of calcareous spar. The pebbles so encased presented a clean and bright surface as though they had been artificially polished."

In this deposit Prestwich found flint pebbles and subangular fragments and blocks of ironstone grit and hard sandstone from the Tertiary beds, small angular flints from the Chalk, both well-rounded and subangular fragments of chert from the Upper Greensand, and quartz pebbles. The underlying surface of the Portland Stone was waterworn.

In the lower part of the deposit were found bones of *Elephas antiquus* Falconer, *E. primigenius* (?) Blumenbach, *Equus, Cervus,* and *Bos.*

Quarrying operations on the Isle of Portland have from time to time disclosed accumulations of bones. Damon states that in 1840, in a quarry on the north-east side of the island a heap equal to several cartloads was obtained. Among them Buckland and Conybeare identified the following :—head bones of a large boar, *Bos urus,* deer, horse (an extinct species), wolf, dog, sheep, mouse.[1] During the excavation of the deep trench on the south side of the Verne Fort " numerous large fissures, some open at bottom but closed at top, and some entirely filled with debris, were met with, traversing the Portland Stone in a direction nearly north and south." In the open ones were found numerous bones, among which Prestwich saw skull and bones of red deer, a metacarpal bone of *Cervus megaceros* (?) Hart, skull of *Bos longifrons* Owen, and skull of a dog. Damon records also *Cervus tarandus* Linné (reindeer) and *Bos urus.* They were thought by Prestwich to be of comparatively recent origin.[2]

Near Encombe House in Purbeck, at a height of about 240 ft. above sea level and ½ mile from the edge of the cliff, bones of *Elephas primigenius* Blumenbach, *Rhinoceros tichorinus* (= *antiquitatis* Blumenbach), *Cervus tarandus* (?) Linné, *Equus,* and *Bos* were found.[3] The level is about 60 ft. lower than the tiny patch of Plateau Gravel (*see* p. 331).

(g) CHESIL BEACH AND THE ORIGIN OF THE FLEET (Pl. XVII).

The great storm beach known as the Chesil[4] Beach or Bank is generally considered to begin (since any point must be chosen arbitrarily) at Bridport. Thence it extends a distance of 18 miles to the Isle of Portland, where it ends abruptly against the cliffs south of Chesilton. " For the first 6 miles of its course it keeps in contact with the coast, but then for 8 miles maintains a beauti-

---

[1] R. Damon, *Geology of Weymouth,* 2nd ed., 1884, p. 144. London.
[2] J. Prestwich, *op. cit.* 1875, p. 30 ; O. Fisher, *The Geologist,* vol. vi, 1863, p. 250.
[3] J. Prestwich, *Quart. Journ. Geol. Soc.,* vol. xlviii, 1892, p. 277.
[4] *Ceosol, Cisel,* Saxon for shingle (cf. Chislehurst).

fully even curve at a distance of 200 to 1,000 yds. from the mainland, enclosing between itself and the shore a shallow salt-water
and brackish lagoon known as the Fleet.[1] For the last 2 miles the
beach strikes boldly out to sea to join itself on to Portland. It
ranges in width from 170 yds. at Abbotsbury to 200 yds. at
Portland, and in height from 22 ft. above high-water mark at
Abbotsbury to 42 ft. at Chesilton. From Abbotsbury to Wyke it
rises at the rate of 1 in 8,450 and from Wyke to Chesilton at the
rate of 1 in 880. The shingle extends to a depth below Low-water
Spring Tides of 6 fathoms at Abbotsbury, 7 fathoms at Fleet, and
8 fathoms at Portland, at which depth it gives way to sand. The
stones of which the visible part of the beach consists increase in
size from Abbotsbury to Portland,[2] but those lying below
Low-water mark diminish in size in the same direction.

  " Borings have shown that the shingle rests on its landward
side upon a floor of clay at a depth of 3 or 4 ft. above Low-water
spring tides. The clay is said to have been exposed on the seaward side after storms, but it was not met with in the borings.
It seems, therefore, to form a shelf upon the edge of which the
beach is built . . .   The main part of the beach above High-
water mark is composed of loose shingle, which is always being
shifted according to the changes of the wind, but the shingle below
this is held in a matrix of sand and grit which is almost, if not
quite, watertight. The tide, therefore, gains access to the Fleet
at its eastward end only, by the narrow opening known as Small
Mouth, and the rise and fall at Abbotsbury does not exceed a few
inches and then only at Spring Tides, when a good deal of water
leaks through the upper unconsolidated part of the bank.[3]

  " In exceptional storms, however, the sea seems to have gained
access somewhat freely to the Fleet. Leland, writing in 1546,
speaks of the south-eastern winds breaking through the bank, and
Camden, in 1590, says the Chesil Beach 'when the south wind
rises, gives and commonly cleaves asunder.' Whatever this
expression may mean, it is recorded that on November the 23rd,
1824, the sea-water stood to a depth of 22 feet 8 inches on the
alluvial meadows at the Decoy, near Abbotsbury, this result
having been brought about not so much by the giving way as by
the overtopping of the bank by waves at high tide. In this same
year the sloop Ebenezer, of 100 tons, ran on the crest of a wave so
high up the bank that she was subsequently launched into Portland
Roads. This occurred about midway between Ferry Bridge and
Chesilton."[4]   In this gale the crest of the bank in places was
washed over the back, and many fishermen's cottages at Chesilton
were destroyed, killing 50 to 60 people.[5] On another occasion, in

---

[1] *Fleet, Fleot,* or *Flot,* Saxon for a shallow sheet of water.
[2] [except in the last 100 yards, when they suddenly change back to fine.]
[3] Statistics from Sir J. Coode, ' Description of the Chesil Bank . . ,' *Proc. Inst.
Civil Engineers,* vol. xii, 1853, p. 520.
[4] A. Strahan, *Purbeck Memoir,* 1898, pp. 203-5.
[5] T. B. Groves, *Nature,* vol. xi, 1875, p. 506.

January 1853, a vessel was lifted by a wave and perched on top of the bank two miles from Small Mouth, and everyone aboard was saved.[1]

The highest and widest section of the beach, between Abbotsbury and Chesilton, as pointed out by Lewis,[2] exactly faces the corridor of open sea between Start Point and Ushant, where ocean waves can roll in uninterrupted from the Atlantic. The present position of the whole beach doubtless represents a compromise between the tendency, shared by all shingle banks, to face the longest fetch of open water at right-angles, and the necessity for adaptation to the corner-stone of Portland Island. As Fisher pointed out,[3] if Portland Island could be moved bodily the beach would undoubtedly advance over the soft clays behind and allow the sea rapidly to consume the Weymouth peninsula. It is a mistake, however, to suppose that the beach has reached stability. It is gradually advancing towards the land throughout its whole length, for each great storm casts pebbles over the top, and they roll down the back slope never to return. The beach is therefore very slowly rolling over on itself, and the new pebbles brought into motion by the sea in each storm to replace those cast over the top have lain still for centuries in the interior, since they in turn were last thrown over to the back, there to be buried by others. The lack of vegetation on any part of the bank at the Portland isthmus shows that this process is going on there faster than elsewhere. Moreover, the rubbish of the old village of Chesilton, accumulated originally on the inner side of the bank, is already being consumed by the sea and stands exposed in a vertical cliff. Near Small Mouth the beach is overwhelming blown sand (*see* p. 348).

The grading of the pebbles from the size of peas near Bridport to large cobbles at Chesilton is one of the most remarkable features of Chesil Bank, though a similar grading on a less spectacular scale can be seen in many shingle beaches. Several causes probably contribute towards this result. When waves strike a shore obliquely they drive pebbles up and down it in a series of curves, so that those on the outer face of the beach travel laterally. It has been proved experimentally on Chesil Beach that any pebbles or stones larger than the average for a given stretch of the beach are moved rapidly south-eastwards until they reach the stretch of beach where they conform to the average. There they form particles of a homogeneous platform and lose their individuality, so that the waves can no longer take hold of them. The process is illustrated by the motions of a few pebbles on a sand beach : the pebbles roll about at the mercy of the waves while the

---

[1] W. H. Hudleston, *Proc. Dorset Nat. Hist. and Ant. Field Club,* vol. xviii, 1902, p. xliii.

[2] W. V. Lewis, ' The Evolution of Shoreline Curves,' *Proc. Geol. Assoc.,* vol. xlix, 1938, p. 115.

[3] O. Fisher, ' On the Origin of the Estuary of the Fleet in Dorsetshire,' *Geol. Mag.,* vol. x, 1870, p. 481.

sand, forming a compact mass, allows the water to glance over it and is scarcely moved. The speed at which large pebbles (the experiment was done with half-bricks, quarter-bricks and three-quarter-bricks) travel until they find their proper position on Chesil Bank was found to be 20 to 25 yds. per hour, or 1 mile in three or four days, in ordinary weather. During rather rougher weather some of the brickbats travelled 80 yards per hour, which would transport them the whole length of Chesil Bank (18 miles) in $16\frac{1}{2}$ days. During storms the rate must be very much greater.[1]

The converse process also contributes towards the grading. A compact platform of large pebbles is not moved by small waves, but the smaller particles are cleaned off its surface and out of the interstices and swept along until they reach the part of the beach where they conform to the average. On Chesil Beach, as pointed out by Vaughan Cornish, waves of very different intensities impinge from two different directions. The large storm waves, when they do not meet the beach head-on, come from west of south-west and move the larger pebbles south-eastwards. But at other times lighter winds blow from the south and south-east, generating waves which are only strong enough to move the smaller pebbles, which therefore shift north-westward.[2] A contributory factor is that big storms tend to throw up the larger pebbles towards the top of the bank and only draw the smaller pebbles and sand back again in the backwash. Thus the larger pebbles are left out of reach of the smaller waves which cause westward travel.

The opposite grading of the pebbles below Low-water Mark needs a separate explanation. In this zone waves have little or no power to move shingle, and any grading must presumably be due to tides. It is known that for 18 hours out of every 24 a tidal current flows from the south-west round West Bay and out south-eastwards past Portland Bill. Tidal currents are better able to shift small pebbles than large, and so the finest material has accumulated at the east end of the bay.

The composition of the shingle has an important bearing on the origin of the beach. Limestone and chert from the Portland and Purbeck Beds are plentiful only at the east end, near Chesilton. For the rest the pebbles are mainly of flint and Greensand chert, but far-travelled rocks like those in the Portland Raised Beach are all present and much more plentiful and larger. At Chesilton perfectly oval or flat-rounded pebbles 4 to 7 ins. in diameter of red, pink, purple and white quartzite like those in the Triassic pebble beds of the neighbourhood of Budleigh Salterton are abundant. There are also black quartzites, purple porphyries, and granites. A pink granite submitted to Dr. J. Phemister is said

[1] N. M. Richardson, ' An Experiment on the Movements of a Load of Brick-bats deposited on Chesil Beach,' *Proc. Dorset Nat. Hist. and Ant. Field Club*, vol. xxiii, 1902, p. 123.

[2] Vaughan Cornish, ' On Sea Beaches and Sandbands,' *Geogr. Journ.*, vol. xi, 1898, p. 628.

by him to resemble Eskdale granite rather than Cornish, and an abundant purple porphyry is likened by the same authority to N. England or S. Scotland porphyries rather than anything from the West of England. How came all these far-travelled rocks into the beach?

Some writers have assumed that the non-local pebbles have crossed the floor of West Bay direct from Devon and Cornwall, but this is impossible. Others have supposed that they have migrated round the shore and are still doing so at the present day. To this Strahan objected that no shingle passes or can pass headlands such as Beer Head and Otterton Point.[1] In his opinion all the materials of the Chesil Beach were brought eastwards in much earlier times and spread over the area now occupied by West Bay, first as Bagshot gravels and then later as Plateau Gravels. The sea in eating its way into the land has winnowed out all the indestructible materials and collected them together to form the present beach. He regarded the supply as now practically shut off.[2]

Though it is true that the winnowings of the lost land in West Bay are represented in Chesil Beach, Strahan's explanation is unsatisfying. The Tertiary and Quaternary gravels of the land that still remains adjacent to the beach, and that will be the next fodder for the sea, would be utterly incapable of supplying the millions of small and large Bunter quartzite pebbles so conspicuous on Chesil Beach, or the large quantities of Permian porphyry. The Bagshot gravels have never been found to contain a single pebble of these substances. In the Plateau Gravels Bunter quartzites are extremely rare and none is known exceeding 5 ins. in diameter. No porphyries have been found. Strahan's theory is only plausible if it be assumed that on the lost land far out in West Bay some ancient river flowed from the west and brought with it deposits of gravel differing entirely in composition from those of the early Frome or the streams of the Weymouth district.

Some may prefer as the agent of transport the floating ice of the Glacial Period. This idea has much to be said for it, when the boulders of granite that have been occasionally recorded from Portland Raised Beach and elsewhere are borne in mind. If large boulders can have been transported up channel by ice, the numerous smaller pebbles can have been brought in the same way; or the larger masses brought earlier can have been reduced in the course of time by attrition on the beach. Ice-transported erratics from the west country have long been known on the coast between Portsmouth and Selsey. There is at present a much higher proportion of quartzite and porphyry pebbles in the coarse-graded part of Chesil Beach from Small Mouth to Chesilton than in the

---

[1] A. Strahan, ' Evidence before Royal Commission on Coast Erosion,' 1907, p. 149, (133).

[2] A. Strahan, loc. cit., 1907 ; and Purbeck Memoir, 1898, p. 207 ; also Geographical Journ., vol. xi, 1898, p. 648.

Raised Beach.   This suggests at first a replenishment since Raised
Beach times, but it may be accounted for by concentration of the
largest and hardest pebbles here owing to their relative indestructi-
bility, from a much longer stretch of destroyed Raised Beach.

We are not, however, driven inescapably to invoke the aid of
floating ice.   The ordinary processes of shore migration by wave
action are capable of introducing all the Permo-Triassic pebbles
into the district, together with those of Greensand grit and chert.
Strahan's difficulty that they could not pass such headlands as
Otterton Point and Beer (or even Golden Cap and Thorncombe
Beacon) is illusory.   Such headlands are but transient details of
a coastline that is always changing as it retreats before the sea.
Their existence depends on local accidents of structure at the
present coastline.   When the coast was farther south there would
have been other headlands at other places, each for a time obstruct-
ing the eastward travel of beach shingle and producing the same
illusion of stability.   But in the end the effects of the south-west
wind would prevail, and as each headland melted away a further
stream of shingle from the Triassic rocks (not of the present Devon
coast but of a lost coast farther south) would be released on another
stage of its eastward journey.   Portland itself, as we have seen,
has come into existence as a headland 4 miles long since the middle
of the Palæolithic period or thereabouts.

The process of shore drift has probably been going on since far
back in the beginning of the Pleistocene period, or even earlier.
The occasional Bunter quartzite pebbles on the land surface round
Weymouth suggest that it began as the Pliocene peneplain began
to rise out of the water; for they cannot have been derived from
the Bagshot gravels and cannot have been brought into their
present positions on any feasible theory of Pleistocene drainage or
glacial transport.[1]

Intimately bound up with the Chesil Beach is the question of
the origin of the Fleet.   Prestwich believed " that the sea for a
time passed between Portland and Weymouth, and that the Fleet
is merely a portion of the old shore-line dammed out by the growth
of the Chesil Bank."   But all other writers are agreed that the
coast-line behind the shingle bank has never been subjected to
marine attack but rather, as Strahan put it, " presents the features
characteristic of subaerial denudation, with but slight modification."   Bristow and Whitaker thought that the Fleet was excavated
by streams which were deflected by the advance of the beach;
while Osmond Fisher regarded it as the half of a submerged valley
(' drowned valley ') and therefore as having been formed by a
river before the beach arrived.   Fisher pointed out that it resembles
the drowned valleys of Radipole Backwater and Lodmoor, and

---

[1] They are too big to have been brought up from Chesil Beach for sling stones
by ancient hunters.   The large cache of sling stones found at Maiden Castle
consisted of pebbles with long axis " seldom more than two inches, often less; never
as big as three inches " (Communication from Lieut.-Col. C. D. Drew, D.S.O.,
F.S.A., Dorset County Museum, Dorchester).

that if Portland Island were removed and the Chesil Beach were allowed to advance across the Weymouth peninsula the time would come when it would bisect the Backwater, leaving a landward half resembling the Fleet (but much shorter).

Fisher was right in regarding the low ground of the Fleet as ' drowned ', but there is no evidence that it ever formed the valley of a continuous river. On the contrary, it runs obliquely across all the drainage lines of the Weymouth district and the south-flowing consequent streams are deflected by it to the south-east, as Bristow and Whitaker observed. Moreover, although Chesil pebbles are scarce on the inner shore of the Fleet[1] and the open sea cannot ever have attacked it, there is a marked parallelism between Chesil Beach and the most prominent parts of the shore-line, which present small straight cliffs.

There can be no doubt that the origins of the Fleet and the Chesil Beach must be sought together. They do not fall readily into place in any classification of shoreline forms, being a combination of several. Morphologically they constitute an offshore bar and lagoon, and the fact that one end of the bar joins Portland Island to the mainland makes it a tombolo. But genetically, since the shoreline is one of submergence, and therefore unsuitable for the origin of true offshore bars, a gigantic bay bar, pushed back almost on to its hinterland, would probably be a more accurate description. On either assumption the Fleet is the last relic of a drowned area, formerly opening into West Bay, and submerged in the Neolithic subsidence (*see* p. 317). The present profile of the Chesil Beach, resting on the edge of a submarine cliff of clay, suggests that it originated as an offshore bar, cast up on a cliff excavated by Atlantic rollers as they entered shallow water.[2] On the other hand longshore drift is so active at the present day that it seems probable that the same process built up the bank in the first place.

At the beginning of the Neolithic subsidence we may picture the Chesil Beach as a bay-mouth bar stretching from an extended Portland Bill westward across what is now West Bay to join some lost headland of Cretaceous and Triassic rocks seaward of Beer Head and Dowlands Cliffs. From the western cliffs long-shore drift brought the pebbles which built up the bar and still form it at the present day, centuries after the supply has been cut off. Landward lay a low tract floored chiefly by Jurassic clays, which gradually drowned during the subsidence. At the same time the shingle bar retreated landward and the big rollers excavated a submarine cliff at its foot. The bank would have tended to swing round to keep parallel with the largest waves, and it is possible that slight changes in the prevalent wind over long periods caused one end to retreat faster than the other, as at present.

---

[1] Except where transported by human agency, as at Langton Herring ferry, whence they have spread for long distances on either side.

[2] D. W. Johnson, *Shore Processes and Shoreline Development*, 1919, pp. 365 ff. New York.

(h) PORTLAND HARBOUR BEACH

This small but interesting beach starts at Portland Castle, then leaves the island and strikes north-westward to join the Chesil Beach about 1,200 yds. beyond the railway-station. After running alongside the Chesil Beach, but on the opposite side of the road and railway, for 800 yds., it diverges northward and ends at Small Mouth. The road and railway are carried along this latter part of it. The two spits together form an example of a " double tombolo."

In composition this beach provides a striking contrast with the Chesil Beach. Although the two run in contact they never mingle. The stones composing it are almost entirely subangular or angular pieces of Portland and Purbeck limestones and cherts from the east cliffs of the Island. Recently there has been a good deal of contamination by human agencies, and the supply of materials from the Island is cut off by the breakwater.

Portland Harbour Beach is broken by a gap through which the tides gain access to a mud flat called the Mere, enclosed in the triangular space between the island and the two beaches. It appears that early in the 16th century the Mere was continuous with the Fleet, [1] but that the eastward advance of Chesil Beach has severed the connexion and forced the Fleet to find a new outlet at Small Mouth.

(i) WEYMOUTH BEACH AND OTHER SHINGLE BEACHES

The part of Weymouth north of the harbour, formerly the separate town of Melcombe Regis, is largely built on a spit of sand and shingle barring the drowned valley of Radipole Backwater. The same beach is continued as a higher and narrower spit across the drowned valley of Lodmoor and along the foot of Jordan Hill to Bowleaze. Opposite Lodmoor it is a true storm beach and the pebbles are larger. There is thus a sorting action which drives the larger pebbles north of the centre and accumulates the sand at Weymouth, and to a smaller extent at Bowleaze. The storm beach almost exactly faces the longest fetch of open water, between Nothe Point and White Nothe, but it and the north end of the beach to Bowleaze are steadily retreating landward like the south end of the Chesil Beach. The main road had to be set back 60 ft. between 1860 and 1890, and was already being overwhelmed again in 1899. [2] After a gale on June 1st, 1938, shingle completely blocked the road and one-way traffic was necessary for a week while clearance was going on. Since then the concrete wall has been doubled in height. " Many thousands of tons of Portland Stone in large blocks were deposited on the shore to form a pro-

---

[1] Leland, quoted in W. J. Black, ' Remarks on the Chesil Beach,' *Trans. Manchester Geol. Soc.*, vol. xv., 1878, p. 46.

[2] T. B. Groves, ' Erosion of the coast near Weymouth,' *Proc. Dorset Nat. Hist. and Antiq. Field Club*, vol. x, 1889, p. 182. Also W. H. Wheeler, *The Sea Coast*, 1902, pp. 155-6. London.

tection " at Jordan Hill and Bowleaze some time between 1860 and 1880.[1] These are now mainly below tide mark.

Changes on Weymouth beach have been accelerated by the construction of Portland breakwater, which has diminished the influence of the S. and S.E. winds and thus given greater effect to those from a more easterly quarter.[2] As Lewis remarks, " probably the breakwaters have caused a slight deflection of the dominant wave fronts by retarding their southern ends, so that the beach is tending to swing round in sympathy.[3] As might be expected, shingle is tending to extend southward and drive some of the Weymouth sand before it, so that in the last half century Weymouth sands have become shorter and wider.[4]

In the $4\frac{1}{2}$ miles eastward to White Nothe is a sinuous coast whose outlines correspond to a varied geological structure. There is much shingle, which alternates with stretches of bare rock, and it is noteworthy how all the principal banks of shingle face southeast, parallel to the Lodmoor-Furzy Cliff part of the Weymouth storm beach. The chief shingle banks are from Redcliff Point to Shortlake ($\frac{3}{4}$ mile), and Ringstead Bay from Bran Point to Holworth House ($1\frac{1}{4}$ mile). The latter stretch of coast is sinuous, and with each undulation the shingle is graded afresh. The larger pebbles travel westward and the storm beaches are banked up at the west end of each stretch (*see* Fig. 79). The westward travel of the pebbles in Ringstead Bay is proved by the eastward increase in abundance of Upper Greensand grits and the absence of Corallian limestones. Otherwise these beaches consist almost entirely of flint and chert.[5]

East of White Nothe the coast gradually escapes from the influence of Portland Island and the shingle banks at first face south (White Nothe to Durdle) and then tend to swing round to parallelism with Chesil Beach, facing south-west into the prevalent wind (Durdle Cove, Man-o'-War Cove, St. Oswald's Bay, Worbarrow Bay, Brandy Bay, Kimmeridge-Egmont Bight). Those at the foot of the chalk cliffs near Lulworth are of remarkably pure chalk flint shingle, that at Worbarrow contains much Wealden quartz grit and Purbeck limestone, and those under the Kimmeridge cliffs are largely of local shale pebbles and would hardly be called shingle in ordinary parlance.

It is noticeable that in circular bays or bays with headlands on both sides the shingle bank and the size of the pebbles both increase towards the centre, to face the open sea. Lulworth Cove and Worbarrow Bay are good examples. Worbarrow best illus-

[1] T. B. Groves, *loc. cit.*
[2] R. Damon, *Geology of Weymouth*, 2nd edit. 1884, p. 155. London.
[3] W. V. Lewis, *Proc. Geol. Assoc.*, vol. xlix, 1938, p. 115.
[4] T. B. Groves, *op. cit*, pp. 185-6.
[5] After south-easterly gales the shingle along the whole of the main stretch of Ringstead Bay (east of the first point east of the smuggler's cottage) is covered with firm coarse sand, brought up from below normal low watermark.

trates the motions of the shingle, for the opposite ends of the bay contribute different rocks.   It is evident that the constituents are sorted solely according to size, irrespective of origin, for pebbles of chalk from the north are mixed thoughout with pebbles of Purbeck limestone from the south and abundant purple quartz grit from the Wealden in the middle.   Therefore all large pebbles travel towards the centre of the bay, where alone the prevalent storm waves strike head-on and there is no tendency to shift later-ally.   When they have remained there long enough to be worn down to smaller sizes they come under the influence of the smaller waves which strike the beach obliquely, and they begin their journey back, arriving finally as coarse sand at one end of the bay or the other.

Swanage beach differs from Weymouth beach in possessing a smaller proportionate length of shingle and in the absence of the return to fine shingle and sand at the end, although the geological conditions are the same and the curve and orientation of the two beaches are identical.   The difference is due to the interference of Portland Island and breakwaters.   The biggest waves that reach Swanage bay strike the shore at Punfield, but the biggest that reach Weymouth bay impinge at Lodmoor.

Blocks of Cornish or Devon granite 6 ins. and more in diameter are sometimes picked up on the shore at White Nothe.   Smaller pebbles (3 to 5 ins.), imperfectly rounded, of quite a different salmon pink granite are common on Ringstead beach as far west as Bran Point and I have found the same granite in Lulworth Cove and Swanage Bay.   Dr. J. Phemister reports that this seems to be a Cumberland granophyre and was probably brought south as ballast.   It does not match any Channel Islands or foreign rock in the Survey collections.   At Lulworth Cove I have also found pebbles of quartzite, green Cornish granite, gneiss, and a porphyry which Dr. Phemister compares with the rhyolite-quartz porphyry series described from the Permian breccias of the Torquay promontory; none of the igneous pebbles was well rounded.

A large quantity of red and green granite in Durlston Bay was introduced by the foundering of a ship near Peveril Point during the war of 1914-18. [1]

(j) SHORE SAND AND BLOWN SAND

Weymouth and Swanage owe their growth and prosperity as seaside towns to their superb sands.   Except at Studland there is no rival beach in Dorset.   At Swanage the Wealden Beds and at Studland the Bagshot Beds provide ample sources of supply; but in fact this has no influence on the accumulation of sand. Worbarrow has the same rocks as Swanage, but it faces west and

---

[1] I have nowhere found east of Chesilton the purple porphyry so abundant there in the Chesil Beach, which Dr. Phemister likens to N. England or S. Scotland rocks (see pp. 340-1); nor has it occurred in the Portland Raised Beach.

has only shingle and a little coarse sand at the extremities. Weymouth, on the other hand, faces east like Swanage and Studland, and the beach is banked on Oxford Clay, with no adequate source of sand in the neighbourhood. The next accumulation of

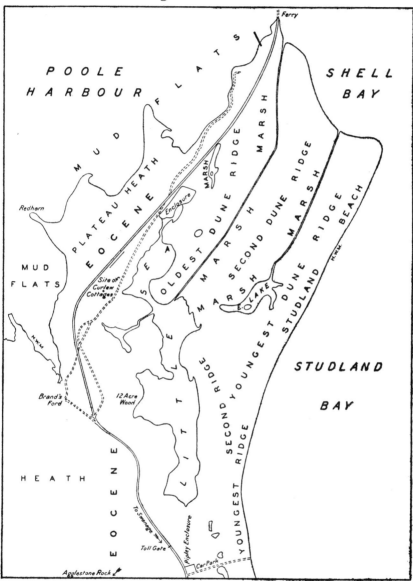

Fig. 83.—*Sketch-map of South Haven Peninsula, Studland.* (Based on Diver).

sand westwards is on the Lias Clay at Lyme Regis, which likewise faces east. In the Isle of Wight the sands of Sandown and Shanklin face east, and there is no equivalent beach in the same geological formations on the west coast. The tendency for sand to accumulate on east-facing or lea shores and shingle on wind-ward coasts is merely an extension of the tendency already observed in individual bays and mentioned in subsection (i). The south ends of east-facing bays never receive the full impact of waves big enough to drive shingle into them, but the deflected ends of the waves, arriving at angles up to 150° from their original direction, are continually piling up sand.

The only other true sandy beach in the area is at Sandsfoot (also facing east). Insignificant accumulations occur also at Bowleaze, Ringstead, Lulworth, Mupe, Worbarrow, Kimmeridge and Chapman's Pool, always in protected places or inlets. At most of these localities it is very fine shingle rather than sand.

Blown sand covers a small area at Small Mouth under the Whitehead Torpedo Works and also on the opposite side of the Fleet, buried under shingle from the Chesil Beach and seen only in excavations. [1]   The only large accumulation is at Studland Bay, where there is a strip 2½ miles long and widening northwards from nil to ⅔ mile in breadth, forming South Haven Peninsula (Fig. 83). The main blown sand area consists of three parallel ridges running a little east of north, separated from each other and from the Tertiary land at the back by strips of marsh with peat and scattered pools, of which the innermost widens south-ward into a freshwater lake 1 mile in length, called Little Sea. The west shore of Little Sea is the original coastline and is marked by a small rise on to higher land (20-50 ft.), formerly a low sea cliff, of which the southward extension can be readily followed, between the sea and Knoll House Hotel, to Studland. The old cliff is aligned with the present seaward shore at Sandbanks, on the opposite side of Poole Harbour mouth, with which it forms an unbroken curve to Hengistbury Head. The blown sand of South Haven Peninsula breaks the curve and juts out into what must once have been part of the bay. It is, in fact, an accretion of surprisingly recent growth.

In an interesting study of this area Diver has shown by collect-ing and comparing the evidence of old maps that Little Sea has been cut off from the sea and the three successive ridges of blown sand have been built up since as recently as the sixteenth century.[2] In the maps by Saxton (1575), Camden (1607) and Speed (1611) the peninsula is shown as nothing but the narrow strip of land corresponding with the Tertiary country west of the old sea cliff. Little Sea is first shown in a map published in 1721. It was then a tidal inlet with a wide opening eastward into the bay, partly enclosed by the earliest of the three dune ridges. By the end of the eighteenth century the inlet had become a lagoon, and the

---

[1] D. F. W. Baden-Powell, *op. cit.*, 1930, p. 508. Shingle from the beach was thrown over it in the great gale of 1824, according to J. B. Groves, *Nature*, vol. xi, 1875, p. 506.

[2] C. Diver, ' The Physiography of South Haven Peninsula, Studland Heath, Dorset,' *Geographical Journal*, vol. lxxxi, 1933, p. 404.

second dune ridge had formed. A survey of 1849 shows the
beginnings of the outermost dune ridge, but it was still invaded
by the sea at highest spring tides, when the water also flowed
behind it into Little Sea, along the course of the present outer

From Camden's Britannia, 1607.

From Avery's survey, 1721.

From Isaac Taylor's map, 1765.

From the Ordnance Survey of 1811.

FIG. 84.—*Four old maps of the South Haven Peninsula, Studland Heath,
showing the growth of the blown sand area and the gradual enclosure of
Little Sea* (Reproduced from C. Diver, in *Geographical Journal*, 1933, p. 407).

trough of marshland. During this general growth of the sand
area the outlines of Little Sea and the other pools passed through
many vicissitudes, and part of the dunes built seawards near the
south end of the area before the eighteenth century was consumed

again by the sea.   At present the land is still growing along most
of the line of Studland Bay, recent surveys showing an advance
of about 80 yds. in the 30 years before 1924, and there are signs
that a fourth dune ridge is beginning to form.   This growth is
counterbalanced, however, by the sea attacking at more than
double that rate on the north-east coast at Shell Bay.

Diver and a team of collaborators tell a fascinating story of the
gradual colonization of this new land by flora and fauna.[1]   Unlike
most coastal blown sand, the Studland sand is almost devoid of
lime, and consequently marram grass gives place to heather much
more quickly, and lime-loving plants and snails are absent.   It is
a white silica sand and in places is of the peculiar quality which
produces " singing sands " when trodden under foot.   It appears
to be derived (via the sea bottom) from the Tertiary sands in the
vicinity.

The cause of the accumulation of so much sand in Studland
Bay is obscure, but it is probably a secondary effect of the advance
of the sea along the Bournemouth and Christchurch cliffs.   The
destruction there has been very rapid in historic times and must
have produced great changes in the curves of the coastline besides
supplying an enormous amount of sand to the neighbouring sea
bed.   The inland cliff behind Little Sea, although, as Diver says,
appearing to continue the curve of the coastline to Hengistbury
Head, must in reality have been the continuation of a flatter
curve a considerable distance farther south.   It is possible that
the recent erosion in Shell Bay may be connected with the checking
of erosion from Bournemouth to Southbourne by the construction
of undercliff drives : the advance of the vanguard having been
stopped, deposition has given place to erosion in the rear.

(k)   ALLUVIUM AND PEAT

Except along the valley of the Frome the amount of alluvium
in the area is small.   A section across the valley of the Jordan
River at Bowleaze shows a few feet of dark alluvial clay full of
recent land and freshwater snails, capped by a few feet (variable)
of recent stream gravel.   At Lodmoor, Radipole Backwater and
the head of the Fleet at Abbotsbury alluvium merges into grass
moor and reed swamp.   On the acid subsoil of the Bagshot Beds
round Poole Harbour it merges into peat with *Sphagnum.*

All the drowned valleys (Poole, Lodmoor, Radipole, West
Fleet) are still silting up with new alluvium brought down by the
streams.

---

[1] C. Diver and R. Good, ' General Scheme of the Survey,' *Journ. Animal Ecology,*
vol. iii, 1934, p. 129 ; R. Good, ' General Ecology of the Flowering Plants and Ferns,'
Journ. Ecology, vol. xxiii, 1935, p. 361 ; C. Diver, ' The Plant-Carpet in relation to
Animal Distribution,' *Proc. Linn. Soc.,* session 150, 1938, p. 124 ; C. Diver, ' The
Study of a Changing Environment,' *Proc. Bournemouth Nat. Sci. Soc.,* vol. xxviii,
1936, p. 57 ; D. Lack and L. S. V. Venables, ' The Heathland Birds,' *Journ.
Animal Ecology,* vol. vi, 1937, p. 62.   There are also other papers on insects.

According to Damon " A bed of peat is at times exposed a little distance from the shore in Weymouth Bay, containing wings of beetles, tangled and partly carbonised plants, etc.' This presumably represents a former extension of Lodmoor or the Backwater, separated by the landward advance of Weymouth beach.

(1) TUFA

At Blashenwell Farm, 1 mile south-south-west of Corfe Castle, a deposit of calcareous tufa occupies an elliptical area 500 yds. long by up to 220 yds. wide. The greatest thickness proved was 9 feet. It can still be seen, and was formerly much excavated, at a pit 250 yds. north of the farm. The tufa is said to rest on a loam with a stony base. The lower part of the tufa is loamy and marly, the upper part hard. It is capped by 1 ft. of black soil with Roman coins, Romano-British pottery, and shells of oyster, whelk, and cockle, proving the date of the tufa to be at least older than the Roman occupation.

The contents of the tufa have been worked out in detail.[2] 21 species of land-snails have been identified, of which ' Helix ' [Cepaea] nemoralis Linné, [C.] hortensis Müller, [Arianta] arbustorum (Linné), [Trochulus] hispida Linné and [Goniodiscus] rotundata (Müller), Oxychilus cellarium (Müller), Clausilia rugosa (Draparnaud) and Pomatias elegans (Müller) are common. There is only one species of freshwater or marsh snail, Limnaea truncatula (Müller), found rarely near the bottom of the tufa. Leaves of hazel, elm and oak have been recognized. Traces of Stone Age man have been found in abundance in all layers of the deposit, in the forms of flaked flints, charcoal, bones of pig, red deer, roe deer and ox, and shells of limpets, periwinkles, Trochus and Scrobicularia, probably brought from the neighbourhood of Chapman's Pool for food. Mr. C. F. C. Hawkes of the British Museum (Dept. of British and Mediæval Antiquities) in 1938 at my request kindly examined all the available flaked flints collected when the tufa was worked for marling the land, and now preserved in Dorchester Museum. He reports that the collection consists entirely of cores and flakes of a microlithic (" pigmy ") industry unmistakably of the later Mesolithic period, probably the ' Atlantic ' phase of post-glacial climate-history. Although most of the material bears a white patina, he considers its uniformly fresh and sharp condition proves it to be contemporary with the deposit. He compares the Blashenwell occurrence with an asso-

---

[1] R. Damon, Geology of Weymouth, 2nd. edit., 1884, pp. 155-6. London.
[2] C. Reid, Proc. Dorset Nat. Hist. and Ant. Field Club, vol. xvii, 1896, p. 67. Reid's detailed description and list of mollusca are reproduced in A. Strahan, Purbeck Memoir, 1898, p. 210. See also J. G. D. Clark, ' Microlithic Industries from Tufa Deposits at Prestatyn, Flintshire, and Blashenwell, Dorset,' Proc. Prehistoric Soc. for 1938, 1939, p. 330.

ciation of similar implements and tufa at Prestatyn, North Wales.[1]

The contents of the Blashenwell tufa make it clear that it was not formed in a lake or swamp, but on the surface of the ground, and at a time when the climate was known to be damp. It was presumably deposited by a spring draining from a sharp synclinal trough of Upper Purbeck Beds which here runs east-and-west from Blashenwell past Lynch for nearly a mile. The spring still rises, but deposition of tufa has long ceased. In the moist climate of late Mesolithic times it was larger and much more highly charged with dissolved bicarbonate of lime, and on rising to the surface carbon dioxide would have been given off and lime deposited.

A tufa of similar origin occurs by the ford at the mouth of Spring Bottom, Ringstead. It covers an area about 200 ft. long by just over 100 ft. wide and has been cut into by the modern stream. It differs from the Blashenwell tufa in the abundance of hard spheroidal nodules about the size of a pigeon's egg. On being broken open these exhibit nests of concentric tufa spheres formed round a small central cavity. The cavity originally contained some fragment of organic (usually vegetable) debris, providing the nucleus around which deposition of lime began. Later the nucleus was dissolved away. No evidence has been found by which to date the Ringstead tufa.

The spring at Lulworth Cove from which the neighbourhood draws its water supply has deposited a tufa cement in the interstices of the surrounding scree of chalk and flint debris, converting it to a rock like concrete. It is a conspicuous object on the north side of the road leading down to the Cove.

(m) LANDSLIPS

On steep coasts built of varied strata landslips are a normal feature and scarcely need description. The cliffs of St. Alban's Head, Hounstout, and White Nothe provide the best examples. A wild undercliff of chalk or limestone boulders encumbers the slopes and often remains stable for many years while a special flora takes possession. Such regions are a paradise for ravens, falcons, foxes and adders. Hollows behind slipped masses fill with marsh, in which helleborine and figwort flourish, or even collect good-sized ponds (as north-west of Goggins Barrow, Osmington). Later the peat or alluvial deposits, with pond snails and plants, become enclosed in fresh landslips and may appear centuries later at sea level beneath a great thickness of rock debris. Examples of this have been noticed below Holworth House, Ring-

---

[1] Abundant Mesolithic implements and plants are found in the Isle of Wight, in the alluvium of the old Western Yar capping the Wealden cliffs at Brook, and in the Medina estuary at Werrar brickyard. See H. F. Poole, ' An Outline of the Mesolithic Flint Cultures of the Isle of Wight,' Proc. I.O.W. Nat. Hist. Arch. Soc., vol. ii, 1937, p. 551 ; and M. H. Clifford, ' A Mesolithic Flora in the Isle of Wight,' ibid., p. 582.

stead, and at Chesilton (p. 335). The ' mud glaciers ' west of Osmington Mills are a special kind of landslip in particularly greasy materials with a low angle of repose, and their motion is a flowing rather than a slipping.

Major landslips inland are more unusual. In our area the principal formation to slip is the Upper Greensand with the Gault. Curtains of slipped Greensand obscure the hill slopes at Abbotsbury and continue towards Portisham. At Osmington Mills the stream valley is excavated for $\frac{1}{4}$ mile through slipped Greensand and its banks and bed resemble those of a torrent cut into a moraine. The chalk pit north-east of the Mills is entirely in a large slipped mass. Again at the east end of Ringstead Bay, the bend in the hills centred on South Holworth Cottages is filled with a triangular mass of slipped Greensand and Gault covering a quarter of a square mile. The slips, which have flowed down the slope at some ancient time probably in the manner of the mud slides of Osmington, have long come to rest, but have left a hummocky topography with marshy hollows. The highest and least distintegrated mass was mapped as Portland Beds, but exposures show nothing but Upper Greensand. Both these and the Osmington Mills slips coincide with the turning of the Greensand outcrop from the direction of strike to the direction of dip.

On the south flank of the saddle between the Poxwell pericline and the Sutton Poyntz pericline, the Upper and Middle Purbeck Beds, tilted southwards at angles of 35-50°, have collapsed and slipped down over the Wealden of the Upton syncline. Part of these slips was exposed in Poxwell road-cutting (p. 143).

About 450 yds. north-east of Chalbury Camp an anomalous stepped outcrop of the cementstones at the top of the Portland Sands, far below their normal position and associated with a spring and marshy ground, may probably be explained as a landslip.

The landslips round the cliffs of the northern half of Portland Island are to some extent intermediate between normal cliff slides and inland slips, for some are ancient and date from the original formation of the escarpment, before the sea approached (*see* p. 335). Others are very recent and are documented with a copious literature. Hutchins records large slips in the seventeenth and eighteenth centuries. The greatest occurred in 1792, when a mass $1\frac{1}{4}$ miles long and 600 yds. broad on the north-east coast slipped down 50 feet. Another mass of 25 acres subsided in 1858 on the west coast, and some garden plots which had previously sloped towards the sea at an angle of 25° were rotated until they sloped at an angle of 45° towards the island. The beach beneath was forced upwards on a bulge of Kimmeridge Clay.[1]

---

[1] R. Damon, *Geology of Weymouth*, 2nd edit., 1884, pp. 157-8. London.

CHAPTER XV

ECONOMIC GEOLOGY

(a) BUILDING, ROAD, AND ORNAMENTAL STONES

The most important and the most ancient industry in the district is that of stone quarrying. The two principal centres are Portland Island (Portland Stone only) and Swanage (Middle Purbeck Beds, with a subordinate amount of Portland Stone quarried in the cliffs between Anvil Point and St. Alban's Head and at Worth under the name Purbeck-Portland).

An account of the quarrying industry of Portland Island is given on pp. 118-121, and of Swanage on pp. 133-135. A much fuller account of the history of the industry will be found in the *Victoria County Histories*, Dorset, vol. ii, 1908, p. 330. The biggest quarry owners on the island at present are the Bath and Portland Stone Firms, Ltd. At and about Swanage there are innumerable firms. Most of the Middle Purbeck building stone is still mined in primitive fashion, but there are now many small open quarries about Acton and Worth, the largest being at Herston, owned by Swanage Quarries Ltd. Most of the quarries do a small trade in rockery stone, bird baths and garden ornaments, but unhappily the beautiful and characteristic Purbeck roofing slabs are now seldom used. Swanworth Quarries, Ltd., work a large open quarry in the Portland Stone at Sheepsleights, about $\frac{3}{4}$ mile north-west of Worth, and the stone for Encombe was got, partly at least, from London Doors Quarry, $\frac{1}{2}$ mile south-west of Kingston; but west of this the Portland Beds change in character and there is little freestone. (*See* pp. 105 ff).

The Purbeck Marble industry is almost extinct, but a little has been raised recently (1937-8), from under a thick shaly overburden, between Blashenwell and Lynch Farms, south of Corfe. (*See* pp. 134-135).

Both Purbeck and Portland stones have been extensively quarried at Upwey and at Portisham, and the Upwey quarries by the Roman road were probably opened by the Romans. No quarrying has been done at either place for some years.

The Corallian Beds yield poor oolitic freestone at Abbotsbury (p. 60), and Forest Marble has been quarried in several places (pp. 18-19). The hard Chalk of the Purbeck Hills was formerly much used for road metal. On the heaths, irony gritstone from the Bagshot Beds (heathstone) has been used for building.

(b) BRICKS AND TILES

The principal sources of bricks and tiles in the area are the Kellaways and Lower Oxford clays at Putton Lane Brickworks, Chickerell (Dorset Brick and Tile Co.) and the Lower and Middle Oxford clay at Chickerell Brickworks, Crook Hill, Chickerell (Webb, Major & Co.). Bricks from these yards have been largely used for Council houses and other developments on the outskirts of Weymouth. Descriptions of the pits will be found on pp. 27, 29, with notes on the clays used.

Hand-made bricks and tiles are produced from the Wealden Variegated Marls by the Swanage Brick and Tile Co., between Godlingston and Ulwell, near Swanage. This was originally the brickyard of the Banks Estate and has been in use for at least two centuries. The company specializes in fine colours and textures for certain work. A band of ferruginous quartz grit is ground up and mixed with the clay to produce a brown colour when needed. Wealden Marls were also made into bricks at Lulworth Cove, where remains of the kilns still stand in the mouth of the glen on the east side of the cove. (*See* pp. 156, 159).

The Reading Beds at one time furnished the chief source of bricks and tiles in the district. At Broadmayne there were no less than six brickyards within ½ mile on the north-east side of the village, producing the famous Broadmayne Speckled Bricks. The pit of Webb, Major & Co. is still (1938) in work and shows the section described, on p. 228. The speckling is due to minute nodules of manganese oxide and does not appear until the brick is well fired. In consequence the bricks at the top of the kiln are a uniform pink, those in the middle are pinkish buff spotted blue, those at the bottom rose pink with black spots with blue centres.

Warmwell also had formerly a brickyard at Brick Hill, ¼ mile west of the church. Bedded loam and a little red clay were worked to a depth of 10 ft.,[1] but a recent boring has proved clay to a depth of at least 84 ft. (*see* p. 228).

Red and white Reading clay, 7 ft. thick, is still made into bricks, tiles and pipes on the Weld Estate at Coombe Keynes. The pit was opened about 1860-70 and the available clay is diminishing in thickness. There is in the middle an impersistent band of ironstone, 0 to 1 ft. thick, which has to be sorted out, but the overburden of sandy soil with a few flints is only 1 ft. deep.

Bagshot clays were formerly worked for bricks at several places. At the brickyard at Moreton Station a 30-foot face was

---

[1] C. Reid, ' Geology of the Country around Dorchester,' *Mem. Geol. Surv.,* 1899, p. 20.

dug, but work stopped in 1915 owing to the high cost of removing from 4 to 6 ft. of overburden and a lens of useless material within the clay.   There was another small brickyard at Studland, ⅓ mile north-west of the village.

The youngest strata in the district that have been used for brickmaking are the Middle Creechbarrow Beds (p. 237), the yellow loam of which served for many years Bond's Brickyard at Cotness Wood, on the north-east side of Creechbarrow Hill (abandoned 1908).

(c) GRAVEL AND SAND

The Bagshot Beds contain an unlimited supply of good builders' sand and the Plateau Gravels are the principal source of gravel.   Where the two are superposed over large areas, on the heaths between Moreton Station and Warmwell, and can be worked in the same pits, an important industry has grown up.   The excavations cover many acres and are up to 40 or 50 ft. deep, providing in summer an illusion of the Libyan Desert.   For about a century the centre of activity was on the south side of Moreton Station, but since 1936 it has spread 1¼ miles to the south-west, where washed and crushed gravel and sand are prepared.   There are smaller pits, abandoned during the last ten years, on the outliers near Warmwell.

A coarse cobble-gravel of Bagshot age is worked in a 30-foot face close to the Hardy Monument on Black Down, and sporadically in other pits near by.   Formerly there were similar pits on Ridgeway Hill or Bincombe Down, by Dorchester Clump, where ballast was got for the railway.

The Angular Flint Gravel is worked for local roads and farm uses at Ringstead, on West Creech Hill, and elsewhere (pp. 323-4).

In Purbeck a small relic of a 100-foot terrace of the Corfe River is worked for local use at Bucknowle (p. 330).   Formerly terrace gravels have been worked also at Langton Herring and Furzedown (p. 330).

The Wealden Quartz Grit is capable of producing a gravel suitable for paths, and is worked at Steeple.

Bagshot Sands from near Wareham and near Creechbarrow have been tested for glass making, but are too impure and are unsatisfactory in grading.[1]

(d) CEMENT, LIME AND MARL

Until shortly before the war of 1914-18 the Lower and Middle Chalk were extensively quarried for making cement at Cocknowle, near Church Knowle, and taken to Ridge, south-east of Wareham. Cement has also been made from bands of argillaceous limestone in the Kimmeridge Clay at Hen Cliff and Broad Bench, Kimmeridge (pp. 73-76) and from Lower Purbeck limestones at

---

[1] P. G. H. Boswell, *Memoir on British Resources of Sands and Rocks used in Glass Making*, 2nd. ed., 1918, p. 73.   London.

Upwey and near Orchard, about 2 miles south-west of Corfe Castle.[1] Other limestones are insufficiently argillaceous and need to be mixed with clay.

Lime has been burnt from the Chalk in all parts of the district, and formerly most of the villages and private estates had their own lime kilns. The hardened Upper Chalk of the Purbeck Hills has been worked for both lime burning and road-metal. The Jurassic limestones have also been burnt for lime locally.

Most of the old chalk pits in the Lower Chalk were worked for marling the land, a practice that has almost died out. Some are very ancient. They are naturally more numerous where there are limeless soils such as those of the Wealden Beds in the vicinity. For instance, round the ridge of Spring Bottom Hill, Ringstead, there are a dozen old pits in the Lower Chalk, some of large size. The Middle Creechbarrow Beds may have been used for the same purpose (*see* p. 238).

(e) PIPE-CLAY OR BALL-CLAY

This industry rivals that of stone quarrying as the most important in the area, and it is the subject of a Geological Survey Memoir : " Ball Clays ", by A. Scott, ' Special Reports on the Mineral Resources of Great Britain,' vol. xxxi, 1929. An account of the industry and the geology is given above on pp. 220-221.

(f) GYPSUM AND ALUM

Gypsum occurs as large isolated masses in the Lower Purbeck Beds of Durlston Bay, where it was formerly collected and used to a limited extent (p. 135), and also at Worbarrow Tout (p. 139).

Many years ago alum was obtained from the Kimmeridge Clay at Kimmeridge and from the spoil-heaps of the Tertiary clays near Corfe.[2]

(g) IRON ORE

An extensive deposit of iron ore in the base of the Kimmeridge formation at Abbotsbury has a high content of iron but is vitiated by too high a proportion of silica. Particulars are given above on pp. 86-8, and more details will be found in ' Special Reports on the Mineral Resources of Great Britain ' (*Mem. Geol. Survey*), vol. xii, 1920, p. 222, by J. Pringle.

(h) WATER SUPPLY

The principal water-bearing formation is the Chalk, though in the past almost every formation except the Fuller's Earth and Oxford and Kimmeridge Clays have been successfully drawn upon for local requirements.

---

[1] A. Strahan, *Purbeck Memoir*, 1898, pp. 106, 237.
[2] A. Strahan, *op. cit.*, p. 237.

Weymouth formerly obtained most of its water from a shallow well near Rodwell House sunk through the Nothe Clay into the Nothe Grits (Corallian Beds) and this was supplemented by a well in the Corallian at Broadwey, springs from the Corallian at Broadwey and Wyke, and wells in the Forest Marble at Radipole. Most of these last, and other wells, are still in use.

In the 'eighties the new waterworks was built at Sutton Poyntz, where exceptionally pure and copious springs flow from the foot of the chalk down. The water is collected and pumped up to a reservoir on the hill spur of Portland Beds west of Preston, whence it supplies the town. The yield varies from 2 million gallons a day in a dry summer to 8 millions in winter.

In 1937, this source proving insufficient to the growing needs of ' greater Weymouth ', a boring was made through the Tertiary beds into the Chalk at West Knighton. Thence the water is pumped through more than 3 miles of pipes to a new reservoir on the top of West Hill, the chalk down above Sutton Poyntz.

The increase of population on Portland Island early presented a problem in water supply. Two small springs at Fortune's Well and Southwell were formerly used but soon proved inadequate. Borings on the island can only draw from the base of the Portland Sand and the catchment is so limited that no great yield can be expected. A well and bore at Southwell was sunk 270 ft. with 130 ft. of headings at 220 ft. and produced 90,000 gallons a day, but the water was contaminated, the level soon fell, and pumping drew in salt water. Another unsuccessful trial was made at Chene. The Island has long drawn its supplies from a well (162 ft.) in the Chalk just north of the Ridgeway Fault at Gould's Bottom, Upwey. The yield varies round about 300,000 gallons a day. More recently this source has been augmented by a new boring near Friar Waddon, which goes down through Purbeck Beds into the base of the Portland Sand in the Upwey syncline. The depth is 360 ft. and the yield about 350,000 gallons a day.

The famous Upwey Wishing Well must derive most of its supplies from the Chalk north of the fault, though the spring rises from the top of the Portland Sand on the southern flank of the Upwey syncline. Its fluctuations synchronise with those in the water level of the well in Gould's Bottom.

Old Swanage obtained its water, up to the beginning of this century, from shallow wells sunk into the Purbeck Beds, and from the springs at the pond near the church and at the foot of Spring Hill. When the town began to grow apace the supplies became both inadequate and unsafe. An attempt was made to tap the springs that are thrown out on a fault in the gap of the hills at Ulwell, by boring into the Chalk and also on the Greensand outcrop. These wells never came up to expectations, though they are still used as an alternative supply. During the war of 1914-18 several attempts were made to find an adequate supply near Studland, but failed, and unfortunately records were not kept of the borings. Eventually the desired source was found in a spring that rises from a joint in the vertical chalk near the junction with the Tertiary beds at Corfe Castle, by the Studland road 100 yds. north-east of the railway bridge. This spring is 5 miles from Swanage, which draws on it at present to the extent of 384,000 gallons a day and still does not exhaust it. While the pumping engine is overhauled every winter the older wells at Ulwell are used. The new reservoir is also at Ulwell.

In the Tertiary syncline north of the Chalk downs there is a mild artesian effect. A boring at Bovington Camp, Wool, penetrates through Tertiary beds (280 ft. thick) into the Chalk to a depth of 726 feet. Water was struck in several layers of the Chalk and rose in the pipe to within 93 ft. of the surface. The artesian pressure was equal to raising a column of water about 270 ft. high. The yield was about 60,000 gallons a day, mainly from the middle part of the Chalk.[1]

Lulworth and district obtain their water from a spring that issues at the foot of the chalk hill midway between the Cove Hotel and the shore of the cove. It is piped from an artificial tank hollowed out of chalk scree cemented by tufa and pumped up to the reservoir by an engine housed close to the beach.

The water supplies of the rural districts are got from very varied local sources. Much information will be found collected together in a separate memoir, " Wells and Springs of Dorset " (*Mem. Geol. Survey,* 1926), by W. Whitaker and W. Edwards, from which also most of the particulars given above have been obtained.

(i) OIL-SHALE

Hundreds of feet of the Kimmeridge Clay consist of bituminous shales which give off an odour of oil, but only one 10-inch band, the Blackstone, is rich enough to have attracted special attention and to have been considered worth working. An account of the workings and of the geology will be found on pp. 68 ff. above, and in more detail in " Special Reports on the Mineral Resources of Great Britain " (*Mem. Geol. Survey*), vol. vii, 1920, by A Strahan. The oil derived from the Blackstone and other parts of the formation contains from 2 to 7 per cent of sulphur, which is costly to extract, whereas the Scottish Carboniferous oil shales seldom contain as much as 2 per cent.

Besides the main outcrop at Kimmeridge, the Blackstone has been met with in many trial borings from Upwey to Portisham.[2]

The Lower Oxford Clay at Chickerell is likewise bituminous (*see* p. 29).

---

[1] W. H. Hudleston, ' Geology in the Field ; part 2.' *Geol. Assoc.,* 1910, pp. 373-6.

[2] *See* A. Strahan, 1920, *op. cit.* ; and for particulars and location of some other borings see W. Whitaker and W. Edwards, ' Wells and Springs of Dorset,' *Mem. Geol. Surv.,* 1926, pp. 84-7, 90-93.

(j) FREE OIL (IMPREGNATIONS AND SEEPAGES)

Search of the Dorset coast by G. M. Lees, A. H. Taitt and other geologists of the D'Arcy Exploration Co. led to their discovering oil impregnations in the Bencliff Grit at Bran Point, in the Purbeck limestones of Peveril Point, Mupe Bay, Lulworth Cove, Durdle Door, Holworth and Chaldon, and in the Wealden Beds of Worbarrow and Mupe Bays and at Lulworth and Dungy Head.[1]

The richest impregnation is that in the topmost Bencliff Grit at Bran Point. " A specimen of the sand from the exposed cliff face has given 12.1 per cent of oil, and where these beds pass below tide level there is a small but active seepage of free oil ". Traces of oil were found on analysing the Portland Sand of Portland and Kimmeridge.

In the Purbeck Beds bituminous limestone was found at Peveril Point, and in the more westerly exposures " fractured limestones . . . show oil residues on the faces of cracks and ooze a little soft bitumen in warm weather." " Purbeck limestones outcropping at Upwey gave a colour on extraction with chloroform, though they lacked visible oil content."

In the Wealden Beds at Worbarrow Bay " there are several sands containing oil. Analysis of one about two-thirds up from the base of the formation showed 2.83 per cent of oil with a specific gravity of 0.96 ". Coarse sandstone boulders in the conglomeratic oil sand at Mupe Bay, mentioned on p. 159 above, yielded a sample containing 7.9 per cent by weight of oil, and there is a second oil sand towards the top of the series. At Dungy Head and Lulworth Cove (east side) the lowest Wealden sandstone is " richly impregnated, chocolate-brown to black in colour, and sticky, due to its oil content ".[2]

The origin of the oil in these impregnations is a mystery. The generally accepted freshwater origin of the Wealden Beds is against their being an original source rock, but Messrs. Lees and Cox consider the Corallian and Purbeck oils may be indigenous to the series in which they are found. Migration from the Oxford and Kimmeridge Clays seems at first the most obvious explanation but on analysis the Corallian residues prove to have less than 0.3 per cent of sulphur and the Purbeck residues less than 1 per cent.

The discovery of so many saturated oil sands at various horizons in this area, and of one actual seepage, showed the possibility of the existence of workable oil reservoirs in the neighbouring anticlinal structures. Accordingly the D'Arcy Exploration Co. in 1936 began a plan of exploration by drilling, which was continued from 1937 to 1939. The first structure to be tried was

---

[1] G. M. Lees and P. T. Cox, ' The Geological Basis of the present Search for Oil in Great Britain . .' *Quart. Journ. Geol. Soc.*, vol. xciii, 1937, pp. 163 *et seq.*
[2] *Ibid.* pp. 165-6.

the Poxwell pericline.   A boring was started on the Portland Freestone outcrop on the south side of the centre, in a position calculated to reach the crests of the Bencliff and Nothe Grits at depth.   This and preliminary shallow borings near the main road south of Poxwell threw much light on the structure of the pericline (see pp. 272-4), but no trace of oil was found.   At the same time a geological investigation was carried on over the surface of the Sutton Poyntz pericline, with revolutionary results; the structure was found to possess such unexpected complications that the prospects did not justify drilling (see p. 266).   A similar investigation of the Chaldon pericline showed a suitable structure the drilling of which would depend on the results obtained at Poxwell, and Poxwell being disappointing Chaldon was not drilled.   A shallow boring was made into the Corallian Beds on the crest of the Ringstead anticline, in the car park near Mine Cottage, Ringstead, but this also gave negative results.   It ended in Nothe Clay at a depth of 161 feet.   A boring on the crest of the Purbeck Anticline at Broad Bench, Kimmeridge, was expected to reach the sands in the Corallian Beds at less than 300 ft., but double the expected thicknesses of basal Kimmeridge Clay and argillaceous Upper Corallian Beds were encountered.   The boring was stopped in Osmington Oolite Series at a depth of 943 ft. and no trace of oil was found (pp. 73-4).

Two other possibilities remained.   Oil might be trapped down the dip in the Wealden Beds near Worbarrow and Mupe Bays, or beneath the Gault unconformity on a prolongation of the Ringstead or Chaldon structures under the Chalk north-west of Lulworth Cove.   These possibilities were under investigation until war broke out in 1939.

APPENDIX I

LIST OF GEOLOGICAL SURVEY PHOTOGRAPHS
(New Series One-inch Sheets 341, 342, 343, with parts of 327 and 328)

Copies of these photographs are deposited for public reference in the Library of the Geological Survey, Exhibition Road, South Kensington, London, S.W.7. Prints and lantern slides are supplied at a fixed tariff on application to the Director.

Reg. No. SHEET 327

A.4948 Fracturing in Portland Beds due to earth-movements. Corton Upwey.

6478 Roadside exposure of ironstone. Blind Lane, Abbotsbury.

7763 Landslip topography, near Abbotsbury. View from Abbotsbury Hill, S. of Wears Farm.

7764 Roadside exposure of ironstone. Red Lane, Abbotsbury.

7765 Landslip topography, near Abbotsbury. View from below White Hill.

7768 General view of Corallian ridge S.E. of Abbotsbury, from top of Blind Lane, Abbotsbury.

7769 General view of Jurassic country looking E. from Abbotsbury Castle.

7774 Gravel pit in ' Head ' beside the Hardy Monument, Blackdown.

7775–6 Gravel pit in Bagshot Beds, just S. of Hardy Monument, Blackdown.

7777 View, looking E., from downs above Portisham village.

7778–9 Fossil tree-trunk from the Purbeck tufa, Portisham quarry.

7780–1 Section of Lower Purbeck beds overlying Portland Stone, Portisham quarry.

7782 View of ' Scar ' limestone in the Portland Sands, Corton Farm.

7783–4 Chert-nodules in Portland Stone having the appearance of flints in chalk. Quarry N. of Friar Waddon Dairy Farm.

7785 View along Ridgeway (with ' Scar ' limestone exposed), N.E. of Friar Waddon Dairy Farm.

SHEET 328

1416 Section of Bagshot Beds. Redcliff, R. Frome, about 1 mile S.E. of Wareham Bridge.

1417 Close view of bed of red and white brecciated loam in No. 1416.

5802–4 Scenery of Eocene and Chalk country near Wareham. View from ½ mile W. of Worgret.

SHEET 341

6479 Topography of hard and soft Jurassic strata south of Abbotsbury View from above Abbotsbury to the Chesil Beach.

6480–1 Topography of Corallian Beds near Abbotsbury.

6482 The Chesil Beach at the Swannery, Abbotsbury, seen from above Shipmoor Point.

6483 View along the Chesil Beach at Abbotsbury.

Reg. No.

A.7766   Topography of Trigonia clavellata Beds and Osmington Oolite on Linton Hill, S.E. of Abbotsbury.

7767   Topography of Sandsfoot Grit and Trigonia Beds near Abbotsbury. View from ¼ mile S. of Abbotsbury.

7768   General view of Corallian ridge S.E. of Abbotsbury, from top of Blind Lane, Abbotsbury.

7769   General view of Jurassic country looking E. from Abbotsbury Castle.

7770   General view of Jurassic country looking S.E. from Abbotsbury Castle.

7771   General view of the Corallian and Kimmeridge country south of Portisham and Abbotsbury, from Goose Hill.

SHEET 342

1311   Cliffs of Portland Stone with slopes below of Portland Sand and Kimmeridge Clay. Chapman's Pool and Swyre Head, from St. Alban's Head.

1315   Cliff of Purbeck and Wealden beds, with Portland stone at base ; showing early stage in cove-formation. Stair Hole, West Lulworth.

1316   Near view of lower part of No. 1315, showing immature cove and junction of Portland and Purbeck beds.

1317   The Lulworth Crumple and inclined Portland and basal Purbeck beds breached by the sea. Stair Hole, West Lulworth.

1318   Lulworth Cove and Crumple. View from N.W. corner of Stair Hole, West Lulworth.

1319   Lulworth Cove. View from footpath to Durdle Door, West Lulworth.

1320   Lulworth Cove. View from coast-guard station, Lulworth Cove.

1321–2   Man o' War Rocks and St. Oswald's Bay, from Durdle Headland, Lulworth.

1323   Man o' War Cove, from cliff W. of Red Hole, W. of Lulworth Cove.

1324   Cliffs of vertical chalk. Bat's Hole and Swyre Head, from Durdle Headland, Lulworth.

1325–6   Arch in nearly vertical Portland stone, with higher cliff at Purbeck beds. Durdle Door, W. of Lulworth Cove.

1327   Arch in nearly vertical Portland Stone, with Isle of Portland in distance. Durdle Door, W. of Lulworth Cove.

1328   Cliff of vertical chalk traversed by a thrust-plane. Durdle Cove, W. of Lulworth Cove.

1329   Caves along a line of thrust in nearly vertical chalk. Cliffs E. of Swyre Head, W. of Lulworth Cove.

1330   Headland of Wealden, Purbeck and Portland beds. Entrance to Lulworth Cove, from East Over.

1331–2   The Fossil Forest and Broken Beds. East of Lulworth Cove.

1333–5   The Fossil Forest. East of Lulworth Cove.

1336–7   Horizontal passage of Purbeck limestone into the condition of Broken Beds. East of Lulworth Cove.

1338   View eastwards over Bacon Hole and Mupe Rocks.

1339   Cliffs of nearly vertical chalk. View of E. side of Arish Mell.

1340   Cliffs of nearly vertical chalk (Arish Mell), with headland of Portland stone (Worbarrow Tout) in distance. View from W. of Arish Mell.

Reg. No.

A.1341 Arish Mell and Mupe Bay, from Flower's Barrow, 1 mile S. of East Lulworth.

1342 Arish Mell, Mupe Rocks and Mupe Bay, from Worbarrow Bay.

1343 Cliffs of Wealden beds ; the Chalk in the background. Worbarrow Bay from near boat-house.

1344 Vertical cliff of Purbeck beds and Portland Stone, with lower slope of Portland Sand. Cliffs of Kimmeridge Clay in the distance. Pondfield and Gad Cliff from Worbarrow Tout.

1345 Cliff-section of Lower Purbeck, including the Broken Beds, resting on Portland Stone. Foot of E. side of Worbarrow Tout, Pondfield.

1346 Headland of Portland Stone and Lower Purbeck beds. Worbarrow Tout, from hill N. of coastguard station, Pondfield.

1347 View of heathlands near Wareham, from Whiteway Hill.

1348 View of Chalk ridge and part of the Tertiary tract, near Whiteway Hill.

1349 Creechbarrow, from the Chalk ridge.

1350 Cliffs of Kimmeridge Clay, Rope Lake Head, E. of Clavell's Hard. St. Alban's Head in distance.

1351 Old level in the " Kimmeridge Coal." Cliffs E. of Clavell's Hard.

1352 Cliffs of Kimmeridge Clay, with bands of cementstone. Clavell's Hard.

1353–4 Cliff of Kimmeridge Clay and ledge of cementstone. Broad Bench and cliffs, E. of Kimmeridge Bay.

1355–6 Chesil Beach from West Cliff, Portland.

1357 Lower Purbeck and top of Portland beds in Tout quarry, West Cliff, Portland.

1359 Cliff of Portland Stone with slopes of Portland Sand and Kimmeridge Clay. View of landslip and West Cliff, point due W. of Easton Church.

1360 View of Weymouth Bay from Furzy Cliff, showing shingle beach between Lodmoor and the sea.

1361 Portland Island and mainland near Sandsfoot. View from Furzy Cliff (continuation of No. 1360).

1362 Coast near Redcliff, E. of Weymouth, from Furzy Cliff.

1363 Coast from Redcliff to Black Head, from old flagstaff, Osmington Mills.

1364 Black Head, from Goggin's Barrow, Osmington Mills.

1365 Corallian beds faulted against Kimmeridge Clay. Cliffs at Osmington Mills.

1366 Corallian beds in cliffs 250 yards E. of Osmington Mills stream.

1367 Chalk, Upper Greensand and Gault resting uncomformably on inclined Kimmeridge Clay and Portland beds. White Nothe, from landslip 200 yards S.S.W. of Holworth House, Ringstead.

1368 Near view of No. 1367.

4942 Cliff section of Purbeck and Portland limestones. Black Nor, Portland.

4943 Eroded joint-fissures in limestone cliffs at Portland Bill, Portland.

4944 Sea-stack (the " Pulpit Rock ") of Portland chert and limestone. Portland Bill.

4945 Section in Portland Beds. Rufus Castle, Church Hope, Portland.

4946 Low cliff of Portland Stone. Portland Bill.

Reg. No.

A.4965   Slipped area of Portland Stone on Portland Sand. Church Hope Cove, Portland.

4966–7   Southwell landslip, Portland.

4971   Slipped mass of Portland and Purbeck limestone. East Weares, Portland.

5020–21   Pleistocene Raised Beach, overlain by 'Head.' Portland Bill.

5802–4   Scenery of Eocene and Chalk country near Wareham. View from ½ mile W. of Worgret.

5807   Section in pipe-clay (Bagshot Beds). Pike Bros. clay pit, Creech Heath, Furzebrook.

5808   Pipe-clay workings, Furzebrook.

5809   Old pipe-clay workings, Furzebrook. View from East Creech.

6484   The Poxwell " Circus."

SHEET 343

1289   Cliff of Portland Stone, with Lower Purbeck Beds forming a retreating brow. Durlston Head, from Tilly Whim.

1290   Same as No. 1289 and showing old quarry (Tilly Whim).

1291   A bay formed in Purbeck Beds ; a headland (Peveril Point) ; chalk cliffs of Ballard Down. Peveril Point and Swanage Bay from Durlston Head.

1292   Middle and Upper Purbeck Beds in cliff. About 100 yards south of Peveril Point coastguard station.

1293   Middle Purbeck Beds, with " Mammal Bed " at base. ½ mile S.W. of Peveril Point coastguard station.

1294   The " Cinder Bed." ½ mile S.W. of Peveril Point coastguard station.

1295   Bay in Lower and Middle Purbeck Beds and headland (Durlston Head) of Portland Stone. Durlston Head, from 100 yards S. of Peveril Point Signal station.

1296   Chalk stacks. By " The Parson's Barn " from boat, Swanage.

1297   Chalk stack. " The Pinnacle," about 100 yards S.W. of " Old Harry," from beach. The Foreland, between Swanage and Studland.

1298   Chalk stacks. " Old Harry," a stack, off the Foreland, Studland Bay, from boat.

1299   Cliff section of Bagshot Sands, partly concreted. Studland Bay.

1300   Headland of Chalk dipping gently under Tertiary Beds. The Foreland, from Studland Bay.

1301   A concreted mass of Bagshot Sand. The Agglestone Rock, near Studland.

1308   Corfe Castle from the west. View across Corfe River gap.

1309   A double breach in the Chalk ridge, the two streams separated by a hill of chalk on which Corfe Castle has been built. Corfe Castle, from barrow on Corfe Common.

1310   Hill with Corfe Castle and undulating country (of Wealden and older formations) in distance.

1311   Cliffs of Portland Stone with slopes below of Portland Sand and Kimmeridge Clay. Chapman's Pool and Swyre Head from St. Alban's Head.

1312   Ancient cultivation terraces (lynchets). West-Man, Winspit, Worth Matravers.

4947   Cliff section of Portland Beds. Seacombe, Worth Matravers.

Reg. No.

A.5801   Double gap in the Chalk ridge : the Corfe gap.   View from Middle-
          bere Heath, 3 miles S.E. of Wareham.

STONE QUARRIES AND QUARRYING

1302   Quarries in Middle Purbeck limestone.   Purbeck Stone quarries,
          Swanage.
1303–4   Top of inclined plane leading into quarry.   Purbeck Stone quarries,
          Swanage.
1305–7   Chipping sheds.   Purbeck Stone quarries, Swanage.
1313–4   Old quarry in Portland Stone.   Winspit, I. of Purbeck.
1358   Quarried blocks of Whit Bed and Base Bed.   Tout quarry, West
          Cliff, Portland.
1419–23   Long Acre quarry, Easton, Portland.
1424–25   Purbeck and Portland limestone quarry, Upwey.
4949   Quarry in Portland Beds, Upwey.
4950   Effect of gully-joints in Perryfield quarry, Portland.
4951   Joint-face in Portland Stone.   Broadcroft quarry, Portland.
4952   General view of Suckthumb quarry, Portland.
4953   Quarry-section in Portland and Purbeck Beds.   Wakeham quarry,
          Portland.
4954   Quarry-section in Portland and Purbeck Beds.   Suckthumb quarry,
          Portland.
4955–6   Quarry in Portland Stone near shore line.   Portland Bill.
4957   Inmosthay quarry, Easton, Portland.
4958–62   Seacombe quarry, Worth Matravers.
4963–4   Worth quarries, Worth Matravers.
4969   Quarry in slipped mass of Portland Stone.   East Weares,
          Portland.
4970   Quarry in slipped mass of Portland and Purbeck beds.   About
          ¼ mile S.E. of Pennsylvania Castle, Church Hope, Portland.
4972   Jack for lifting blocks of stone.   Bowers quarry, Portland.
4973   Hand cranes for lifting blocks of stone.   Wakeham East quarry,
          Portland.
4974   Steam cranes for lifting blocks of stone.   Silklake quarry, Portland.
4975   Removing ' top rubble ' (Purbeck Beds) overlying Portland Stone.
4976   Building a ' waste beach ' of rubble from Purbeck Beds.   Suck-
          thumb quarry, Portland.
4977   ' Beach,' or waste dump, of rubble from Portland Stone quarries.
          Suckthumb quarry, Portland.
4978   Rubble ' beach ' and quarry face in Portland Beds in juxtaposition.
          Broadcroft quarry, Portland.
4979   Debris from old quarrying operations.   East Weares, Portland.
4980   Removal of old ' beach ' and quarrying Base Bed of Portland
          Stone.
4981   ' Channeler ' at work.   Bowers quarry, Portland.
4982   Quarry face in Portland Stone.   Seacombe quarry, Worth
          Matravers.
4983   ' Rising ' (splitting off) Roach stone from Portland Building
          stone.   Inmosthay quarry, Portland.
4984   ' Pitted ' block of Portland Stone ready for separation.   Inmosthay
          quarry, Portland.

Reg. No.

A.4985   Raising a block of stone from quarry. Seacombe quarry, Worth Matravers.

4986   ' Pitting ' a block of Portland stone. St. Paul's quarry, Portland.

4987–8   Splitting a block of Portland stone. St. Paul's quarry, Portland.

4989   Large block from Base Bed of Portland Stone. Cottonfields quarry, Portland.

4990   Bedding plane in Portland stone. Cottonfields quarry, Portland.

4991–2   ' Scappled ' (trimmed and squared) blocks of Portland stone. Easton, Portland.

4993   Blocks of ' scappled ' Roach stone. Portland Bill.

4994   Old blocks of stone reputed to have been trimmed for use in St. Paul's Cathedral. East Weares, Portland.

4995   Transport of Portland stone from quarry. Easton, Portland.

4996   Loading blocks of stone into railway truck.

4997   Stack of unsawn and partly-sawn blocks of stone. Easton, Portland.

4998   Sand-saws cutting blocks of stone. Easton, Portland.

4999   ' Roughing out ' a block of stone before turning on lathe. Easton, Portland.

5000   Section of stone column being turned on lathe. Easton, Portland.

5001–3   Circular saw for cutting stone. Easton, Portland.

5004   Coulter planing machine at work on stone. Easton, Portland.

5005   Masonry on stone : scratching. Easton, Portland.

5006   Masonry on stone : rubbing. Easton, Portland.

5007   Hand-carving in stone. Easton, Portland.

5008–9   General view of mason's workshop. Easton, Portland.

5010   Stack of masonry in Portland stone. Easton, Portland.

5011   Travelling crane lifting block of masonry. Easton, Portland.

5012   Stack of finished masonry. Easton, Portland.

5013   Tombstone of Portland stone, dated 1675, with little trace of decay. Church Hope, Portland.

5014   Carved block of Portland stone above entrance of the Borstal Institution, Portland.

5015   Roach used as building stone. St. George's church, Easton, Portland.

5016–7   Decayed pillars, worked in Curf from Portland Beds. St. Peter's church, Easton, Portland.

5018   General view of quarry, with quarrying plant. Worth quarries, Worth Matravers.

5019   Plant for crushing Portland stone for road-metal. Worth quarries, Worth Matravers.

5022   Near view of block of Roach stone. Duncecroft quarry, Portland.

APPENDIX II

Some books and articles of general interest not referred to in the footnotes. (This list includes references to some papers published too late to be referred to in the memoir.)

1874 & later   Thomas Hardy. The Wessex novels referring specially to our area are ' Far from the Madding Crowd ',.' The Trumpet Major ', ' The Well Beloved ', ' Wessex Tales '.

1882   C. E. Robinson, ' Picturesque Rambles in the Isle of Purbeck '. London.

1883   Thomas Bond, ' History and description of Corfe Castle '. London

1885   O. P. Cambridge, ' Megalithic remains at Poxwell,' *Proc. Dorset Nat. Hist. Ant. F. Club*, vol. vi, p. 55.

1891   A. M. Wallis, ' The Portland stone quarries,' *ibid.*, vol. xii, p. 187.

1898   J. Meade Falkner, ' Moonfleet '. London.

1905   C. G. Harper, ' The Dorset Coast '. London.

1905   Barrett, W. B., ' Flora of the Chesil Bank and the Fleet,' *Proc. Dorset Nat. Hist. Ant. F. Club*, vol. xxvi, p. 251.

1906   Sir F. Treves, ' Highways and Byways in Dorset '. London.

1912   Barrett, W. B., ' Contributions to a flora of Portland,' *Proc. Dorset Nat. Hist. Ant. F. Club*, vol. xxxiii, p. 96.

1921   W. C. Norman, ' Sandsfoot Castle, Weymouth,' *ibid.*, vol. xli, p. 34.

1922   F. J. Harvey Darton, ' The Marches of Wessex'. London.

1928   R. H. Cunnington, ' The Scenery of Dorset and the geological factors to which it is due,' *Proc. Dorset Nat. Hist. Ant. F. Club*, vol. xlix, p. 147.

1933   Anton Fägersten, ' The Place-Names of Dorset '. Uppsala.

1934   Earl of Ilchester, ' The Abbotsbury Swannery,' *Proc. Dorset Nat. Hist. Arch. Soc.*, vol. lv, p. 154.

1935   G. M. Davies, ' The Dorset Coast, a geological guide '. London.

1935-1937   R. E. M. Wheeler, ' The Excavation of Maiden Castle,' *Proc. Dorset Nat. Hist. Arch. Soc.*, vols. lvi-lviii.

1936   C. P. Chatwin, ' The Hampshire Basin and Adjoining Areas'. British Regional Geology, Geological Survey.

1940   Eric Benfield, ' Purbeck Shop : a stoneworker's story of stone'. Cambridge.

1940   Ronald Good, ' The Old Roads of Dorset '. Dorchester.

1940   W. J. Arkell, ' Dorset Geology, 1930-1940,' *Proc. Dorset Nat. Hist. Arch. Soc.* vol. lxi, p. 117.

1941-1942   W. J. Arkell, ' Some Topographical Names in South Dorset,' *ibid.*, vol. lxii, p. 39, and vol. lxiii, 1942, p. 33.

1942   D. F. W. Baden-Powell, ' On the marine mollusca of Studland Bay, Dorset, and the supply of lime to the sand-dunes,' *Journ. Animal Ecology*, vol. xi, p. 82.

1945   W. J. Arkell, ' The names of the strata in the Purbeck and Portland Quarries,' *Proc. Dorset Nat. Hist. Arch. Soc.*, vol. lxvi.

INDEX

Fossils are entered only when figured in the text

Abbotsbury : ironstone, 8, 10, 62, 63, 74, 86-88, 249, 357 ; name, 8 ; oil-shale, 86 ; scenery, 4, 86, 116, 242, 249, 319, 350 ; swannery, 4, 21 ; Forest Marble, 19, 179, 249 ; Cornbrash, 21, 23 ; Oxford Clay, 25, 60 ; Corallian, 50, 59-63, 249, 355 ; Kimmeridge Clay, 85-88 ; Portland Beds, 116 ; Gault, 179, 353 ; Chalk 252 ; Chesil Beach, 338, 339.

Abbotsbury Fault, 19, 34, 63, 85, 194, 244, 245, 247, 249-253, 258-264, 266, 268, 269, 271, 274, 277.

Abscherung, 248.

Accommodation effects. *See* Adjustment folds.

Acheulian culture and period, 324, 326, 328, 333.

Actaeonella cf. *oliviformis*, 168.

Actaeonella ? verneuilli, 168.

Actinocamax plenus, 199.

Actinocamax quadratus, 200.

Acton, 133, 354.

Acton Turville Beds, 19.

Adjustment folds, 243, 291, 292, 294, 296, 299, 304, 311.

Agglestone, The, 8, 224.

Agglestone Grit, 216, 217, 218, 224, 227, 229, 235.

Agriculture, 3, 4, 318, 356, 357.

Aish, 125, 146, 147.

Albian Stage, 10, 80, 178-185, 196, 197, 293 ; earth-movements and unconformity, 163, 179, 246, 247, 251, 275, 279, 281, 282.

Algae, 95, 101, 126, 133.

Alluvium, 10, 317, 350, 351.

Alum, 69, 357.

Alum Bay Leaf Bed, 217, 219.

Amblotherium (jaw and tooth), 127.

America, 126, 169, 185.

Ammonites : Jurassic, 6 ; Fuller's Earth, 18 ; Cornbrash, 21, 23, 24 ; Kellaways Beds, 26, 27 ; Oxford Clay, 26-34, 257 ; Corallian Beds, 37, 39, 41, 47, 49, 53, 54, 58, 61, 62, 257 ; Kimmeridge Clay, 66, 67, 71-88 ; Portland Beds, 92-94 ; Lower Greensand, 165-167, 170, 172-174 ; Gault and Upper Greensand, 180-193 ; Chalk, 197-200, 204, 206, 208, 210, 212.

Amoeboceras anglicum, 74.

Amoeboceras krausei, 74.

ANDERSON, F. W., 129, 130, 151, 153.

Anglo-Saxon occupation, 7 ; place names, 7-9.

Angular Flint Gravel, 10, 211, 313, 324, 330, 356.

Anomia laevigata, 170.

Anvil Point, 3, 95, 97, 138, 303, 354.

Aptian Stage, 10, 154, 163, 166, 246.

Aptychus latus, 65.

Aptyxiella portlandica, 97.

Archaeoniscus brodiei, 131.

D'Arcy Exploration Co., 64, 85, 248, 261, 266, 272, 275-277, 279, 360.

Ardennes, 149, 163.

Arish Mell, 5, 206, 207, 300, 301, 303, 319.

Arne, 8, 226, 327.

Arrhaphoceras studeri, 182.

Artifacts : of blackstone, 69 ; of flint, 231, 313, 316, 324-331, 336, 351 ; of septaria, 27 ; of Purbeck marble, 134 ; of Purbeck stone, 354.

Ashford (Kent), 151.

Astarte hilpertonensis, 20.

Astarte subcostata, 170.

Astarte zonata, 40.

Atherfield Clay, 10, 166, 167, 169-176.

Atlantic phase, 351.

Aulacostephanus sp., 74.

Avon River, 316, 325, 329, 333.

Aylesbury (Bucks.), 93.

Backwater, The. *See* Radipole.
Bacon Hole, 9, 108, 109, 114, 139-141, 296-298.
Bacon Tier, 146.
BADEN-POWELL, D. F. W., 330-335, 348.
Bagshot Beds, 10, 216-233, 235, 244, 256, 312, 327, 346, 350, 355, 356.
BAILEY, E. B., 268, 269.
Ballard Down, 1, 8, 185, 195, 204, 205, 243, 304-311 ; Fault, 205, 244, 304-311.
Ball Clay industry. *See* Pipe-clay.
Barbatia aptiensis, 170.
BARBER, C. T., 261.
Bargate Beds, 164, 165, 174.
Barnston, 3.
Barremian Stage, 150.
BARROIS, CHARLES, 6, 180, 189, 196, 307.
Barton Beds, 217, 219, 235.
Bartonian Stage, 217, 219.
Basal Shell Bed, 92, 95, 112-115, 120-122, 285.
Basalt Stone, The, 71, 75, 76.
Base Bed Freestone, 113, 120-122.
Bath and Portland Stone Firms, Ltd., 119, 354.
BATHER, F. A., 78.
Bathonian Stage, 10, 11, 15-24, 152.
Bat's Head, 208-210, 285-289, 305, 308, 311.
Beaches, 10, 322, 331-333, 337-348 ; erratics in, 340-342, 346 ; grading of pebbles in, 339, 340, 345, 346 ; limestone, 344–346 ; orientation, 339, 345, 346 ; Portland Harbour, 344 ; raised 331-333, 340-342 ; sand, 346-348 ; septaria in, 34 ; shale, 345 ; shingle, 344-346. *See also* Chesil Beach.
BECHE, Sir H. T. DE LA, 6, 39, 41, 51, 81, 125, 145, 251.
BECKLES, S. H., 135.
Beef, 123, 124, 137, 142, 143, 144, 332, 334.
Belemnitella mucronata, 200.
Belemnites, 18, 28, 32, 79, 196, 198-201, 203, 204, 210.
Bembridge Limestone, 10, 217, 234, 235, 239-241, 244.
Bembridgia cincta, 239.
Bencliff Grit, 36, 37, 39, 41, 42, 47, 48, 51, 54, 57, 59, 360, 361.
Berkshire Oolite Series, 41.
BEURLEN, K., 83.
Bicavea rotaformis, 199.
Bincleaves, 54. *See* Bencliff.

Bincombe, 315 ; inlier, 245, 258, 260-262 ; name, 8 ; structures, 251, 256, 260-262, 265, 266 ; Forest Marble, 260-262 ; Cornbrash, 24, 260-262 ; Oxford Clay, 34, 35, 258, 260-262 ; Kimmeridge Clay, 261, 262 ; Portland Beds, 115, 260-262 ; Purbeck and Wealden Beds, 162, 260-262 ; Greensand, 179, 194, 213, 258, 260-262 ; Chalk, 212, 213 ; Eocene, 229-232, 356.
Bincombe tunnel, 144, 213, 255, 258. *See* Ridgeway cutting.
Bindon Hill, 8, 300, 315.
Bituminous Shales, 72, 80, 103, 359 *and see* Oil-shales.
Black Down, 230-233, 246, 315, 356.
Blackdown Greensand fauna, 182, 193.
Blacker's Hole, 9.
Black Head, 5, 34, 48-50, 74, 84, 85, 281, 282.
Black Nore Beds, 92, 114, 120, 121.
Black Sandstones, The, 91, 92, 100, 102, 106, 107, 110, 111, 114.
Blackstone, 69, 72, 76-78, 80, 81, 85, 86, 88, 359.
BLACK, W. J., 344.
BLAKE, J. F., 6, 39, 44, 53, 56, 57, 61, 67, 70-73, 79, 86-88, 90, 93, 94.
Blashenwell, 240, 304, 351, 352, 354.
Blown sand, 10, 348-350 ; in Chalk 12.
Blue Pool, The, 220, 225, 226.
Bogs. *See* Marshes.
Boiling Rock Syncline, 263, 264, 281.
Bolonian Stage, 67.
Bone fissures, 336, 337.
Bononian Stage, 67.
Borings : Bovington Camp, 227, 359 ; Chaldon Down, 179, 277 ; Creechbarrow, 235, 237, 238 ; Friar Waddon, 117 ; Goulds Bottom, Upwey, 358 ; Kimmeridge, 73-75, 361 ; Lulworth, 361 ; Lyme Regis, 248 ; Portland Island, 358 ; Portsdown, 130, 148, 165 ; Poxwell, 74, 81, 85, 272-274, 277, 361 ; Ringstead, 361 ; Ulwell, 358 ; Upwey, 358, 359 ; Warmwell, 228 ; West Knighton, 228, 358.
Boscombe Sands, 217.
BOSWELL, P. G. H., 356.
Bothenhampton, 19.
Boueti Bed, 15, 16, 18, 19, 274.
Boulonnais, The, 32, 67, 94, 132, 148, 164.
Bournemouth, 217, 218, 316, 318, 325, 350.

Bovey Tracey (Devon), 220.
Bovington Camp, 227, 229, 359.
BOWER, W. J., foreman, of Winspit, 102.
Bowleaze Cove, 51, 344, 345, 348, 350.
Boxworth Rock (Cambs.), 39.
Brachiopods, 6, 16-24, 39, 44, 50, 56, 65, 66, 79, 87, 88, 90, 94, 106, 107, 196, 198-204, 212, 213, 231, 249, 267.
Bracklesham Beds, 217-219, 235.
Bradford Clay, 19.
BRADLEY, P. C. S., 130, 232.
BRAJNIKOV, B., 324.
Brandy Bay, 68, 73-76, 78, 81, 303, 345.
Bran Point, 42, 43, 45-47, 49, 50, 58, 284, 345, 346, 360.
Bransgore Terrace, 316, 329, 333.
Breccias : crush, 292, 302 ; fault, 142, 288, 293, 307 ; Permian, 332, 346 ; Purbeckian, 123, 140, 142, 143, 243, 297-299, and see Broken Beds ; Cretaceous, 164, 200, 264-266 ; Eocene, 223, 227, 230 ; Recent, 352. See also Head.
Brick-making, 27, 29, 156, 159, 227, 228, 230, 234, 237, 355, 356.
Bride River, 319.
Bridport, 4, 15, 18, 19, 337, 339.
Brimstone Bottom, 323, 324.
BRISTOW, H. W., 6, 135, 139, 141, 142, 261, 277, 312, 342, 343.
British place names, 7.
Broad Bench, 64, 68, 73-75, 302, 303, 356, 361.
Broadmayne, 7, 228, 229, 241, 355.
Broadwey, 7, 59, 327, 329, 358.
BRODIE, P. B., 128, 129, 135.
Broken Beds, 123, 124, 138-143, 243, 294, 295, 297-299, 301, 302 ; origin, 297, 299.
Broken Shell Limestone, 124, 137, 142, 144, 304.
Bronkham Hill, 255, 315.
BRYDONE, R. M., 196, 203, 207, 210, 211.
BUCKLAND, W., 6, 39, 41, 51, 81, 125, 145, 152, 251, 337.
BUCKMAN, S. S., 29, 30, 53, 70, 77-79, 84, 88, 90, 91, 93, 94, 99, 101.
Bucknowle, 8, 320, 330, 356.
Building Research Station, 119, 121.
Building-stones, 3, 60, 95, 97, 113, 118-122, 124, 133-135, 354, 355.

BULLEN, R. A., 334.
Bunter quartzite, 231, 232, 329-332, 341, 342.
Burning Cliff, 81, 82, 112, 285.
Burrs, 126, 133, 138, 141, 144.
Burton Bradstock, 15, 18.
BURTON, H. ST. J., 315.
BURY, HENRY, 240, 314-317, 319.
Bushey, 225, 327.
BUSK, H. G., 311.
Byle Brook, 318.

Cainozoic era, 10, 11, 215.
Callihoplites auritus, 182.
Callihoplites tetragonus, 182.
Callovian Stage, 10, 15, 21, 25.
CALKIN, J. B., 128.
Calne (Wilts.), 37, 164.
Calvert (Bucks.), 29.
Cambridge Greensand fauna, 184.
CAMDEN, W., 338, 348, 349.
Campanian Stage, 202.
Candona ansata, 129.
Candona bononiensis, 129.
Cannon balls, 48, 53.
Caps, 100, 101, 105, 108, 124, 125, 129, 138, 141, 142, 146, 147, 297, 299.
Cardiaster fossarius, 186.
Cardioceras costicardia, 34.
Cardioceras praecordatum, 34.
Cardioceras quadrarium, 34.
Cardium ibbetsoni, 170.
Carstone, 166, 173, 188.
Cassiope helvetica, 168.
Cassiope lujani and var. crassa, 168.
Cassiope pizcuetana and var. renevieri, 168.
Castleton, 88.
Cattle Ledge Shales, 72.
Caves, 4, 97, 208, 305.
Cayton Bay (Yorks.), 53.
Cement-making, 356, 357.
Cenomanian Stage, 10, 185, 189, 195-199, 204, 206-209.
Chalbury Camp, 114, 115, 117, 144, 263, 266, 353.
Chaldon, 8, 161, 179, 193, 194, 210, 211, 275-281, 315, 320, 321, 323, 360.
Chaldon Pericline, 248, 266, 275-279, 281, 320, 321, 323, 361.

Chalk, The : cement, lime, marl, 356, 357 ; marmorized, 264-266 ; origin, 12, 195 ; palaeontology, 197-203, 272, 279 ; piping, 216, 222, 227, 228, 232, 256 ; relation to Albian, 196, 197, 204, 206-209 ; relation to Eocene, 215, 216, 221, 222, 225, 229, 244, 256 ; scenery, 1, 2, 5, 195, 242 ; slips, 5, 80, 84 ; source of water, 357-359 ; structure, 242-248, 252-256, 264, 275, 277-280, 286-293, 296, 297, 300, 301 ; thickness, 195, 197, 199, 207 ; zones, 196, 197, 200-203 ; in Purbeck, 204-207, 234, 242, 301, 302, 304-312, 355 ; Lulworth, 207-211, and see Structure ; Ringstead, 209, 211 ; Chaldon-Portisham, 211-214, 252–255, 264, 272, 274, 275, 277-279.

Chalk Rock, 200.

CHANDLER, M. E. J., 219.

CHAPMAN, F., 130.

Chapman's Pool, 75, 78-80, 98, 318, 348, 351.

Characea, 124, 133.

Charmouth, 317.

Charnel, 68.

CHATWIN, C. P., 151, 176, 314.

Chellian culture, 325, 326.

Chene, 358.

Chert : origin, 89, 90, 141 ; Palaeozoic, 149, 230 ; Jurassic, 89, 90, 100-102, 105, 107, 108, 110, 111, 115-117, 121-124, 133, 135, 141-143, 277, 298, 299, 301, 302 ; Cretaceous, 179, 189, 191, 192, 194, 213 ; in Tertiary, 215, 229, 230, 231, 244 ; in Pleistocene gravels, 321, 324, 325, 329-331, 337 ; in beaches, 332, 344, 345.

Cherty Freshwater Bed, 130, 135, 138, 142-144.

Cherty Series, 92-95, 99-102, 105-122, 132.

Chesil Beach, 4, 7, 25, 337-344 ; description, 337, 338 ; composition, 340, 346 ; grading, 339, 340 ; motions, 339, 340 ; origin, 340-342 ; storms on, 338 ; substratum, 118, 338, 348.

Chesilton, 335, 337-341, 346, 353.

Chickerell, 9, 23-27, 30, 355, 359.

Chloritic Marl, 204, 212.

Christchurch (Hants.), 350.

Church Hope, 8.

Church Knowle, 8, 135, 205, 356.

Cidaris florigemma (spine), 40.

Cimmerian movements, 163.

Cinder Bed, 124, 132, 135, 138, 141-145, 231, 263, 275, 295, 296, 334.

Clactonian culture, 324.

CLARK, J. G. D., 351.

CLARKE, W. B., 307-309, 311.

Clavell's Hard, 9, 69, 72, 75, 76, 303.

CLAVELL, Sir W., 69, 70.

Clayhanger, 60, 61.

Claywell, 221, 225.

Clay-with-Flints, 324.

Cleavage. See Fracture cleavage.

Cliff End, 15, 18, 19.

CLIFFORD, M. H. 352.

Cliffs : erosion, 68, 318, 342, 343 ; inland, 348 ; names, 8 ; scenery, 3, 4, 9, 97-99, 105, 178, 195, 343.

Coal-money, 69.

Coarse Quartz Grit, The, 157-162, 224, 356.

Coastline : configuration, 4, 8, 205, 318, 322, 343, 348-350 ; erosion, 68, 318, 342-345, 350 ; nomenclature, 8 ; scenery, 9 ; stacks, 4, 205.

Cochlostoma heterostoma, 239.

Cockpit Head, 195, 207.

COKER, J., 69.

COLLIGNON, M., 197.

Condensed beds, 37.

Conglomerates, 150, 157-161, 227, 233, 241, 247, 252, 264, 360. See also Pebble beds.

CONYBEARE, W. D., 6, 288, 307, 337.

COODE, Sir J., 338.

Coombe Keynes, 8, 211, 227, 355.

Coombe Rock, 10, 334-336.

COQUAND, H., 163, 169.

Corallian Beds, 5, 10, 36-63, 281-284 ; oil impregnations, 360, 361 ; palaeontology, 36-39 ; scenery, 4, 242 ; thickness, 36 ; Weymouth, 54, 358 ; Fleet Shore, 57-59 ; Abbotsbury-Broadwey, 59-63, 249, 358 ; Osmington-Ringstead, 41-50, 281-284, 360, 361 ; under Purbeck 73, 361.

Coral Rag, 37, 42.

Corals, 37, 40, 42, 49, 50, 95, 199.

Corbula alata, 131.

Corbula Beds, 124, 130, 137, 144.

Corbula durlstonensis, 131.

Corbula striatula, 170.

Corfe (Castle), 3 ; cement-making, 356, 357 ; name, 7 ; river gaps, 318, 320, 331 ; structures, 205, 206, 303, 304, 312 ; water supply, 359 ; Wealden Beds, 150, 153, 156, 157 ; Lower Greensand, 165, 174-177 ; Chalk, 195, 199, 205, 312 ; Eocene, 216, 218, 220, 221, 224-226, 312 ; Oligocene, 233, 234 ; Pleistocene, 330, 331 ; Holocene, 240, 251.
Corfe Hill (Radipole), 7.
Corfe River, 318, 319, 330, 356.
Cornbrash, 10, 20-24, 257, 260-262, 266-268.
CORNES, H. W., 151.
Cornish rocks, 159, 216, 220, 223, 229, 231, 325, 333, 341, 346.
CORNISH, VAUGHAN, 340.
Corton, 7, 60, 77, 86, 116, 121, 253.
Coryates, 7, 86, 92, 117.
Cotness, 220, 226, 233, 234, 237, 356.
Cow Corner, 188, 189, 206, 207.
Cowstones, 193.
Cox, L. R., 91, 95, 122, 240, 241.
Cox, P. T., 160, 248, 360.
Crackers Group, 166, 168-172, 174-176.
Cranborne, 216.
Crania egnabergensis, 200.
Creech, 1, 7, 220, 221, 226, 233, 237, 312, 323, 327, 356.
Creechbarrow, 6, 206, 216, 217, 220, 226, 233-241, 312, 315, 355.
Creechbarrow Beds, 216, 217, 233-241, 244, 356, 357.
Cretaceous System, period, 10, 11 ; duration, 12 ; earth-movements, 163, 179, 246, 247, 248, 268, 271, 275, 279 ; easterly tilt, 246 ; fauna, 128, 149, 152, 185 ; lower limit, 125, 149 ; mapping, 6 ; relation to Cainozoic, 215, 216 ; thickness, 11, 12 ; transgression, 162-165 ; unconformity, 148, 193, 194, 249-251, 258, 260, 267, 268, 271, 279.
Crinoids, 19, 28, 31, 65, 78, 81, 86, 200-203, 207, 210, 213.
Crook Hill Brickyard, 26, 355.
Crumples, 243, 291, 292, 294-296, 298, 304.
Crushed Ammonoid Shales, 71, 79, 98.
Crustacea, 6, 39, 87, 95, 99, 129, 130, 167, 168, 172.
Cuddle, 72, 75, 76.
Cuisian Stage, 10, 217, 218.
CUNNINGTON, R. H., 180, 185.
Curf, 122.
Currendon, 223.

Cycads, 125, 133, 147, 152.
Cycles of deposition, 36, 37, 89.
Cypridea fasciculata, 129.
Cypridea paucigranulata, 129.
Cypridea punctata, 129.
Cypridea spinigera, 151.
Cypridea tuberculata, 151.
Cypridea valdensis, 151.
Cyprimeria vectensis, 170.
Cyprina anglica, 170.
Cypris Freestones, 124, 130, 141-145, 272, 292, 294, 296, 297, 301.
Cypris purbeckensis, 129.

———

DAMON, ROBERT, 6, 19, 24, 25, 42, 46, 51, 57, 60, 68, 119, 121, 332, 337, 345, 351, 353.
Dancing Ledge, 3, 99, 138, 303.
Dartmoor, 149, 220.
DAVIES, A. MORLEY, 217.
DAVIS, A. G., 218.
Décollement. See Abscherung.
Deshayesites deshayesi, 170.
Deshayesites punfieldensis, 170.
Devon, 182, 193, 313, 324, 332, 333, 336, 340-343, 346.
Dicey Clays, 71, 72.
Dicroloma trifida, 28.
Diestian Stage, 314.
? *Dimorphosoma* cf. *calcarata*, 168.
DINES, H. G., 314.
Dirt Beds, 115, 123, 124-126, 135, 138, 140, 142-147, 299, 302.
Discina latissima, 65.
Discoidea dixoni, 199.
Distichoceras bicostatum, 30.
Disturbances. See Structure.
DIVER, C., 347-350.
DIXON, E. E. L., 216.
Dorchester, 215, 229, 244, 248, 325 ; museum, 69, 218, 325, 326, 328, 342, 351.
Dorset Brick and Tile Co., 27, 355.
Dorset-Hampshire Basin. See Hampshire Basin.
DOUGLAS, J. A., 21, 24.
DOUVILLÉ, H., 88.
Downshay, 134, 152, 156, 303.
Drag, 251, 252, 255, 259, 288, 293, 309, 310 ; -joints, 291 ; -folds, see Adjustment folds.
Drainage (natural), 313-323, 343, 350.
DREW, C. D., 342.
Drowned valleys, 317, 342, 343, 350.
Dry valleys, 320, 321, 323, 336.
Dungy Head, 108-111, 114, 141, 160, 246, 293, 294, 360.

DUNKER, W. B. R. H., 132, 153.
Durdle Door and Cove : beach, 345 ; name, 7 ; structure, 246, 288-294 ; Purbeck Beds, 141, 142, 292-294, 297, 298, 360 ; Wealden Beds, 160, 161, 246, 293 ; Gault and Greensand, 178, 190, 246, 293 ; Chalk, 199, 208.
Durlston Bay, 7, 123, 129, 132, 133, 135-138, 304, 346, 357.
Durlston Head, 3, 97, 137, 138, 297, 303, 304.
Durnovarites subquadratus, 182.

East Fleet (village), 23, 26, 27.
East Weares, 119.
Echinocorys scutata, 200.
Echinoids (Jurrassic), 20-24, 39, 40, 46, 60, 87, 131, 132, 135 ; (Cretaceous) 180, 184, 187, 188, 190, 193, 198-203, 208-210, 212-214, 231, 307.
Economic geology, 354-361.
EDMUNDS, F. H.; 119, 121.
EDWARDS, F. E., 239.
EDWARDS, W., 226, 359.
EDWARDS, W. N., 95.
Egdon Heath, 1.
Egmont Bight, 75, 79, 345.
Elsworth Rock (Cambs.), 33.
Elwell, 7.
Elworth, 8, 62, 86.
Emmit Hill, 8, 77, 90-92, 98, 104, 303.
Emmit Hill Marls, 91, 92, 98, 103, 104, 108.
Empool Pumping Station, 228, 229.
Encombe, 331, 337, 354.
ENGLEFIELD, Sir H. C., 6, 97, 133, 307.
Engonoceras grimsdalei, 182.
Eocene System, 10, 12, 215, 217, 241, 244, 246, 310, 324 ; beach pebbles, 327, 329 ; climate, 218, 219 ; fauna and flora, 218, 219 ; relation to Cretaceous, 215, 216, 221, 228, 229, 232, 244 ; thickness, 222, 223, 224, 226, 227 ; zones, 217, 218.
Erosion, 13, 68, 313, 318, 342-345, 350.
Erratic pebbles : in beaches, 332, 334, 340-342, 346 ; on Portland Island, 334, 337 ; in sediments, *see* Cornish rocks.
Exogyra conica, 186.
Exogrya nana, 40.

Exogyra nana Beds, 44, 50, 56, 84, 88, 106-110, 112-116, 118, 263.
Exogyra Rock, 179, 185-192.
Exogyra sinuata Beds, 165, 166, 168.
Exogyra tuberculifera, 170.
Exogyra virgula, 65.

Faringdon (Berks.), 11, 164.
Faults, 6, 7, 11, 42-44, 68, 80, 81, 84, 111, 138, 142, 161, 179, 205, 249-312 ; adjustment, 291, 311 ; dip, 247, 262, 268, 271 ; double-action, 259, 264, 269, 271, 273, 274, 277 ; onion-scale, 311 ; over-thrust, 6, 7, 243, 251, 253, 258, 264-266, 268-273, 288-292, 296, 300, 307-311 ; reversed, 142, 225, 251, 256, 258, 272, 303 ; step, 138, 304 ; strike, 142, 161, 193, 194, 225, 247, 262, 268, 282, 292, 293, 304 ; tear, 271 ; trough, 304 ; two-way, *see* double-action ; underthrust, 307-309, 311.
Fayle and Co., 221, 224, 225.
Ferns (fossil), 152, 218, 219.
Ferny Hole, 86, 249.
Ferruginous Sands, 166, 167, 169-172, 174.
Filholia elliptica, 239.
FISHER, OSMOND, 6, 135, 144, 152, 162, 232, 256-258, 261, 299, 339, 342, 343.
Fishes, 6, 67, 95, 123, 128, 137, 152, 172.
FITTON, W. H., 6, 91, 92, 126, 132, 137, 149, 153, 154, 165.
Five Marys, The, 210, 276-279.
Flats, The, 66, 73-75.
Fleet Backwater (The Fleet) : Jurassic rocks exposed on, 14, 16, 19, 21, 23, 25, 30, 32, 34, 57-59, 88 ; locality map of shores, 14 ; marshes, 350 ; name, 7 ; origin, 329, 337, 338, 342, 343.
Fleet Common, 14, 18, 23, 329.
Fleet River, 329, 330, 342, 343.
Flints : Chalk, 197, 200, 202, 203, 206, 208-213, 254, 288, 300 ; Eocene, 215, 216, 222, 227-233, 246, 277 ; Oligocene, 217, 234, 237-241, 327 ; Pleistocene, 321, 323-332, 336, 337 ; in beaches, 332, 345 ; implements, 231, 313, 316, 324, 336, 351 ; shattered, 254, 298, 305, 307, 323, 324.
Flora (fossil), 152, 218, 219, 240, 298, 351. *See also* Trees, Ferns, Cycads.

Flower's Barrow, 186.
Folds. *See* Structure, Purbeck Fold, Weymouth Anticline, Adjustment folds, etc.
Folkestone (Kent), 182, 314.
Folly Hollow, 86, 249.
FORBES, EDWARD, 6, 149.
FORDHAM, H. G., 180, 185.
Foreland, The, 195. *See* Handfast Point *and* Old Harry Rocks.
Forest Beds ; Jurassic, 123, 125, 126, 140, 141, 144-147 ; Pleistocene or Holocene, 317.
Forest Marble, 10, 11, 16, 18-19, 63, 249-251, 260-262, 266-268, 274, 355, 358.
Fortune's Well, 358.
Fossil Forest, 140, 141, 297, 298.
FOSTER, C. LE N., 314.
Fracture cleavage, 244, 278, 296, 300, 301.
France, 169, 324, 325, 339. *See also* Boulonnais, Normandy, Paris Basin.
Freestone Series, 92-95, 97, 99-101, 105-122.
Freshwater faunas, 6, 11, 123, 124, 130-132, 134, 152, 219.
Freshwater Steps, 9, 70, 75, 78, 79, 98, 318.
Friar Waddon, 116, 117, 145, 162, 253, 255, 358.
Frome River, 5, 7, 227, 316-319, 323-325, 350.
Fucoid beds, 36, 54, 59, 89, 257.
Fuller's Earth, 10, 15-18, 29, 177, 246, 249, 274 ; Rock, 15 ; scenery, 4.
Furzebrook, 219, 220, 225.
Furzedown, 26, 32, 330, 356 ; Clay, 26, 32, 34.
Future of the area, 9.

Gad Cliff, 3, 8, 78, 81, 90, 92, 94, 97, 100, 105-108, 110, 111, 114, 301, 302.
Gales, effects of, 4, 338, 340, 344, 345.
GARDNER, J. S., 218.
Gastropods ; Fossil, 6, 28, 31, 33, 40, 46, 58, 59, 60, 85, 87, 95-97, 123, 124, 130-132, 135, 138, 139, 142-144, 152-154, 156, 168, 169, 172, 177, 199, 231, 234, 239-241, 257 ; Recent, 331, 332, 334, 335, 351, 352.

Gault, 10, 178-194 ; basement bed, 176, 177, 178, 185, 188-192, 275, 293 ; palaeontology, 181-187 ; slips, 5, 80, 178, 353 ; thickness, 178, 185, 188-190, 192 ; unconformity below, 80, 81, 111, 164, 177, 179, 191, 193, 194, 247, 268, 275, 277, 281, 282, 293, 296 ; zones, 180, 181 ; Purbeck, 179, 185-189 ; Lulworth, 189, 190 ; Ringstead, 111, 191, 192 ; Sutton Poyntz, 268.
Gaulter('s) Gap, 9, 73-75.
GERARD, THOMAS, 69.
Germany, 39, 66, 77, 78, 93, 130, 132, 149, 150, 153, 154, 163, 247, 248.
Glacial periods. *See* Ice Ages.
Glass sands, 69, 356.
Glauconite, 112, 114, 175, 176, 178, 188, 189, 192, 196, 197, 204, 206, 207, 212, 213, 215, 227-229, 272, 275, 277.
Glos Oolite Series, 41.
Godlingston, 3, 152, 156, 157, 355.
Goggins Barrow, 84, 192, 352.
Golden Cap, 342.
Goniomya literata, 22.
GOOD, RONALD, 350.
Gorwell, 86.
Gould's Bottom, 145, 251, 254, 287, 358.
Grammatodon carinatum, 186.
Granite : detritus in sediments, 12, 149, 220, 230, 231 ; erratics in beaches, 332-334, 340, 341, 346.
Gravels, 313, 316, 322, 341, 356 ; chert, 321 ; cobble, 315 ; commercial, 356 ; erratic, *see* Cornish rocks, Quartzite pebbles ; flint, 10, 211, 313, 323, 324 ; pebble, 327, 329 ; plateau, 10, 229, 230, 313, 315, 316, 324-331, 337 ; submerged, 317 ; terrace, 316, 324-331, 333.
Great Oolite Series, 16, 19.
Green Hill (and Greenhill Barton), 114, 116, 121, 144, 260, 263-266, 285.
Greenhill Gardens, 25, 32.
GREEN, J. F. N., 316.
Greensand. *See* Upper- and Lower-.
Greywethers. *See* Sarsen Stones.
GRIMSDALE, T. F., 180, 185, 192.
Grossouvria cf. *miranda*, 30.
GROVES, A. W., 149.
GROVES, T. B., 338, 344, 345, 348.
Gryphaea Beds, 165.
Gwyles, 9, 42, 318.
Gypsum, 135, 139, 243, 248, 299, 357.

HAACK, W., 129.
Hackness Rock, 30.
Haldon Hills (Devon), 231.
Ham Anticline (Hants.), 242.
Hamble River, 314.
Hambury Tout, 7, 227, 232, 288, 289.
Ham Cliff, 26, 33, 34, 48, 51-53, 281-283.
Hampen Marly Beds, 17.
Hampshire Basin, 1, 12, 217, 218, 242, 246, 248, 255, 313, 316, 318, 359.
Hamstead Beds, 217, 244.
Handfast Point, 1, 204, 205, 316.
HANDLIRSCH, A., 129.
Hardy Monument, 230-232, 356.
Haslemere (Surrey), 176.
Hauterivian Stage, 150.
HAWKES, C. F. C., 351.
HAWKINS, H. L., 132.
Head, 10, 331-335.
Headon Beds, 217, 235.
Heathstone, 355.
Hecticoceras aff. *nodosum*, 30.
Hemicidaris purbeckensis, 131.
Hen Cliff, 66, 69, 72-76, 302, 356.
Hengistbury Head (Hants.), 217, 348, 350.
Herbury, 16, 18, 19.
Herston, 133, 354.
Hewish Hill, 8, 61.
Hibolites hastatus, 28.
Highcliff Sands, 217.
HINDE, G. J., 133.
Hobarrow Bay, 68, 73, 74, 302, 303.
Hog's Back, The, 164, 242.
Holaster planus, 199.
Holaster subglobosus, 199.
HOLLINGWORTH, S. E., 143, 299.
Holme Heath, 327.
Holocene System, 10.
Holworth, 8, 81-83, 111-113, 118, 144, 161, 191, 193, 194, 209, 211, 275, 277, 278, 281, 282, 285, 321, 323, 324, 335, 345, 352, 353, 360.
Honeycomb weathering, 102, 107.
Hope's Nose (Devon), 333.
Hoplites dorsetensis, 186.
Hounstout, 3, 7, 68, 70, 75, 79, 90, 92, 97, 98, 102, 352.
Hounstout Clay, 71, 79.
Hounstout Marl, 71, 79, 104, 108.
HUDLESTON, W. H., 6, 39, 44, 53, 56, 57, 61, 77, 86-88, 99, 113, 152, 224, 225, 227, 233–235, 237-241, 312, 339, 359.
HUMMEL, K., 163.

HUTCHINS, J., 68, 70, 133, 134, 353.
Hydrobia chopardiana, 131.
Hysteroceras varicosum, 182.
Hythe Beds, 164.

———

IBBETSON, L. L. B., 256.
Ice Ages and Ice Action, 313, 317, 324, 333, 334, 341, 342.
Ichthyodorulites, 128.
Inconstans Clay, 42, 44, 50, 56, 84, 88.
Infra-Valanginian Stage, 150, 151.
Inoceramus labiatus, 199.
Insects, 123, 124, 128, 129, 135, 144, 219, 351.
Ironstones, 50, 86-88, 175, 176, 227, 357.
Isastraea explanata, 40.
Isle of Purbeck. *See* Purbeck.
Isle of Wight, 5, 150, 152-154, 164-172, 174-176, 195, 217, 218, 242-244, 312, 315, 316, 347, 352.
Isopods, 123, 129, 131.
Itchen River, 314.

———

JACCARD, S. A., 132.
JEFFREYS, J. GWYN, 332.
JOHNSON, D. W., 343.
JONES, INIGO, and use of Portland Stone, 118.
JONES, O. T., 271, 299, 307, 311.
JONES, T. RUPERT, 6, 130, 153.
Jordan Cliff Clays, 26, 33, 34.
Jordan Hill, 9, 25, 51, 53, 54, 344, 345.
Jordan Stream, 266, 267, 319, 350.
JUDD, J. W., 173, 176, 241.
JUKES-BROWNE, A. J., 149, 180, 185, 190, 199, 202, 204, 206, 213.
Jura Mountains, 30, 32.
Jurassic System and period, 10, 11, 25, 258 ; duration, 11 ; lower limit, 11 ; upper limit, 125, 149 ; mapping, 6 ; palaeontology, 6, 128, 152 ; thickness, 11, 303 ; zones, 6.

———

Kaolin, 12, 220, 221.
KEEPING, H., 6, 235, 238-240.
Kellaways Beds, 10, 18, 25-28, 266, 268, 355.
Kemble Beds, 19.
Kent, 148, 151, 152, 314.
KENT, P. E., 267, 272-274.

Kimmeridge, 68, 302, 303, 345, 348 ; alum works, 357 ; bóring, 73-75, 361 ; cement-making, 356 ; coal, 64, 68-70, 72, 359 ; ledges, 68 ; spelling, 68 ; test-holes, 70.

Kimmeridge Clay, 10, 64-88 ; mapping, 34 ; palaeontology, 65-67 ; relation to Portland Sand, 90-92 ; scenery, 3 ; thickness, 64, 70-73, 82, 84, 85, 361 ; source of alum, 357, cement, 356, fuel, 69, gault or marl, 9, oil, 359; zones, 6, 67, 71-80 ; Purbeck, 64, 67-80, 301-303, 361 ; Ringstead, 41-44, 80-85 ; Osmington Mills, 48-50, 84, 85, 283; Bincombe and Sutton Poyntz, 260-262, 266, 267 ; Weymouth, 56, 85, 86, 88, 249-251 ; Portland, 88.

Kimmeridgian Stage, 5, 10, 64, 66, 67.

Kingbarrow Quarries, 122, 146.

Kingston, 134, 354.

KIRKALDY, J. F., 149, 164, 169, 174, 176, 177.

KITCHIN, F. L., 86, 164.

Knaps, 8, 63, 157.

Knoll House, 348.

Knoll, The, 8, 115, 260, 261, 263, 264.

Knowle, 3.

KOERT, W., 132.

Kosmoceras compressum, 30.

Kosmoceras Shales, 26, 27.

Kosmoceras spinosum, 30.

Kosmoceras tidmoorense, 30.

———

LACK, D., 350.

Lamellibranchs ; Mesozoic, 6 and throughout chapters II-XI, especially 17-24, 27, 28, 38, 40, 46-48, 53, 58, 65, 82, 87, 94-96, 99-103, 111-113, 131, 132, 167, 170-172, 181, 182, 184, 187, 198, 199 ; Tertiary, 219, 240, 241. *See also* Oyster Beds.

Landslips, 4, 80, 84, 99, 116, 118, 194, 249, 251, 263, 281, 284, 285, 323, 335, 352, 353.

Langtonia setina, 129.

LANG, W. D., 317.

Langton Herring, 16, 17, 18, 246, 303, 330, 343, 356.

LATTER, M. P., 91.

Lattorfian Stage, 10, 217.

Ledian Stage, 217.

LEES, G. M., 160, 248, 360.

LELAND, J. 338, 344.

Lenham Beds (Kent), 314.

Lepthoplites cantabrigiensis, 182.

LEWIS, W. V., 339, 345.

Lias Rocks, The, 78, 81.

Lignite, 144, 152, 154, 158, 173, 177, 216, 225, 230 ; thick beds used as fuel, 225.

Lima rigidula, 22.

Lime-burning, 356, 357.

Lingula ovalis, 65.

LINTON, D. L., 314, 315, 320.

Linton Hill, 60-63, 86.

Listy Bed, 100, 101.

Little Bredy, 255.

Little Mayne, 7, 229.

Littlemore Clay Beds, 37, 47, 48, 50, 59, 84.

Little Sea, 224, 347-350.

Lobster Beds, 166, 168, 173, 174.

Lodmoor, 4, 7, 9, 25, 317, 318, 327, 342, 344-346, 350.

London ; Portland Stone in, 118-119.

London-Ardennes Ridge, 149.

London Clay, 10, 216-219, 221, 222, 225, 227, 229, 234, 244.

London Doors Quarry, 354.

Long Ebb, 73, 74.

Lord's Barrow, 276-279, 319, 321.

LORIÈRE, G. DE, 169.

LORIOL, P. de, 132.

Lorton House, 329.

Lott and Walne, Ltd., 228.

Lower Calcareous Grit, 26, 37, 41. *See also* Nothe Grit.

Lower Greensand, 10, 11, 163-177 ; palaeontology 154, 167-172 ; relation to Wealden Beds, 155, 158, 163-165, 173, 176, 247 ; relation to Gault, 177, 179, 247 ; thickness, 165 ; zones, 165-167 ; Purbeck, 173-176 ; Lulworth, 177, 179.

Lucina minuscula, 65.

Luckford Lake, 7.

Lulworth : axis, 303 ; beach, 345, 346, 348 ; brick-making, 355 ; building stone, 97 ; castle 1 ; cove 3, 4, 108, 141, 159, 189, 208, 295-297, 318, 345 ; crumple, 159, 243, 292-296, 298, 304 ; drainage, 320, 323 ; fossil trees, 125 ; name, 8 ; oil prospects, 360, 361 ; springs, 352 ; structures, 243-246, 288, 291-300, 303, 305, 307 ; water supply, 359 ; Portland Beds, 108-111, 114 ; Purbeck Beds, 123, 139-142, 292 ; Wealden Beds, 159, 355 ; Lower Greensand, 177, 179 ; Gault 178, 179, 189, 190 ; Chalk, 206, 208, 210, 211 ; Eocene, 227 ; gravel, 324.

Lumachelles, 16.

Lutetian Stage, 217.
LYELL, Sir CHARLES, 219, 223.
Lyme Regis, 81, 216, 248, 347.
Lynch Farm (Kingston), 304, 352, 354.
Lynch Farm (Wyke), 26, 32.

———

Magas pumilus, 200.
Maiden Castle, 213, 256, 342.
MAILLARD, G., 132.
Mammals : Jurassic, 123, 124, 126-128, 135, 138, 152 ; Tertiary, 235 ; Pleistocene, 317, 337.
Mammoths, 317, 337.
Man : Anglo-Saxon, 7-9 ; Celtic, 7 ; as geological agent, 138, 145, 220, 344, 345, 346 ; Mesolithic, 317, 351, 352 ; Neolithic, 317, 318, 343, 351 ; Paleolithic, 313, 325-331 ; Roman, 69, 119, 134, 220, 351, 354.
Manganese deposits, 228, 337.
Man o' War Cove and Head, 190, 199, 208, 289, 292, 293, 345.
MANSEL-PLEYDELL, J. C., 69.
MANTELL, G. A., 154.
Maple Ledge, 72-76.
Maps of the area : Geological Survey sheet-lines and numbers, 2 ; Webster's, 5 ; Bristow's, 6 ; Reid and Strahan's, xii, 6 ; early topographical, 348, 349.
Marehill Clay, 174, 179.
Marl, 356, 357.
Marnhull and Todber Freestone, 60.
MARSDEN, M. H., 325, 326, 328.
Marshes, bogs, fens, 1, 4, 7, 25, 148, 317, 318, 334, 335, 348-353.
Marsupites testudinarius, 200.
Massive Bed, The, 80, 90-92, 103, 104, 106, 108.
Matcham pits, 224, 225.
Melcombe Regis, 8, 344.
Meleagrinella echinata, 20.
Meon River, 314.
Mere, The, 344.
MERRETT, E. A., 130.
Merry Hill, 60.
Mesolithic culture and period, 317, 351, 352.
Mesozoic era, 10, 11, 244, 245.
Metacypris fittoni, 151.
Metacypris forbesii, var. verrucosa, 129.
MEYER, C. J. A., 173, 176.
Micraster coranguinum, 200.
Micraster cortestudinarium, 200.
Micraster leskei, 199.

Middle Bottom, 210, 286-288, 300, 305, 312, 336.
Miocene period, 240, 241, 244, 313-315, 323.
MITCHELL, E. W., 279, 280.
Modiola bipartita, 28.
Moigns Down, 114, 143, 211, 272, 275.
MOIR, J. REID, 231, 324.
Montian Stage, 217.
Moreton, 216, 228-230, 316, 325-328, 355, 356.
Morinina dorsispinata, 151.
Morrison formation, affinities of Purbeck mammals with, 126.
MOTTRAM, B. H., 260.
Mountain-building movements, 12, 313.
Mud-slides, 5, 84, 192, 193, 281, 282, 330, 353.
Mupe Bay, 3, 5, 139, 158, 159, 165, 177, 188, 189, 206-208, 291, 300, 301, 319, 320, 348, 360, 361.
Mupe Rocks, 5, 108, 297.
Musculus autissiodorensis, 97.
Mytilus suprajurensis, 97.

———

NEAVERSON, E., 76, 77, 79, 82.
Neithea quadricostata, 186.
Neocomian Stage, 10, 148, 149, 151, 152, 163, 247.
Neolithic culture and period, 317, 318, 343, 351.
Neomiodon medium, 131.
Netley Heath (Surrey), 314.
Neuburg fauna, 77-78.
New Forest (Hants.), 315.
Newton, 221, 224.
Nine Barrow Down, 303, 315.
Nodular Rubble, 37, 46, 58, 60, 61.
Norden, 220, 221, 224, 225, 312.
Norfolk chalk, 195.
Normandy, 19, 30, 32, 33, 39, 134.
Nothe Clay, 36, 37, 41, 42, 47, 48, 51, 52, 54, 59, 84, 358, 361.
Nothe Grit, 36, 37, 47, 48, 51-55, 59, 257, 258, 358, 361.
Nothe Point (The Nothe), 8, 25, 54.
Nottington, 8, 19.
Nucleolites clunicularis, 20.
Nucleolites scutatus, 40.
Nucula calliope, 28.
Nummulites, 217, 218.

Oakley, K. P., 195, 317.
Oddens Wood, 60, 61.
Offaster pilula, 200.
Oil : impregnations, 47, 142, 159, 160, 360, 361 ; explorations, 73-75, 266, 267, 272-277, 360, 361.
Oil-Shale, 3, 29, 68-70, 72, 86, 359.
Old Harry Rocks, 205.
Oligocene System, 6, 10, 215, 217, 218, 240, 241, 244.
Onion-scale faulting, 307, 311.
D'Orbigny, A., 66, 76.
Orchard, 135, 357.
Ornithella classis, 20.
Ornithella digona, 17.
Ornithella lagenalis, 22.
Ornithella obovata, 20.
Ornithella siddingtonensis, 22.
Osborne Beds, 217, 235.
Osmington, 8, 161, 268, 271, 281, 319 ; cascade, 47, 53, 284, 318 ; stream, 321, 330.
Osmington Mills : Oxford Clay, 34, 35 ; Corallian Beds, 41-50, 54, 282-284 ; Kimmeridge Clay, 41-44, 48-50, 84-86, 283 ; Gault, 179, 181, 184, 188, 192-194 ; Chalk, 211, 281 ; gravel, 323, 330 ; ledges, 284 ; mud-slides, 5, 84, 192, 193, 281, 282, 352, 353 ; slips, 283, 284, 353 ; structure, 48, 281-285.
Osmington Oolite Series, 37, 41, 42, 46, 48, 51, 54, 57-62, 84, 361.
Ostlingoceras puzosianum, 182.
Ostracods, 123, 124, 129, 130, 143, 147, 151-153, 155, 252.
Ostrea alimena, 28.
Ostrea delta, 65.
Ostrea dilatata, 28.
Ostrea distorta, 131.
Ostrea gregarea, 40.
Ostrea hebridica, 16, 17.
Ostrea marshii, 22.
Ostrea minuta, 17.
Overthrusts. See Faults.
Owen, Sir Richard, 6.
Ower, 133.
Ower Heath, 325.
Owermoigne, 212, 228, 278.
Oxford and district, 26, 30, 33, 37, 79, 82, 92, 148.

Oxford Clay, 5, 10, 11, 18, 25-35, 36, 359, 360 ; bricks, 355 and refs. ; scenery, 4 ; thickness, 25, 249 ; zones, 26 ; Weymouth, 33, 34, 54, 60 ; Fleet and Chickerell, 26-33, 355, 359 ; inliers, 34, 35 ; Ridgeway, 257-259 ; Bincombe, 260-262; Sutton Poyntz, 266-268 ; Poxwell boring, 273, 274.
Oxfordian Stage, 10, 25, 26, 36, 41.
Oxytoma sp. (*inequivalve* group), 28.
Oyster beds, 16, 17, 18, 36, 42, 44, 50, 56, 83, 94, 95, 99, 109, 110, 115, 118, 123, 124, 135, 143, 257, 263. See Cinder Bed, Exogyra Beds, Gryphaea Beds.

Pachychilus manselli, 131.
Palaeoglandina costellata, 239.
Palaeolithic terrace, 325.
Palaeoliths, 313, 316, 324-331.
Palaeoxestina occlusa, 239.
Palaeozoic rocks, 11.
Parallel Bands, The, 91, 92, 102, 104, 106, 107, 111.
Paravirgatites Clays, 71.
Paris Basin, 218.
Pavlovia rotunda, 78.
Pavlow, A. P., 67, 93.
Peat, 10, 225, 317, 348, 350, 351, 352.
Pebble beds : Mesozoic, 18, 125, 140, 141, 142, 149, 154, 157-161, 164-167, 173-176, 179, 185, 188, 275, 302 ; Tertiary, 216, 223, 227-233, 327 ; Pleistocene, 327, 337 ; Bunter-quartzite, 231, 232.
Pecten asper, 186.
Pecten fibrosus, 38-39.
Pecten lamellosus, 97.
Pecten laminatus, 17.
Pecten midas, 38-39.
Pecten qualicosta, 40.
Pecten splendens, 38-39.
Pecten vagans, 17.
Pectinatites cf. *nasutus*, 78.
Pectinatites Clays, 71.
Peltoceras ? prespissum, 30.
Peneplanation, 313-315, 319, 323.
Pentacrinus sp., 28.
Perisphinctes cautisrufae, 34.
Perisphinctes kobyi, 30.
Permo-Triassic Systems, 11, 127, 248, 332, 341, 342, 346.
Perna Bed, 164, 166, 167, 169-172, 174, 176.
Petrockstow (Devon), 220.
Peveril Point, 135-138, 243, 304, 346, 360.

Phascolestes (jaw and tooth), 127.
PHEMISTER, J., 340, 346.
PHILLIPS, W., 307.
Phosphatic nodules, 37, 82, 85, 164, 188, 190, 192, 197, 199, 204, 208, 211, 212.
Physa bristovii, 131.
Pictonia densicostata, 74.
Pier Bottom, 80, 98.
Pike Bros., 220, 226, 235, 327.
Pipe-clay, 12, 216, 220, 221, 223-226, 229, 230, 233-235, 237, 312, 357.
Piping of the Chalk. *See* Solution Pipes.
Pisolite, 47, 48, 58, 84.
Place-names, 7-9, 140.
Plagiaulax (jaw), 127.
Planorbis fisheri, 131.
Plateau Gravel, 10, 229, 230, 313, 315, 316, 324-331, 337, 341.
Pleistocene System, 10, 313-337.
Plenus Marl, 197, 199, 200, 204-206, 208, 209, 213, 234, 291, 295-297, 300, 301.
Pleuromya alduini, 65.
Pliocene period, 228, 232, 241, 244, 313-315, 319, 321, 323, 330, 342.
Poland, 93.
Polychaete worms, 39.
Polyzoa, 19, 201, 202, 208.
Pondfield, 4, 9, 90, 97, 105, 139, 298, 301, 302, 320.
Pon(d) Freestone, 95, 97, 100, 101, 105, 108.
Poole Harbour, 4, 5, 218, 221, 224, 226, 317-319, 348, 350.
POOLE, H. F., 352.
Porphyry erratics in beaches, 332, 340, 341, 346.
Portisham, 4, 70, 85, 86, 95, 111, 116, 118, 126, 142, 145, 232, 233, 241, 249-253, 255, 298, 305, 329, 353, 354, 359.
Portland : age of Island, 342 ; Bill, 95, 118, 298, 331, 334, 340 ; breakwater, 88, 119, 344-346 ; Chesil Beach at, 337-340, 343 ; cycads, 133, 147 ; ferry, 9, 338 ; Harbour, 83, 88 ; Harbour beach, 344 ; head, 334, 335 ; Kimmeridge Clay, 83, 88 ; landslips, 353 ; mammal drift and bone fissures, 337-340, 343 ; Portland Beds, 118-122 ; Purbeck Beds, 145-147, 298 ; quarries, 118-122, 145-147, 354 ; raised beach, 10, 331-333, 340-342 ; Roads, 88, 118, 338 ; Rufus Castle, 118 ; scenery, 4 ; structure, 242 ; water supply, 358.

Portland Beds, 10, 89-122 ; palaeontology, 92-96 ; relation to Purbeck Beds, 124, 147 ; scenery, 3, 4, 5, 242 ; thickness, 90, 95, 111, 114, 117, 118 ; zones, 92-94 ; in Portland, 92, 118-122, 331, 360 ; in Purbeck, 92, 95-108, 120, 301-303, 360 ; Lulworth, 97, 108-111, 114 ; Ringstead to Portisham, 82, 92, 263-277, 285, 358.
Portland Clay, 92, 114, 115, 120, 121.
Portland Stone. *See* Portland Beds and Building Stones. Competence, 243, 299 ; as piston rock, 266, 285.
Portlandian Stage, 5, 10, 66, 67, 89, 92.
Portlandkalk, 66, 76.
Portland Screw, 95-97, 113, 122, 147.
Portsdown Anticline and boring, 130, 148, 165, 242, 314.
Portsmouth, 341.
Povington, 8.
Poxwell : boring, 74, 81, 85, 272-274, 277, 361 ; Chalk, 211, 212, 274, 275 ; circle 241, 274 ; drainage, 319 ; gravel, 324 ; landslip, 353 ; name, 8 ; pericline, 114, 194, 248, 266, 271-275, 277, 281, 321, 361 ; Portland Beds, 111, 114, 272 ; Purbeck Beds, 142, 143, 272, 297 ; road-cutting, 143, 353 ; serpulite, 95 ; structure 247, *and see* pericline.
Prestatyn (Flintshire), 351, 352.
Preston, 8, 85, 111, 114, 281, 358.
Preston Grit, 37.
PRESTWICH, J., 331-337, 342.
Prickle Bed or Puffin Ledge, 100, 102, 110, 111.
PRINGLE, J., 86-88, 164, 357.
Procerithium damonis, 28.
Promathildia microbinaria, 131.
Prorasenia sp., 74.
Protocardia purbeckensis, 131.
Provirgatites albani, 77.
Pseudoceratites, 183, 185.
Pseudomelania heddingtonensis, 40.
Ptychostylus harpaeformis, 131.
Ptychostylus philippii, 131.
Puckstone, 8, 224.
Pulborough (Sussex), 174.
Puncknowle, 19.
Punfield, 9, 150, 153, 155, 165-174, 184-186, 197, 199, 204, 346.
Punfield Formation, 173.
Punfield Marine Band, 166-169, 173-176.

Purbeck, 1, 242 ; building stones, 95, 97, 124, 128, 133-135, 144 ; coal-money, 69 ; coastline, 4, 5, 318 ; drainage, 315, 316, 318-320 ; pene-planation, 315, 318 ; pipe-clay, 220, 221 ; stone-mines, 134 ; struc-ture, 301-304 ; topography, 1-4, 315 ; Kimmeridge Clay, 64-80 ; Portland Beds, 95-108 ; Purbeck Beds, 133-139, 301, 302 ; Wealden Beds, 150, 152-158 ; Lower Green-sand, 173-176 ; Gault and Upper Greensand, 179, 185-189 ; Chalk, 204-207, 304-312 ; Eocene, 216-227 ; Oligocene, 233-241 ; gravels, 330, 331.

Purbeck Beds, 10, 11, 89, 123-147, 152 ; brecciation, see Broken Beds ; climate, 129, 130 ; conditions of deposition, 89, 123 ; conformity with Portland and Wealden Beds, 124, 138, 139, 147-149, 247 ; oil impregnations, 360 ; palaeontology, 126-133, 152 ; as pebbles in Eocene, 216, 230-232, 244 ; as piston rock, 266, 298 ; scenery, 3-5 ; thickness, 123, 141, 142, 301 ; zones, 124, 130 ; in Purbeck, 133-139, 301-304, 356-358 ; Lulworth, 139-142, 293, 295-299 ; Chaldon inlier, 275-277 ; Ringstead to Portisham, 81, 114, 115, 142-145, 162, 251, 252, 263-277 ; Portland, 145-147, 335.

Purbeck Fault, 288, 305, 306, 312. See Ballard Down Fault.

Purbeck Fold, 4, 12, 13, 195, 242-248, 285-312 ; adjustment in, 291-296, 304, 311 ; attenuation in, 290, 293 ; axis, 68, 302, 303 ; breccia-tion, see Broken Beds ; change of strike, 300, 301, 303 ; chert in, 90 ; core rocks, 301-303 ; date, 241, 242 ; foresyncline, 244, 286-288, 300, 308, 311 ; middle limb (vertical), 205, 206, 243, 288-301, 307, 308, 312 ; minor structures, see Broken Beds, Fracture cleavage, Shears, etc. ; pitch, 246, 296 ; Kimmeridge Clay in, 68, 301-303 ; Portland Beds in, 90, 301-303 ; Purbeck Beds in, 301-304 ; Chalk in, 195, 301, 304-312.

Purbeck Hills, 1, 3, 186, 195, 205, 206, 220, 234, 236, 242, 301, 303, 311, 312, 323, 355, 357.

Purbeckian Stage, 5, 10, 123.

Purbeck Marble, 124, 133-138, 140, 141, 304, 354.

Purbeck-Portland building stone, 95, 354.

Putton Lane Brickyard, 26, 27, 355.

Quarr, 134.

Quartzite pebbles (Bunter), 231, 232, 329-332, 341, 342.

Quaternary deposits, 10. See Pleistocene.

Quenstedtoceras brasili, 30.

Quenstedtoceras lamberti (and var. intermissum), 30.

Quenstedtoceras leachi, 30.

Quenstedtoceras mariae, 34.

Radiolaria, 149, 230.

Radipole, 7, 19, 327, 358 ; Back-water, 7, 24, 25, 27, 29, 32, 33, 317, 318, 342-344, 350.

Ragged Rocks, The, 99.

Raised Beaches, 10, 331-333, 340-342, 346.

Rasenia cf. cymodoce, 74.

Rasenia cf. mutabilis, 74.

Reading Beds, 10, 215, 217, 218 221, 222, 225, 227-230, 234, 241, 244, 324, 355.

Recent deposits, 337-353.

Red Beds, 39, 46, 49, 61.

Redcliff, 9, 48, 51-53, 59 ; Redcliff Point, 25, 34, 281, 345.

Redcliff (Wareham), 227, 230.

Redend Point and Sandstone, 216, 222-225.

Red Hole, 227, 289, 290.

Red Lane, 86.

Red Nodule Beds, 26, 32, 33, 34, 257.

REHBINDER, B., 154, 169.

REID, CLEMENT, 6, 215, 216, 227-231, 256, 315, 317, 319, 351, 355.

REID, E. M., 219.

Reigate (Surrey), 151, 176.

Rempstone Hall, 1, 205, 220, 225, 312, 327.

Reptiles, 6, 39, 66, 78, 87, 95, 126, 128, 137, 152, 162.

REYNOLDS, S. H., 19.

Rhaetic Beds, 123, 126.

RHODES, J., 173, 175.

Rhynchonella and Lingula Beds, 71, 79, 98.

Rhynchonella boueti, 17.

Rhynchonella cerealis, 22.

Rhynchonella cuvieri, 199.

Rhynchonella inconstans, 65.

Rhynchonella smithi, 16.

Rhynchonella yaxleyensis, 20.

RICHARDSON, N. M., 340.
Ridgeway Anticline, 248, 254-256.
Ridgeway Fault, 164, 194, 213, 214, 232, 244, 247, 251-266, 315.
Ridgeway Hill, 194, 213, 252, 254-256, 319, 356.
Ridgeway cutting, 34-35, 123, 129, 144, 152, 162, 194, 251, 256-260.
Ringstead, 9 ; Anticline, 42, 80, 246, 320, 361 ; beach, 345, 346, 348 ; boring, 361 ; faults, 81, 82, 284, 285 ; landslips, 353 ; ledges, 42, 43, 284 ; structures, 270, 281-285 ; unconformity, 179, 193, 247 ; Corallian Beds 41-47 ; Kimmeridge Clay, 42-44, 74, 80-85 ; Portland Beds, 111-114, 284, 285 ; Purbeck Beds, 142, 143, 285, 297 ; Gault and Greensand, 179, 191-194, 285 ;   Chalk, 209, 211, 285 ; Reading Beds, 324 ; gravels, 211, 323, 324, 335, 336, 356 ; tufa, 352.
Ringstead Coral Bed, 39, 41-44, 48-50, 56-58, 84, 85.
Ringstead Waxy Clay, 41-44, 49, 50, 56.
Ripple-marks, 18.
River history, 314-321, 324-331, 342, 343, 350.
Roach, 83, 89, 95, 99, 111-113, 147.
Road-metal, 355.
ROBINSON, C. E., 134, 219.
Rodden, 8, 23, 60, 61, 62, 86, 319, 329 ; Brook, 329, 330.
Rodwell, 57, 358.
Roman artifacts of Blackstone, 69 ; markings in Portland quarries, 119 ; pottery and coins, 351 ; use of pipe clay, 220 ; use of Purbeck Marble and stone, 134, 354.
Roofing flags, 135, 354 ; tiles, 355.
Rope Lake Head, 72, 75, 78, 81 ; Hole, 9, 75, 76, 78.
Rothamsted (Herts.), 314.
Rotunda Clays and Nodules, 71, 79, 98.
ROUCHADZÉ, J., 167.
ROWE, A. W., 6, 196, 199, 202, 204, 205, 207, 210, 211, 306-308.
Rupelian Stage, 217.
Russia, 93, 169.

Saccocoma sp., 65, 78, 81, 86.
St. Alban's Head, 3, 8, 80, 90-92, 97-105, 114, 138, 242, 301, 303, 354.
St. Alban's Head Marls, 91, 92, 98, 103, 107, 118, 352.

St. Oswald's Bay, 190, 208, 291-293, 300, 345.
SALFELD, HANS, 6, 66, 70, 76, 77, 81, 83, 85, 88, 93.
Salisbury Plain (Wilts.), 243.
Salt : deposits, 248, 299 ; marshes, 4 ; works, 69.
Sand : beach, 322, 345-348 ; blown, 4, 10, 347-350 ; builders', 356 ; dunes, 4, 347-350 ; glass, 69, 356 ; singing, 350.
Sandbanks, 348.
SANDBERGER, C. L. F., 132.
Sandgate Beds, 164, 165, 174.
Sand Holes, 331, 332.
Sandrock Series, 166, 167, 174, 179.
Sandsfoot Castle, 54, 348.
Sandsfoot Clay, 36, 41, 42, 44, 48-50, 54-58, 61.
Sandsfoot Grit, 36, 41, 43, 44, 49, 50, 56-59, 62, 63, 86-88.
Sarsen Stones, 7, 227, 233, 241, 336.
SAXTON's map, 348.
Scaphites aequalis, 199.
Scaphites Group, 165.
Scarborough (Yorks.), 30.
Scar Cementstones, 114, 116, 118, 263, 268, 272.
Scenery, 1-4.
SCHAFFER, R. J., 119, 121.
Schloenbachia varians, 199.
SCHNEID, T., 77, 78.
SCOTT, A., 221.
Scratchy Bottom, 209, 269, 336.
Seacombe, 3, 90, 95, 97, 99-102, 138, 303, 318.
Sea currents, 340, 343.
Sea stacks, 4, 205.
Seawell Knap, 63.
SEDGWICK, ADAM, 6, 39.
Seend (Wilts.), 37, 164.
Selsey Bill, 341.
Senonian Stage, 10, 195, 202-205, 207, 209, 210.
Septaria, 26, 27, 34, 82, 83, 84, 88, 225.
Serpula coacervata, 131.
Serpula concava, 186.
Serpulite, 89, 92, 94, 95, 101, 102, 112, 113, 117, 132.
SEWARD, Sir A. C., 133, 152.
Shears, 206, 243, 244, 264, 287-293, 300, 301, 307-309 ; sequence-dating, 288-291.
Shell Bay, 1, 347-350.
SHERBORN, C. D., 6.
Shilvinghampton, 8, 60, 61.
Shingle. See Beaches.
Shipmoor Point, 21, 23.

Shipstal Point, 226, 327.
Shortlake, 25, 33, 48-50, 281, 330, 345.
SHOTTON, F. W., 311.
Shrimp Bed, 94, 95, 97, 99, 100, 105, 108, 113, 302.
Silton (N. Dorset), 62.
SIMPSON, G. G., 126, 127.
Singing sands, 350.
Slatt, 123, 143, 145, 146.
Slumped beds, 302.
Small Mouth, 54, 81, 88, 330, 338, 339, 344, 348.
Smedmore, 69, 70.
Solent, 5, 316, 317.
Solent River, 316, 324.
Solifluxion, 324, 333-336.
Solution pipes, 216, 222, 227, 228, 232, 241, 256, 314.
Somme River, 325.
Southampton docks, 317.
South Down Farm, 113.
South Haven Peninsula, 347-350.
Southwell, 145, 358.
SOWERBY, J. DE C., 154, 257.
Spain, 154, 163, 168, 169, 175.
Spalacotherium (jaw), 127.
SPATH, L. F., 29, 31, 70, 77-79, 91, 93, 94, 151, 165, 167, 174, 180, 185, 188, 197.
SPEED's map, 348.
SPENCER, W. K., 195, 205.
Spithead, 5, 316.
Sponges, 39, 90, 124, 133, 195, 202, 209, 213, 215, 230.
Spring Bottom, 269, 281, 323, 352, 357.
Spring Bottom Syncline, 193, 194, 211, 270, 281, 282, 285.
Springs, 7, 8, 352, 353, 358, 359.
Stages, 10, 217.
Stair Hole, 4, 9, 135, 141, 142, 294-296.
Starfish, 190, 199, 203, 204, 209.
Start, The, 333, 339.
Steeple, 3, 157, 206, 224, 324, 356; Brook, 318, 320, 330, 331.
Steeple Ashton (Wilts.), 50.
STEINMANN, G., 153.
STILLE, HANS, 163, 248.
Stinkstone, 91, 103.
Stoliczkaia dispar, 182.
Stonehill Down, 312.
Stone-quarrying, 354, 355 and refs.
Stonesfield Slate, 126, 128.
Storms, effect of, 4, 338, 340, 344-346.
Stour River, 316, 325, 329, 333.

STRAHAN, Sir AUBREY, 6 (and constantly throughout the memoir). Especially : on overthrusting, 6, 7, 258, 305 ; on the pre-Gault unconformity, 6, 247 ; on the Wealden Beds and Lower Greensand of Swanage and Corfe, 156, 173-175 ; on abnormal Chloritic Marl, 189 ; description of Chesil Beach 337, 338 ; on the origin of Chesil Beach, 341.
Strain-slip cleavage. See Fracture cleavage.
STRUCKMANN, C. E. F., 132.
Structure, 6, 11, 12, 13, 68, 80, 84, 90, 111, 114, 118, 123, 148, 164, 179, 195, 213, 225, 226, 242-312. See also Faults, Drag, Adjustment folds, Purbeck Fold, etc.
Studland : brick-making, 356 ; Chalk, 195, 203-205 ; Eocene, 215, 216, 218, 221-225, 229, 244 ; gravels, 327 ; name, 8 ; sand and dunes, 4, 346-350 ; structures, 305, 310, 312 ; water supply, 358, 359.
Sublithographic Stone, 89, 95, 108.
Submergence, 317, 318, 343, 351.
Subplanites cf. *grandis*, 78.
Subplanites pseudoscruposus, 77.
Subplanites sp. (typical), 78.
Superimposed drainage, 319.
Sutton Poyntz : inlier, 245, 258, 264 ; pericline, 266-271, 361 ; thrust-faulting, 212, 268-271, 274 ; waterworks, 358 ; Cornbrash, 24, 266-268 ; Oxford Clay, 34, 35, 179, 258, 266-268 ; Kimmeridge Clay, 266-268 ; Portland Beds, 114, 266 ; Greensand and Gault, 179, 194, 258 ; Chalk, 211, 212.
Swanage : Bay, 3, 9, 154-156, 173, 185, 304, 346 ; beach, 346, 347 ; brick-making, 355 ; fossil mammals and crocodiles, 127, 128 ; golf-links, 223, 227, 230, 237, 312 ; name, 8 ; palaeolith from, 331 ; stone quarries, 95, 97, 133, 134, 354 ; structures, 302-312 ; water supply, 358, 359 ; Purbeck Beds, 123, 304 ; Wealden Beds, 150, 152, 154-156, 169, 346 ; Lower Greensand, 165, 173, 174, 179 ; Gault and Upper Greensand, 179, 185, 186 ; Chalk, 204, 205, 304-311 ; Eocene, 223, 224.
Swanage Brick and Tile Co., 156, 355.
Swan Brook, 133, 154.

Swanworth Quarries, Ltd., 97, 354.
Swindon (Wilts.), 77, 94.
SWINTON, W. E., 128, 152.
Swyre, 19.
Swyre Head (Kingston), 3, 8, 75, 315.
Swyre Head (Lulworth), 8, 209, 286, 289, 301.
Swyre Head (Puncknowle), 8.

———

TAITT, A. H., 267, 272-277, 279, 307, 311, 360.
TARR, W. A., 137.
Tatton, 8.
Tectonics. *See* Structure.
Tellina subconcentrica, 170.
Terebratula intermedia, 20.
Terebratula langtonensis, 17.
Terebratulina lata, 199.
Terebratulina rowei, 200.
Terrestrial fauna and flora, 6, 11, 123, 151, 216, 218, 219, 240, 241, 332, 334, 335, 337, 351, 352. *See also* Mammals, Trees, etc.
Tertiary era and rocks, 10, 215-241 ; duration, 12 ; erratics on Portland, 334, 336, 337 ; fauna and flora, 12, 218, 219 ; mapping, 6 ; peneplanation 16, 313-315, 319, 323 ; scenery, 1, 5 ; structures, 242-246, 250-312 ; syncline, 359 ; vulcanicity, 12. *See also* Eocene, Oligocene, Hampshire Basin, etc.
Test, River, 316.
Thames, River, 316, 318.
Thamnasteria concinna, 40.
Thanet Beds, 217.
Thecosmilia annularis, 40.
Thorncombe Beacon, 342.
Three White Stone Bands, The, 71, 78-81.
Thrusts. *See* Faults.
Thurlestone (Devon), 7.
Tidmoor Point, 30-32 ; Clays, 26, 30-32.
Tiles, 355 and refs.
Tilly Whim, 3, 8, 95-99, 263.
Tisbury star-coral, 95.
Titanites Bed, 99, 105, 108.
Tombolos, 343, 344.
TOPLEY, W., 149, 314.
Topography ; development, 313-323 ; place-names, 7-9.
Torquay (Devon), 11, 333, 346.
Touts, 7, 263, 301.
Trees (fossil), 115, 123, 125, 133, 141, 144-147, 152, 167, 172.
Triassic system, 127, 248, 332.

Triconodon (jaw), 127.
Trigonia angulata, 20.
Trigonia clavellata, 38-39.
Trigonia (clavellata) Beds, 37, 39, 41, 42, 45, 46, 48, 54, 57-62.
Trigonia gibbosa and vars. *manseli* and *damoniana*, 97.
Trigonia hudlestoni, 38-9.
Trigonia hudlestoni Bed, 37, 41, 48, 51-53.
Trigonia incurva, 97.
Trigonia sp. cf. *irregularis*, 28.
Trigonia rolandi, 20.
Tropaeum Beds, 166.
Tufa : Jurassic, 115, 117, 123, 125, 126, 138, 141, 143-147, 297, 301, 302 ; Oligocene, 217, 240, 241 ; Holocene, 10, 351, 352, 359.
Turonian Stage, 10, 195, 199-202, 204, 207-209.
Turrilites acutus, 199.
Turtles, 128, 137.
Turtle Stones, 27, 29.
Tyneham, 3, 157, 206, 302 ; Brook, 320.

———

Uintacrinus westfalicus, 200.
Ulwell, 7, 154, 156, 205, 312, 255, 358, 359.
Ulwellia menevensis, 151.
Ulwellia ventrosa, 129.
Under or Bottom Freestone, 97, 100, 101, 105, 108.
Unio porrectus, 131.
Upper Calcareous Grit, 41, 44, 48, 56.
Upper Greensand, 10, 19, 178-194 ; palaeontology, 181-185 ; pebbles in Eocene, 215, 216, 229-231, 244 ; relation to the Chalk, 186, 196, 197, 204, 206-209, 212, 213 ; slips, 5, 80, 84, 194, 249, 281, 285, 353 ; thickness, 178 *and see* Gault ; unconformity, 34, 83, 179, 249-251, 258, 260, 267, 268, 275, 279 ; zones, 180, 181 ; Purbeck, 185-189, 205, 206 ; Lulworth, 189, 190, 296 ; White Nothe and Osmington, 189, 191, 248, 285, 353 ; Chaldon to Sutton Poyntz, 267-274 ; Bincombe, 213, 258, 260-262, 264 ; Ridgeway, 257-260 ; Abbotsbury, 249-251.
Upton Syncline, 161, 247, 248, 264, 279, 281, 321, 324, 353.
Upwey, 7, 59-61, 111, 114, 116, 142, 144, 145, 242, 250-252, 254, 255, 329, 354, 357-360 ; Wishing Well, 8, 358.

Upwey Syncline, 145, 162, 250-252, 256, 259, 358.
U shaped burrows, 39.
USSHER, W. A. E., 333.

Valanginian Stage, 150, 151, 163.
Vale of Kingsclere (Hants.), 148, 242.
Vale of Pewsey (Wilts.) Anticline 12, 314.
Vale of Wardour (Wilts.) Anticline, 12, 94, 148.
Valvata helicoides, 131.
Variegated Marls and Sandstones, 150 ff. *See* Wealden Beds.
VAUGHAN, A., 19.
VELLACOTT, C. H., 88, 135.
VENABLES, L. S. V., 350.
Verne Fort, 118, 121, 336, 337.
VERNEUIL, E. DE., 169.
Vines Down, 279.
Virgatotome ribbing, 67, 77, 93.
Viviparus cariniferus, 131.
Viviparus inflatus, 131.
Viviparus subangulatus, 131.

WAAGEN, W., 6, 41, 83.
Waddon, 8, 116, 117, 145, 162, 253, 255, 358. *See* Friar Waddon.
Wallington River, 314.
Wareham, 219, 221, 224-227, 230, 325, 327, 356.
Warmwell, 7, 216, 228-232, 325, 355, 356.
Warmwell Pits, Ltd., 230, 325.
Washing Ledge, 73, 75, 76.
Waterfalls, 318.
Water supply, 357-359.
Watton Cliff, 15, 16, 17, 18.
Wave action, 4, 68, 322, 338-340, 342-350.
Weald, The, 12, 164, 165, 174, 243, 244, 314, 318.
Wealden Beds, 10, 11, 148-162, 216 ; brick-making, 355 ; classification, 125 ; oil impregnations, 360, 361 ; palaeontology, 130, 151-154, 169 ; relation to Purbeck Beds, 124, 139, 148, 149, 247 ; relation to Lower Greensand, 158, 159, 163, 176, 177, 247 ; scenery, 3, 5 ; thickness, 148, 156, 158, 159, 161, 301, 303 ; Swanage, 154-156, 346 ; in Purbeck, 154-158, 356 ; Lulworth, 139, 158-161, 246 ; Chaldon, Osmington, Ridgeway, 161, 162, 252, 257-259.

Wealden Shales, 150-156, 165, 169, 176.
Wears Hill, 315.
Webb, Major and Co, 27, 288, 355.
WEBSTER, THOMAS, 5, 6, 97, 125, 133, 138, 149, 288, 307.
West Bay, 4, 231, 244, 340, 341, 343.
Westbury (Wilts.), 50 ; Iron Ore Beds, 56.
West Knighton, 214, 228, 229, 358.
WESTON, C. H., 256-258.
West Stafford, 216, 325, 336.
West Weare Cliffs, 121, 146.
West Weare Sandstones, 92, 114, 120, 121.
Weymouth : Backwater, 34 *and see* Radipole Backwater ; Bay, 25, 344 ; beach, 344-347 ; brick-making, 355 ; coast erosion, 342, 343 ; drainage and topography, 315, 319, 342 ; extension, 9 ; faulting and folding, 163 ; harbour, 54-57, 344 ; name, 7 ; pottery, 30 ; scenery, 4 ; water supply, 358 ; Oxford Clay, 26, 33, 355 ; Corallian Beds, 50, 54-57 ; Kimmeridge Clay, 56, 88 ; Portland Beds, 111-122.
Weymouth Anticline, 4, 242, 303, 319 ; age, 244, 319 ; continuity with Purbeck Anticline, 303 ; drainage, 319 ; Fuller's Earth in, 15, 17 ; Forest marble in, 19 ; Oxford Clay in, 25, 33 ; Corallian Beds in, 54 ; Kimmeridge Clay in, 85 ; Portland Beds in, 116, 118.
Weymouth Waterworks Co., 229.
Wey, River, 7, 319, 327, 329, 330, 333.
WHEELER, W. H., 344.
Whin, 8.
WHITAKER, W., 141, 142, 226, 331, 342, 343, 359.
Whit Bed, 113, 120-122.
Whitcombe, 214.
White Band, The, 71, 75, 76, 78, 80-82, 85.
White Cementstone, The, 91, 103, 104, 108.
White Hill, 315.
WHITE, H. J. OSBORNE, 153, 165, 210-214, 246, 248, 252-256, 264, 266, 269, 274, 278, 315, 317, 320, 321, 329.
White Horse Hill, 194, 211, 267, 268, 271, 315.
White Nothe, 4, 8, 9, 80, 190-192, 195, 197, 199, 202, 209, 284, 285, 315, 323, 345, 352.
White Septarian Band, 78, 81.

Winchester Anticline (Hants.), 314.
Wind gaps, 319, 321.
Windsbatch, 145.
Winfrith, 7, 210, 279, 320-321, 325 ;
 Brook, 7, 320-323.
Winslow, 8, 281.
Winspit, 3, 8, 95, 97, 99-102, 138, 318.
Winterborne Anticline, 248, 255.
Woodham Brick-pit (Bucks.), 30.
WOODS, G. and R. M., 336.
WOODS, HENRY, 99, 171, 175.
WOODWARD, Sir A. SMITH, 128, 152.
WOODWARD, H. B., 6, 18, 19, 24, 57,
 60, 68, 90, 101, 116, 139, 216, 298,
 299.
Woodyhyde, 3.
Wool, 7, 203, 210, 211, 227, 229, 307,
 325, 359.
Worbarrow Bay and Tout, 3, 5, 7,
 105, 107, 139, 150, 157, 175, 186,
 195, 206, 301, 303, 319, 320 ; beach,
 345, 348 ; structures, 291, 301,
 303 ; Purbeck Beds, 123, 139, 301,
 302, 357 ; Wealden Beds, 148, 150,
 156-158, 360, 361 ; Lower Greensand, 165, 168, 174-176, 179, 247 ;
 Gault, 178, 179, 186-189 ; Chalk,
 205-207, 301 ; gravel, 323.
Worth Matravers, 97, 101, 138, 354 ;
 Quarry, 97, 99-101.

WREN, Sir CHRISTOPHER, and use of
 Portland Stone, 118, 119.
WRIGHT, C. W., 158, 175, 178, 182,
 195.
WRIGHT, E. V., 182.
WRIGLEY, A., 218.
Wychwood Beds, 19.
Wyke Regis, 8, 9, 26, 32, 34, 58, 60,
 338, 358.
Wyke Wood, 329.

———

Yellow Ledge, 66, 72, 75, 76.
Ypresian Stage, 10, 217, 218.

———

Zones : of Cornbrash, 21 ; of Oxford
 Clay and Kellaways Beds, 26 ;
 of Corallian Beds, 41 ; of Kimmeridge Clay, 67, 71-80, 83-85, 88 ;
 of Portland Beds, 92-94 ; of Purbeck Beds, 124 ; of Lower Greensand, 166 ; of Gault and Upper
 Greensand, 180-184 ; of Chalk,
 196, 197-203, 279, 280 ; of Eocene,
 217, 218.

Printed in England for Her Majesty's Stationery Office by The Scolar Press Limited, Ilkley, West Yorkshire.

Dd 587312   K24